S. LALOMIA

D1159695

ELEMENTARY
STRUCTURAL ANALYSIS and DESIGN

Steel, Timber, and Reinforced Concrete

ELEMENTARY STRUCTURAL ANALYSIS and DESIGN

Steel, Timber, and Reinforced Concrete

SECOND EDITION

LINTON E. GRINTER, Ph.D., C.E.
RESEARCH PROFESSOR AND DEAN, THE GRADUATE SCHOOL
THE UNIVERSITY OF FLORIDA

THE MACMILLAN COMPANY, NEW YORK
COLLIER–MACMILLAN LIMITED, LONDON

© Copyright, The Macmillan Company, 1965

All rights reserved. No part of this book may be reproduced or transmitted in any form or by any means, electronic or mechanical, including photocopying, recording or by any information storage and retrieval system, without permission in writing from the Publisher.

Third Printing, 1967

Earlier edition copyright *1942* by *The Macmillan Company*

Library of Congress catalog card number: 64-21965

THE MACMILLAN COMPANY, NEW YORK
COLLIER–MACMILLAN CANADA, LTD., TORONTO, ONTARIO

PRINTED IN THE UNITED STATES OF AMERICA

FOREWORD

Some of you who study from this textbook will be college students or apprentice engineers who plan to become structural designers; many will be aero-space engineers, electrical engineers, mechanical engineers, architects, or others who study this subject to extend their knowledge of engineering. A reasonable understanding of structural design should form the common background of all engineers and architects. Our technological civilization depends directly upon transportation and machine power. Transportation is impossible without bridges, viaducts, wharfs, docks, hangars, and similar structures. Machine power demands industrial buildings, cranes, towers, warehouses, and office buildings. Rockets, satellites, and planetary landing gear present unique structural problems. An engineering leader in any field must be familiar with structures and be able to aid in planning new ones, although he need not be prepared to execute a detailed design.

It will soon become evident to you that the study of structural analysis and design requires the solution of many problems. Actually, the professional life of a designing engineer is largely spent solving similar problems, irrespective of whether his field is electricity, power, machine design, or structures. Fortunately, the general method of attack upon design problems in any field of engineering is always the same.

1. We set down all the known data carefully.
2. We list the assumptions that we intend to make.
3. We perform and record all steps of analysis and design.
4. We explain adjustments made in the light of engineering judgment.
5. We record all results, making free use of sketches for illustration.

You can also adopt a standard form of problem analysis that will serve in any field. As an example of form, a large number of the problems in this book are worked out on special design sheets. You need not follow this form at all, but you should adopt a form of your own and hold to it consistently. It will soon become a habit, and you will present your calculations in attractive form wherever they may be used. The old saying that "anything worth doing is worth doing well" applies proverbially to engineering studies. Accuracy, completeness, and neatness are the three standards upon which engineering reports, engineering drawings, and design calculations are judged.

L. E. GRINTER

Gainesville, Florida

PREFACE

This book has been prepared because of the writer's conviction that a larger proportion of all engineering students would profit from the study of structural design. Those students considered were architects, mechanical and environmental engineers, all non-structural civil engineers, aero-space engineers, and others who have a common interest in building and miscellaneous structures, but who are not likely to become bridge designers. This group of students is also homogeneous in the need for an understanding of steel, timber, and reinforced concrete structures along with simple wall and column footings. All of this material may have to be discussed in one semester. It must, therefore, be treated simply and briefly.

The greatest emphasis is given to steel structures, since steel serves for tanks, towers, trusses, and supporting frames of every description as well as for industrial buildings and office buildings. The principles involved also apply to light-weight structures of aluminum alloys and other metals. Reinforced concrete receives considerable attention because of its wide use not only for buildings and bridges but for footings and foundation structures. Timber, which serves for temporary or low-cost buildings, storage bins, and other non-fireproof structures, is treated adequately. Special chapters are devoted to plastic design for steel and ultimate strength design for reinforced concrete, and also to prestressed concrete.

The need for conserving time leads to less emphasis upon theory and more consideration of design than has been common in introductory texts. In fact, only a small part of the book is drawn from the author's *Theory of Modern Steel Structures*, while a number of chapters are rearranged from *Design of Modern Steel Structures*. Of course, it was necessary to revise such material to agree with a more elementary point of view. The five chapters on reinforced concrete structures and prestressed concrete make use of the *Building Code for Reinforced Concrete* of The American Concrete Institute. Specifications of The American Institute of Steel Construction are used for design with all structural steels. Specifications needed in studying the text are included in the final chapter.

A knowledge of elementary mechanics (statics) and of the strength of materials is an evident prerequisite to the use of this textbook. In turn, these subjects are usually preceded by a study of calculus, although short courses are available for designers without calculus as a prerequisite. This leads the writer to mention that many apprentice engineers have studied the first edition of this text without the benefit of formal enrollment in a course and have written to express appreciation for its brevity and clarity.

The writer has been closely associated with the curricular investigations that have produced a somewhat more scientific background for engineers with a corresponding reduction of practical knowledge and early capacity to design. In this book design is presented as the basic objective, analysis being the essential tool. As more and more non-professionalized subject matter finds a place in the civil engineering curriculum, it is quite possible that the condensed presentation in this text may represent the extent of the attention that can be given to the subjects of steel and concrete design in many undergraduate civil engineering curricula. This possibility has been considered in the arrangement of the chapters and in bringing into the book for the first time a condensed presentation of such subjects as plastic design of steel, ultimate load design of concrete, and prestressed concrete. Perhaps a clearer title for this revision would be "Elements of Structural Analysis and Design," because some of the material added can hardly be classed as elementary. However, comparatively little attention has been given to whole structures, the emphasis in a textbook prepared for the first courses in analysis and design necessarily being addressed mainly to design of structural elements.

CONTENTS

LIST OF TABLES

TABLES IN SPECIFICATIONS

LIST OF ABBREVIATIONS AND SYMBOLS

ABBREVIATIONS

AASHO	American Association of State Highway Officials
AISC	American Institute of Steel Construction
AREA	American Railway Engineering Association
ASCE	American Society of Civil Engineers
ASTM	American Society for Testing Materials
AWS	American Welding Society
NLMA	National Lumber Manufacturer's Association
CG; cg	center of gravity
d	penny designation for nail sizes
DL or D	dead load
FS	factor of safety
k	kips
LL or L	live load
NA	neutral axis
WF	wide flange beam section
WL or W	wind load

CLASSIFICATIONS

*A*7, *A*373, *A*36, *A*440, *A*441, *A*242	structural steels of different yield strengths
*A*141, *A*195, *A*406	rivet steels of different strengths
*A*307, *A*325, *A*354	bolt steels of different strengths
*E*60, *E*70	classes of electrodes for welding
SAW-1, *SAW*-2	grades of submerged-arc welding

GENERAL NOTATION

a	distance, length, or thickness
A	area
A_f	area of flange
A_v	area for shear
A_w	area of web
b	breadth or distance, flange width
c	distance such as that from neutral axis to extreme fiber
C	compressive force, arm of a couple
d	diameter, depth, or distance
e	eccentricity
E, E_t	modulus of elasticity, tangent modulus
f	fiber stress

GENERAL NOTATION (*continued*)

f_y, F_y	yield stress for plastic design
F, F'	forces
g	gage distance
G	torsional modulus of rigidity, also specific gravity
h	height, also diameter of a rivet hole
H	horizontal reaction
I, J	moment of inertia, polar moment of inertia
k	ratio, depth of flange to toe of fillet for steel beam
K	stiffness, also special factor defined in text
l, L	lengths
M, M_e	bending moment; moment of eccentricity
M_p, M_y	plastic moment of a section; yield moment
n	number of bolts or rivets, also a ratio
p	unit wind pressure
P, P_n	load, wind force normal to the roof
Q	statical moment of an area
r	radius of gyration, also a ratio
R	rivet stress, radius, reaction, or resultant
s	rivet spacing between holes in line of stress
S	section modulus, also total stress
t	thickness
T	tensile force or total tension, also torque moment
V	vertical reaction, or total vertical shear, also wind velocity
w	uniform load per unit length or area
W	work, total uniform load
W_u, W_c	ultimate collapse loading for plastic design
x, y	coordinates or distances
$\bar{y}$	distance to the center of gravity
Δ	deflection
ϵ	unit strain
θ	slope or angle
μ	Poisson's ratio
σ	unit stress normal to a plane
Σ	summation
τ	unit shearing stress along a plane

NOTATION FOR STEEL DESIGN BY *AISC* SPECIFICATIONS

a	center-to-center distance between transverse stiffeners
A_b	nominal body area of a bolt
A_f	area of compression flange
A_{st}	cross-sectional area of stiffener or pair of stiffeners
A_w	area of girder web
C_c	column slenderness ratio dividing elastic and inelastic buckling; equal to $\sqrt{\frac{2\pi^2 E}{F_y}}$
d	depth of beam or girder; also diameter of roller or rocker bearing
e	horizontal displacement, in the direction of the span, between top and bottom of simply supported beam at its ends
E, E_c	modulus of elasticity of steel; modulus of elasticity of concrete
f_a, f_b	computed axial stress; computed bending stress

f_t, f_v	computed tensile stress; computed shear stress
f_{vs}	shear between girder web and transverse stiffeners, in pounds per linear inch of single stiffener or pair of stiffeners
F_a	axial compressive stress permitted in the absence of bending stress
F_{as}	axial compressive stress, permitted in the absence of bending stress, for bracing and other secondary members
F_b	bending stress permitted in the absence of axial stress
F_b'	allowable bending stress in compression flange of plate girders as reduced because of large web depth-to-thickness ratio
F_e'	Euler stress divided by factor of safety; equal to $149{,}000{,}000/(L/r)^2$
F_p	allowable bearing stress
F_t, F_v	allowable tensile stress; allowable shear stress
F_y	specified minimum yield point of the type of steel being used
h	clear distance between flanges of a beam or girder
l_{cr}	critical unbraced length adjacent to plastic hinge, in inches
L	span length, in feet; unbraced length in inches
M_D; M_L	moment produced by dead load; by live load
M_p	plastic moment
P; P_y	applied load; plastic axial load
r, r_b	radius of gyration about axis of concurrent bending
r_y	lesser radius of gyration
t, t_f	girder or beam web thickness, flange thickness
V, V_u	statical shear; "ultimate" shear in plastic design
w	web thickness of plastically designed rolled beams

Notation for Timber Design by *NLMA* Specifications

A	cross-sectional area of timber
b	breadth of section, often larger dimension
c	allowable unit stress in compression parallel to the grain
$c_\perp$	allowable unit stress in compression perpendicular to the grain
d	depth of a rectangular column section, usually least side, also diameter of bolt or screw
E	modulus of elasticity of wood
f	allowable unit stress in flexure
G	specific gravity of wood when oven dry
h	depth of cross-section of a beam
H	allowable unit stress in horizontal shear
I	moment of inertia of a section
L	span of a beam in feet and length of a column in inches
N	load allowed at an angle θ to the grain
θ	angle between direction of load and direction of grain
p	allowable withdrawal load per inch of penetration for nail or screw
P	load on member or connector parallel to the grain, also allowable lateral load on nail, screw or connector parallel to the grain
Q	load on screw, bolt or connector perpendicular to the grain
t	allowable unit stress in tension parallel to the grain
u	unit allowable pressure at angle θ by Hankinson's formula

Notation for Reinforced Concrete Design by *ACI* Specifications

a, a_b	depth of equivalent rectangular stress block $= k_1c$; k_1c_b
A_c	area of core of spirally reinforced column to outside of the spiral

A_g	gross area of beam or column section
A_s; A_s'	area of tensile reinforcement; compressive reinforcement
A_t	nA_s or transformed area of tensile steel
A_v	area of tensile web reinforcement in length s of beam
α	angle of inclined web bars to axis of member
b	width of compression face of flexural member
b'	width of web for I and T-sections
b_o	perifery of critical section of a slab or footing
c	distance from extreme compression fiber to neutral axis
d, d'	distance from extreme compression fiber to centroid of A_s; of A_s'
D	nominal diameter of reinforcing bar
D_s	diameter of circle through centers of longitudinal bars for column
e	eccentricity of resultant load on column or any section
e_b	maximum permissible eccentricity of N_b
E_c; E_s	modulus of elasticity of concrete; of steel
f_a	axial load divided by area of member A_g
f_c	compressive stress in concrete
f_c'	compressive strength of concrete
f_s	calculated stress in tensile steel
f_t	calculated stress in transformed tensile steel $= f_s/n$
f_v	tensile stress in web reinforcement
f_y, F_y	minimum specified yield strength of steel reinforcement
F_a	allowable axial stress $= 0.34\ (1 + p_g m)f_c'$
F_b	allowable bending stress for bending alone
h	actual unsupported length of column; $h' =$ effective length
I, I_c	moment of inertia of beam or column, I_c for concrete
j	ratio of distance between centroid of compression and centroid of tension to the depth d
k_1	0.85 for $f_c' < 4000$, 0.80 for $f_c' = 5000$, and 0.75 for $f_c' = 6000$, etc.
K	stiffness factor $E_c I_c / L$
L	length of clear span, $L_1 =$ clear span perpendicular to L
L'	average of two adjacent clear spans for negative moment
m, m'	$f_y/0.85f_c'$; $m' = m - 1$
M, M'	bending moment, modified bending moment
M_u	ultimate resisting moment
n	ratio E_s/E_c
N	load normal to cross-section including tension due to shrinkage and creep
N_b	value of N below which the allowable eccentricity is controlled by tension
ΣO	sum of perimeters of bars used in computing bond stress
ϕ	capacity reduction factor = 0.90 for flexure; 0.85 for shear and bond; 0.75 for spiral columns; and 0.70 for tied columns
p, p'	A_s/bd; A_s'/bd; for a column, substitute area of concrete for bd
p_f, p_w	$A_{sf}/b'd$; $A_s/b'd$
p_g	ratio of vertical reinforcement to gross area A_g of column
P	allowable column load unreduced by eccentricity
q	$A_s f_y / bdf_c'$
r	radius of gyration of transformed cross-section
r'	ΣK of columns to ΣK of floor members in a plane at one end of a column
R	a reduction factor for long columns
s	spacing of stirrups or bent bars along axis of beam

t	minimum thickness of a beam or slab, depth or diameter of a column section
u,u_u	unit bond stress; ultimate bond stress
v,v_c	unit shear stress; shear stress carried by the concrete
V,V'	total shear; shear carried by web reinforcement
V_u,V_u'	total ultimate shear; ultimate shear carried by web reinforcement

ELEMENTARY STRUCTURAL ANALYSIS and DESIGN

Steel, Timber, and Reinforced Concrete

CHAPTER 1

DESIGN AND CONSTRUCTION

1. The Process of Building. The engineer looks at a finished structure and in his mind's eye, he sees the succession of steps that were performed to produce it. If we neglect consideration of the financing of the project, the legal process for acquiring the site, and the human relations between owner, engineer, and builder, there is still a long succession of events involved. A decision must be made as to the purpose to be accomplished by the structure, and its form must be chosen to fulfill its function. Costs need to be studied in comparison with the probable length of useful life of the structure, and this study will lead to a choice of material, that is, wood, steel, or concrete, or a combination of these. Then comes an estimate of the loads to be carried, followed by an analysis of the stresses in the members. The design of the structure involves the choice of member sizes and their connections, after which the shop work of fabricating individual members or parts of members proceeds. Finally, the field construction work takes place, and the finished structure appears. Each of these steps will now be considered briefly.

2. Form and Function. Whether we are considering an office building, a factory, a dock, or a support for some tank or machine, the size, shape, and arrangement of parts should depend upon the function to be performed. There is no reason why a machine tool plant should have the same external form or internal appearance as a warehouse. These buildings serve different purposes, and each should be arranged to aid in the fulfillment of that purpose. For instance, the factory may need a great deal of natural light while the warehouse may be more effective if built without windows and with artificial ventilation.

A power plant has often been an unattractive, square building showing no design for function other than the requirement that it provide the necessary floor space and an adequate height to hold the boilers. We see in Fig. 1 a power plant of functional design with the various services of boiler house, turbine house, and switch house segregated and given proper space under appropriate roof levels. Inside, convenience and purpose control floor levels, materials, and arrangement of equipment. The resulting structure is attractive, serviceable, and economical, although probably not cheap.

Another example of form being controlled by function of a building may be seen in Fig. 2. The desire of the owner for uninterrupted floor space is fulfilled by large floor spans, few interior columns, and no wall columns, the floors being cantilevered outward beyond the interior columns. The glass enclosure therefore had to be supported by vertical mullions to resist the wind pressure. Again to reduce obstructions inside the building, the mullions are exposed on the face of the building as a prominent architectural feature. Notice that the ceilings are uniformly lighted so that desks and offices may be moved as desired.

Courtesy Eng. News-Record

Fig. 1. Power Plant Building Functionally Designed.

Architect's sketch of power plant, with roof levels from high to low corresponding to boiler house, turbine house, and switch house. Small structure at right is screen house over intake tunnel.

3. A New Development in Architecture. A great deal of interest is engendered by the architectural features of America's modern buildings. Early office buildings were often criticized as esthetically unsatisfactory, the blame being placed by most critics upon the commercial motive. It was frequently pointed out that the most beautiful structures of the world had all been inspired by some influence other than the desire for a profitable investment. This argument has come back upon the critics, however, by the widespread acceptance of the belief that our industrial and office buildings and also apartment buildings constructed since 1940 have developed an entirely new type of monumental architecture, now called contemporary, which has taken its place with the other great schools of architecture. A glance at Fig. 2 is convincing evidence that here is a new conception of building architecture that cannot die without a change in the life of America, because it mirrors the age that it serves.

4. Life and Cost. A structure may be built for almost any period of use from 10 years to 100 years or more. Of course, the cost will increase with the need for permanency. There are hazards that may destroy any except the most permanent structures. Hurricanes produce wind velocities over small areas of more than 200 miles per hour, while we ordinarily design buildings to resist severe wind storms of from 60 to 100 miles per hour. Earthquakes have produced horizontal accelerations of 0.2 g or more, but we usually design for less than this acceleration even along the West Coast. Corrosion of steel, weathering of concrete, and decaying of timber may be delayed or prevented at increased cost. Hence, the designer considers *initial cost*, *maintenance*, and *useful life* as controlling factors in selection.

Courtesy Ingalls Iron Works Co.

FIG. 2. MANUFACTURERS TRUST COMPANY BUILDING, NEW YORK.

This simple 3-storey structure with floors cantilevered beyond the columns and with exposed steel mullions supporting the glass face has unusual distinction.

5. Materials. We will center our interest in steel, timber, and reinforced concrete as the main structural materials. Brick, tile, artificial stone, pressed board, glass block, gypsum, and plastics are used for enclosing space but not primarily for carrying load or providing strength. Steel is tough, ductile, and strong. Its allowable flexural stress of 20,000 to 33,000 psi, depending upon the steel chosen, permits the use of slender members in keeping with modern architecture. Steel softens and loses a large part of its strength below red heat and, therefore, is not fireproof. When covered with 2 in. of concrete or tile, steel is usually considered to be safe from fire and corrosion. Timber decays when it becomes alternately dry and moist. It is easily burned unless it is used as heavy beams and posts. But it can have a long life if it is painted regularly and maintained continuously dry. Reinforced concrete does not have the strength of steel, but it is stronger than timber. Steel is introduced into concrete columns to reduce the required area and thus to save floor space. Steel bars must be provided near the tension faces of concrete beams because concrete is very weak in tension and must be strengthened by the use of steel reinforcing bars. Reinforced concrete is subject to deterioration due to freezing and thawing, but this action can be minimized by the use of a proper concrete mix. Prestressed concrete is precompressed by stressed wires. It resists tension in flexure merely by a reduction of its precompression.

Each structural material is available in different strengths. Structural steel, for example, is available under *A*7 specifications at a yield strength of 33,000 psi, *A*36 at a yield strength of 36,000 psi, *A*242 and *A*441 for which the yield strength varies from 50,000 psi for material up to ¾ in. thick to 42,000 psi for material over 1½ in. thick. Similarly, for concrete or timber a wide range of strengths is available at differing unit costs. The designer should determine for each structure the optimum strength of material for use in each part so that the overall cost to meet all requirements is a minimum.

6. Loads. We first estimate the *dead load* of the structure and then revise this estimate as the design proceeds. The *live load* may consist of a crowd of people, of stored materials, of operating machines, or of moving trucks. It is evident that the live loading must be chosen to approximate operating conditions in as simple a manner as possible. *Impact* caused by moving loads or vibration is taken into consideration as an increment of the live loading except for timber structures where its effect is considered negligible. The *wind load* is chosen as a horizontal or inclined pressure (normal to the surface) varying with the locality. Its range is usually from 15 to 40 psf. Snow loading varies from 0 to 30 psf on a horizontal surface. Horizontal earthquake forces have been mentioned. Water pressure occurs on the inside surfaces of tanks, reservoirs, and dams and is readily computed.

7. Stress Analysis. Since we will be dealing with statically determinate structures, or those that may be made statically determinate by use of reasonable assumptions, our analysis will be based upon the equations of statics, $\Sigma F_x = 0$, $\Sigma F_y = 0$, and $\Sigma M = 0$. First, the reactions are calculated. From the loads and reactions we determine by statics the bar stresses for the trusses, the direct stresses for the columns, and the moments and shears for the beams and girders. Either algebraic or graphical methods may be used with requisite accuracy. We expect to maintain *a standard of accuracy of about 1 per cent of error* in either graphical analyses or slide-rule calculations. Obviously, greater accuracy can never be translated into tons of steel and cubic yards of concrete. Even a somewhat greater percentage of error would

Courtesy Bethlehem Steel Co.

FIG. 3. STRUCTURAL STEEL DETAILS.

not be serious, but it might lead to careless habits. Because a designer can maintain an accuracy represented by an error of about 1 per cent without extreme care in performing graphical analysis or in setting the slide rule, this standard of accuracy is accepted for most stress analysis.

Machine Calculations. There is wide use of digital computers in engineering offices for making stress computations. The machine follows coded instructions known as a *program.* A simple program might instruct the machine to sum the numbers above each number in a column (representing forces) and multiply each summation by the sine of an angle taken from a second column of numbers and then divide the result by an area taken from a third column. The result might be a set of unit stresses for the diagonal members of a tower obtained in a few seconds of machine operation. However, the writing of the program in machine code and its use on one or more towers for which the stresses were known, to assure its correctness, along with the necessary "debugging", may take several times the time used in making slide-rule calculations. Therefore, the value of machine calculations lies in standardized programs that can be used over and over, or in sophisticated studies that would require an unreasonable amount of hand calculation. The latter occur in analyses of statically indeterminate structures based upon many simultaneous equations and in dynamic studies for which a complete stress analysis may have to be repeated for changed dynamic loads for each successive fraction of a second over a time span of several minutes. Machine calculations use from five to ten significant figures to avoid loss of accuracy although the results may be no more meaningful than hand calculations of slide-rule accuracy. Every engineer needs to understand how digital computers are operated so that he may decide when a machine computation may be desirable as contrasted to hand computation and also what aid may be obtained from the machine in the study of highly complex structural action. The latter is beyond the scope of this book.

8. Structural Design. When the moments, shears, and direct stresses have been determined, it is possible to select the member sizes. In its essential features, this problem has been considered as a part of the course in the strength or mechanics of materials, but the types of members and the number of special cases will need to be extended here. The *direct-stress formula* ($f=P/A$) and the *beam-flexure formula* ($f=Mc/I$) will be used frequently. Then, of equal importance will be the design of connections

Courtesy Reynolds Metals Co.

FIG. 4. ALUMINUM GIRDER HAS V-SHAPE CROSS-SECTION.

between the members. Riveted, bolted, pin-connected, or welded joints in steel structures; nails, screws, bolts, and connectors for timber structures; and the bending and anchoring of reinforcing bars and prestressing wires in

Courtesy Timber Structures, Inc.

Fig. 5. Structural Roof in Timber.

concrete structures are of the greatest importance in design. More structures have failed because of inadequate connections between the parts than because of weak members. Both in the design of members and of joints, we will depend greatly upon standard specifications and building codes. Those to be used most frequently are American Institute of Steel Construction (*AISC*) *Specifications for Structural Steel for Buildings*; American Welding Society (*AWS*) *Code for Fusion Welding of Buildings*; American Concrete Institute (*ACI*) *Building Code Requirements for Reinforced Concrete.* These specifications are given in abbreviated form in Chapter 17. Since they are numbered consecutively, we will find it convenient to refer to them by number and thus save repeating common specifications many times.

9. Fabrication and Construction. After the designer has selected the members and designed the joints, the detailer makes the detail drawings of the structure. For steel, the details locate every rivet and weld, fix all sizes and dimensions, and specify bearing surface finish. For concrete, the details list all bar sizes and lengths, locate bends in the reinforcing bars, and give the dimensions of the concrete members. Quality of the concrete is covered by the job specifications. For timber, the details list commercial sizes and exact lengths. Holes for bolts or connectors are located, and bolts are specified as to size and strength. Each piece of timber is given a commercial strength designation, as for example, 1200c, which means that this timber must be able to resist a column compressive stress of 1200 psi. Construction details for steel, aluminum, and timber structures are shown in Fig. 3, Fig. 4, and Fig. 5.

The detail drawings go to the shop where steel members are fabricated, reinforcing bars are cut to length and bent, and large timbers are bored and shaped. Some of this work may be performed in the field (especially for timber structures), but field work is usually more expensive than shop fabrication. For large complex structures of steel or timber, a complete or partial shop erection may be performed to assure rapid field work.

In the field the builder is at the mercy of the weather, but his unique ability to overcome this and other obstacles is proverbial. However, it is the duty of the designer, the detailer, and the shop superintendent to provide the construction engineer with as nearly a perfectly fabricated structure as is feasible. Small delays in the field are inordinately expensive. Aside from the vagaries of the weather, field delays are usually due to some error in the design office or the shop. It is evident that careful *routing of material* through the shop so that it will reach the job when it is needed and not greatly before is a critical matter. All persons involved in routing materials must agree upon the transportation facilities to be used between the shop and the field.

CHAPTER 2

THE TOOLS OF STRESS ANALYSIS

10. Loads on Beams and Trusses. Loads on structures will be discussed very briefly here because it is necessary to study this matter in detail in the following chapter. However, even for a study of the mechanics of stress analysis, it must be understood that the roof system of an industrial building and the floor system of a bridge serve the purpose of carrying the live load and most of the dead load to the panel points of the supporting trusses. It may be assumed in the analysis that each truss member carries its own

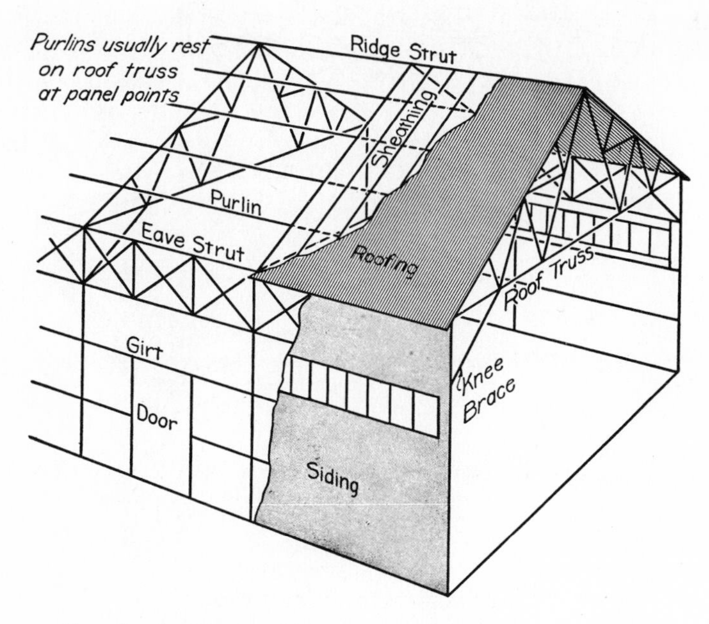

FIG. 6. STRUCTURAL FRAME OF AN INDUSTRIAL BUILDING.

weight equally to the two adjacent panel points. Thus, there is a concentrated load at each joint of one half of the dead weight of all members framing into that joint. Accordingly, when a truss diagram is shown with arrows which represent concentrated loads at the panel points, it should be remembered that these forces are computed as *reactions* produced at the panel points by the roof system, the floor system, or the truss members themselves, as the case may be. A study of roof framing for an industrial building (Fig. 6), of floor framing for a highway bridge (Fig. 7), or of the floor system of an office building (Fig. 8) will help to clarify these statements.

In contrast to the way in which loads are applied as joint concentrations to trusses, *uniform or distributed loads* do come directly upon the top flanges of beams and girders. Such loads might be carried there by a concrete floor slab or roof slab. Small beams frame at right angles into larger beams or girders, and their reactions produce concentrated loads upon the larger beams. (Note the arrangement of floor girders supporting floor joists in Fig. 8.) A girder also must carry a uniform load composed of its own weight and probably the dead load of a small amount of the floor slab that rests directly upon its upper flange.

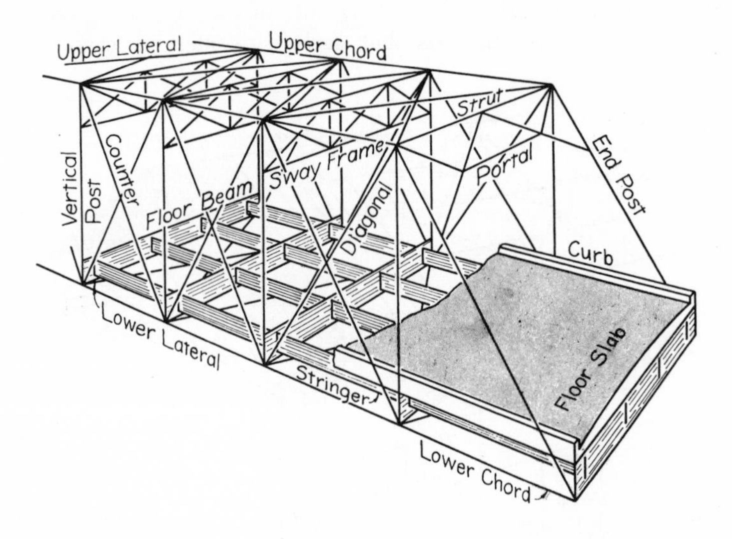

FIG. 7. TRUSSES, FLOOR SYSTEM, AND BRACING OF A THROUGH-TRUSS HIGHWAY BRIDGE.

EQUILIBRIUM OF STRUCTURES

11. The Laws of Statics. The statement that a body is in *static equilibrium* simply means that it is not moving. A structure may move; for example, an airplane frame or a lift bridge moves; but the individual members of a single structural unit do not move relative to each other, for the structure would then become a *machine.* All stationary structures, and indeed all moving structures when acceleration or inertia forces are included, must be acted upon by a set of forces (loads and reactions) that are in equilibrium. The laws of statics state: *for any set of coplanar forces in equilibrium, the algebraic sum of the components of these forces along any axis in this plane is equal to zero; and further, the moment of these forces about any point in this plane is equal to zero.* It is unnecessary to consider here the general case of forces in space, because the loads, reactions, and stresses for a beam or truss usually may be considered to act in a *single plane.*

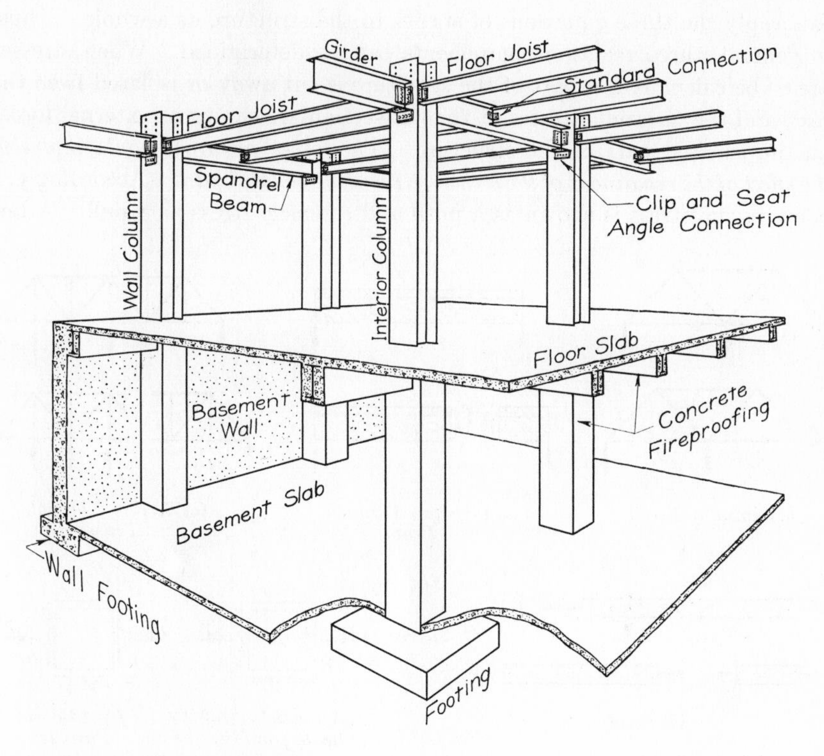

FIG. 8. THE FIREPROOFED STRUCTURE OF A STEEL FRAME BUILDING.

The Equations of Statics. For convenience, structural engineers are accustomed to write the laws of statics for coplanar forces in shorthand as follows:

(1) $\Sigma F_x = 0$ (sometimes written $\Sigma H = 0$).

(2) $\Sigma F_y = 0$ (sometimes written $\Sigma V = 0$).

(3) $\Sigma M_C = 0$ (for center of moments C).

The equations $\Sigma F_x = 0$ and $\Sigma F_y = 0$ refer to the summation of the force components along horizontal and vertical axes. Any pair of rectangular axes may be used with equal confidence. Axes chosen parallel and perpendicular to main truss members are sometimes found convenient in the analysis of roof trusses. The equation of moments, $\Sigma M = 0$, has no such limitation, since it applies to the moment of the forces about *any point in the plane of the loads.*

12. Stress Analysis by Statics, Free Body Diagrams. Any structure, part of a structure, truss joint, truss number, part of a number, or even any infinitesimal particle of a beam or truss must be acted upon by a set of forces that are in equilibrium. In order to compute the values of the reactions, we can apply the three equations of statics to the structure as a whole. Thus, in general, three reaction components can be determined. When stresses are to be calculated, a part of the structure is cut away or isolated from the rest, and the internal stresses at the cut section are shown as external forces on the isolated part of the structure. *The forces pictured should represent the effect of the remainder of the structure upon the isolated part.* Accordingly, a compressive stress is shown as a push and a tensile stress as a pull. A few

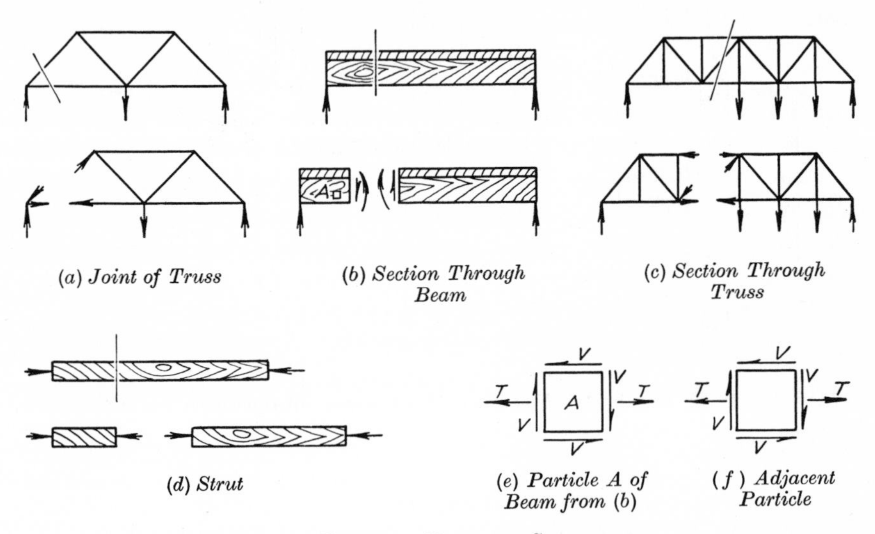

Fig. 9. Isolated Parts of Structures.

structures are cut by sections and the isolated parts are shown in Fig. 9. Such isolated parts of structures with all contact and body forces shown are called "free body diagrams." Notice that the sum of the forces placed at the opposing faces of the cut section will always be zero, since no actual *external* forces exist there.

The Number of Stresses Determinable by Statics. In general, three unknown forces can be calculated for an isolated body by use of the three equations of statics. Only two unknowns can be determined from the equations $\Sigma F_y = 0$ and $\Sigma M = 0$ for *parallel coplanar forces,* such as the vertical reactions of a truss or beam. The equation $\Sigma F_x = 0$ merely shows that no horizontal reaction is needed when all loads are vertical. Two unknowns can be found for *concurrent coplanar forces* by use of the equations $\Sigma F_x = 0$ and $\Sigma F_y = 0$. The equation $\Sigma M = 0$ is not needed because any group of concurrent forces that obeys the equations $\Sigma F_x = 0$ and $\Sigma F_y = 0$ must have a zero moment about any point in its plane. All three of the equations of statics are independent for *non-concurrent non-parallel forces in a plane*, and three unknown forces can be determined. Such forces exist at a cross-section of a beam and at most sections that are cut through trusses. (See Fig. 10.)

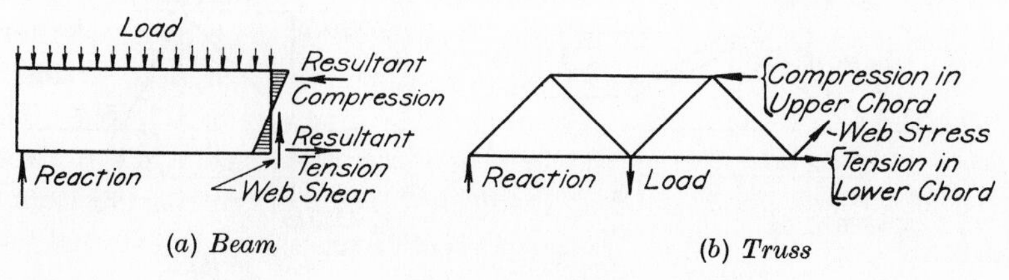

(*a*) *Beam* (*b*) *Truss*

Fig. 10. Comparison of Internal Stresses.

It is of interest to observe in Fig. 10 the correspondence of loads, reactions, flange stress and chord stress, web shear and web stress between the beam and the truss. This similarity should be studied because it is the basis of a simplified method of truss analysis.

Use of Resultants. An error is made frequently by the novice in attempting to replace several loads on a structure by their resultant. It is permissible to replace all loads on a structure by their resultant when calculating reactions by *use of the entire structure as a free body*. Only those forces acting to the right or left of a cut section may be replaced by their respective resultants when the shears or moments in a beam, or the internal stresses in a truss, are computed. This limitation will be clear if we recall that only those forces to the left of a given section would even be shown on a free-body sketch of that portion of the structure to the left of this section. A resultant that included some forces to the right of the section certainly should not be used. The ability to draw free-body diagrams is of great importance in structural analysis.

PROBLEMS

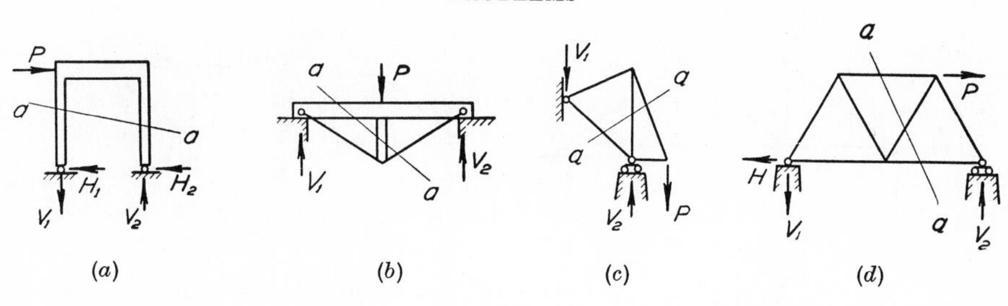

Problem 201.

201. Draw neat sketches showing the isolated parts of each structure as cut by the section *a–a*. Study the directions of the loads and reactions in order to show the internal forces and moments acting in their correct directions on each free-body diagram.

202. Isolate each bar of these structures and show the forces acting on each. Determine the direct stresses in the bars.

HINT. Start by isolating the entire structure as a free body to find the reactions at B.

Ans. to (*a*), $S_{BC} = 2130$ lb. C.
Ans. to (*b*), $S_{BC} = 1490$ lb. C.

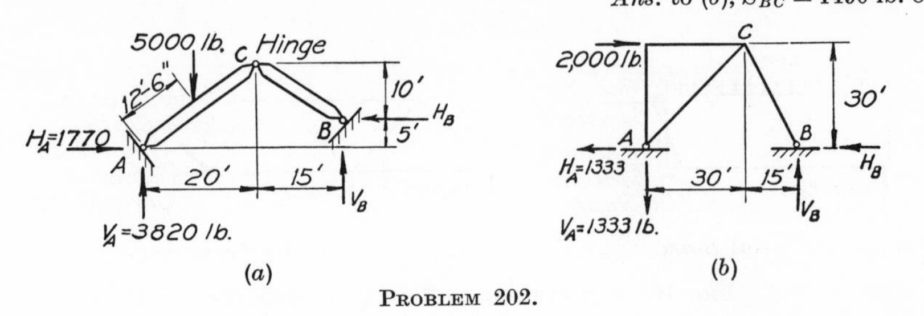

PROBLEM 202.

203. In Problem 202 (*a*) keep the reactions and the point of application of the load unchanged in position but draw in a different shape of structure to support the load. Choose a statically determinate form of structure and supports so that you may compute the reaction at B and the internal forces.

204. Same as Problem 203 except use the sketch for Problem 202 (*b*).

GRAPHICAL ANALYSIS

13. Graphical Conditions of Equilibrium—Concurrent Coplanar Forces. Corresponding to the mathematical requirements that the equations $\Sigma F_x=0$ and $\Sigma F_y=0$ must be satisfied for a set of concurrent forces in static equilibrium, there is the necessary and sufficient condition of graphical analysis that *the force polygon must close.* Consider the four concurrent forces acting at the left-hand end of the truss of Fig. 11(*a*). These forces are drawn to scale in (*b*) with the arrows pointed continuously around the polygon. The polygon (*c*) is drawn to show that closure is obtained when the forces are taken in a different order. *The order chosen is immaterial,* but the arrows must point continuously around the polygon.

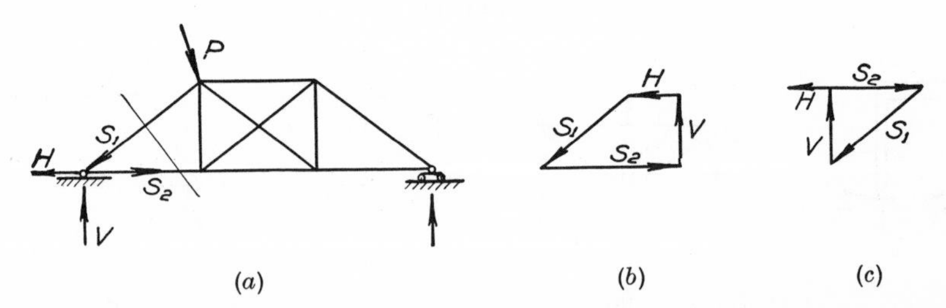

FIG. 11. FORCE POLYGONS FOR THE LEFT-HAND REACTION JOINT.

14. Graphical Conditions of Equilibrium—Non-concurrent Coplanar Forces. Non-concurrent forces in equilibrium must satisfy the same conditions as concurrent forces plus the requirement expressed by the equation of statics, $\Sigma M=0$. The mathematical requirement expressed by this equation is satisfied graphically by the necessary condition that *the equilibrium polygon shall close.* The procedure for drawing the equilibrium polygon or funicular[1] polygon will be explained in the following sections. The equilibrium polygon is a useful device, but it is not possible to give it quite the physical significance that is so evident in the force polygon.

15. Bow's Notation. In order to obtain the greatest saving of time by graphical constructions, it is necessary to follow a standardized system of notation. Bow's notation (Robert Bow—England, 1873) consists of the use of two letters or figures placed at the two ends of a vector in the force polygon to designate the force represented by it. Then the same letters or figures are written on the two sides of the action line of the same force. Figure 12 represents the use of Bow's notation. In (*a*) and (*b*) the load P_1 is properly termed *force A-B with action line a-b*; the reaction R_2 is *force D-E with action line d-e.*

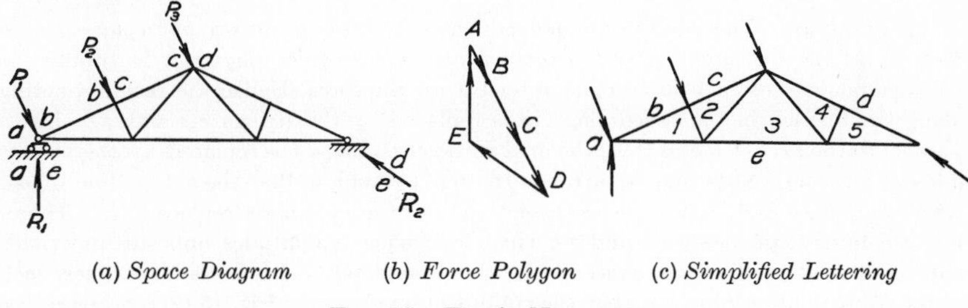

(*a*) *Space Diagram* (*b*) *Force Polygon* (*c*) *Simplified Lettering*

FIG. 12. BOW'S NOTATION.

The sketch (*c*) shows how lettering can be economized by placing a single letter between each pair of forces. It also shows how internal stresses can be designated by numbers. The force 3-*E* would represent the stress in the center member of the lower chord while the force 2-3 would represent the stress in the adjacent web member.

16. The Equilibrium Polygon. The forces in Fig. 13 are lettered with lower-case letters in the space diagram and with upper-case letters in the force polygon. We will assume that the forces shown (loads and reactions) are in equilibrium. A pole *O* is chosen conveniently to either side of the force polygon and the rays *O-A*, *O-B*, etc. are drawn. Clearly *A-O* and *O-B* are components of the force *A-B*. (Law of the triangle of forces from mechanics.) Similarly, *B-O* and *O-C* are components of *B-C*. Note then that the force *O-B* acting as a component of *A-B* is equal but oppositely directed to the force *B-O* acting as a component of *B-C*. When each ray is thus looked upon as representing two equal and opposite force components, the entire set of rays forms a substitute force system that will replace the

[1] This is also called the *string* polygon. *Funicular* simply means string-like. We will define the *equilibrium* polygon to mean the special case of the string or funicular polygon when the forces considered are in equilibrium.

effect of the original force system on the structure. Hence, if these equal and opposite pairs of forces can be shown to be collinear, both the original force system and the substitute force system must be in equilibrium. In the construction of the equilibrium polygon, as will be shown, we will place each pair of equal and opposite force components along the same line of action so that the conditions of equilibrium will be fulfilled.

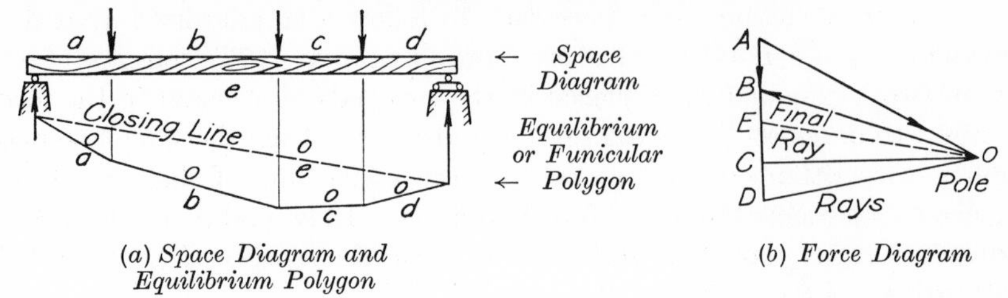

FIG. 13. GRAPHICAL CONSTRUCTION OF THE EQUILIBRIUM POLYGON.

PROCEDURE. The equilibrium polygon in Fig. 13(*a*) is drawn *by replacing each force in the space diagram by its two components from the force diagram.* Naturally the two components of each force must intersect on the force. Hence the reaction acting along the line *e-a* in the space diagram is replaced by the strings *e-o* and *o-a* drawn parallel to the rays *O-E* and *O-A*; the load with action line *a-b* is replaced by the strings *a-o* and *o-b*; etc. Note that we arrange the replacement so that the action line of *o-a* when we replace *E-A* is the same as the action line of *a-o* when we replace *A-B*. Therefore, the force components *o-a* and *a-o* which have equal magnitudes, opposite directions, and the same line of action, cancel each other completely. In the same manner, each string (from *o-a* to *o-e* inclusive) of the equilibrium polygon in Fig. 13 (*a*) represents the action line of two equal and opposite force components which cancel each other. But this will only be true *for all strings* if the string or funicular polygon is actually closed. It follows that *the original forces which form a closed force polygon must be in equilibrium when the string polygon also closes.* If the string polygon does not close, one pair of equal and opposite force components will not have the same line of action but will have parallel lines of action. In that case the original forces cannot be in moment equilibrium. Instead, their resultant will be a couple. For example, the loads and the end reaction for one half of a simple span truss with symmetrical loading would obey the equation $\Sigma F_y = 0$ but not the equation $\Sigma M = 0$. The resultant of these forces is a couple. The string polygon will not close but will present two parallel strings that are not collinear. The value of the couple is one force multiplied by the perpendicular distance between the parallel strings.

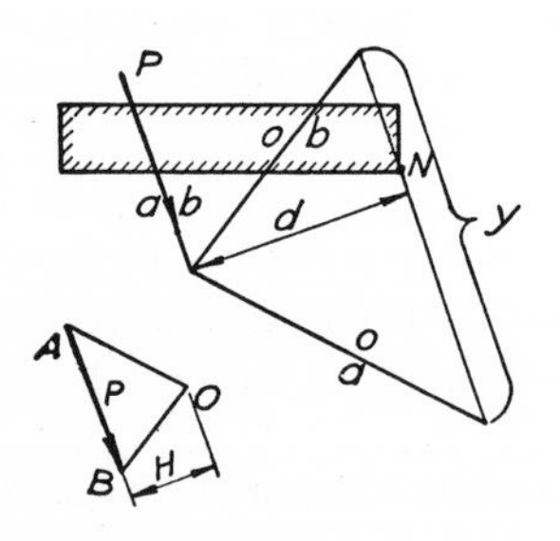

FIG. 14. MOMENT BY GRAPHICS.

17. The Equilibrium Polygon and the Equation $\Sigma M = 0$. Consider the body shown in Fig. 14 acted upon by the force P or A-B, which may properly be considered to represent the resultant of several forces, such as loads and reactions to the left of a section. The rays O-A and O-B are drawn from a pole O in the force diagram, and these rays are paralleled by the strings *o-a* and *o-b* on the space diagram. The intercept between these strings on a line drawn through the point N parallel to the resultant force P is called y. The pole distance H in the force diagram is taken perpendicular to the force P, as is the distance d in the space diagram. Then, from similar triangles, we find

$$\frac{y}{d} = \frac{P}{H}, \quad \text{or} \quad Hy = Pd = M_N, \tag{4}$$

the moment of P about the point N. Observe that the intercept y must be measured on a line through the moment center parallel to the resultant load P, and that the pole distance H must be measured normal to the resultant load.

Moment Diagram by Graphics. In Fig. 15, the intercept of the string polygon under the point N, or y_1, lies between the strings *o-b* and *o-d*. Accordingly, y_1H represents the moment of the force *D-B* (whose components are *D-O* and *O-B* in the force diagram) about the point N. Note that DB is also the resultant of the load and reaction to the left of section N.

By definition the moment about the section of the resultant force to the left of the section is the bending moment at the section. Hence y_1H is the value of the bending moment at the section N in Fig. 15. In general we may state that a vertical intercept of the equilibrium polygon for a horizontal beam when multiplied by the horizontal pole distance gives the bending moment in the beam at a position corresponding to the intercept.

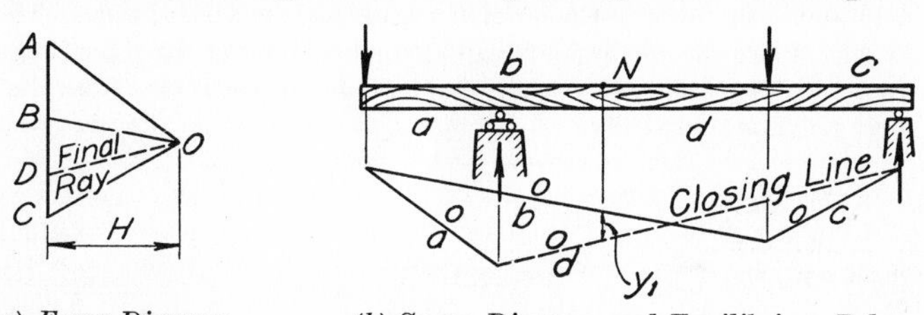

(*a*) *Force Diagram* (*b*) *Space Diagram and Equilibrium Polygon*

FIG. 15. BENDING MOMENT OBTAINED GRAPHICALLY.

Units for Graphical Moments. The pole distance furnishes the scale for measuring intercepts on the equilibrium polygon. More specifically, intercepts from the equilibrium polygon measured to the scale of the space diagram (ft.) can be multiplied by the pole distance measured to the scale of the force diagram (lb.) to obtain bending moments in corresponding units (ft-lb.). *Hence the equilibrium polygon is the bending moment diagram to scale when the pole distance in the force diagram is chosen as unity.* It is more common to choose a pole distance of 1000 lb. or 10,000 lb. Then the intercept on the equilibrium polygon measured in feet is simply multiplied by 1000 or 10,000 to obtain the bending moment in foot-pounds.

Graphical Criterion for Rotational Equilibrium. The force *D-B* in Fig. 15 is either the resultant of *D-A* and *A-B*, the forces to the left of N, or, *with sign reversed*, it may represent the resultant of B-C and C-D, the forces to the right of N. The product y_1H may therefore represent the moment about N either of the forces to the right or left of the point N. Since these equal moments have opposite signs, we conclude that the total moment of all forces about N is zero, or that the structure is in rotational equilibrium about this point. But, as N was taken to represent any point on the structure, the general statement may be made that closure of the equilibrium polygon is proof that the structure is in rotational equilibrium about all points in its plane, that is, the loads and reactions satisfy the equation of statics $\Sigma M = 0$.

PROBLEMS

205. Show how to obtain graphically the resultant of a series of concurrent forces that are not in equilibrium. Set up a numerical case and draw the force polygon to scale.

206. Four vertical forces of 2500 lb. each act at intervals of 20 ft. alternately up and down so that each pair of adjacent forces forms a clockwise couple of known value. Draw a string polygon and note that the initial and final strings are not collinear. Scale the values of these strings in pounds and the distance between them in feet and compare the moment obtained with the magnitudes of the two couples.

207. Determine the dead-load stresses for the highway bridge truss shown, by drawing a separate force polygon for each joint. Each of the two trusses weighs 38,800 lb. The total weight of steel in the stringers, floor beams, laterals, sway frames, portals, and handrails is 62,300 lb. The 18-ft. roadway requires a concrete floor slab 19½ ft. wide and 8 in. thick. Each curb is 9 in. high and 9 in. wide. The concrete weighs 150 pcf. Place the entire dead load at the lower-chord panel points.

SUGGESTION. Two unknown stresses can be found at each joint from the condition that the force polygon must close. *Ans.* $S_{\text{max.}} = 119$ kips.

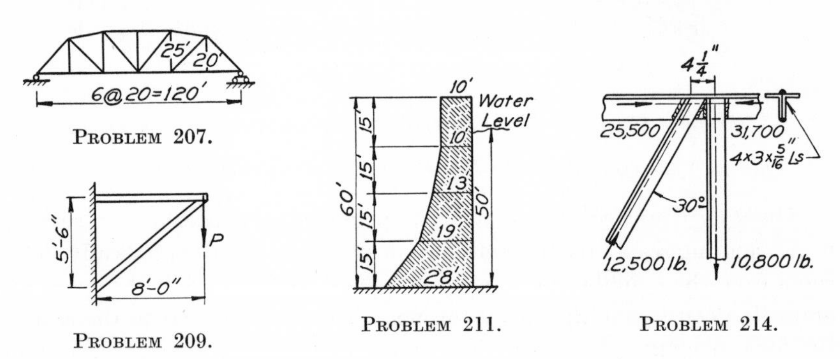

PROBLEM 207.

PROBLEM 209.

PROBLEM 211.

PROBLEM 214.

208. Same as Problem 207 but increase width of roadway to 27 ft. and increase weight of steel 30 per cent.

209. The welded cantilever crane has a horizontal tension member composed of two steel bars 2 in. by 5/16 in. If the crane was designed equally strong in all parts, what load would it lift at a working stress of 20,000 psi in the horizontal member?

Ans. 17,200 lb.

210. Develop a graphical procedure for determining the resultant of a series of non-concurrent forces that are not in equilibrium. Consider the use of partial resultants. Set up and solve a numerical example.

SUGGESTION. Where intersections of the forces do not occur on the sheet, it is necessary to use the uncancelled strings of the funicular polygon. The strings are components of the resultant and the resultant must therefore pass through their intersection.

211. Determine the resultant base pressure per lineal foot for the dam shown. Estimate the weight of masonry at 145 pcf. For stability, the resultant pressure must be within the middle third of the base. Is this dam stable against overturning? Check your graphical work by algebraic calculations. In practice a wider base would be used. *Ans.* R per lineal ft. = 154 kips acting at 18.5 ft. from heel.

212. Same as Problem 211 but reduce the water level to 45 ft.

213. Graphically determine the moment diagram for a simple beam or cantilever uniformly loaded. Treat the uniform load as a series of ten concentrations. Show that the polygon obtained approximates a parabola.

214. By drawing a force polygon and an equilibrium polygon, show that the resultant of the stresses meeting at this joint is a couple whose value is 45,900 in-lb. Assume that each top-chord member resists one third of this moment. Determine its flexural stress. Sketch an improved detail. *Ans.* 6200 psi.

REACTIONS OF STRUCTURES

18. Supports for Beams and Trusses. The function of the reactions of a structure is to resist the tendency of the loads to move the structure in certain directions while permitting other necessary movements. For

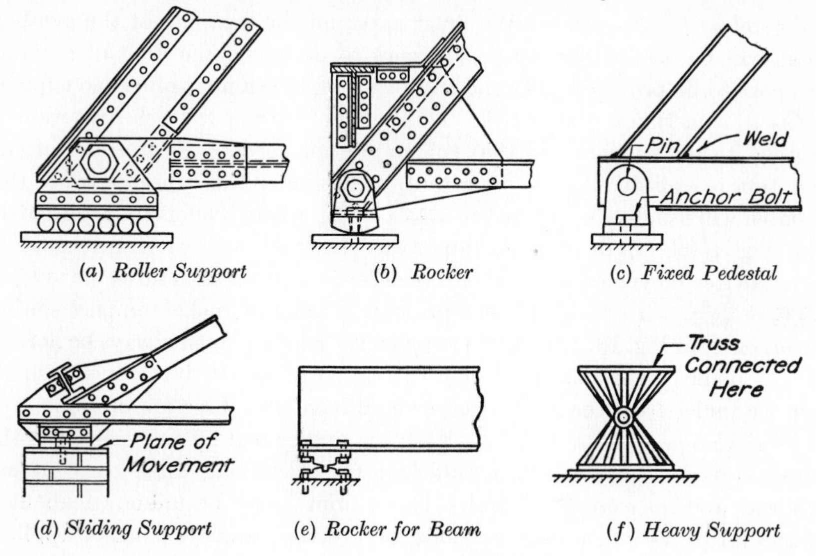

FIG. 16. REACTION SUPPORTS FOR BEAMS AND TRUSSES.

example, a bridge must have one end supported on rollers or rockers to allow for the movement that occurs from increase or decrease in the span length because of temperature change. A fixed support with a rotating pin is desirable at the other end to take care of the end rotation that accompanies vertical deflection of the structure. A roller, a rocker, a sliding shoe, and a fixed support are shown in Fig. 16. Each of these types of support is used in bridges or buildings. It is assumed that the reader will familiarize himself with the appearance and use of such elementary structural devices as rollers, pins, hinges, rockers, and links. A reaction pin and a roller box are seen in Fig. 17.

Courtesy American Bridge Co.

FIG. 17. EXPANSION SHOE.

Symbols for Reactions. We must agree on the meaning of the symbols that will be needed for use on sketches to designate the kind of reaction support to be provided. At the end of a simple beam a knife-edge support is sometimes designated. This symbol means that the reaction is normal to the support and that rollers are not needed. If freedom of end rotation is considered very important, as at the end of a bridge truss, this symbol will usually be changed to or where a pin is to be provided. See Fig. 16(*c*), (*e*), or (*f*). In important structures it is often necessary to provide free movement normal to a reaction. In such structures the symbol or with three circles represents a roller or rocker support similar to (*a*) or (*b*) of Fig. 16. At such a support the reaction must always be normal to the plane of the rollers. When the support symbol shows only a single pin we understand that the reaction may have any direction or slope.

Calculation of Reactions. It should be understood by this time that the three equations of statics are sufficient for calculating three reaction unknowns and *no more than three.* Three things may be unknown about a single force: its magnitude, its slope or direction, and its point of application. This information can be obtained if its x component, its y component, and its point of application are known. Ordinarily the point of application of the reaction is known, and one or both of its two components are to be determined. Since two sloping reactions (unknown in value and direction) have four components, which could not be calculated by the three equations of statics, it is usually necessary to arrange the manner of support so that one component of one reaction will be zero. This requirement is met by placing one end of the truss on rollers in order to make the horizontal component of reaction equal to zero at that end. This arrangement also allows for free temperature expansion or contraction. Trusses that have more than three reaction components are called *statically indeterminate* in regard to the external forces. Structures of both types are shown in Fig. 18.

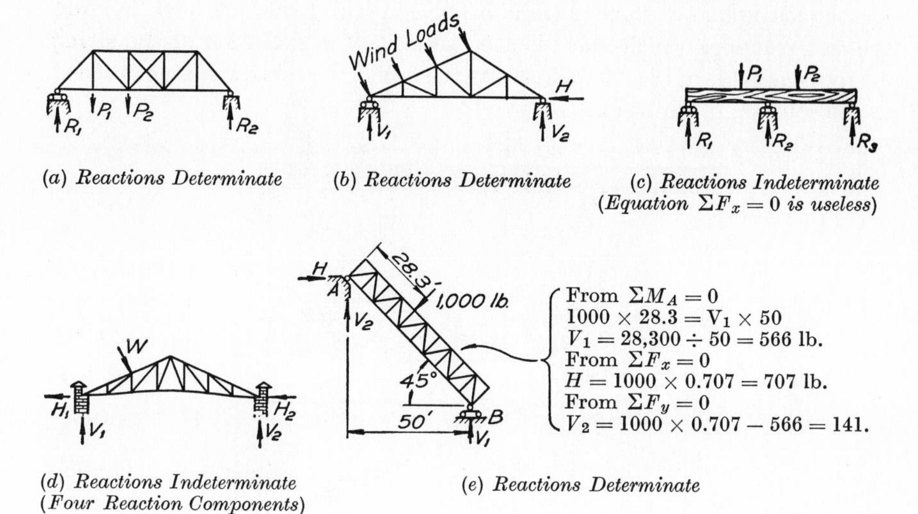

(*a*) *Reactions Determinate* (*b*) *Reactions Determinate* (*c*) *Reactions Indeterminate* (*Equation $\Sigma F_x = 0$ is useless*)

(*d*) *Reactions Indeterminate* (*Four Reaction Components*) (*e*) *Reactions Determinate*

Fig. 18. Statically Determinate and Indeterminate Reactions.

19. Reactions Under a Simple Span—Vertical Loads. *The algebraic solution* of this problem is quite elementary. The equation of statics, $\Sigma M = 0$, when written for a center of moments at the right-hand reaction, can be solved for the left-hand reaction. We then determine the right-hand reaction from the equation $\Sigma F_y = 0$. The values of the reactions can be checked by use of an equation of moments about the left-hand reaction.

The graphical procedure for determining the vertical reactions under a horizontal span is in exact correspondence with the algebraic method. We first draw a partial force polygon (reactions as yet unknown) and a partial funicular or string polygon. Figure 19 shows these constructions in solid lines. Then the string *o-a* is extended (broken line) until it intersects the reaction line *d-e* at *r*. Note that the intercept *q-r* or y between the strings *o-a* and *o-d*, when multiplied by the pole distance H, is equal to the moment of the three loads about R_2. Hence, $R_1 = yH \div s$. However, if the closing line *m-q* (string *o-e*) is drawn and paralleled by the ray *O-E* in the force polygon, it is noticed that the triangle *A-O-E* is similar to the triangle *r-m-q* since corresponding sides are parallel; therefore we may write

$$\frac{y}{s} = \frac{E\text{-}A}{H}. \tag{5}$$

But since $R_1 = yH \div s$ we may write

$$R_1 = \frac{yH}{s} = \frac{(E\text{-}A)H}{H} = E\text{-}A, \tag{6}$$

and it follows that $R_2 = D\text{-}E$. Hence we conclude that a ray drawn parallel to the closing line of the equilibrium polygon will divide the load line into the two reactions which may then be scaled. The extension of the string *o-a* to *r* was made in Fig. 19 to illustrate the proof given above; it is not needed in the solution of problems.

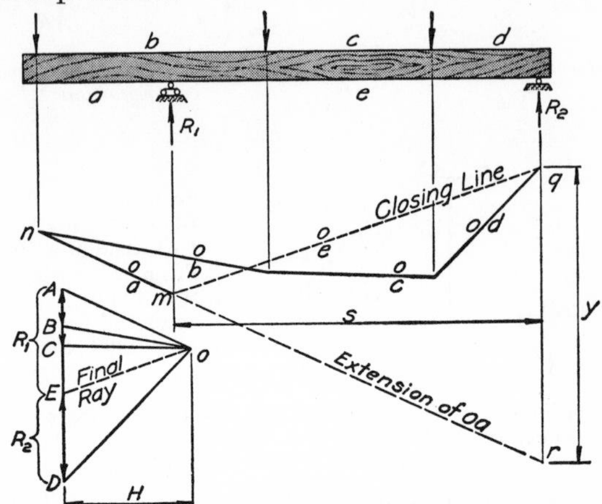

Fig. 19. Reactions of a Simple Overhanging Beam.

20. Reactions of a Roof Truss—Wind Loads. This is the general problem of determining two reactions, one known in direction and point of application and the other known in point of application only. *Algebraically*, the equation $\Sigma F_x = 0$ shows that the x component of R_1 (see Fig. 20) is equal and opposite to the x component of the loads when R_2 acts vertically. Then, an equation of moments about the left-hand pin contains but the one unknown R_2, which is determined. Finally, the equation $\Sigma F_y = 0$ makes possible the calculation of the y component of R_1, after which the reaction R_1 can be found both in magnitude and direction from its two known components.

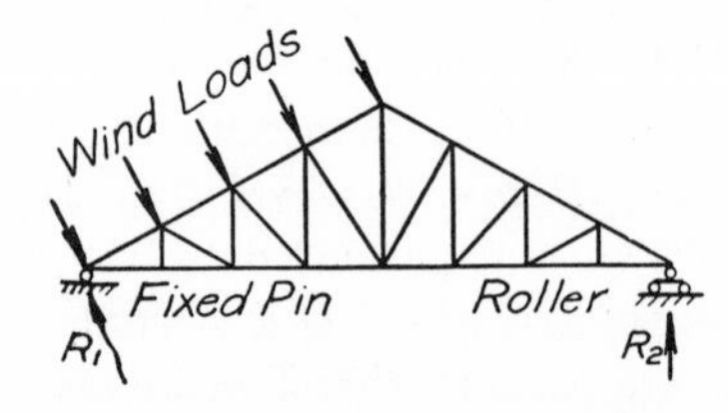

Fig. 20. Wind Reactions for a Roof Truss.

Roller supports are more common for bridge trusses where the length of span usually justifies the cost.

Graphically, the procedure is almost identical with the method already discussed for determining the vertical reactions under a simple span. Lay out the force diagram A-B-C-D-E-F, Fig. 21(b). Choose a pole O and draw in the rays O-A to O-F inclusive. The location of G is unknown, but, since R_2 is vertical, G must lie on a vertical line above the point F. (F-$G = R_2$.) Observe that *the loads and reactions are drawn in a clockwise order.*

The funicular polygon must be started at the one known point on the action line of the sloping reaction, which is the point m in Fig. 21(a). The funicular polygon is then constructed to an intersection at r on the action line of R_2. Note that the string o-a parallel to the ray O-A connects two intersecting forces at their point of intersection and hence disappears. The closing string o-g (line r-m) is paralleled in the force diagram by the ray O-G, which is extended to an intersection with a vertical line through F. The force F-G is scaled to obtain the magnitude of the reaction R_2, while the force G-A represents both the magnitude and direction of R_1.

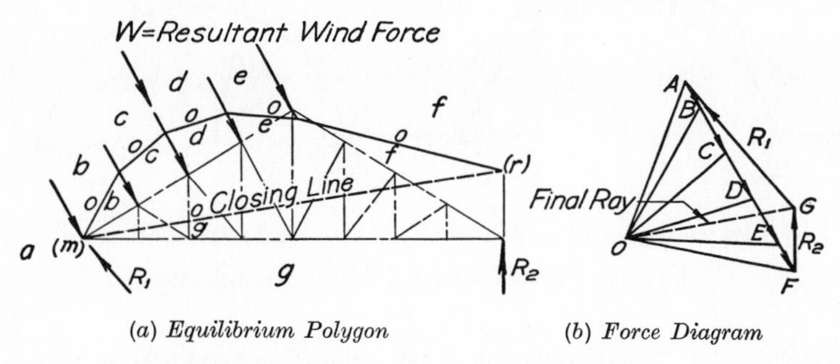

(a) *Equilibrium Polygon* (b) *Force Diagram*

FIG. 21. TRUSS REACTIONS FROM WIND.

Simplification. This problem can be much simplified in most cases by replacing all wind loads by their *resultant force* [see W in Fig. 21(a)] before starting the force polygon. However, the use of a resultant load is recommended only when the line of action of W may be determined by inspection. This simplification is also useful in the algebraic method.

21. Reactions for a Three-Hinged Arch. The structure of Fig. 22 has two sloping reactions or four reaction components. However, it is not statically indeterminate, since the hinge at the crown furnishes an extra equation, $\Sigma M_{\text{crown}} = 0$, which makes *the algebraic determination of the reactions* possible by statics.[2] In Fig. 22, the two reaction points are shown on the same level. Hence the equation $\Sigma M_B = 0$ contains only the one unknown, V_1, which can be determined. Then the equation of moments for

[2] A frictionless pin cannot resist moment. However, we do not obtain an *independent* equation by writing $\Sigma M_C = 0$ for the entire arch as a free body. This equation must hold true for equilibrium even without a pin at the crown. Instead, we isolate as a free body the part of the structure to one side of the crown and obtain an entirely new and independent equation, $\Sigma M_C = 0$ for the forces acting on the half arch as a free body.

the forces to the left of C, $\Sigma M_C = 0$, will contain but one unknown, H_1. This equation can be solved for the value of H_1. If the supports are at different levels, these two equations will each contain the two unknowns, H_1 and V_1. Such equations must be solved simultaneously. As soon as H_1 and V_1 are known, H_2 and V_2 can be determined from the equations $\Sigma F_x = 0$ and $\Sigma F_y = 0$ applied to the entire structure.

The graphical determination of the reactions is illustrated in (*b*) of Fig. 22. The action line of R_2 (reaction on the unloaded side of the arch) must pass through the center hinge, because the bending moment there (moment of R_2, the only force to the right of C) must be zero. The two reactions, being components of the load, must intersect somewhere on the action line of the load. When their action lines have been determined in the space diagram,

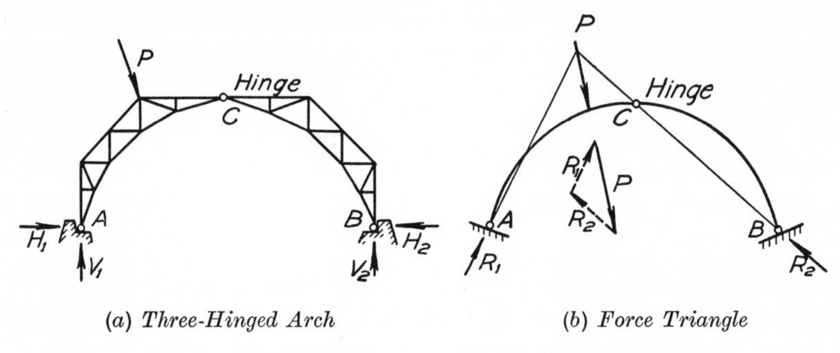

(*a*) *Three-Hinged Arch* (*b*) *Force Triangle*

FIG. 22. REACTIONS OF A THREE-HINGED ARCH.

the values of the two reactions may be found from the force diagram. This method can be used to determine the reactions for each of several forces separately and then these partial reactions can be combined into a resultant reaction. It is more convenient to make use of two resultant loads, one for each half of the arch. A *single resultant for loads on both halves of the arch* can not be used conveniently because neither reaction for this case will pass through the central pin. The moment of a reaction about the center hinge is not zero when a load exists between that reaction and the hinge.

22. Two Sloping Reactions for a Roof Truss. Unlike the three-hinged arch, the roof truss becomes statically indeterminate externally if there are two sloping reactions, both unknown in direction. Small roof trusses may be constructed cheaply by bolting both ends down to pillars or masonry walls. This arrangement produces four unknown components of reaction. Since the stresses in such trusses are small, it is considered satisfactory to assume the direction of one or both of the reactions. For instance, in Fig. 23(*a*), the assumption is made that the line of action of each reaction is parallel to the resultant of the wind loads.

Algebraically, the two reactions in Fig. 23(*a*) can be computed from two equations of moments about the reaction points. An alternate assumption that is sometimes used is that each of the two horizontal components of reaction is equal to one half of the horizontal component of the entire wind load. See Fig. 23(*b*) where $H_1 = H_2$. Each of these assumptions gives reactions that are only approximations. These approximate methods of computation should not be used for large trusses until a careful study has shown that the greatest possible error in the reactions will not endanger the structure.

Graphically, the determination of two sloping reactions assumed to act parallel to the wind loads needs no explanation. The procedure becomes self-evident from Fig. 23(*a*). It is almost identical with the determination of the vertical reactions under a simple span. Figure 23(*b*) shows how the reactions must be divided into components when the horizontal components of the reactions are taken as equal. One must observe a regular order, either clockwise or counterclockwise, in laying out the force polygon.

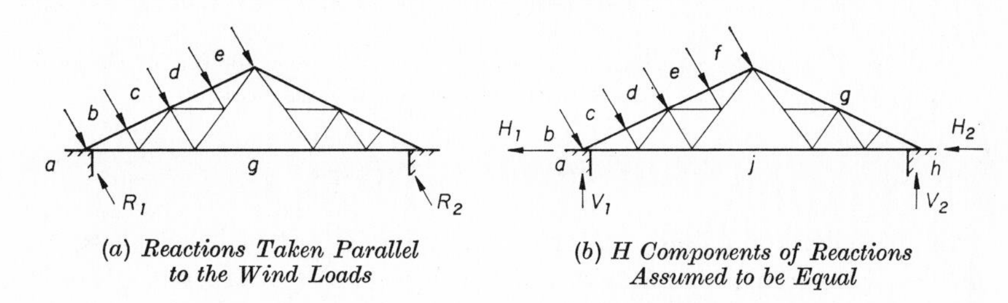

(*a*) *Reactions Taken Parallel to the Wind Loads*

(*b*) *H Components of Reactions Assumed to be Equal*

FIG. 23. REACTIONS DETERMINED BY ASSUMPTION.

23. Directions or Signs of Reactions. Since the reactions hold the loads in equilibrium, their directions can usually be determined by inspection. When one is not certain of the direction of a reaction, he may assume its direction. Then its *algebraic sign*, when determined by the equations of statics, will be positive if the assumed direction is correct, and negative if the assumed direction must be reversed. The sign or direction of the reaction can also be found from the *graphical requirement* that all arrows must point continuously around the closed force polygon of the loads and reactions.

PROBLEMS

215. Compute the values of the reactions for the roof truss as caused by a wind pressure of 25 psf of roof surface acting normal to the roof. Trusses are spaced 16 ft. apart. Assume that the right-hand end of the truss is supported on rollers. Check your calculations by graphical determination of the reactions.

Ans. Right-hand reaction = 2500 lb. Left-hand reaction = 6800 lb.

216. Same as Problem 215 but use the truss illustrated for Problem 224.

217. Same as Problem 215 but assume that the reactions act parallel to the wind load. *Ans.* Right-hand reaction = 2810 lb.

218. Same as Problem 215, but assume that the horizontal components of the two reactions are equal. *Ans.* Right-hand reaction = 3200 lb.

219. Compute the values of the reactions for the three-hinged arch caused by the dead load of 3000 lb. per ft. acting from *A* to *D*. Then place a single vertical load of 30,000 lb. (representing a road roller) at point *B* and determine the reactions both algebraically and graphically. *Ans.* D. L. reaction = 516,000 lb.

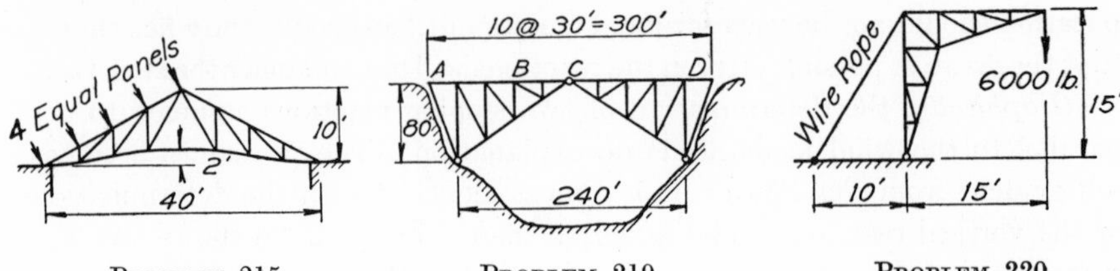

PROBLEM 215. PROBLEM 219. PROBLEM 220.

220. Graphically determine the values of the reactions for the cantilever truss illustrated. Check result algebraically. *Ans.* Rope stress = 10,800 lb.

HINT. Start a string polygon at the one known point on the action line of the right reaction.

221. Use a graphical procedure to check the reactions given for one of the problems on p. 43, Vol. 1, *Theory of Modern Steel Structures*, Revised Edition.

STRESS ANALYSIS OF TRUSSES

24. Definition of a Truss. A truss is any framework of bars[3] placed together to form triangles. An exterior bar forms a side of one triangle only, but an interior bar forms a side of each of two triangles. A truss of this simple type is called statically determinate *internally* because all of the stresses in the bars can be calculated by use of the three equations of statics. Figure 24(*a*) represents a simple type of statically determinate truss, and (*b*) represents another common type of bridge truss which is also determinate. The highly irregular structure shown in (*c*) fulfills the preceding definition of a statically determinate truss.

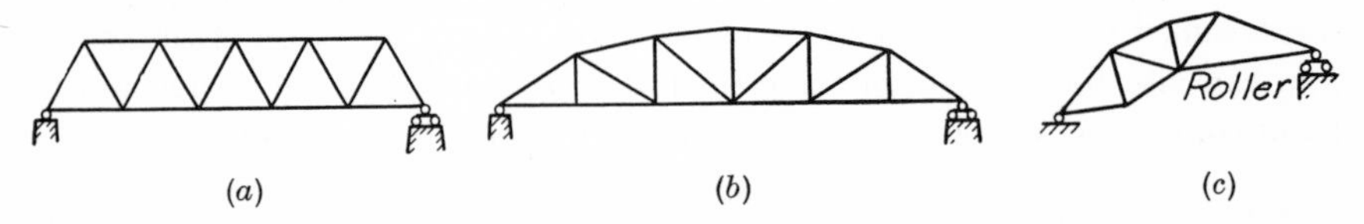

FIG. 24. STATICALLY DETERMINATE TRUSSES.

Double Diagonals. The truss shown in Fig. 25(*a*), with double diagonals in the center panel, is a common type of bridge or building truss. Usually this structure is treated as if it were statically determinate. The explanation is that the double diagonals are tension members that are *incapable* of resisting compression. We conclude that only the diagonal stressed in tension actually is in operation, as shown in (*b*). When both diagonals are stiff compression members, the truss is statically indeterminate. The common procedure of analysis for stiff diagonals is to assume that they are stressed

[3] The word *bar* commonly is used to signify any truss member. Actually, an eye *bar* is a tension member of rectangular cross-section drilled at each end for connection to a pin.

equally, one in tension and the other in compression. Then, each diagonal resists one half the stress that it would receive if it acted alone. The analysis of true stresses for a statically indeterminate truss is beyond the scope of this text. Such problems are treated in the author's *Theory of Modern Steel Structures*, vol. II, Revised Edition.

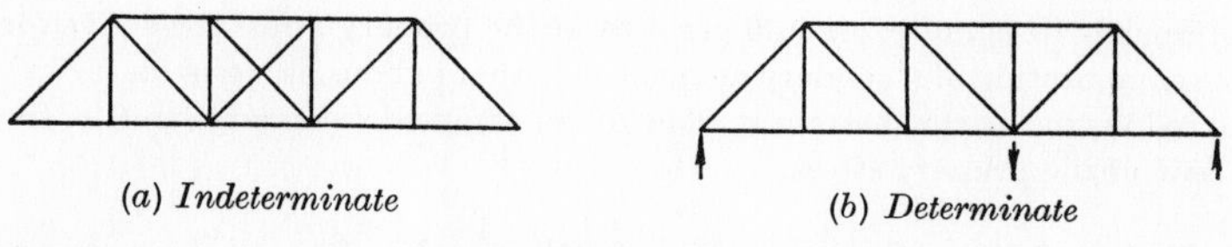

(*a*) *Indeterminate* (*b*) *Determinate*

FIG. 25. INTERNAL REDUNDANCY.

25. Fundamental Assumptions. Certain fundamental assumptions are made in truss analysis with which the reader must become familiar.

(1) The gravity lines of all bars meeting at a joint intersect at a single point.

(2) There is a frictionless pin at each joint of the truss.

(3) There is no bending in any member of the truss. Assumption (3) also summarizes (1) and (2). The assumption that there is no bending in any truss member is incorrect, of course, because any bar which is not vertical must act as a beam to carry its own weight to the adjacent joints. In long heavy members this bending stress may be of significance. However, the specifications for design usually require such deep sections that the flexure caused by the weight of the member may be neglected.

It is possible to make the first assumption practically true by detailing the members and joints properly. The correct procedure is to lay out the truss members by placing their gravity axes on the center lines of the truss, which in turn intersect at a single point at each joint. The only approximation usually allowed is that the gage line of an angle is taken as its gravity axis. A joint detail where the members meet at a point is shown in Fig. 26(*a*). Joint details where these assumptions are incorrect are shown in (*b*) and (*c*).

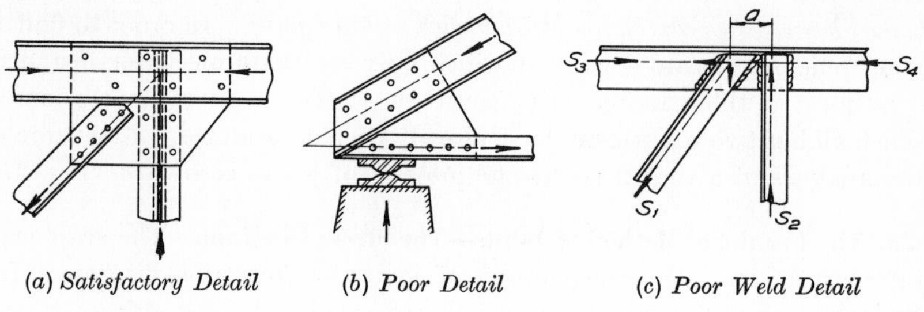

(*a*) *Satisfactory Detail* (*b*) *Poor Detail* (*c*) *Poor Weld Detail*

FIG. 26. STRUCTURAL JOINTS.

EXAMPLE. *Flexure of Truss Members.* If the action lines of all forces at a joint do not meet at a single point, flexure is produced in the members. Consider the joint shown in Fig. 26(*c*). The stress S_1 is resolved into its horizontal and vertical components at its intersection with S_3 and S_4. We can see that there must be a bending moment equal to $(S_2 \times a)$ resisted by the members at this joint because the vertical component of S_1 is equal to S_2 and these two parallel forces form a couple of this value. It follows that this joint does not fulfill assumption (3) above.

Secondary Flexure. When a truss deflects, there is a slight change in the angle between each pair of members. Riveted or welded joints resist this internal adjustment and force each member to bend into an S-shape or a reversed curve producing *secondary moments.* The corresponding fiber stresses in the bars are called secondary stresses, in contrast to the direct or primary stresses. Experiment has shown that the secondary stress ordinarily does not exceed 30 per cent of the primary stress for a given member. Since the computation of secondary moments is rather tedious, it is customary in building codes to reduce the working stress to allow for an assumed secondary stress of from 30 to 40 per cent of the primary stress.

26. Rules of Stress Components. In the study of mechanics, components of stress are found by use of functions of angles. In stress analysis, the engineer prefers to use the known lengths of the members to represent these functions of angles. It will be remembered that the force and space triangles are similar. Hence, from the proportionality of sides we see that

$$\frac{\text{Stress}}{\text{Component of stress}} = \frac{\text{Length of member}}{\text{Corresponding component of length}} \tag{a}$$

By transposition we may write two other useful rules:

$$\text{Stress} = \frac{\text{Component of stress} \times \text{Length of member}}{\text{Component of length}} \tag{b}$$

or,

$$\text{Component of stress} = \frac{\text{Stress} \times \text{Component of length}}{\text{Length of member}}. \tag{c}$$

27. Truss Analysis by the Method of Joints. The external loads and internal bar stresses acting at an isolated joint of a truss form a set of forces that intersect at a single point and are in equilibrium. If the equations $\Sigma F_x = 0$ and $\Sigma F_y = 0$ are used to calculate the unknown bar stresses, the equation $\Sigma M = 0$ gives no additional information. Accordingly, *only two unknown bar stresses can be found from each isolated joint.* In order to find a starting point we locate a joint at which only two bars meet, for instance the end joint at the reaction. One can then proceed in succession to joints at which all but two bar stresses have already been determined. An example of the analysis of a roof truss by the method of joints is given in Fig. 27.

28. The Graphical Method of Joints—The Stress Diagram. The graphical counterpart of the algebraic method of joints is the stress diagram. In reality, the stress diagram is a group of superimposed force polygons, one for each joint of the truss. This correspondence is illustrated by Fig. 28 where the separate force polygons are drawn for each joint. These force polygons are superimposed upon one another in (*f*) to form the stress diagram. Note that in the separate force polygons all vectors corresponding to the bar stresses are drawn twice, but that this duplication is avoided in the stress diagram by superposition of equal but opposite vectors. Hence each of the dotted lines in the stress diagram (*f*) represents two equal and

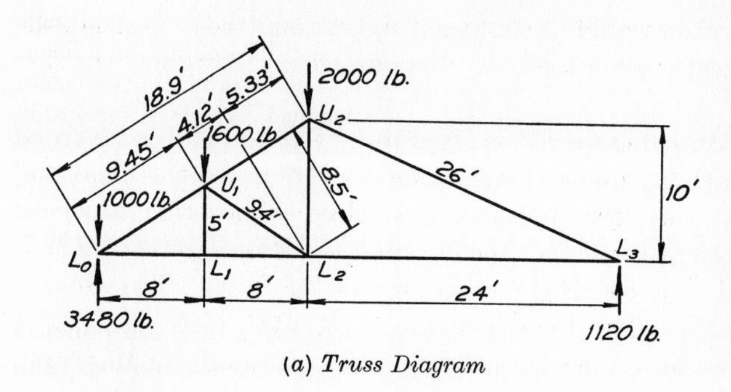

(a) *Truss Diagram*

Stress Table

L_0U_1	-4680 lb.
L_0L_1	$+3970$ "
L_1L_2	$+3970$ "
L_1U_1	0 "
U_1U_2	-3180 "
U_1L_2	-1500 "
U_2L_2	$+800$ "
U_2L_3	-2910 "
L_2L_3	$+2690$ "

L_0U_1 L_0L_1 R = 2480(net)

(b) *Joint* L_0

From joint L_0

$$(\Sigma F_y = 0)\ L_0U_1 = -2480 \times \frac{18.9}{10} = 4680 \text{ C. (lb.)}$$

$$(\Sigma F_x = 0)\ L_0L_1 = 2480 \times \frac{16}{10} = 3970\ T.$$

0 3970 3970

(c) *Joint* L_1

From Joint L_1

$$(\Sigma F_x = 0)\ L_1L_2 = L_0L_1 = 3970\ T.$$

From Joint U_1

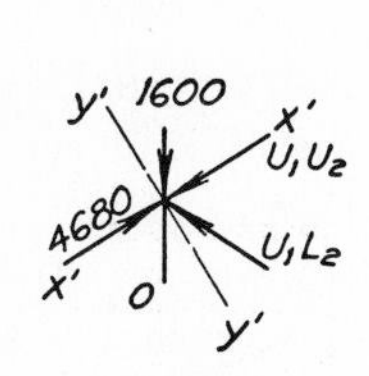

(d) *Joint* U_1

$$(\Sigma F_{y1} = 0)\ U_1L_2 = \left(1600 \times \frac{16}{18.9}\right)\frac{9.4}{8.5} = 1500\ C.$$

$$(\Sigma F_{x1} = 0)\ U_1U_2 = 4680 - 1600 \times \frac{10}{18.9} - 1500 \times \frac{4.1}{9.4}$$

$$= 4680 - 850 - 650 = 3180\ C.$$

From Joint L_2

$$(\Sigma F_x = 0)\ L_2L_3 = 3970 - 1500 \times \frac{8}{9.4} = 2690\ T.$$

$$(\Sigma F_y = 0)\ L_2U_2 = 1500 \times \frac{5}{9.4} = 800\ T.$$

1500 L_2U_2 3970 L_2L_3

(e) *Joint* L_2

From Joint U_2

$$(\Sigma F_y = 0)\ U_2L_3 = \left(2000 + 800 - 3180 \times \frac{10}{18.9}\right)\frac{26}{10}$$

$$= 2910\ C.$$

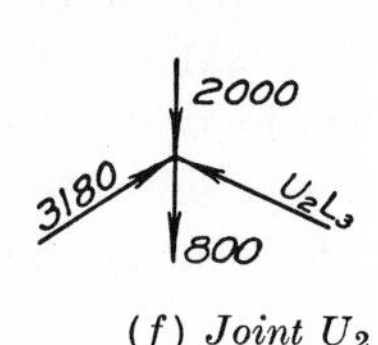

(f) *Joint* U_2

$$(\Sigma F_x = 0)\ 3180 \times \frac{16}{18.9} - 2910 \times \frac{24}{26} = 0 \quad 0 = 0.$$

Check.

Another check may be made at L_3.

FIG. 27. SIMPLE TRUSS ANALYZED ALGEBRAICALLY BY THE METHOD OF JOINTS.

opposite vectors. Arrows would be confusing and are omitted. Instead, the arrows are placed directly upon the truss diagram where they show the *sign of the stress*.[4]

29. Procedure for Drawing the Stress Diagram. The first step in drawing the stress diagram is to lay out a complete force polygon for the loads and reactions. Naturally, this force polygon must close. The order used can be clockwise or counterclockwise, but the *forces must be drawn consecutively* as they are encountered as a pencil is moved around the truss. The order is clockwise in Fig. 28(f). The force polygon A-B, B-C, C-D, D-E, E-A forms a straight line because there are only vertical forces acting on this truss.

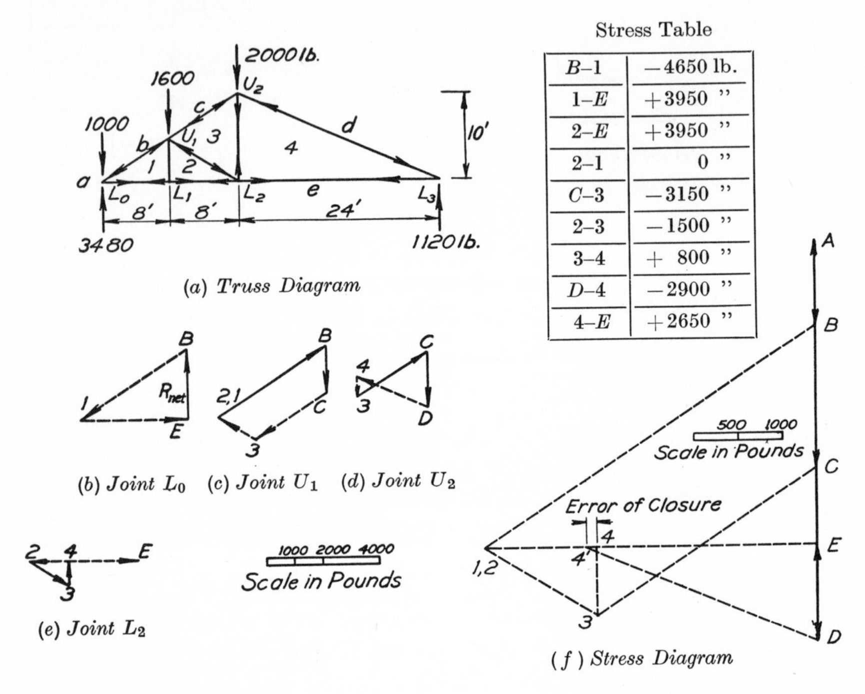

Stress Table

B–1	–4650 lb.
1–E	+3950 "
2–E	+3950 "
2–1	0 "
C–3	–3150 "
2–3	–1500 "
3–4	+ 800 "
D–4	–2900 "
4–E	+2650 "

(a) *Truss Diagram*

(b) *Joint* L_0 (c) *Joint* U_1 (d) *Joint* U_2

(e) *Joint* L_2

(f) *Stress Diagram*

Fig. 28. Graphical Analysis of the Truss of Fig. 27.

The next step is to draw a force polygon for the reaction joint L_0. This force polygon is E-A-B-1-E of Fig. 28(f). Observe that the order in which the forces are taken around the joint is clockwise. The order used in drawing the force polygon for the external loads was clockwise, and *these two orders must agree.* The direction arrows for the stresses are directed from B to 1 and from 1 to E as in (b). Note that E-B in (b) is the net reaction at

[4] A member that is resisting compression will lengthen when the stress is released. Such a member must therefore be pushing outward against its end joints. The arrows, which picture the action of the member on its two end joints, must be directed *outward* for a compression member and *inward* for a tension member.

L_0, or 2480 lb. Thus we establish the directions of the arrows shown at the joint L_0 in (*a*).

The second force polygon drawn is for the joint U_1, that is, 1-*B*-*C*-3-2-1. (The stress in U_1L_1 obviously is zero, which makes the point 2 coincide with point 1.) Here the vector 1-*B* is reused from the previous polygon for L_0. but its arrow is reversed. Force polygons may now be drawn for the joints L_2 and U_2, which completes the stress diagram.

Error of Closure. The work may be checked by observing whether or not the stress vectors for *E*-4 and 4-*D* form a triangle with the right-hand reaction *D*-*E*. This triangle *D*-*E*-4 is the force polygon for L_3. Unless it is a perfect triangle, there is an error in the drafting, or in the scaled value of the reaction, or in both. This error may be expressed in terms of an "error of closure" since the location of the point 4 has been obtained twice. See (*d*) and (*e*) of Fig. 28. *The error of closure is the scaled value in pounds of the distance between the two locations of the point* 4. Careful work will reduce the error of closure so that no important stress will be in error more than one or at most two per cent. A small unimportant stress may show a considerably larger percentage of error, and this can not be avoided in graphical work. However, by comparing the stresses obtained graphically in Fig. 28 with those obtained algebraically in Fig. 27 we find a maximum variation of only 1.5 per cent.

30. The Method of Sections. A fundamental objection to the method of joints and to the stress diagram is that they are not easily applied to the determination of the stress in a single member near the center of a truss. By these methods it is necessary to compute the stresses from one end of the truss up to the bar in question. On the other hand, the method of sections permits us to cut a section anywhere through the structure, and to compute the values of *three unknown non-concurrent stresses* cut by this section. The section chosen may cut any number of bars, but all except three must have known stresses. These three stresses must be non-concurrent if their values are to be calculated by statics.

EXAMPLE. Two sections are cut through the truss of Fig. 29 and several stresses are calculated. The other stresses are given, so that they may be checked by the reader for practice. The section 1–1 illustrates the calculation of the stress in a diagonal web member from the shear in the panel. The equation $\Sigma F_y = 0$ shows us that the vertical component of the stress in a diagonal is equal to the vertical shear in the panel, which is the left end reaction minus any loads to the left of the section. This concept is valid only for a *truss with horizontal chords*. It may be stated as a rule that applies both to diagonals and verticals:

$$\text{Stress in web member} = \text{Panel shear} \times \frac{\text{Length of member}}{\text{Height of truss}}. \tag{7}$$

Chord members are analyzed by means of the equation $\Sigma M = 0$. The stress in the member *BC* is determined from the section 1–1 by an equation of moments about *c*.[5] The point *c* is chosen because it is the intersection of the bars *Bc* and *bc*, the other two members cut by the section 1–1. Hence, for a *truss with parallel chords*,

[5] When a truss is lettered with capital and lower-case letters we read *Bc* as *B major*, *c minor*, and *bc* as *b minor*, *c minor*, etc.

$$\text{(8)} \qquad \text{Stress in chord member} = \frac{\text{Moment about intersection of other members cut}}{\text{Height of truss}}.$$

We find the equation $\Sigma F_x = 0$ to be useful for the determination of the chord stresses in a truss with vertical web members. The section 2–2 clearly illustrates the use of this equation to show that the horizontal members BC and cd must have equal and opposite stresses since the web member cut is vertical.

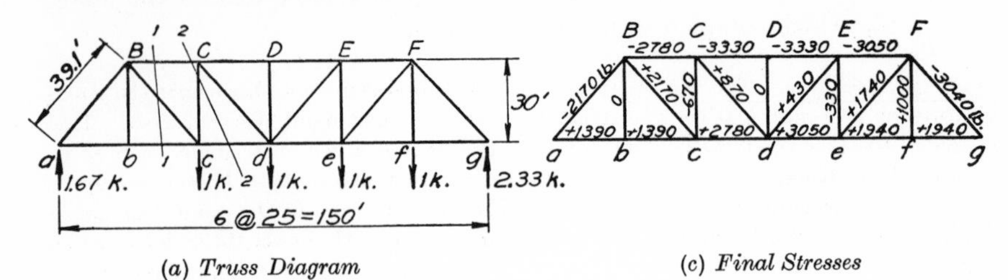

(a) *Truss Diagram*

(c) *Final Stresses*

From Section 1–1.

$$S_{Bc} = 1670 \times \frac{39.1}{30} = 2170 \text{ lb. } T. \qquad (\Sigma F_y = 0.)$$

$$S_{BC} = 1670 \times \frac{50}{30} = 2780 \text{ lb. } C. \qquad (\Sigma M_c = 0.)$$

From Section 2–2.

$$S_{Cc} = 1670 - 1000 = 670 \text{ lb. } C. \qquad (\Sigma F_y = 0.)$$

$$S_{cd} = -S_{BC} = 2780 \text{ lb. } T. \qquad (\Sigma F_x = 0.)$$

(b) *Sections*

(d) *Stress Calculations*

FIG. 29. TRUSS ANALYZED BY METHOD OF SECTIONS.

31. The Method of Moments. All stresses in a truss with sloping chords can be found quite easily by the method of moments, a variation of the method of sections. Three equations of moments involving the three unknown stresses acting on any cut section can always be obtained. We commonly choose the moment centers[6] at the intersections of pairs of unknown stresses, so that each of the moment equations will contain only a single unknown. See Fig. 30(*a*).

Use of Stress Components. A variation of the method of moments is obtained by the use of components. The need for simultaneous equations can be eliminated by selecting the moment center at the intersection of two of the unknowns. Then the third unknown is broken up into components at a point selected so that one of these components *also passes through the moment center.* The other component is the only unknown in the moment equation. Figure 30(*b*) illustrates the method of moments by the use of

[6] If the three moment centers chosen are on a straight line, an unknown force of any magnitude might act along this line without affecting the moment equations. In general, two of the equations of moments will be *dependent* if the three moment centers lie on a straight line.

components of stress. The horizontal component of S_3, marked $_HS_3$, for example, passes through the moment center F, and therefore drops out of the equation $\Sigma M_F = 0$.

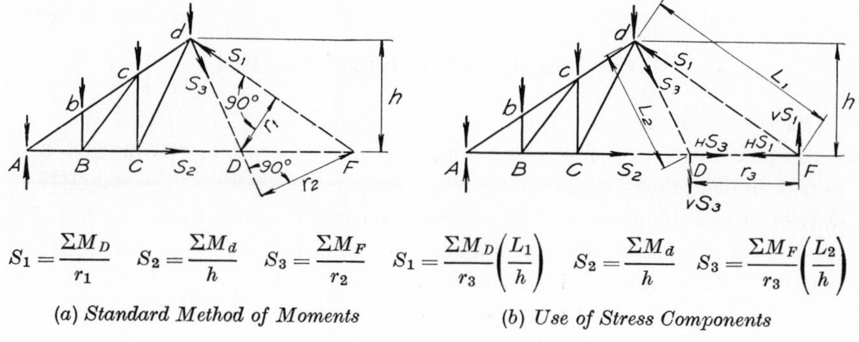

$$S_1 = \frac{\Sigma M_D}{r_1} \quad S_2 = \frac{\Sigma M_d}{h} \quad S_3 = \frac{\Sigma M_F}{r_2}$$

(a) Standard Method of Moments

$$S_1 = \frac{\Sigma M_D}{r_3}\left(\frac{L_1}{h}\right) \quad S_2 = \frac{\Sigma M_d}{h} \quad S_3 = \frac{\Sigma M_F}{r_3}\left(\frac{L_2}{h}\right)$$

(b) Use of Stress Components

FIG. 30. STRESS ANALYSIS BY THE METHOD OF MOMENTS.

PROBLEMS

222. Analyze for the stresses that would be produced in this Pratt bridge truss by a line of motor cars extending from a to x. Consider the line of cars to be represented by a uniform load determined on the assumption that the average car weighs 3300 lb. and takes up a space of 20 ft. including the space between cars. Remember that the loads come onto the floor system which produces panel concentrations on the truss.

Ans. $EF = -11{,}100$; $eF = +7400$; $ef = +6000$ lb.

223. Same as Problem 222 except that the live load extends from a to d.

224. Compute the snow-load stresses in the Howe roof truss. The trusses are spaced 15 ft.-5 in. apart and the snow load is 20 psf of roof surface. Use the method of joints and check by drawing a stress diagram.

Ans. $U_3U_4 = -8300$; $L_3U_4 = -3500$; $L_3L_4 = +10{,}000$ lb.

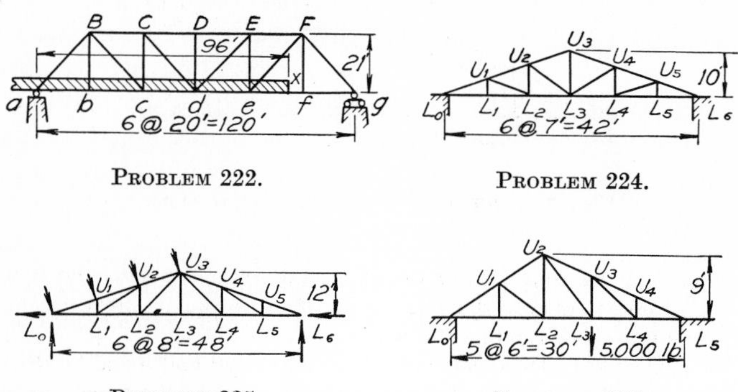

PROBLEM 222.

PROBLEM 224.

PROBLEM 225.

PROBLEM 227.

225. Compute the wind-load stresses in the Pratt roof truss. Assume that the reactions have equal horizontal components. The trusses are spaced 20.0 ft. apart. The wind pressure is 25 psf normal to the roof. Use the method of joints and check by calculating the stresses in U_2U_3, L_2U_2, and L_1L_2 by the method of moments.

Ans. $U_2U_3 = -13{,}000$; $L_2U_2 = -7500$; $L_1L_2 = +9600$ lb.

226. Same as Problem 225 except use the graphical method of analysis. Assume that the reactions are parallel to the wind loads.

227. Determine the stresses in this roof truss caused by the crane load of 5000 lb. at L_3. Use any method you prefer and check at least three stresses by one other method.

Ans. $U_2U_3 = -6700$; $U_3L_3 = U_3L_4 = 0$; $L_3L_4 = U_2L_3 = +6000$ lb.

Shear and Moment Diagrams for Beams

32. Shear Diagrams. When the loads upon a beam are fixed in position, a complete analysis of stresses may be made from the information contained in the shear diagram and the moment diagram. The method of drawing these diagrams will be reviewed particularly in regard to *signs*. If the resultant force to the left of a section is upward, the shear is considered positive. This upward force must be accompanied by a downward resultant force to the right of the section, a condition that also defines positive shear.

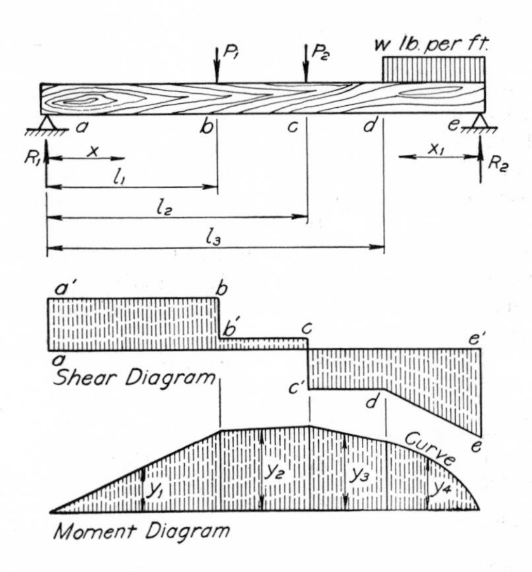

Fig. 31. Shear and Moment Diagrams.

Procedure. In drawing a shear diagram, start with the left-hand reaction and draw a vertical ordinate equal to the value and in the direction of the reaction, as *a-a'* in Fig. 31. Extend the horizontal line *a'-b* to indicate constant shear. (The weight of the beam is being neglected.) Draw *b-b'* vertically downward and equal to P_1. Extend *b'-c* horizontally to indicate constant shear. Draw *c-c'* vertically downward and equal to P_2. Extend *c'-d* horizontally to indicate constant shear. Draw *d-e* sloping downward by an increment of w for each foot horizontally. Finally, draw the line *e-e'* vertically upward and equal to R_2. There is a check here since the ordinate *e-e'* should bring the shear diagram back to the horizontal base line. This procedure may be used either as an *algebraic* or *graphical* method.

33. Moment Diagrams. The moment diagram is of great importance in beam and girder analysis, for it is in effect a diagram of extreme fiber stresses for a beam of constant cross-section. Usually, a sketch of the moment diagram will be as useful as a scale drawing, provided that two or three numerical values of critical ordinates are written upon it. These critical ordinates exist at concentrated loads, at the ends of pieces of distributed load, and always at points of zero shear, points which will be shown to correspond to points of maximum moment.

The bending moment at any section may be computed *algebraically* by taking the moment about the section of all forces either to the right or to the left of the section. The determination of the moment diagram *graphically* follows from the discussion of §17. The equilibrium polygon for the loads and reactions is in effect a bending-moment diagram. The scale of the resultant moment diagram involves the combined scales for forces and distances, as explained in §17.

Sign of the Bending Moment. The usual rule of signs is that the bending moment is positive when the moment of the forces to the left of the section is clockwise or when the moment of the forces to the right of the section is counterclockwise. An easier way to remember this rule of signs is to recall that positive moment causes tension in the bottom fibers, as in a simple beam, and that negative moment causes tension in the top fibers, as in a cantilever beam.

34. Shape of the Moment Diagram. It will be shown that the moment diagram is a straight line between points of concentrated loads when no uniform load exists and that it becomes a parabola when there is a uniform load. Actually, a piece of beam without a uniform load can exist only when the beam is vertical. Any sloping or horizontal beam must carry its own weight. However, when the weight of the beam is small as compared to the values of the concentrated loads, its weight is frequently neglected in drawing the shape of the moment diagram.

Proof. The bending moment for each section of the beam shown in Fig. 31 may be expressed as follows:

(9) From a to b: $$y_1 = R_1 x.$$

(10) From b to c: $$y_2 = R_1 x - P_1(x - l_1).$$

(11) From c to d: $$y_3 = R_1 x - P_1(x - l_1) - P_2(x - l_2).$$

(12) From d to e: $$y_4 = R_1 x - P_1(x - l_1) - P_2(x - l_2) - \frac{w(x - l_3)^2}{2},$$

or, by using the right-hand end of the beam, we obtain

(13) $$y_4 = R_2 x_1 - \frac{w x_1^2}{2}.$$

Equations (9), (10), and (11) are linear in x and must represent straight lines. Equation (12) looks rather complicated, but it is identical with equation (13), which is clearly a first-degree curve or a straight line minus a second degree curve or a parabola. The resultant curve is therefore parabolic.

35. Moments Computed from Areas under the Shear Curve. The area of the shear diagram between two concentrated loads that act normal to a beam as in Fig. 32 (where the weight of the beam is neglected) is equal to the constant value of the shear times the distance between the loads. Evidently, then, this area is equal numerically to the change in moment in the beam between the two load points. Note that any area from a shear diagram is computed as a product of a shear ordinate (pounds) multiplied by a horizontal length (feet) and is therefore obtained directly in the proper units for bending moment (foot-pounds). We will also show that these statements still apply when there are intermediate concentrated loads.

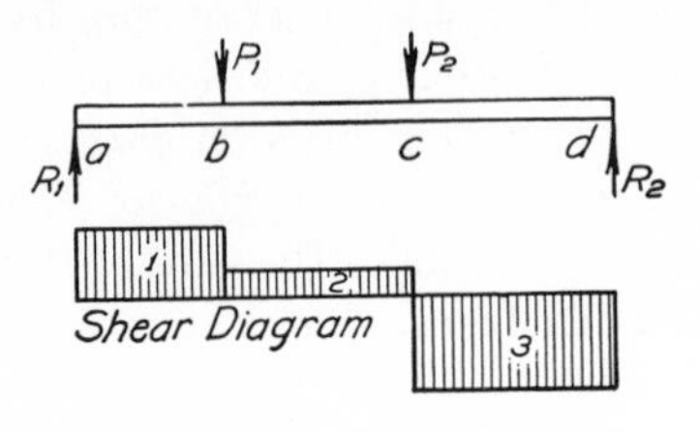

FIG. 32. SHEAR AREAS.

The loads and reactions here are normal to the axis of the beam. A couple may be produced by loads parallel to the axis of the beam. In that case the moment is not obtainable as an area under the shear diagram.

DEMONSTRATION. The area (1) of Fig. 32 represents the change of moment from a to b, and the area (2) represents the change in moment from b to c. Therefore, the area (1) plus the area (2) represents the change in moment from a to c. No further proof is needed for the case of a uniform or distributed load because any distributed load can be treated as a large number of small concentrated loads. Accordingly, we may state that the area of the shear diagram between any two points along a beam is identical (both numerically and in actual units) with the change in bending moment between the same two points. Of course, this statement applies only to change in moment due to normal loads. A moment may be applied at one point through a bracket by a horizontal force, thus producing a sudden change or break in the moment diagram which may not be expressible as a shear area.

Again, by referring to Fig. 32, we conclude that the area (1) plus the area (2) equals the area (3) because the area from either end to the point c represents the bending moment at the point c when the end moments are zero. Evidently the positive and negative shear areas are always equal *for a simple beam.* It is possible to use the area of the shear diagram in the computation of bending moments. For instance, the bending moment in a cantilever beam at any point is equal to the area of the shear diagram between that point and the free end.

36. Points of Maximum Moment. It will be shown that the point of zero shear in a beam is also a point of maximum positive or negative moment. If we start to sum areas of the shear diagram for a horizontal beam by moving inward from an end where the moment is zero, the total summation of area or change in moment will *increase* either negatively or positively with increase of the distance x from the end until the shear diagram crosses the base line. At this point we must start numerically to *subtract* succeeding areas, and the moment will start to decrease. A point of maximum positive or negative moment must have existed where the shear diagram crossed the base line. The quickest way to obtain the maximum negative and positive moments for selecting the size of a beam is first to locate the points of zero shears and then to compute the bending moments at these points.

PROBLEMS

228. The entire weight of one 20-ton truck rests directly on one girder of a 60-ft. girder bridge. The truck has axles spaced 14 ft. apart, and 80 per cent of the weight is on the rear axle. Compute the maximum moment at the center allowing for a dead load of 1400 lb. per ft. of girder. *Ans.* 1,174,000 ft-lb.

229. Repeat Problem 228 for maximum moment at the quarter point and for a point 22 ft. from one end. *Ans.* 894,000 and 1,100,000 ft-lb.

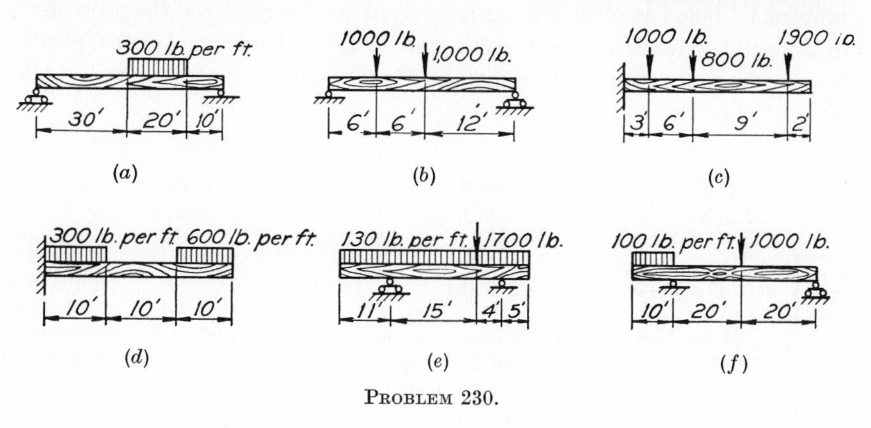

PROBLEM 230.

230. Plot shear and moment diagrams to scale for each of the beams shown. Write values of *all* critical ordinates on the diagrams. Answers given are for maximum moments. *Ans.* (*a*) 66,700; (*b*) 9,000; (*c*) 44,400; (*d*) 165,000; (*e*) 6,350; (*f*) 12,500 ft-lb.

MAXIMUM COMBINED STRESSES

37. Critical Stresses. In the design of tension members, columns, and beams, it is usual to consider (in each instance) only a single controlling stress. However, the designer will inevitably be confronted from time to time with structural design problems where two kinds of stress combine at a given point. The problem is to determine *the direction of the maximum stress and its magnitude.* For example, tensions or compressions may occur at right angles to each other and produce a resultant stress greater than either. The calculations of such resultants are common engineering procedure. On the other hand, we are prone to forget that a direct stress and a shear acting on the plane *A* may produce a greater direct stress or a greater shear on the plane *B*.

Failures of Materials. Whether failure is caused by direct stress, by shear, or by strain has never been determined for the general case. It seems probable that each may control failure for special materials and special conditions of loading. For the purpose of design, however, we will accept the maximum stress-shear theory of failure; that is, we will so design the structure that the maximum direct stress will be within its specified allowable value and the maximum shearing stress will be below its specified limitation. This necessitates a knowledge of how to compute the maximum unit direct stress at a point and the corresponding maximum unit shearing stress.

38. Formulas for Determining Principal Stresses and Shears. These results will be presented as a group of special cases that cover many practical problems. The formulas will not be derived since their derivations are given in all complete texts on the strength of materials. Table 1 presents formulas for stresses on inclined planes and also for maximum stresses termed "principal values."

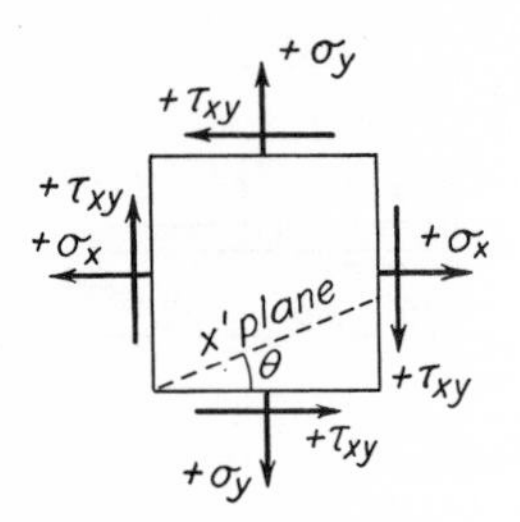

FIG. 33. PLANAR STRESSES AT A POINT ACTING ON A DIFFERENTIAL ELEMENT.

The combination of biaxial normal stresses plus shears acting at a point is the most general case of stresses in a plane. A stress field of this nature is found in the webs of beams, in walls, and in very thin plates. The illustrations in Table 1 are special cases of stresses acting at a point for which Fig. 33 represents the general case.

Notation. Books on elasticity have standardized the use of the Greek letter σ (sigma) for unit stress rather than the English s or f. For unit shear they have adopted the Greek letter τ (tau). The latter is particularly convenient, since unit shear in structures books has varied between s_s, s_t, v, and other symbols. In this section we will adopt the use of σ for unit stress and τ for unit shear, since familiarity with this notation is useful in reading the literature of engineering mechanics.

For θ, as indicated in Fig. 33, the plane of zero shear or of maximum normal stress is defined by

$$\tan 2\theta = \frac{2\tau_{xy}}{\sigma_y - \sigma_x}, \tag{14}$$

and for the principal stresses,

$$\sigma' = \frac{\sigma_y + \sigma_x}{2} \pm \sqrt{\left(\frac{\sigma_y - \sigma_x}{2}\right)^2}. \tag{15}$$

The maximum shears occur at 45 degrees to the planes of the principal stresses

$$\tau' = \sqrt{\left(\frac{\sigma_y - \sigma_x}{2}\right)^2 + \tau_{xy}^2}. \tag{16}$$

The maximum shear is one half of the difference between the principal stresses or $1/2(\sigma_y' - \sigma_x')$ when σ_y' has its maximum value. The specialized formulas given in Table 1 are determinable from equations (14), (15), and (16).

TABLE 1

STRESSES ON INCLINED PLANES AND THEIR MAXIMUM VALUES

STRESSES ON INCLINED PLANES	PRINCIPAL VALUES	SLOPE θ
(17) $\sigma_y' = \sigma_y \cos^2 \theta = \frac{1}{2}\sigma_y(1 + \cos 2\theta)$	Max. $\sigma = +\sigma_y$	$\theta = 0$
(18) $\tau_{x'y'} = \sigma_y \sin \theta \cos \theta = \frac{1}{2}\sigma_y \sin 2\theta$	Max. $\tau = \frac{\sigma_y}{2}$	$\theta = 45°$
(19) $\sigma_y' = \sigma_y \cos^2 \theta + \sigma_x \sin^2 \theta =$ $\frac{1}{2}(\sigma_x + \sigma_y) + \frac{1}{2}(\sigma_x - \sigma_y) \cos 2\theta$	Max. $\sigma = \sigma_y$ or σ_x	$\theta = 0°$ (or 90°)
(20) $\tau_{x'y'} = \frac{1}{2}(\sigma_y - \sigma_x) \sin 2\theta$	Max. $\tau = \frac{1}{2}(\sigma_y - \sigma_x)$	$\theta = 45°$
(21) $\sigma_y' = \sigma_y (\cos^2 \theta - \sin^2 \theta)$ $= \sigma_y \cos 2\theta$	Max. $\sigma = \pm\sigma_y$	$\theta = 0°$ (or 90°)
(22) $\tau_{x'y'} = \sigma_y \sin 2\theta$	Max. $\tau = \sigma_y$	$\theta = 45°$
(23) $\sigma_y' = \tau_{xy} \sin 2\theta$	Max. $\sigma = \pm \tau_{xy}$	$\theta = 45°$ (or 135°)
(24) $\tau_{x'y'} = -\tau_{xy} \cos 2\theta$	Max. $\tau = \tau_{xy}$	$\theta = 0°$ (or 90°)
(25) $\sigma_y' = \frac{1}{2}\sigma_y(1 + \cos 2\theta) + \tau_{xy} \sin 2\theta$ (when $\tan 2\theta = 2\tau_{xy}/\sigma_y$)	(25a) Max. $\sigma = \frac{\sigma_y}{2} \pm \sqrt{\frac{\sigma_y^2}{4} + \tau_{xy}^2}$	
(26) $\tau_{x'y'} = \frac{1}{2}\sigma_y \sin 2\theta - \tau_{xy} \cos 2\theta$	(26a) Max. $\tau = \sqrt{\frac{\sigma_y^2}{4} + \tau^2_{xy}}$	

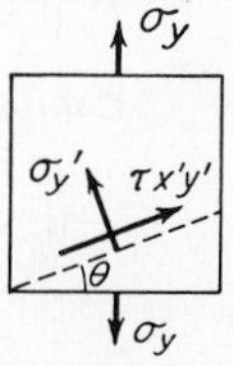

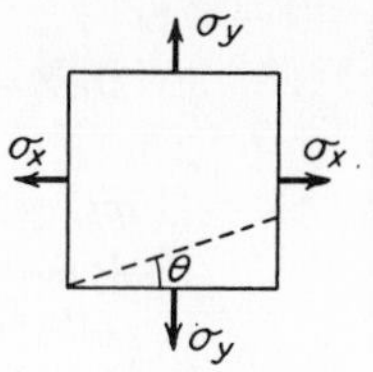

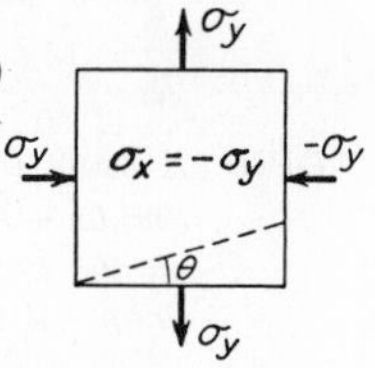

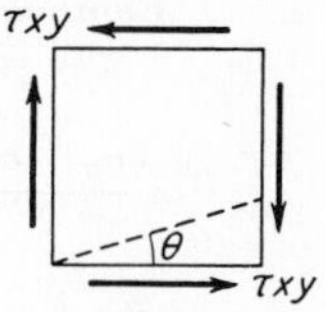

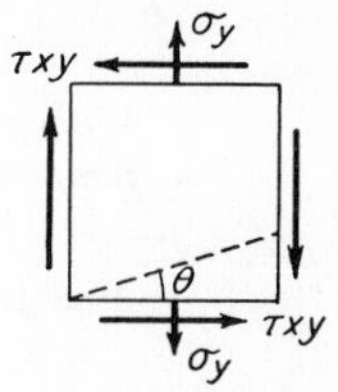

Comparison of Signs. The formulas of Table 1 are commonly derived in books on mechanics of materials and elasticity. However, there is often a difference of signs involved. In making comparisons one should observe whether the angle θ or its complement is used and whether θ is measured in the first or fourth quadrant which changes the signs of its trigonometric functions. Also, a positive shear may be defined oppositely to the positive direction of τ as defined herein.

DP1a. *An anchor bolt carries an initial tension of 12,000# and a positive shear of 8000#. Select a diameter such that the combined tension will not exceed 24,000 psi and the combined shear will not exceed 15,000 psi.*
Trial diameter = 1.0″; area = 0.785 in.^{2}
Unit direct stress, $\sigma_y = 12{,}000 \div 0.785 = 15{,}300$ *psi.*
Unit cross shear (average), $\tau_{xy} = 8000 \div 0.785 = 10{,}200$ *psi.*

Combined Stresses: *Equations (25a) and (26a), Table 1*

$$\text{Max. } \sigma = \frac{\sigma_y}{2} \pm \sqrt{\frac{\sigma_y^2}{4} + \tau_{xy}^2} = \frac{15{,}300}{2} + \sqrt{\frac{15{,}300^2}{4} + 10{,}200^2}$$

$$= 7650 + 12{,}750 = 20{,}400 \text{ psi.}$$

$$\text{Max. } \tau = \sqrt{\frac{\sigma_y^2}{4} + \tau_{xy}^2} = \sqrt{\frac{15{,}300^2}{4} + 10{,}200^2} = 12{,}750 \text{ psi.}$$

The 1″ diameter is larger than needed, but a ⅞″ bolt would not serve.
At the root of thread, the net tension is 12,000 ÷ 0.55 = 21,800 psi.
If the bolt undergoes flexure, τ_{xy} *might more properly be taken as the maximum beam shear on a circular section, which is ⅓ larger than the average unit shear.*

DP1b. *A beam web near the flange is stressed to 14,000 psi in horizontal compression and to −7000 psi in vertical and horizontal shear. Can a vertical load be placed on the beam that will stress the web in compression in a vertical direction to 8000 psi without exceeding a permissible combined compression of 20,000 psi?*

Combined Stresses: *Equations (14), (15), and (16).*
The principal stresses are

$$\frac{\sigma_y + \sigma_x}{2} \pm \sqrt{\left(\frac{\sigma_y - \sigma_x}{2}\right)^2 + \tau_{xy}^2}$$

$$= -11{,}000 - 7600 = -18{,}600 \text{ psi.}$$

Without the vertical load, the combined compression is

$$\text{Max. } \sigma = \frac{\sigma_x}{2} \pm \sqrt{\frac{\sigma_x^2}{4} + \tau^2} \qquad (\sigma_x \text{ being } -14{,}000)$$

$$= -\frac{14{,}000}{2} - \sqrt{\frac{(-14{,}000)^2}{4} + 7000^2} = -7000 - 9900 = -16{,}900 \text{ psi.}$$

The maximum shear in either case is the value of the radical; i.e., 7600 psi with the vertical load and 9900 psi without it.

Comment: *The design is satisfactory, and the vertical load may be carried safely.*

DESIGN SHEET 1

Combined Stress Calculations. *Design Sheet* 1. There are many instances of combined stresses where the ordinary design procedure does not take the real principal stresses into consideration. For example, we know that hot driven rivets have initial tension stresses. Such rivets are designed for shear or bearing with no reference to combined stresses. The justification is that all test joints that have been used to set allowable working stresses in shear and bearing also have had rivets with initial tension. Therefore, combined stresses are considered indirectly in riveted joint design.

BOLT SELECTION, *DP1a*. The design problem *DP1a* shows how the maximum tension and the maximum shear can be determined in a bolt or rivet resisting tension and shear. This combined stress is quite significant for a bolt, since working stresses for bolts are not intended to allow for stress combinations. When large anchor bolts are being designed, the safety of the structure may be involved to as great an extent as in the design of a main member. A determination of the maximum tension and of the maximum shear is the only safe procedure.

BEAM STUDY, *DP1b*. The design problem *DP1b* shows how the combination of stresses may properly influence the selection of a beam for special loadings. The addition of a vertical load on the top flange is shown to increase the diagonal compression in the web from 16,900 to 18,600 psi. It is interesting that this same load application happens to reduce the web shear at the point under consideration from 9900 to 7600 psi. Of course, *either* combined shear is greater than the applied shear of 7000 psi. It is to be noted that beam design does not ordinarily make use of combined stress calculations. Neverthless, if unusual loads are to be considered, a study of the combined stresses will be the designer's best approach to safe design.

PROBLEMS

231. A beam under negative moment near a support has a tensile stress at the top of the web of $\sigma_x = +20$ ksi. A vertical load on the upper flange at that point produces a web compression of $\sigma_y = -10$ ksi. If the maximum web shear at that point is $+20$ ksi, find the principal stresses and the maximum shear.

Ans. max. $\sigma_y' = +30$; max. $\sigma_x' = -20$; max. $\tau = +25$ ksi; $\theta = 63°$.

232. A material having low tensile strength usually has good strength in compression and shear when tension is absent. When such material is loaded to 10 ksi in biaxial compression and 10 ksi in shear on x and y planes, find the principal stresses and the maximum shear. First determine that principal stresses occur at 45 degrees to the x and y planes. *Ans.* principal stresses are -20 ksi and zero; max. $\tau = 10$ ksi.

39. Survey of Elementary Stress Analysis. This chapter has been limited to a study of a few of the many applications of statics to stress analysis. Structural analysis begins with the study of the laws of statics. The reactions, the bar stresses, the distribution of loads to welds, rivets, and pins, and even the stresses in the most minute fibers within these small parts are all controlled by the laws of statics. Statics may not be sufficient for the complete analysis of a complicated structure, but, nevertheless, the stress distribution obtained by the aid of some other tool must *always* satisfy the equations of statics, $\Sigma F_x = 0$, $\Sigma F_y = 0$, and $\Sigma M = 0$ if the forces occur in a single plane. There are six equations of statics applicable to any group of forces in space.

Both algebraic and graphical methods of analysis have been given for the determination of the reactions and stresses in trusses, and the reactions, shears, and moments in beams. Probably every algebraic method has a graphical counterpart, but this does not mean that both are always of equal importance. In truss analysis, for instance, the main advantage of the graphical treatment lies in the fact that forces at many angles may be handled almost as easily as horizontal and vertical forces. Moreover, it is not necessary that we even know the angles at which such forces act provided that a *scale* drawing of the structure with its loads is available. This fact is sufficient reason for choosing a graphical construction in preference to an algebraic method when such conditions exist. The common point of view is that graphical analysis is preferable for roof trusses, but that the stresses in most bridge trusses and the reactions for all structures are perhaps more easily obtained algebraically.

Use of Computers. The stress analysis of simple structures is so readily performed by hand that the use of a digital computer is unnecessary. However, if a structure is of a standard type and if an available computer program that has been tested for accuracy (debugged) is usable without revision, it may be convenient and may save the time of engineers. The use of a computer also may permit study of the effects of different positions of the loads or of several load systems without use of extra time of the designer. Of course, algebraic analysis is the basis of machine computation. In all cases the designer should make one or more hand calculations to check the reasonableness of the machine results before accepting them for use. Errors in machine analysis are occasionally due to a faulty machine but more frequently to a small inaccuracy in the program language. Errors are often very difficult to locate if they are of this nature. However, any competent engineer will be prepared to complete an approximate analysis by slide-rule computation so that he may quickly approve or disapprove the results of a machine analysis.

CHAPTER 3

INDUSTRIAL BUILDINGS

40. Types of Industrial Buildings. The term *industrial building* has come to mean any building structure used by industry where at least a part of the enclosed area is of one-story height. Included are buildings for steel mills, structural shops, train sheds, automotive assembly plants, and space-craft factories. These diverse structures all have the common requirement of large open floor areas frequently requiring roof trusses that provide adequate headroom for the use of an overhead traveling crane.

The Structural Frame. A simple type of steel building frame is shown in Fig. 34(*f*). Around the main figure are small line diagrams of several types of building bents that are in common use. These are, of course, merely roof trusses that are connected rigidly to their supporting columns. The diagrams show bents with several kinds of roof trusses, with roof ventilators, with two stories, and with side sheds.

It is seen from a study of Fig. 34(*f*) that the industrial building frame consists of diagonally braced side bents or portals and several transverse bents formed from each roof truss with its supporting pair of columns. The whole structure is made rigid by the use of diagonal bracing in the planes of the top and bottom chords of the roof trusses.

Purpose of Diagonal Bracing. Since each truss with its columns and knee braces forms a rigid bent, the function of the diagonal bracing is largely to *square* the building during erection and to prevent the building from *twisting* under a diagonal wind. Theoretically, bracing in one bay would serve this purpose, but it has been found that a light structure tends to vibrate and rack itself to pieces unless a considerable amount of diagonal bracing is used. It is necessary, then, to brace two bays, and it will be found advisable to *brace alternate bays* in all except temporary structures.

In connection with the diagonal bracing, all buildings require the use of continuous longitudinal struts for the full depth of the structure. These struts reduce vibration and act as members of the systems of bracing in the planes of the upper and lower chords. A ridge strut, two eave struts, and at least one strut connecting the lower chords of the roof trusses are required. These may be seen in the center sketch in Fig. 34. Similar struts for a flat roof building are visible in Fig. 35.

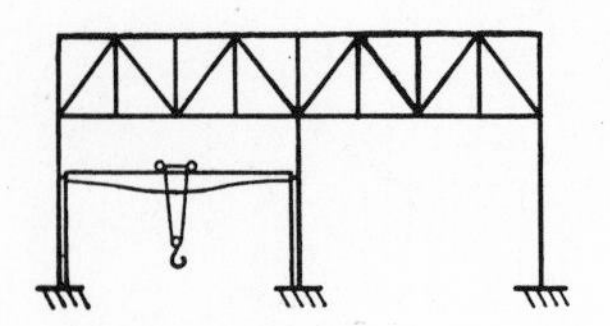

(a) *Warren Type Double Bent*

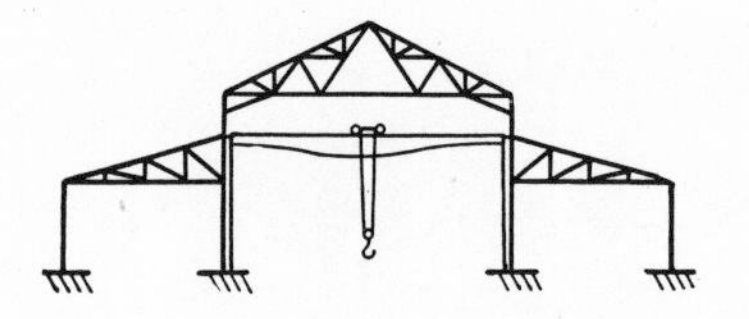

(b) *Bent with Side Sheds*

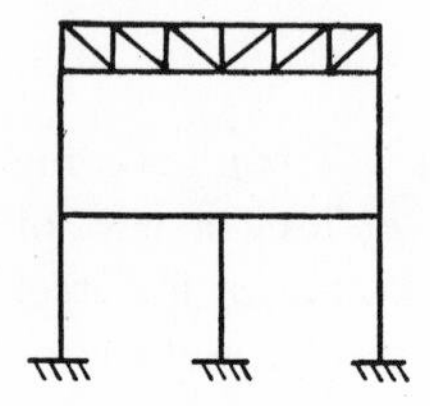

(c) *Two-Story Bent*

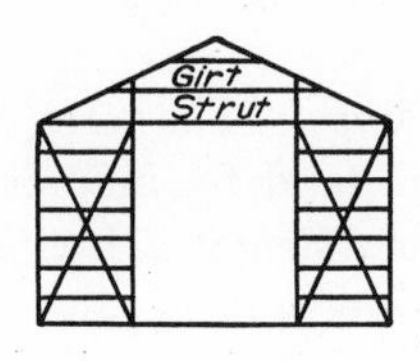

(d) *End Framing*

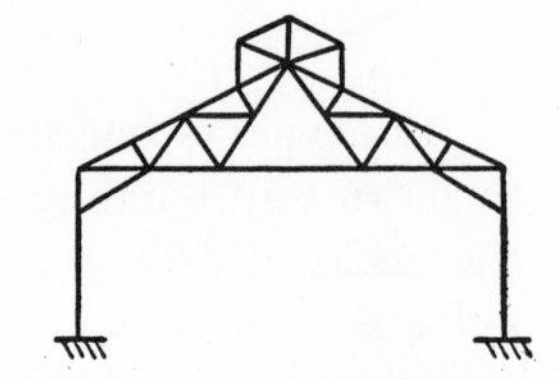

(e) *Fink Type with Skylight*

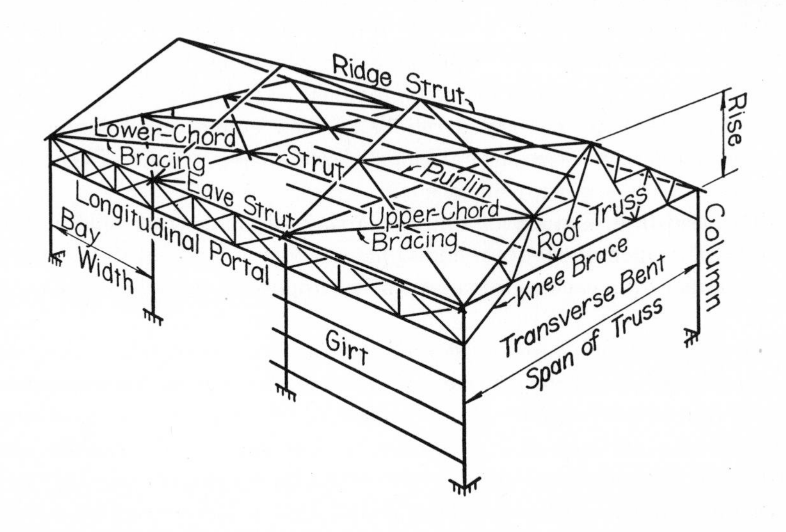

(f) *Standard Building Frame*

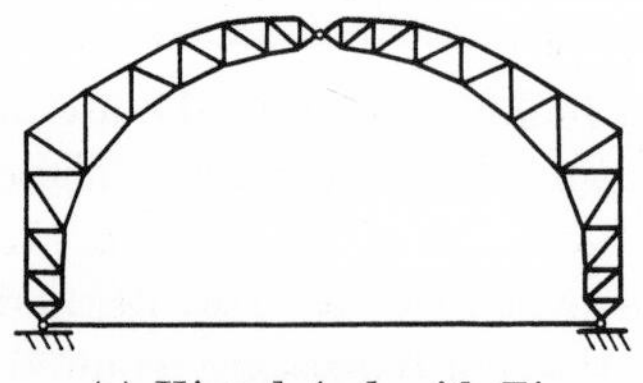

(g) *Hinged Arch with Tie*

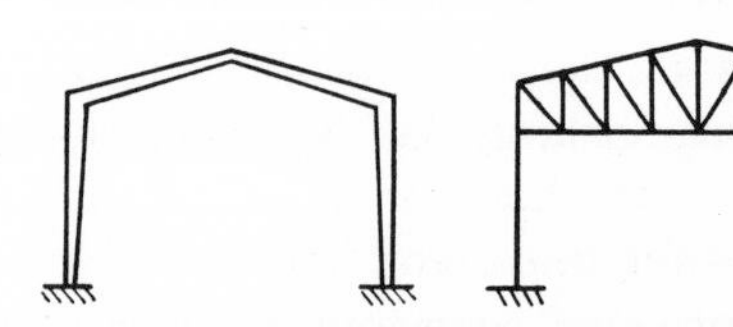

(h) *Flat Slopes, Girder and Truss Types*

Fig. 34. Industrial Building Frames.

Courtesy American Institute of Steel Construction

FIG. 35. INDUSTRIAL BUILDING UNDER CONSTRUCTION.

41. Structural Variations. Many variations of the industrial building frame shown in Fig. 34(f) are found in common use. However, the structural elements are essentially the same except for a few variations:

(1) *Diagonal Side Bracing.* In some buildings where it is not necessary to have wide openings in all bays of the sides, it is possible to substitute diagonal side bracing for the longitudinal portals. A more rigid structure as well as a less expensive one can be obtained in this way. It is necessary to place diagonal bracing in at least two bays of each side, and the use of bracing in alternate bays is desirable. A frame which has diagonal bracing in two bays of the side is shown in Fig. 36.

(2) *Continuous Roof Bracing.* Another variation of the standard type of industrial building frame occurs when knee braces are omitted in the interior bents and the *entire wind load* is transferred to the ends of the building by continuous roof bracing. This bracing may be placed only in the plane of the lower chords of the roof trusses or in both planes of the chords. In either case, it is necessary to make use of solid masonry end walls or of diagonally braced end frames to resist the thrust of the wind. A knee-braced end bent would seldom be used in such a building because the heavy bending moments in the columns could not be resisted *economically.* Diagonally braced end frames are shown in Fig. 36.

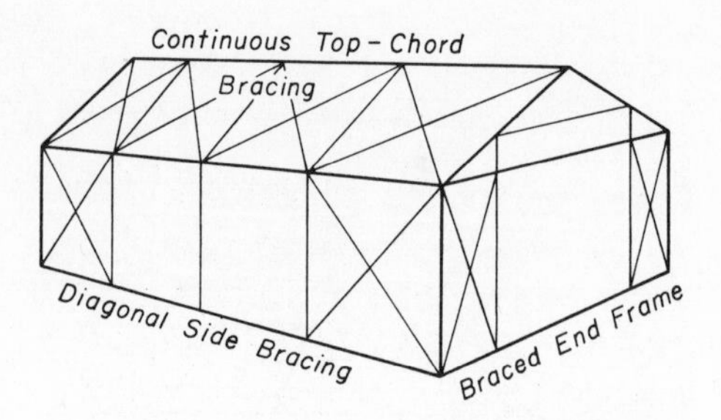

FIG. 36. STEEL BUILDING FRAME.

(3) *The Hinged Arch.* A third variation of the standard industrial building is the two-hinged or three-hinged arch structure. See Fig. 34(*g*). If diagonal bracing is used either continuously or in alternate bays, the arch will be braced properly. The arch building is used only where relatively great clear spans are desired, as, for instance, for an armory, a hanger, or a colosseum. A horizontal tie rod may be used to furnish the necessary horizontal reaction at the base if concrete abutments prove to be too costly. A diagram of a *tied arch* is shown in Fig. 34(*g*). A photograph of a hinged roof arch is shown in Fig. 37.

Courtesy American Bridge Co.

FIG. 37. HINGED ARCHES OF THE GOODYEAR AIRSHIP DOCK, AKRON, OHIO.

42. Roof Construction. The roof of an industrial building must span between the roof trusses. Since the roof trusses are seldom spaced closer than 15 ft., reasonably heavy beams are required to span between the trusses and carry the roof load. These beams are called *purlins*. Their spacing will be found to vary from 3 to 7 ft. depending upon the allowable span of the roofing material or of the *sheathing*. Originally sheathing consisted of a wood deck resting on the purlins and covered by a light metal or mastic roofing. Modern construction with its flat or slightly sloping roofs often makes use of precast slabs of light-weight concrete that span from 4 to

7 ft. between the purlins. Such slabs may be only 1½ in. thick since they are machine cast with stiffening ribs along each edge. A slab with ribs, size 3 × 6 ft., will weigh about 350 lb. which permits some handling by hand. The concrete deck is covered with several coats of asphalt and roofing paper.

No sheathing is required under a corrugated metal roof or a corrugated asbestos roof, but roll roofings as well as composition shingles, slate, and tile, all require sheathing for their support. Corrugated metal roofs or corrugated asbestos roofs are therefore cheaper and are usually selected for temporary or low-cost industrial buildings.

43. Wall Construction. The sidewall of a low-cost industrial building is commonly constructed in the same manner as the roof. *Girts* are used to span between the columns and either corrugated steel, aluminum, or corrugated asbestos siding is attached to the girts. Except in the cheapest buildings this thin surface material will be backed up by insulation and an inside finish material. Much study and effort has been given to the problem of machine production of prefabricated wall panels. This method of construction is rapidly superseding fabrication by hand on the job. Windows and glass panels take up a great deal of the sidewall area. Steel or aluminum sash and frames are used. Special girts must be placed above and below the windows for their support. Sidewall between windows may be constructed of cement plaster on expanded metal, brickwork, concerte blocks, or modern prefabricated sandwich panels.

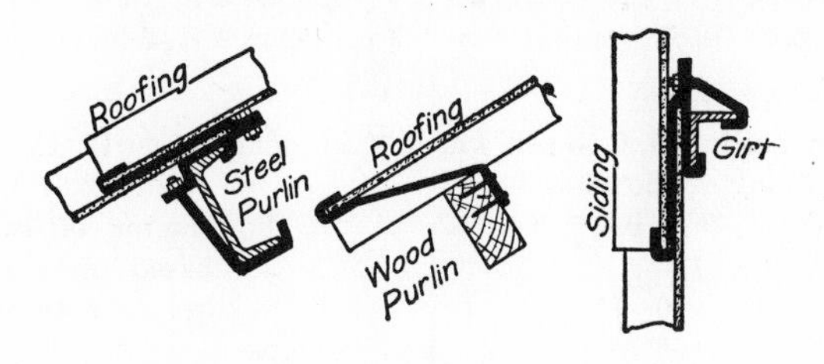

Fig. 38. Clips for Attaching Corrugated Asbestos.

Details. The reader is referred to Sweet's Architectural Catalogue for details of roof and sidewall coverings, windows, doors, etc. Clips for attaching corrugated asbestos roofing to purlins and girts are shown on Fig. 38. Corrugated metal roofing is often attached to steel members with hammer-driven self-threading screws.

Expansion of Roof Truss. The manner in which the roof trusses are attached to the brick walls is of importance. For roof trusses of short span, the change in length of the bottom chord from temperature change will be small, and the ends of the trusses may be bolted down to the walls. When the trusses exceed 40 ft. in. length, it is usually the practice to place one end of the truss upon a *sliding plate* to take care of expansion. A truss of greater span than 70 ft. when supported on masonry walls should have one end resting on a *rocker* or on *rollers*. The reaction of such a support is assumed to be vertical; a truly vertical reaction would exist if the rollers were frictionless. All horizontal reaction must be furnished by the opposite support.

Dead Loads and Live Loads for Buildings

44. Weight of Roof and Sidewalls. When a steel-frame building is selected because of its cheapness the entire construction is often made as light as possible. For this reason a roofing material that is self-supporting is desirable. Corrugated steel sheets can be obtained to span from 3 to 4½ ft. between purlins. Corrugated asbestos roofing will span from 4 to 6 ft. between purlins. These same materials may be used to enclose the sides of the building, where they will span from 4 to 7 ft. between girts.

Corrugated Roofing. The following weights of corrugated steel, aluminum, and corrugated asbestos are recommended where the load is in lb. per sq. ft. *of roof surface.* The use of corrugated asbestos and corrugated aluminum has increased rapidly because of neat appearance and freedom from maintenance. Corrugated metals are available in several patterns for architectural effects.

Corrugated Steel. Load 40 psf.
No. 22 gage (U.S. Standard) wt. 1.5 psf, span 3 ft.-6 in.
No. 20 gage (U.S. Standard) wt. 1.8 psf, span 3 ft.-10 in.
No. 18 gage (U.S. Standard) wt. 2.3 psf, span 4 ft.-6 in.

Corrugated Aluminum.
0.032-in. thickness, 0.56 psf, width 35 in., length 5 to 12 ft. (pitch 2.67 in., depth 0.87 in.)

Purlin Spacing	Allowable Load	
7′ — 0″	25 psf	For factor of safety of 2.0 based upon ultimate flexural strength of 35,000 psi.
6′ — 0″	35	
5′ — 6″	40	
5′ — 0″	50	
4′ — 0″	80	

Corrugated Asbestos. Load 40 psf.
¼-in. thickness, wt. 3 psf, span 4 ft.-0 in.
⅓-in. thickness, wt. 4 psf, span 5 ft.-0 in.
⅜-in. thickness, wt. 4½ psf, span 6 ft.-0 in.
For a load of 30 psf, decrease to the next lighter weight.
For a load of 50 psf, increase to the next heavier weight.

The following *weights of roofing materials* are suggested per square foot of roof surface. They are given as upper and lower limits, since considerable variation of weight is possible.

Roof Covering	*psf*
Wood sheathing (2 in. thick)	6 to 8
Concrete roof slab (3 in. thick, depending on aggregate)	20 to 35

Roof Covering	*psf*
Thin, precast concrete ribbed roof panels	15 to 20
Tiles	8 to 20
Composition shingles	2 to 5
Composition sheet roofing	0.5 to 1.5
Tar and gravel roofing (3- to 5-ply felt)	5 to 8

45. Weights of Steel Purlins. The main structural members in the roof are the steel purlins. The weight of purlins varies with the spacing between purlins, with the amount of dead load and live load, and particularly with the spacing of roof trusses. Because of these variables, the weight of steel purlins can be stated only within wide limits. Usually this weight will be found within the limits of 2 and 4.5 psf of roof surface. The lower value is applicable where the span between roof trusses is short (under 16 ft.) and the loads are light. The upper value of 4.5 psf may be exceeded for greater spacing of trusses (over 20 ft.) where a heavy type of roof such as precast slab sheathing is selected.

46. Weight of Roof Truss and Roof Bracing. Roof trusses are of many types, depending upon the slope of the roof and upon the number of panel points needed for the support of the purlins. If the purlins are allowed to rest upon the top chord of the roof truss between joints, a heavy top-chord section will be required, which may increase the weight of the roof truss considerably. The major factors that influence the weight of a roof truss are the span, the amount of load to be carried, and the *pitch*.[1] A roof truss of large pitch (steep slope) will certainly weigh less per square foot of roof surface than one of small pitch. The rules given below for estimating the approximate weights of roof trusses are satisfactory for design purposes.

Roof Truss. The *weights of roof trusses* of from $\frac{1}{3}$ to $\frac{1}{4}$ pitch may be assumed to vary from 2.0 to 3.5 psf of roof surface where the span is 40 ft. The lower value may be used for welded construction when a corrugated metal roof or a corrugated asbestos roof is used. The gusset plates used with riveted construction will increase the truss weight about 15 per cent. For longer spans, add $\frac{1}{2}$ psf for each additional 10 ft. up to 80 ft. For flat roofs, increase the above weights from $\frac{1}{2}$ psf to 1 psf, and for very steep roofs, decrease the weights from $\frac{1}{2}$ psf to 1 psf. The formula, $w = 0.5 + 0.05L$, may be used as a guide to the variation of weight per square foot of roof surface with the span L (in feet) for trusses of $\frac{1}{4}$ pitch.

Roof Bracing. In addition to the weight of the roof trusses, there is the weight of diagonal bracing and longitudinal struts to be considered. This bracing may be assumed roughly to add from $\frac{1}{2}$ to $1\frac{1}{2}$ psf to the dead load. The lower value applies to small structures where diagonal bracing is not needed in the plane of the lower chord.

[1] The *pitch* of a roof truss is the rise divided by the span. [See Fig. 34(f).] The pitch is *not* the tangent of the angle at the eave; it is *one half* of the tangent of that angle.

47. Snow Load.[2] The amount of snow load that should be used in the design of an industrial building is largely a matter of opinion. Certainly, the actual snow load will be larger in the northern states than in the southern states. Probably the value of the snow load should represent the maximum weight of damp snow that can reasonably be expected to fall in any particular locality over a period of several winters. Dry snow is of little importance since it is readily swept from the roof by the accompanying wind. In general, it may be said that the weight of snow usually considered in design varies from 5 to 30 psf of roof surface. For roofs of $\frac{1}{3}$ or $\frac{1}{4}$ pitch, a snow load of from 12 to 20 psf is commonly assumed for the central states where a 24-in. snow is exceptional and from 5 to 10 psf for the southern states. These values may be halved for very steep roofs and they should be nearly doubled for flat roofs. They are given in pounds per square foot of roof surface.

48. Wind Load. The wind load depends upon wind pressure which in turn depends upon velocity of the wind. Early tests gave the relationship $p = 0.004V^2$ as the total force in pounds on a rectangular plate 1 sq. ft. in area when exposed to a constant wind velocity of V miles per hour. A part of this force p is a pressure on the windward face and a part is accounted for by suction on the leeward face.

More recent tests have indicated that the actual pressure on the windward face of a building of reasonable depth is but one half of the value given above or $0.002V^2$ and that a suction of about $0.0013V^2$ will occur on the leeward face. Hence, the recommendations of the *ASCE* Committee on Wind Bracing in Steel Buildings (Transactions *ASCE*, vol. 105, p. 1715) was that the total wind force on the building be computed from the relationship

$$p = 0.0033V^2 \text{ (pressure plus suction)} \tag{1}$$

Here p is the wind force in pounds per square foot and V is the wind velocity in miles per hour.

49. Wind Pressure on Low Buildings. If we accept the *ASCE* formula ($p = 0.0033V^2$) we see that a velocity of 77.8 miles per hour produces a total wind force (part pressure and part suction) of 20 psf of exposed face. It is generally considered that 20 psf is a safe pressure for the design of a low building shielded by other neighboring structures where the average 5-min. velocity controls design. In an exposed or isolated location a design pressure of 30 psf corresponding to a gust velocity of 95 miles per hour is recommended. Bridges are placed in unprotected sites, which explains the fact that they must be designed for a wind pressure of from 30 to 50 psf. Towers in hurricane areas have been designed for wind velocities as high as 125 miles

[2] A. F. Meyer, *Elements of Hydrology*, Wiley, pp. 81–89. Survey of snow and ice fall, with illustrations. Also see *Snow loads on buildings*, Eng. News-Record, July 7, 1949, p. 76.

per hour. For the design of tall structures wind velocity must be varied with elevation y, i.e.,

$$V_y = V_0\left(\frac{y}{y_0}\right)^{1/7}. \tag{2}$$

Here V_0 is the base velocity at elevation y_0, which is usually 30 ft. above ground. Equation (2) is known as the "one-seventh power law." It has not been established for universal applications. For greater safety some structures in areas subject to hurricanes have been designed for velocity change based upon the one-fifth power of y/y_0.

Internal Wind Forces. Open windows, doors, or glass broken by a storm will cause internal wind pressure if openings may occur on the windward side. A suction or internal negative pressure will occur if openings can exist on the leeward side. The following formulas were recommended in the *ASCE* report. The factor n is the percentage of wall surface composed of windows, doors, and other openings ranging from 0 to 30 per cent.

$$p_{ip} = 4.5 + 0.25n \quad \text{(internal pressure in pounds per sq. ft.)}. \tag{3}$$

$$p_{is} = 4.5 + 0.15n \quad \text{(internal suction in pounds per sq. ft.)}. \tag{4}$$

It is recommended that the internal pressure or suction be used in the design of walls and for anchorage of the roof. The most unfavorable combination with external pressure or suction is to be chosen for each part of the structure. For example, on a wall parallel to the direction of the wind the internal pressure from equation (3) is to be combined with an external suction specified to be 9 psf for checking the resistance of the wall to being blown outward.

Sloping and Rounded Roof Surfaces. The *ASCE* specified wind pressures *in pounds per square foot of roof surface* are as follows:

Windward Slope. (Where θ is the angle with the horizontal.)

(*a*) For θ not greater than 20 degrees, an external suction of 12 psf. When $\theta = 0$ (for a flat roof) this external suction force must not be neglected.

(*b*) For θ from 20 degrees to 30 degrees an external suction of

$$p_{es} = 1.20\theta - 36. \tag{5}$$

(*c*) For θ from 30 degrees to 60 degrees an external pressure of

$$p_{ep} = 0.30\theta - 9. \tag{6}$$

(*d*) For θ above 60 degrees an external pressure of 9 psf along with (*e*) on the leeward slope.

Leeward Slope.

(*e*) For θ greater than 0 degrees an external suction of 9 psf, which is raised to 12 psf for a flat roof.

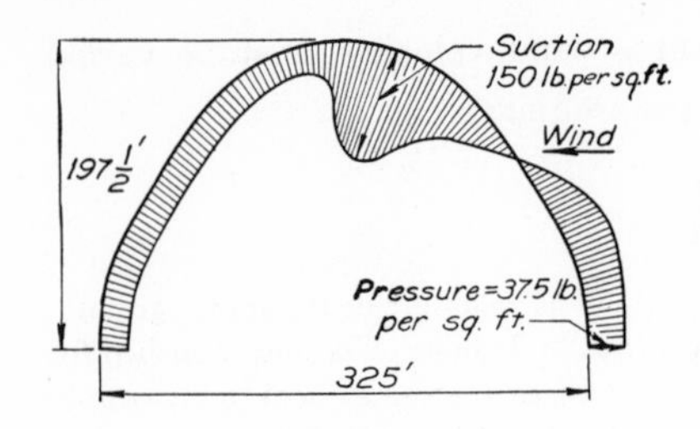

FIG. 39. WIND PRESSURE ON THE GOODYEAR ZEPPELIN DOCK.

Rounded Roofs.

(*f*) For varying rise ratios and for each quarter of the arc the *ASCE* report (Transactions *ASCE*, Vol. 105, p. 1717) gives a different formula to control the design pressure or suction. Fig. 39 illustrates the need for careful study of the pressure and suction variation across a curved roof surface. The extremely high value of negative pressure or suction near the crown of the arched roof is noteworthy.

Empirical Formulas for Sloping Roofs. Several formulas have long been in use for determining the total wind force (pressure plus suction) to be used in the design of a sloping roof truss. In the use of these formulas the wind is considered to be merely a pressure effect on the windward side of the roof which tends to give conservative stresses for design in most cases. *θ is the angle at the eave.* The pressure p_n is normal to the roof.

(7) $$p_n = p\left(\frac{2\sin\theta}{1+\sin^2\theta}\right)$$ (Duchemin formula, original tests made in 1829).

(8) $$p_n = p\sin\theta^{1.84\cos\theta - 1}$$ (Hutton formula),

(9) $$p_n = p\frac{\theta}{45}$$ (Ketchum or straight-line formula).

The Duchemin formula is considered to be the most reliable, but the straight-line formula has been much used because of its simplicity. The Hutton formula and the straight-line formula are in close agreement below an angle of 35 degrees (about ⅓ pitch).

50. Load Combinations to be Used in Design. Observation shows that a heavy snow will be blown from a sloping roof before the wind velocity approaches 60 miles per hour. Therefore we do not consider it necessary to use both *full snow load and full wind load* in the design of a roof. Instead, the following load combinations are used. The design stress in any member is the largest stress produced by any one of these three combinations:

(1) Dead load and snow load.
(2) Dead load and wind pressure from either direction.
(3) Dead load, *one-half* snow load, and wind pressure from either direction.

The term *one-half snow load* as used here means snow or rather ice over the entire roof of one half the weight of the maximum snow load. It does not mean full snow load on one half of the roof, which is a very improbable loading when combined with full wind load. However, snow load over a part of the roof area is covered by Spec. 2.

Alternate Loading. The use of a uniform vertical load over the entire area of the roof in place of the combined effect of dead load, snow load, and wind is entirely reasonable where the trusses are supported on masonry walls. A minimum vertical load of 30 psf frequently is specified.

PROBLEMS

301. The plan of an industrial building is 60×180 ft. Roof trusses are spaced 20 ft. apart. The purlin spacing is 5.6 ft. The roof is of ¼ pitch. The roofing material is corrugated asbestos. Estimate the probable dead load to be supported by one interior roof truss. Tabulate your estimate in neat form.

302. A gymnasium roof spans 80 ft. and the trusses are spaced 22 ft. apart. The rise of the roof is 3 ft.-6 in. A 3-in. concrete slab spans 5 ft. between steel purlins and carries a 5-ply tar and gravel roof. The concrete weighs 100 pcf. Produce a neat tabulated estimate of the total dead load acting on one truss.

303. Plot the Duchemin, Hutton, and straight-line formulas for the special cases of $p = 20$ and $p = 30$ psf. Plot all graphs on a single sheet. Add *ASCE* data from §49. Values of p_n are to be plotted as ordinates and values of θ as abscissas.

304. A building is 160 ft. long, 60 ft. wide, and 25 ft. to the roof. It has a flat roof. Find the resultant pressure on the windward side of the building caused by a wind blowing 50 miles per hour at an angle of 30 degrees with the shorter side. Use *ASCE* formula, $p = 0.0020V^2$, for pressure on the windward side. Make use of the Duchemin formula. Neglect skin friction. *Ans.* 20,800 lb.

305. A solid concrete cylinder 2 ft. in diameter and 7 ft. high forming a gate post is found overturned by the effect of a hurricane. Both the post and its base are undamaged. Assume that the concrete weighs 150 pcf and calculate the necessary wind velocity. Use $p = 0.0033V^2$ for the combined effects of pressure and suction but reduce p by a factor of 0.75 for a cylindrical shape. *Ans.* 165 m.p.h.

306. Compute the height to which a free-standing brick wall may be constructed before it will be blown over by a wind of 60 m.p.h. The wall is 12 in. thick and weighs 120 pcf. Use $p = 0.0033V^2$, equation (1). Repeat for a concrete block wall weighing 72 pcf. Neglect bond of uncured mortar. *Ans.* (*a*) 10 ft.; (*b*) 6 ft.

Roof-Truss Analysis

51. Types of Roof Trusses. There are numerous variations of the standard types of roof trusses. However, the principles of analysis are the same for all. Truss diagrams are shown in Fig. 40 for a number of roof trusses. Of those shown, the Fink, and Pratt types are most used for roofs of large rise ratio and the Warren and Pratt types are most used for flat roofs.

Note that the diagonals of the two Pratt trusses shown in Fig. 40(*c*) and (*d*) slope in opposite directions. The Pratt truss is constructed so that the diagonal web members will be in tension under dead load. In contrast, the Howe truss has its verticals in tension and its diagonals in compression under dead load. The reason for this difference is that the Howe truss is usually of wood construction with steel verticals. Wood diagonals are quite capable of resisting compression, but long steel diagonals should be sloped in the opposite direction to act in tension. The quadrangular truss is used for long spans and is constructed of steel. The diagonals are reversed near the center of the span where they would otherwise be acting in compression.

The French and Fan trusses are less important variations of the standard Fink truss. *Saw-tooth* trusses are used in modern construction to obtain adequate sky light for a wide building. The glazed surfaces should be faced north to avoid direct sunlight.

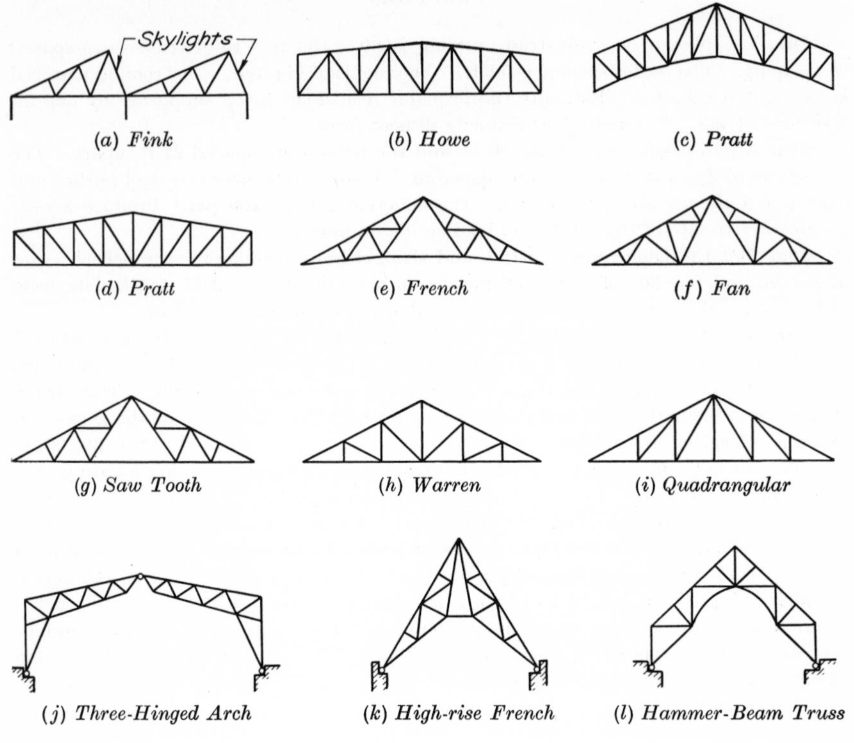

Note that (*i*) (*k*) and (*l*) are roof structures that produce horizontal thrusts on side walls or abutments.

Fig. 40. Roof Trusses of Varying Slopes.

52. Calculations of Loads and Reactions. Panel concentrations of snow load and wind load are obtained by multiplying the area tributary to each panel point by the load per square foot. The entire dead load of roofing material, sheathing, purlins, and truss is divided among the upper-chord panel points according to their tributary areas. The refinement of placing a part of the dead load of the trusses at the lower-chord panel points would be wasted precision. Ceiling loads may be caused by suspended ceilings, hanging balconies, light fixtures, shafts, and suspended machinery, or monorail cranes. These loads, including the effect of impact, must be taken into consideration in the design.

Reaction at a Sliding Plate. The calculations for standard cases of truss reactions caused by dead load and wind have been discussed in Chapter 2.

A special case arises when a sliding plate is used at one end of the truss. The horizontal reaction at the sliding end is limited to the product of the vertical reaction there (caused by vertical loading as well as wind) and the coefficient of friction (about $\frac{1}{3}$ as a rough estimate). The value of the vertical reaction is *independent* of the coefficient of friction. Of course, if the plates corrode and fail to move (a very probable condition for steel plates) both ends of the truss become fixed. In that case a better approximation of the stresses may be obtained by making the horizontal reaction at each end equal to 50 per cent of the horizontal component of the wind load.

53. Algebraic and Graphical Methods of Analysis. All the standard tools of algebraic and graphical truss analysis have already been discussed. Roof trusses are commonly analyzed by means of the stress diagram. The algebraic method of joints is preferred by some. In order to obtain accurate stresses by the graphical method, one must start with a large-scale drawing of the truss drawn with extreme care. Most inaccuracies develop from failure to obtain lines in the stress diagram that are exactly parallel to the corresponding truss members.

54. Ambiguous Trusses. *Algebraic Analysis.* The analysis of the Fink truss of Fig. 41(*a*) may be started by the method of joints. From joint L_0, one continues by the usual procedure to U_1 and L_1. Nevertheless, despite the fact that all stresses cut by the section *a-a* are now known, there remain three unknown stresses at each of the joints U_2 and L_2. It is possible, however, to cut the section *b-b* and to compute the stress in L_2L_3 from an equation of moments about U_4. With the stress in L_2L_3 known there are but two unknown stresses at the joint L_2. Therefore it becomes possible to continue by the method of joints in the following succession: L_2, U_2, U_3, M_1, U_4, etc.

Semi-Graphical Analysis. The same difficulty of ambiguity develops in drawing the stress diagram in Fig. 41(*b*). The points 1, 2, and 3 are located by drawing force polygons for the joints L_0, L_1, and U_1. Since three unknowns exist both at U_2 and L_2, the diagram cannot be continued. The semi-graphical method of procedure involves the algebraic determination of the stress 7-*G* from an equation of moments about the joint U_4. Then the location of the point 7 on the diagram is determined by scaling the value of 7-*G* backward from *G*, as a tension stress. The stress diagram can then be continued in the order of joints mentioned above.

Graphical Analysis. An entirely graphical method of removing the ambiguity from the Fink truss is shown in Fig. 41(*c*) and (*d*). The members 4-5 and 5-6 in (*a*) are removed and the single member 4′-6 is substituted for these two members. The stress diagram for the substitute structure is drawn in the usual manner until the point 7 is located. Evidently the stress in the member 7-*G* and therefore the location of the point 7 would be the same for the original truss and for the substitute truss, since the moment

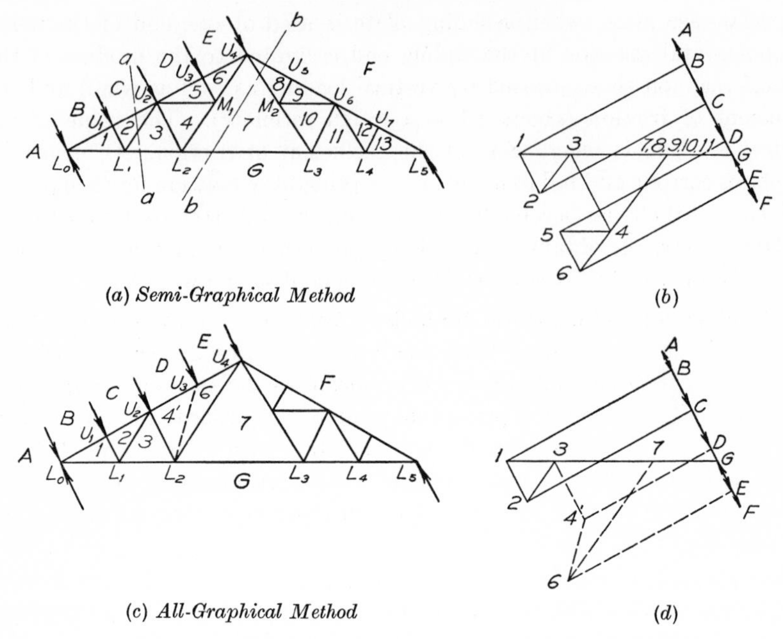
(a) *Semi-Graphical Method* (b)

(c) *All-Graphical Method* (d)

FIG. 41. GRAPHICAL ANALYSIS OF A FINK ROOF TRUSS.

about the joint U_4 is the same in both. Also the points 1, 2, 3, and 6 would not be moved. With the point 7 located as shown by the broken lines in (*d*), it is possible to replace the original truss members as in (*a*) and to complete the diagram, which will then appear as in (*b*).

This study justifies the conclusion that ambiguity is caused by an unusual arrangement of members. It is in no way connected with statical indeterminacy.

55. Example of the Analysis of a Flat Warren Truss. The truss shown in Fig. 42 will be analyzed and the maximum stresses determined. The truss

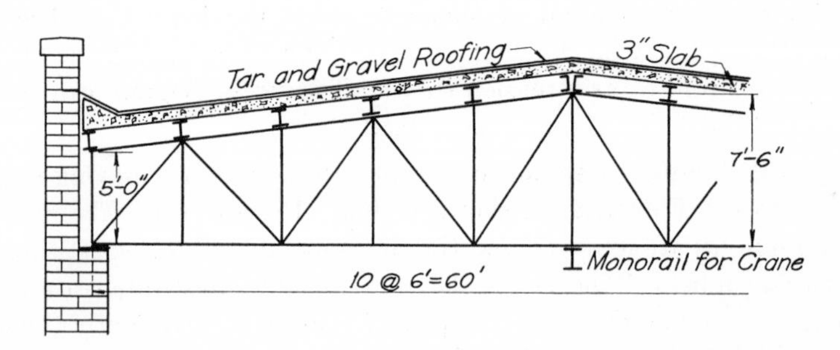

FIG. 42. ROOF OF AN INDUSTRIAL BUILDING WITH WARREN TRUSSES.

must carry the dead load of the roof, a snow load of 30 psf, and a concentrated load at mid-span of 20,000 lb. caused by a monorail crane. The truss is protected by a parapet wall, and therefore no positive wind load will be considered. The roof should be checked for stability under a suction of 12 psf as specified for flat slopes in §49 and the internal wind pressure given by equation (3).

DATA.

Type of truss: Warren with verticals.
Span: 60 ft.-0 in.
Height: 7 ft.-6 in. at center, 5 ft.-0 in. at each end.
Spacing of roof trusses: 15 ft.-0 in.
Purlin spacing: 6 ft.-0¼ in. between panel points.
Snow load: 30 psf of roof surface.
Crane load: 20,000 lb. at center of truss (including impact).
External wind suction following §49 = 12 psf.
Internal wind pressure for 30 per cent openings by equation (3) $= 4.5 + (0.25 \times 30) = 12$ psf.
Total upward wind force on roof of $12 + 12 = 24$ psf.

PANEL LOADS.

Roof slab: 3-in. slab constructed with light-weight aggregate (100 psf); weight, 25 psf of roof surface. (Adequate to resist lifting force of wind.)
Roof covering: 5-ply tar and gravel roofing; weight, 7¾ psf of roof surface.
Purlins: 6-in. standard I-beams at 12.5 lb. per ft.; weight per sq. ft. of roof surface $= 12.5 \div 6 = 2.1$ psf.
Roof truss: The loading is not particularly heavy; hence the basic weight (40-ft. span) is taken midway between the limits of 2 and 3.5 psf, or 2.75 psf. See §46. This weight is increased 1 psf to account for the 60-ft. span and 1 psf to allow for the flat pitch. The estimated weight is 4.75 psf of roof surface.
Bracing: Diagonal bracing will be used in the planes of the upper and lower chords. The estimated weight is 1.0 psf of roof surface.

Summary of panel loads:

Roof slab	= 25.0 psf
Roof covering	= 7.75
Purlins	= 2.1
Roof trusses	= 4.75
Bracing	= 1.0
Snow load	= 30.0
Total	= 70.6 psf
Panel load	$= 70.6 \times 6.02 \times 15 = 6370$ lb.

STRESS CALCULATIONS.

Stress Diagram for Dead Load and Snow Load. Since there is no wind load to be considered, a combined diagram for dead load and snow load is drawn. See Fig. 43(*b*). The stresses are placed on the truss diagram in (*d*). Note that the symmetry of truss and loading makes it unnecessary to draw the stress diagram for the right-hand half of the truss. If we should become interested in the dead-load stresses, they may be obtained by multiplying the combined dead-load and snow-load stresses by the *constant ratio* 40.6/70.6.

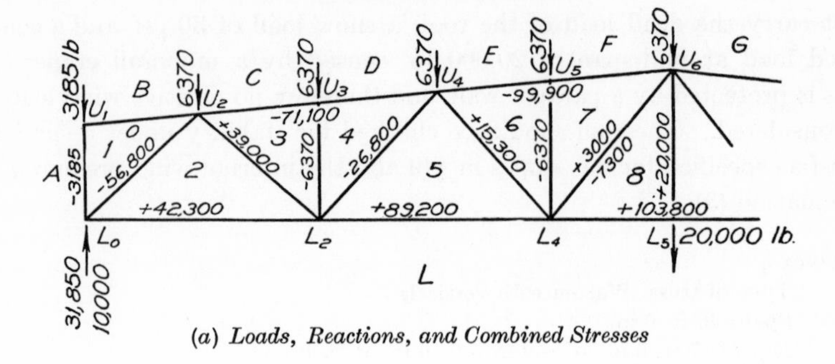

(a) *Loads, Reactions, and Combined Stresses*

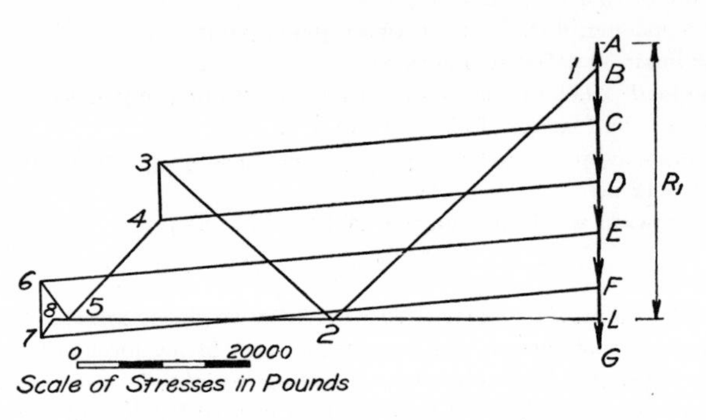

(b) *Stress Diagram (Dead and Snow Load)*

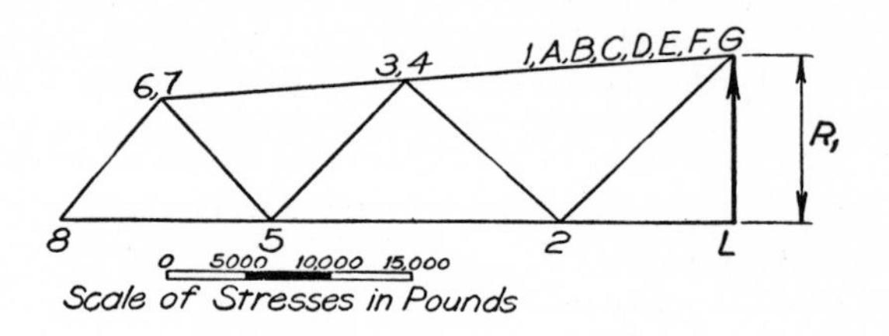

(c) *Stress Diagram (Crane Load)*

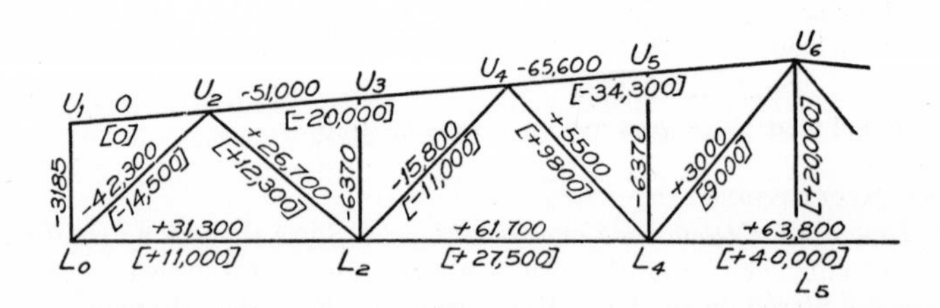

(d) *Scaled Values of Stresses (Crane Load Stresses in Brackets)*

FIG. 43. ANALYSIS OF A FLAT WARREN ROOF TRUSS BY GRAPHICAL METHOD.

Stress Diagram for the Monorail Crane Load. This diagram is shown in (*c*) of Fig. 43. The stresses are placed on the truss diagram in (*d*). These stresses are shown enclosed in brackets. The analysis presents no special difficulties.

Combined Stresses. Combined stresses for design are given on the truss diagram, Fig. 43(*a*). For all members except L_4U_6, the combined or maximum stresses may be obtained by summing the stresses as given in (*d*). The dead-load and snow-load stress in L_4U_6 is $+3000$ lb. and the crane-load stress is -9000 lb. The maximum possible tension clearly is 3000 lb., as recorded in (*a*). The maximum compression is the crane-load stress of 9000 lb. *minus* the dead-load tension of 3000(40.6/70.6), or $-9000 + 1700 = -7300$ lb. This value is recorded as the other combined stress for L_4U_6 in (*a*). The member must be capable of resisting *either of the combined stresses.*

56. Example of the Analysis of a Fink Roof Truss. The truss shown in Fig. 44 will be analyzed and the maximum stresses determined. The truss must carry the dead load of the roof, a snow load of 15 psf on the horizontal, and a wind pressure of 20 psf on the vertical.

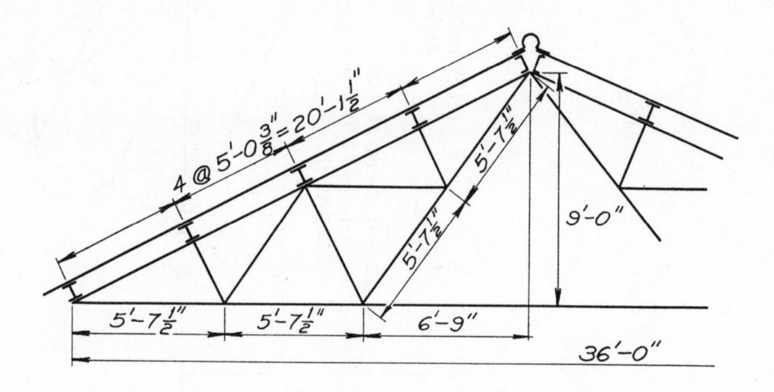

FIG. 44. ROOF WITH FINK TRUSS.

DATA.

Type of truss: Standard Fink.
Span: 36 ft.-0 in.[3]

Rise: 9 ft.-0 in.
Spacing of roof trusses: 16 ft.-3 in.
Snow load: 15 psf on a horizontal surface.
Wind load: 20 psf on a vertical surface.

DEAD LOAD.

Roof coverings: 3/8-in. corrugated asbestos; weight, 4½ psf.
Purlins: Steel purlins at 5-ft. centers to carry light loads for a span of 16 ft. are estimated to weigh 3 psf of roof surface.
Roof trusses: Estimated at the lower limit of 2 psf of roof surface because of the short span and light loads.
Bracing: Adequate bracing is estimated to weigh 1 psf of roof surface.
Fixtures and shafts: An allowance of ½ psf of roof surface will care for such light loads.

[3] A short-span truss is selected here to reduce the number of members and computations. Trusses are seldom used for spans under 50 ft .or even 60 ft. since welded girder bents are more economical either for flat roofs or pitched roofs of intermediate spans.

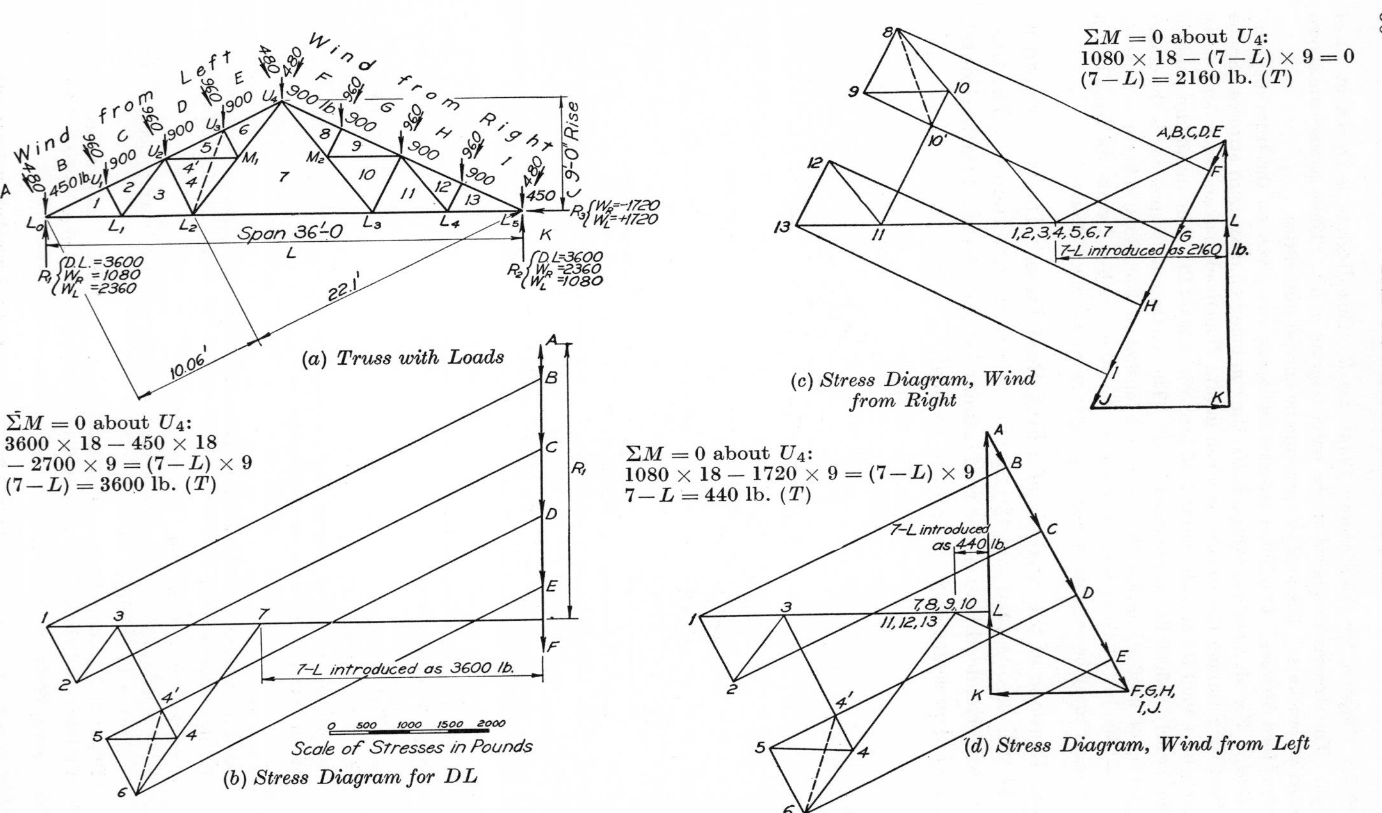

FIG. 45. STRESS DIAGRAMS FOR A FINK ROOF TRUSS.

DEAD PANEL LOAD.

Roof covering	=	4.5 psf
Purlins	=	3.0
Roof trusses	=	2.0
Bracing	=	1.0
Fixtures, shafts	=	0.5
Total	=	11.0 psf
Panel load	=	$11.0 \times 5.03 \times 16.25 = 900$ lb.

SNOW LOAD. 15 psf on the horizontal corresponds to about 10 psf on a roof of ¼ pitch.

Panel load $= 10 \times 5.03 \times 16.25 = 820$ lb.

WIND LOAD. The wind pressure on a roof of ¼ pitch ($\theta = 26°{:}40'$) is $p_n = 20 \times 26.67 \div 45 = 11.8$ psf (straight-line formula).

Panel load $= 11.8 \times 5.03 \times 16.25 = 960$ lb.

STRESS CALCULATIONS.

Stress Diagram for Dead Load. This diagram, shown in Fig. 45, presents no difficulty other than the need for overcoming the ambiguity of the Fink truss. The use of the substitute member U_3L_2 and the introduction of the calculated value of the stress $7\text{-}L$ are both illustrated on the diagram.

Stress Diagrams for Wind. Two wind-stress diagrams are shown on Fig. 45. Two diagrams are required because the entire horizontal reaction occurs at the right-hand end of the truss, and, therefore, the stresses produced by wind from the left are not simply reversed from those produced by wind from the right.

Combined Stresses. Table 2 shows how the stresses may be combined for maximum. In filling out this table, we obtain column (2) for snow load from the dead-load stresses of column (1) by direct proportion using the ratio of the corresponding panel loads, that is, $820/900 = 0.91$. Maximum combined stresses are given in column (7). There are no members that undergo a reversal of stress. All corresponding stresses for the two halves of the truss are equal except for the members of the *lower chord*. For every member, the combination of $DL + ½$ *Snow* + *Wind* gives a larger stress than $DL +$ *Snow*. This result is to be expected where the snow load is relatively small.

Alternate Loading. Column (8) of Table 2 gives the stresses for an alternate vertical loading of 25 psf of roof surface. The chord stresses range from 98 to 118 per cent of their computed maximum values. The web stresses range from 86 to 90 per cent of their maximum stresses. A large amount of roof-truss design is based upon an alternate vertical loading. Of course, the alternate loading for a longer span may be much greater than 25 psf.

Anchorage. For a roof slope of 26°-40′ the specified external suction is 9 psf on the leeward slope and $1.20\theta - 36 = (1.20 \times 26.7) - 36 = -4$ psf on the windward slope (equation 5, §49). By equation (3) §49 for 30 per cent openings, there may be an internal pressure of $4.5 + 0.25 \times 30 = 12$ psf of roof surface. The maximum lifting force on one half the roof is $(9 + 12) \times 16.25 \times 18.0 = 6150$ lb. Because this lift is greater than the dead load of one half of the truss, anchor bolts will be needed.

57. Stress Coefficients and Nomographic Chart. The bar stresses in a given roof truss of *fixed pitch* vary directly with the panel load and are *independent* of the span. If the panel load is taken as 1 lb., the corresponding bar stresses are called stress coefficients. Tables of stress coefficients are available for most standard trusses in the structural handbooks. Figure

46 is a nomographic chart, prepared by Professor J. R. Griffith, from which either the dead-load stresses or the wind stresses can be obtained for a standard eight-panel Fink truss for any given panel loading. A new chart is required for each change in pitch and for each new arrangement of members. Any span may be assigned since the stresses are dependent upon the pitch rather than the span for fixed panel loads. The wind stresses in Fig. 46 are based upon the assumption of parallel reactions. Draw a straight line from the value of the panel load through the number of the member on the vertical center line and extend to the scale of the total stress. Try this method of checking the dead-load stresses in Table 2 for the truss of Fig. 45.

TABLE 2

STRESSES IN POUNDS FOR THE FINK TRUSS OF FIG. 45

Stress	(1) Dead Load	(2) Full Snow	(3) Half Snow	(4) Wind from Left	(5) Wind from Right	(6) Columns to be Combined for Maximum	(7) Maximum Stress	(8) Stress Caused by a Vertical Load of 25 psf as an Alternate Loading	Member
1–B	−7050	−6420	−3210	−4320	−2440	1, 3, 4	−14,580	−16,100	U_1L_0
2–C	−6650	−6050	−3030	−4320	−2440	1, 3, 4	−14,000	−15,100	U_1U_2
5–D	−6250	−5700	−2850	−4320	−2440	1, 3, 4	−13,420	−14,200	U_2U_3
6–E	−5850	−5320	−2660	−4320	−2440	1, 3, 4	−12,830	−13,300	U_3U_4
13–I	−7050	−6420	−3210	−2440	−4320	1, 3, 5	−14,580	−16,100	U_7L_5
12–H	−6650	−6050	−3030	−2440	−4320	1, 3, 5	−14,000	−15,100	U_7U_6
9–G	−6250	−5700	−2850	−2440	−4320	1, 3, 5	−13,420	−14,200	U_6U_5
8–F	−5850	−5320	−2660	−2440	−4320	1, 3, 5	−12,830	−13,300	U_5U_4
1–L	+6300	+5730	+2860	+3650	+2160	1, 3, 4	+12,810	+14,300	L_0L_1
3–L	+5400	+4920	+2460	+2600	+2160	1, 3, 4	+10,460	+12,300	L_1L_2
7–L	+3600	+3280	+1640	+ 440	+2160	1, 3, 5	+ 7,400	+ 8,200	L_2L_3
11–L	+5400	+4920	+2460	+ 440	+4300	1, 3, 5	+12,160	+12,300	L_3L_4
13–L	+6300	+5730	+2860	+ 440	+5400	1, 3, 5	+14,560	+14,300	L_4L_5
1–2	− 810	− 740	− 370	− 960	0	1, 3, 4	− 2140	− 1840	U_1L_1
2–3	+ 900	+ 820	+ 410	+1070	0	1, 3, 4	+ 2380	+ 2050	U_2L_1
3–4	−1620	−1480	− 740	−1920	0	1, 3, 4	− 4280	− 3680	U_2L_2
4–5	+ 900	+ 820	+ 410	+1070	0	1, 3, 4	+ 2380	+ 2050	U_2M_1
5–6	− 810	− 740	− 370	− 960	0	1, 3, 4	− 2140	− 1840	U_3M_1
6–7	+2700	+2460	+1230	+3200	0	1, 3, 4	+ 7130	+ 6130	U_4M_1
4–7	+1800	+1640	+ 820	+2130	0	1, 3, 4	+ 4750	+ 4090	M_1L_2
13–12	− 810	− 740	− 370	0	− 960	1, 3, 5	− 2140	− 1840	U_7L_4
12–11	+ 900	+ 820	+ 410	0	+1070	1, 3, 5	+ 2380	+ 2050	U_6L_4
11–10	−1620	−1480	− 740	0	−1920	1, 3, 5	− 4280	− 3680	U_6L_3
10–9	+ 900	+ 820	+ 410	0	+1070	1, 3, 5	+ 2380	+ 2050	U_6M_2
9–8	− 810	− 740	− 370	0	− 960	1, 3, 5	− 2140	− 1840	U_5M_2
8–7	+2700	+2460	+1230	0	+3200	1, 3, 5	+ 7130	+ 6130	U_4M_2
10–7	+1800	+1640	+ 820	0	+2130	1, 3, 5	+ 4750	+ 4090	M_2L_3

Roof Truss Stresses

Eight Panel Fink Truss of 1/4 Pitch

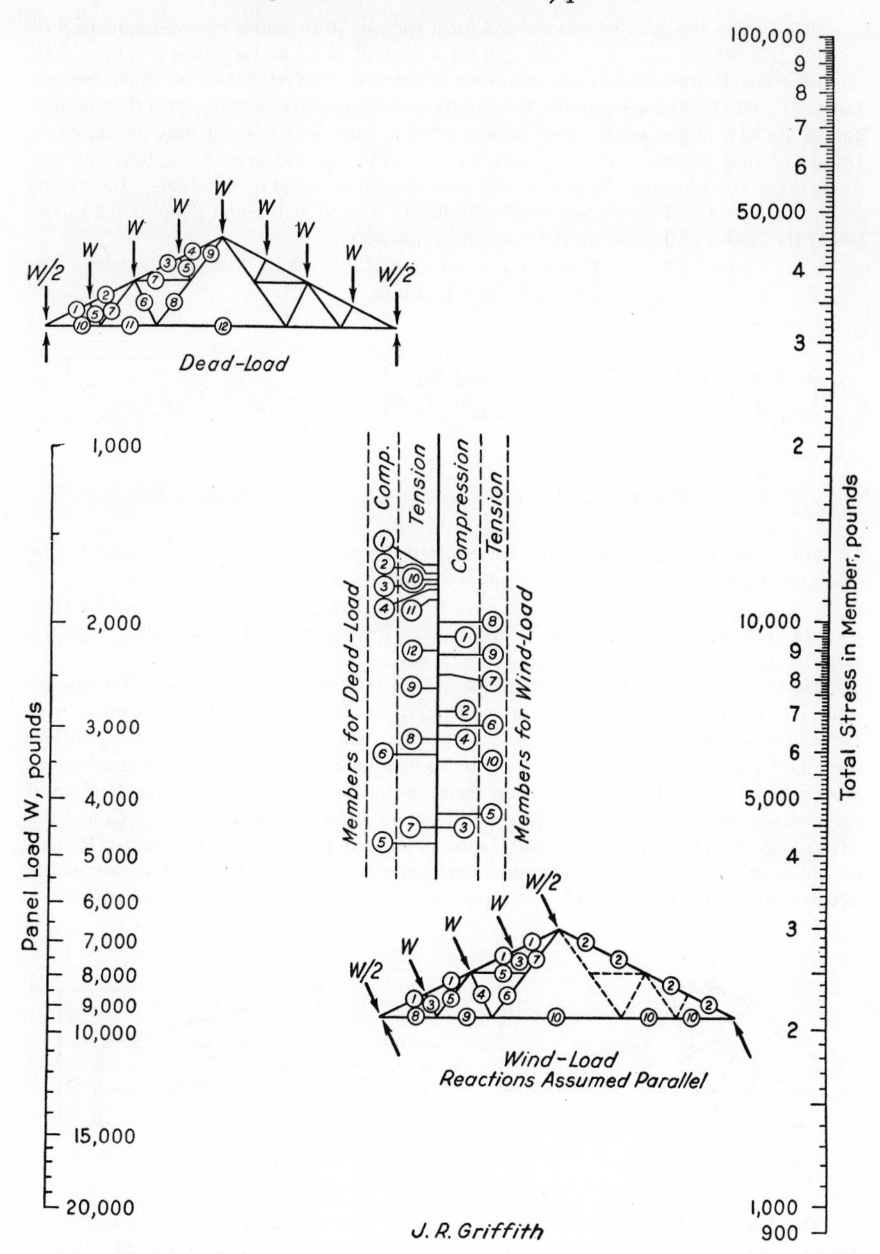

Fig. 46. Nomograph of Stresses for a Standard Fink Roof Truss.

Draw a straight line from the value of the panel load through the number of the member on the vertical center line and extend to the scale of the total stress at the right.

PROBLEMS

307. Revise the calculations for §55 for a span of 70 ft. and a center height of 8 ft.

308. Revise the calculations for §56 for a span of 45 ft. and a center height of 9 ft.

309. The Pratt truss shown supports a concrete roof slab 2½ in. thick (weight 150 pcf). The trusses are spaced 20 ft. apart and the purlins are 8-in., 11.5-lb. channels placed at each upper joint. The weight of roof truss and bracing may be taken at 7.5 psf of roof surface. The roof covering is 5-ply tar and gravel weighing 6.5 psf. Analyze the truss for dead load and for a snow load of 25 psf of roof surface. Determine the stresses produced by a crane load of 10,000 lb. placed at the first panel point to the left of the center and combine for maximum stresses.

Ans. $L_6L_7 = +145$; $U_5U_6 = -146$; $U_6U_7 = -139$; $L_6U_6 = +4.3$ or -2.6; $U_5L_6 = +7.8$; $U_6L_7 = -13.3$ kips.

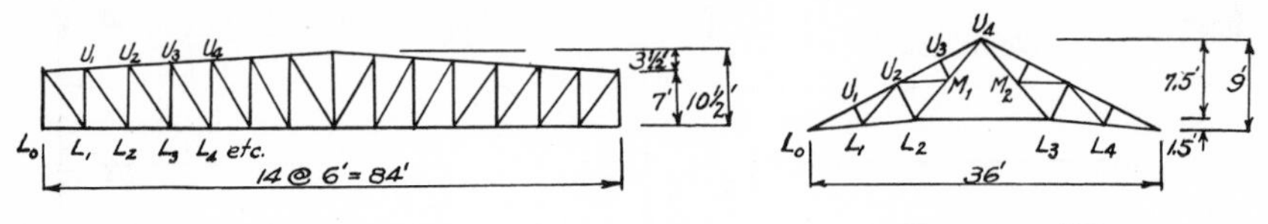

PROBLEM 309. PROBLEM 310.

310. Analyze the French truss for exactly the same loads that were used in the example of §56. Assume that the wind reactions are parallel to the wind loads.

Ans. $L_2L_3 = +8.2$; $U_3U_4 = -19.2$ kips.

311. Lay out a Warren truss to replace the Pratt truss of Problem 309. Use the same loads and determine the maximum stresses.

312. The Fan truss shown carries a dead load of 14 psf of roof surface. Trusses are spaced 16 ft. apart. The snow load is 12 psf of roof surface and the wind pressure is 15 psf on a vertical surface. Calculate normal wind pressure by the straight-line formula ($p_n = p\theta/45$). The left end of the truss rests on a sliding plate having a friction coefficient of 0.3. Allow for a friction reaction due to $DL + Wind$. If the horizontal component of the wind load is less than twice the maximum possible friction reaction at the left, divide this H-component equally between the two reactions. For a larger H-component of wind load all excess above the maximum value of the friction reaction at the left will be resisted at the right. Compute the wind stresses and the design stresses.

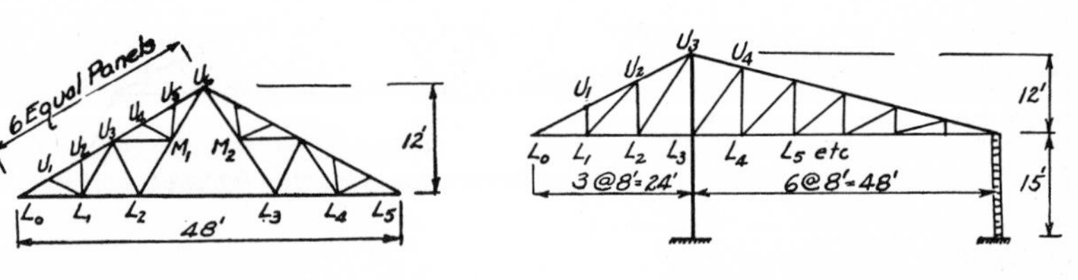

PROBLEM 312. PROBLEM 313.

313. The cantilever truss covers a grandstand. Panel lengths along the lower chord are all equal. Dead load is estimated at 15 psf of roof surface. Trusses are 20 ft. apart. No snow is to be considered, but the wind may blow from either direction with a pressure of 25 psf on the vertical. Make use of the Duchemin formula and determine design stresses.

Stress Analysis of Framed Portals

58. Portals and Bents. Whenever clear openings must not be restricted by diagonal bracing, the engineer turns to the use of a bent or portal. In the illustration Fig. 34(f) we see a series of framed portals along the side of the building to produce longitudinal stability. Also, there are transverse bents (each consisting of a roof truss, its supporting columns, and two knee braces) at intervals down the length of the building. Since the analysis of a portal is simpler than the analysis of a building bent with roof truss, it will be considered first.

59. Girder Portal with Pin-End Columns. The simplest type of girder bent or portal has pin-end columns, as shown in Fig. 47(a). A free-body diagram of the structure is shown in (b). Since the moments at the base must be zero (pin-end columns) there are but four reactions, and the structure is statically indeterminate to the *first* degree. In order to determine the reactions by statics, it is necessary to make an assumption which will eliminate *one* unknown. The usual assumption is that $H_1 = H_2$. Then, from the equation of statics $\Sigma F_x = 0$, it is seen that $H_1 = H_2 = P/2$; from $\Sigma F_y = 0$ it is seen that $V_1 = -V_2$; and from $\Sigma M_B = 0$, it is found that numerically $V_1 = V_2 = Ph/a$. The directions of the reactions are as shown in (b) of Fig. 47.

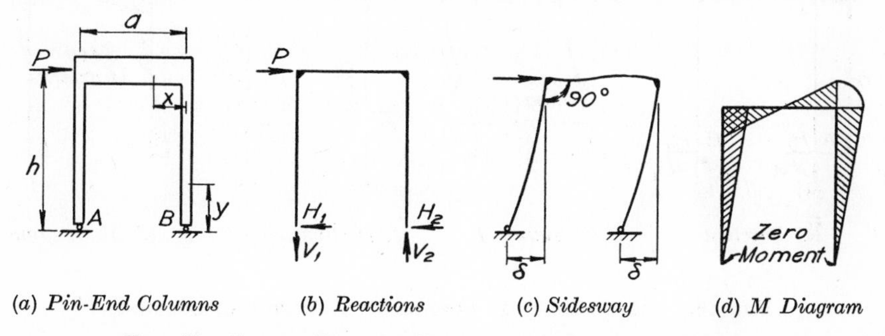

(a) *Pin-End Columns* (b) *Reactions* (c) *Sideway* (d) *M Diagram*

Fig. 47. Girder Bent or Portal with Pin-End Columns.

Shear and Moment Diagrams. The shears and moments may be calculated at any point in the structure from the values of the reactions. The shear at any point in the column is equal to $H = P/2$, and the column moment is $(P/2)y$. The shear at any point in the girder is $V = Ph/a$, and the girder moment at any point becomes $(P/2)h - (Ph/a)(x)$. The moment diagram for the portal as shown in (d) is plotted on the tension sides of the members.

Approximation Justified. A justification for the fundamental assumption that $H_1 = H_2$ is easily found. Since the girder is made of the same material as the columns, that is, steel, its small direct stress produced by the load P will not shorten it appreciably. The elastic deflection curves of the two columns as shown in Fig. 47(c) are therefore practically identical. The columns may be looked upon as identical cantilever beams (extending downward from the girder) loaded with the forces H_1 and H_2. In order to have equal elastic deflections, these identical cantilever beams must resist the same shears and moments, which leads us to conclude that H_1 and H_2 are equal.

60. Girder Portal with Fixed-End Columns. This structure, shown in Fig. 48(a), has six components of reaction. It follows that the fixed-end portal is statically indeterminate to the third degree. The deflected structure (b) shows plainly the points of contraflexure near the mid-heights of the columns. Since points of contraflexure are points of zero moment, that part of the structure above these points may be isolated, as in (c), and treated as a portal with shortened columns and pin-end bases. The calculations for the reactions, shears, and moments follow as for the pin-end portal. A final moment diagram is shown in Fig. 48(d).

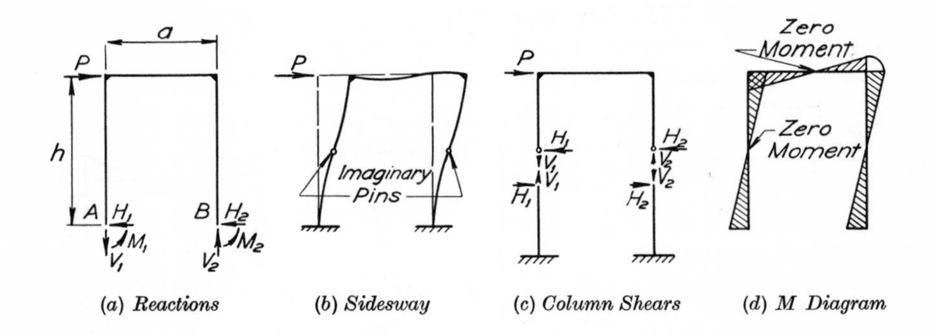

(a) *Reactions* (b) *Sidesway* (c) *Column Shears* (d) *M Diagram*

FIG. 48. GIRDER BENT OR PORTAL WITH FIXED-END COLUMNS.

61. Example of the Analysis of a Framed Portal. The portal shown in Fig. 49 will be analyzed for the stresses caused by a horizontal force of 1000 lb. acting at the top. The columns are assumed to be fixed at their lower ends. The shear in each column is taken as one half of the load, or 500 lb. The points of contraflexure are located at the mid-height from the base to the foot of the knee brace or 5 ft. above the base.

Signs of Stresses. In the calculations that follow, each force is assumed to be acting in the direction shown in Fig. 49. A negative value for a stress simply means that the assumed direction should be reversed.

VERTICAL REACTIONS. Use the isolated section above the points of contraflexure, Fig. 49(*a*).

$$\Sigma M_C = 0; \quad 1000 \times 12 - V_2 \times 14 = 0; \quad V_2 = 860 \text{ lb.} \quad (C).$$
$$\Sigma F_y = 0; \quad V_1 = -V_2 = 860 \text{ lb.} \quad (T).$$

MOMENT AT COLUMN BASE.

$$M_A = M_B = 500 \times 5 = 2500 \text{ ft-lb.}$$

STRESS IN *EI*. Isolate the left-hand column above the point of contraflexure as in (*b*) of Fig. 49.

$$\Sigma M_G = 0; \quad 500 \times 12 - x\text{-comp.}S_{EI} \times 7 = 0; \quad x\text{-comp.}S_{EI} = +860 \text{ lb.}$$
$$S_{EI} = 1.41 \times 860 = 1210 \text{ lb.} \quad (T).$$

STRESS IN *GI*. Use the same section as for the member *EI*.

$$\Sigma F_y = 0; \quad -860 + y\text{-comp.}S_{EI} - y\text{-comp.}S_{GI} = 0; \quad S_{GI} = 0.$$

STRESS IN *GK*. Use the same section as for the member *EI*.

$$\Sigma M_C = 0; \quad 1000 \times 12 + x\text{-comp.}S_{EI} \times 5 - S_{GK} \times 12 = 0;$$
$$S_{GK} = 1360 \text{ lb.} \quad (C)$$

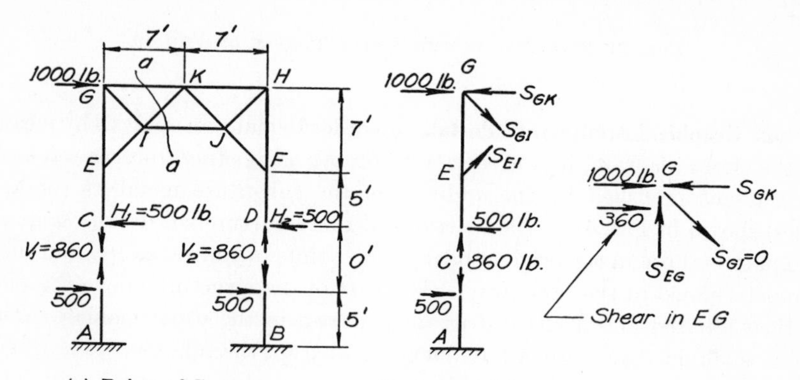

(*a*) *Points of Contraflexure* (*b*) *Isolated Column* (*c*) *Joint G Isolated*

FIG. 49. ANALYSIS OF A SIMPLE PORTAL.

Moment and Shear Diagrams. These diagrams may now be drawn for the left-hand column. They are shown in Fig. 50(*b*) and (*c*). The remainder of the stresses may be obtained by any desired combination of the methods of joints, moments, and sections. For instance, the use of the section *a–a* of Fig. 49 and the equation $\Sigma F_y = 0$ is a convenient way to determine the stress in the member *IK*. Evidently the stress is $1.41 \times 860 = 1210$ lb. (*T*). A casual inspection of the joint *G* might mislead us into thinking that the stress in the member *GK* is 1000 lb. (*C*); ($\Sigma F_x = 0$). This conclusion is erroneous because the equation $\Sigma F_x = 0$ at *G* [Fig. 49(*c*)] *must include the shear at G in the post EG.* The stress in the member *GK* then becomes $1000 + 360 = 1360$ lb. (*C*), which agrees with the value determined above.

Final Stresses. The computed stresses are given in Fig. 50(a). Considering the stresses in the members KH, JH, and JF as forces on the right-hand column, we may determine its shear and moment diagrams, which should be identical with those for the left-hand column. The equilibrium of the right-hand column may be checked under the action of the reactions and of the stresses in the connecting members.

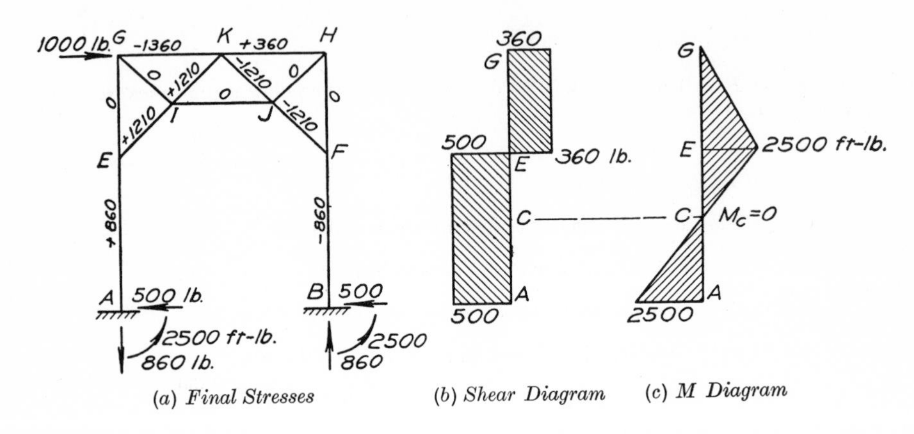

(*a*) *Final Stresses* (*b*) *Shear Diagram* (*c*) *M Diagram*

FIG. 50. STRESSES IN THE SIMPLE PORTAL OF FIG. 49.

62. Graphical Analysis of a Portal. In order to make an analysis by means of the stress diagram, it is necessary to *remove all bending from the columns.* This is accomplished by the addition of the substitute members (broken lines) shown in Fig. 51. The reactions of this structure will be the same at the pins as those in the original bent at the points of contraflexure, and they are determined in the same way. The part of the structure above the pins is then isolated and a stress diagram is drawn in the usual manner. The stresses obtained are correct for all members except the columns. The direct stresses in the columns and their shear and moment diagrams can be obtained algebraically, as has been explained in the preceding section.

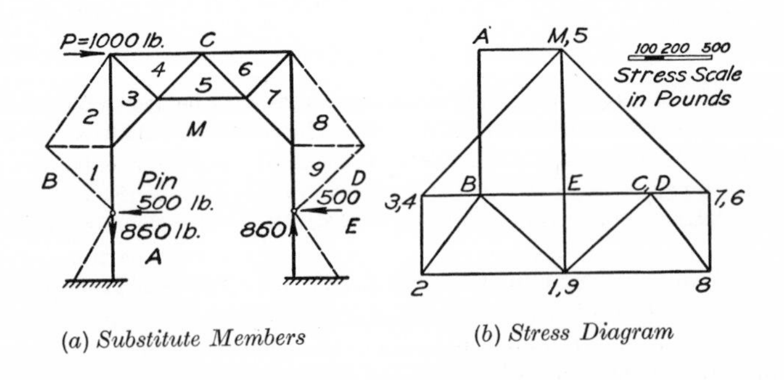

(*a*) *Substitute Members* (*b*) *Stress Diagram*

FIG. 51. GRAPHICAL ANALYSIS OF A PORTAL.

PROBLEMS

314. The stiff frames (*a*), (*b*), (*c*), and (*d*) have one end on rollers. These rollers and pins can resist uplift. Compute the values of critical moments and draw the shear diagrams.

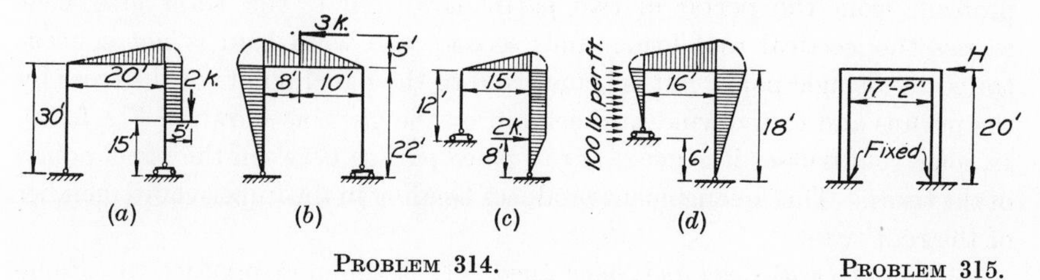

PROBLEM 314. PROBLEM 315.

315. The welded bent shown is formed of 12-in. beams with their webs in the plane of the bent. Find H to produce a fiber stress of 20,000 psi in the column at the bottom of the girder. The section modulus is 100 in.³ and the area is 18.9 in.² for all members. Repeat with pin ends. *Ans.* $H = 16{,}700$ lb. (pin ends).

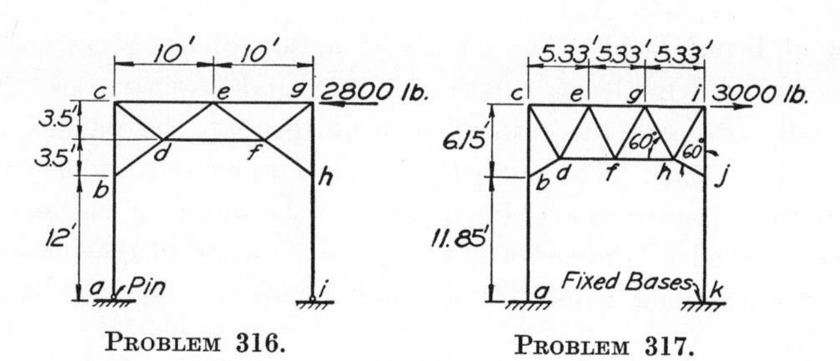

PROBLEM 316. PROBLEM 317.

316 to **318.** Analyze for the stresses in these portals produced by the loads shown on the sketches. Draw shear and moment diagrams for the columns.

Ans. The maximum stress for each portal is successively:

316. $S_{eg} = -5200$; **317.** $S_{gi} = +4130$; **318.** $S_{ce}, S_{eh} = \pm 3460$ lb.

319. Analyze for the stresses in this portal and draw shear and moment diagrams for the columns. Divide the vertical shear equally between the stiff diagonals.

Ans. $S_{be} = -2520$ lb.; $S_{ce} = +4170$ lb.

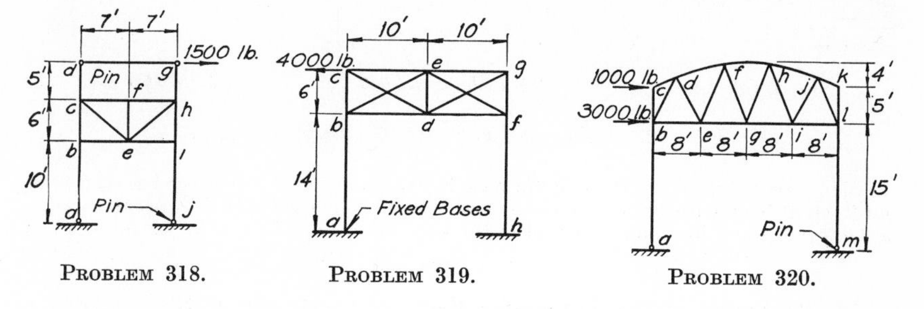

PROBLEM 318. PROBLEM 319. PROBLEM 320.

320. Analyze this portal by the graphical method and then draw shear and moment diagrams for the legs. The upper panel points lie on a parabola whose maximum rise is 4 ft. above point k. *Ans.* $S_{eg} = -790$ lb.; $S_{il} = -5240$ lb.

Stress Analysis of Transverse Bents

63. The Transverse Bent. The transverse bent presents a different problem from the portal in two particulars. First, the transverse bent carries the vertical roof loads, and, second, the wind load is not concentrated at a single point, but is transferred to the panel points of the truss by the purlins and to the windward column by the girts, as shown in Fig. 52(*a*). In some roof trusses it is necessary to place purlins between the panel points of the truss. This arrangement produces bending in the upper-chord member of the roof truss.

Action of Dead Load and Snow Load. It is common practice to assume that the stresses in the truss from dead load and snow load may be calculated just as though the truss were simply supported on masonry walls. In other words, the stress in the knee brace is taken as zero, and the column is considered to have direct stress only. This procedure will be followed here.

Action of Wind Load. The combined action of the truss and columns is to be considered in the calculation of the wind-load stresses. The wind loads actually come to the transverse bent through the purlins and girts, as shown in Fig. 52(*a*). Temporarily, however, in order to make the method of analysis clear, the wind load on the side of the building will be considered to be concentrated at the top and bottom of the column, as shown in Fig. 52(*b*). Concentrations come from *tributary areas*. See the explanation below Fig. 52.

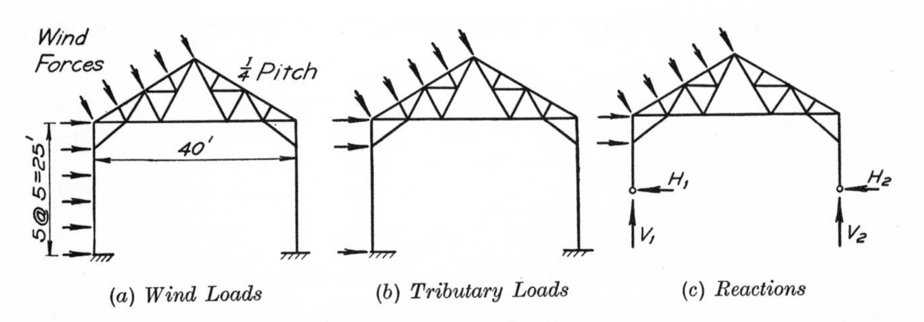

Fig. 52. Reactions for the Transverse Bent.

Side area tributary to the column base is $10d$ where d is the distance between bents, and the half-height from the base to the foot of the knee brace is 10 ft. Areas tributary to the top of the column and the foot of the knee brace are $2.5d$ and $12.5d$, respectively.

64. Reactions of the Transverse Bent. Exactly as in the analysis of portals, the locations of the points of contraflexure in the columns will be determined from a consideration of top and bottom restraints. The point of contraflexure may be taken as one half of the distance from the base up to the foot of the knee brace when the column anchorage is designed to resist the greatest possible moment at the base of the column. For safety, pin-end conditions should be assumed if the degree of restraint is unknown.

It needs to be emphasized that the transverse bent is a statically indeterminate structure. With pin-end columns it is statically indeterminate to the first degree, and with fixed-end columns it is indeterminate to the third degree. Therefore, any analysis by statics is approximate in that it requires that the number of unknowns be reduced by the aid of one or more assumptions.

Column Shears. The total horizontal component of the resultant of the wind forces that are concentrated above the points of contraflexure, as seen in Fig. 52(*b*) and (*c*), will be assumed to produce *equal shears at the points of contraflexure.* This is not the assumption that has been most used in the past, but it will be found more satisfactory.[4] The usual assumption has been that the horizontal reactions at the bases of the columns are equal, but this assumption is seriously in error.

Vertical Reactions. The structure above the assumed points of contraflexure will be isolated, as in (*c*). The vertical reaction V_1 can be found from the equation $\Sigma M = 0$ for a center of moments at the point of contraflexure in the right-hand leg, and V_2 can then be found from the equation $\Sigma F_y = 0$ applied to the isolated part of the structure above the points of contraflexure.

65. Stresses in the Transverse Bent. From here on, the procedure may be made identical with the analysis of the single-bay portal. The left-hand column above the point of contraflexure is isolated, as shown in Fig. 53. The stress S_1 can be obtained from the equation $\Sigma M_B = 0$. Then the stress S_3 follows from $\Sigma F_y = 0$. Finally, the stress S_2 can be found from the equation $\Sigma M_D = 0$. Note that the moment about the point C of all the forces above C is *not zero*, but is the *bending moment* in the column at the point C. The same statement is true in regard to the moment about C of the forces below the point C. In order to set the moment about the point C equal to zero, we must consider all forces shown in Fig. 53 in the equation of moments. This equation is not needed.

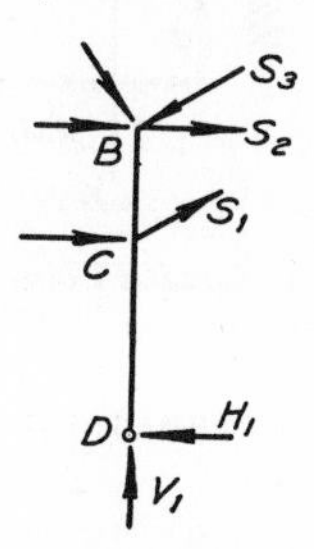

FIG. 53. ISOLATED COLUMN.

Use of the Stress Diagram. It has been most convenient up to this point to use algebraic analysis. Since the truss members are found to have nearly as many different slopes as there are members, it may save time to complete

[4] A comparison of the reactions for the bent of Fig. 52 as obtained by the author's method and from a model test by Professor J. B. Griffith is significant. The wind pressure is taken as 30 psf and the spacing of bents is 15 ft. By model analysis, $H_1 = 9733$ lb., $H_2 = 5015$ lb. By the method of §64, $H_1 = 9630$ lb., $H_2 = 5120$ lb.

the analysis by a graphical construction. A stress diagram can readily be drawn for the remainder of the truss by starting with the known stresses S_1, S_2, and S_3 as external forces.

ALGEBRAIC CHECK. The stresses for those members that frame into the right-hand column are obtained from the completed stress diagram. At the same time, it is wise to isolate the column above the point of contraflexure and to check the forces acting on this part of the column for equilibrium. This is a complete check upon the graphical construction.

66. Shear and Moment Diagrams. The shear diagram and the moment diagram for the leeward column are identical in appearance with those for a simple portal. Equal maximum moments occur at the base and at the foot of the knee brace. The value of the maximum moment is equal to the shear in the leeward column times one half the height from the base to the foot of the knee brace. Fixed bases are assumed.

Windward Column. In drawing the shear diagram and the moment diagram for the windward column, we must remember that the true loading is as shown in Fig. 52(*a*) and not as was assumed in Fig. 52(*b*). This change

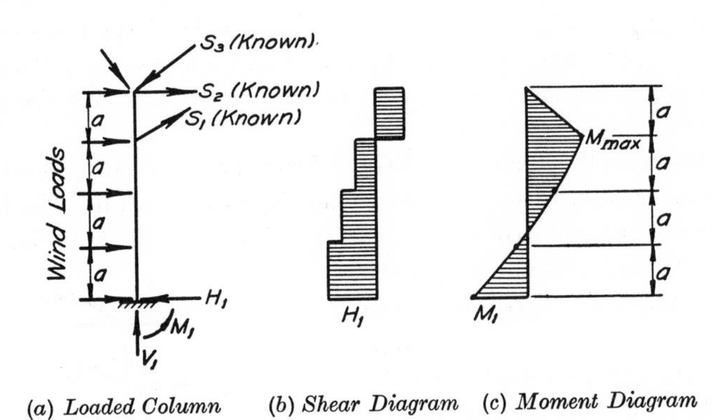

(*a*) *Loaded Column* (*b*) *Shear Diagram* (*c*) *Moment Diagram*

FIG. 54. SHEAR AND MOMENT DIAGRAMS FOR THE WINDWARD COLUMN OF A TRANSVERSE BENT.

in loading is assumed to have no effect upon the stress in any member except the windward column. The determination of the shear diagram and the moment diagram for the windward column from the true loading and the stresses in the adjoining members completes the analysis. This procedure is illustrated by Fig. 54. The horizontal reaction H_1 can be found from the equation $\Sigma F_x = 0$ for the forces of (*a*). The shear diagram is shown in (*b*). The moment M_1 can be found by taking moments of all forces in (*a*) about the base; the moment diagram as shown in (*c*) can be completed by calculating the moment about each load point of the known forces above that point shown in (*a*).

Location of Point of Contraflexure. It will be found that the point of zero moment in the windward column is considerably below its assumed location, which was at the mid-height. This fact will not affect the design of the structure, however, because the maximum base moment as originally calculated still exists at the base of the leeward column. The maximum moment in the windward column, found at the foot of the knee brace, has not increased appreciably from its first assumed value. All necessary information regarding column moments can therefore be obtained without actually drawing the moment diagrams.

67. Pin-End Columns. Transverse bents with pin-end columns are analyzed just as was explained above for the part of the anchored bent above the points of contraflexure. Again, the windward reaction (horizontal) should be greater than the leeward reaction by the amount of the force F_1 (Fig. 55), which is obtained from the area tributary to the base of the windward column. Figure 55 also shows how substitute members may be introduced (broken lines) just as in Fig. 51, to obtain a complete graphical analysis. Note that the substitute members actually form vertical trusses that take the bending away from the columns.

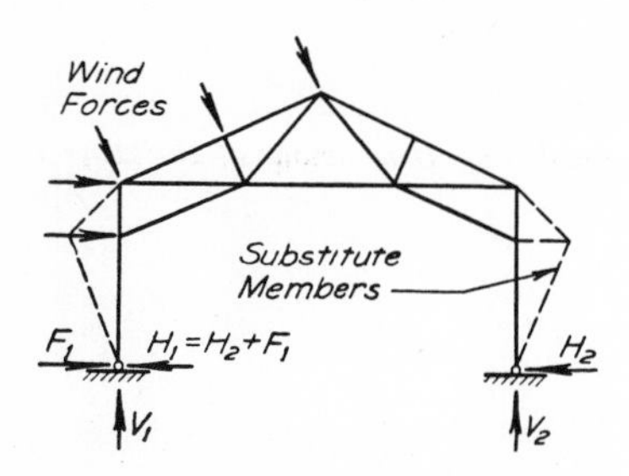

FIG. 55. REACTIONS FOR A PIN-END BENT.

68. Combined Stresses. The same procedure that was followed for the ordinary roof truss is suggested for obtaining the design stress for any member of a transverse bent. That is, design each member for the maximum and minimum stresses caused by any of three load combinations: (1) dead load plus full wind load from either direction, (2) dead load plus full snow load, (3) dead load plus one-half snow load plus full wind load from either direction. The proper combinations and the final design stresses are given in Table 3 for the bent analyzed in Fig. 56.

Equivalent Vertical Loading. The method of the equivalent vertical load is satisfactory for the analysis of wall-bearing trusses, but it seems entirely misused in the analysis of a transverse bent because it does not account for the important stresses introduced by the knee brace. (See Table 3.)

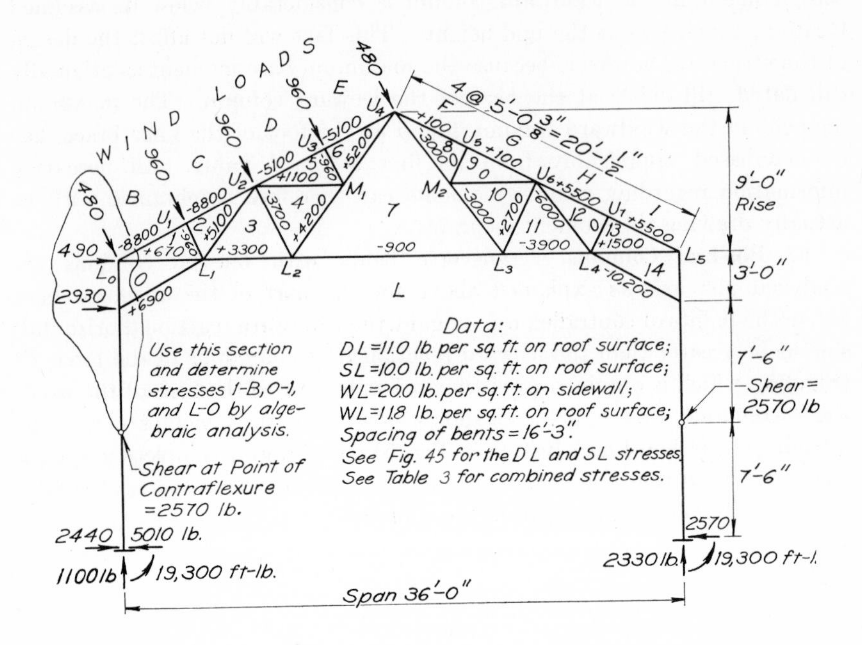

(a) *Loads and Dimensions of Building Bent*

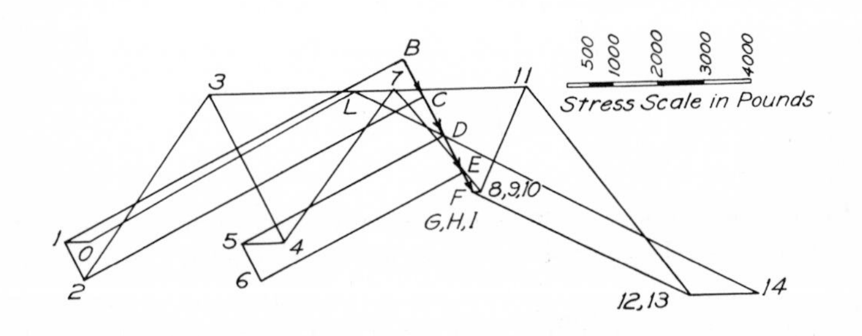

(b) *Stress Diagram for Wind*
(*Starting with L-O, O-1, and 1-B Known*)

FIG. 56. WIND-STRESS ANALYSIS OF A TRANSVERSE BENT.

TABLE 3

STRESSES IN POUNDS FOR THE MEMBERS OF THE TRANSVERSE BENT OF FIG. 56

STRESS	DEAD LOAD (1)	FULL SNOW (2)	HALF SNOW (3)	WIND FROM LEFT (4)	WIND FROM RIGHT (5)	COLUMNS TO BE COMBINED FOR MAXIMUM		MAXIMUM STRESSES		STRESS CAUSED BY AN ALTERNATE VERTICAL LOAD OF 25 PSF	MEMBER
						Tens.	Comp.	Tens.	Comp.		
1–B	−7050	−6420	−3210	−8800	+5500		1, 3, 4		−19,060	−16,100	U_1L_0
2–C	−6650	−6050	−3030	−8800	+5500		1, 3, 4		−18,480	−15,100	U_1U_2
5–D	−6250	−5700	−2850	−5100	+ 100		1, 3, 4		−14,200	−14,200	U_2U_3
6–E	−5850	−5320	−2660	−5100	+ 100		1, 3, 4		−13,610	−13,300	U_3U_4
13–I	−7050	−6420	−3210	+5500	−8800		1, 3, 5		−19,060	−16,100	U_7L_5
12–H	−6650	−6050	−3030	+5500	−8800		1, 3, 5		−18,480	−15,100	U_7U_6
9–G	−6250	−5700	−2850	+ 100	−5100		1, 3, 5		−14,200	−14,200	U_6U_5
8–F	−5850	−5320	−2660	+ 100	−5100		1, 3, 5		−13,610	−13,300	U_5U_4
1–O	+6300	+5730	+2860	+ 670	+1500	1 & 2		+12,030		+14,300	L_0L_1
3–L	+5400	+4920	+2460	+3300	−3900	1, 3, 4		+11,160		+12,300	L_1L_2
7–L	+3600	+3280	+1640	− 900	− 900	1 & 2		+ 6,880		+ 8,200	L_2L_3
11–L	+5400	+4920	+2460	−3900	+3300	1, 3, 5		+11,160		+12,300	L_3L_4
13–14	+6300	+5730	+2860	+1500	+ 670	1 & 2		+12,030		+14,300	L_4L_5
1–2	− 810	− 740	− 370	− 960	0		1, 3, 4		− 2140	− 1840	U_1L_1
2–3	+ 900	+ 820	+ 410	+5100	−6000	1, 3, 4	1 & 5	+ 6410	− 5100	+ 2050	U_2L_1
3–4	−1620	−1480	− 740	−3700	+2700	1 & 5	1, 3, 4	+ 1080	− 6060	− 3680	U_2L_2
4–5	+ 900	+ 820	+ 410	+1100	0	1, 3, 4		+ 2410		+ 2050	U_2M_1
5–6	− 810	− 740	− 370	− 960	0		1, 3, 4		− 2140	− 1840	U_3M_1
6–7	+2700	+2460	+1230	+5200	−3000	1, 3, 4	1 & 5	+ 9130	− 300	+ 6130	U_4M_1
4–7	+1800	+1640	+ 820	+4200	−3000	1, 3, 4	1 & 5	+ 6820	− 1200	+ 4090	M_1L_2
13–12	− 810	− 740	− 370	0	− 960		3, 5		— 2140	− 1840	U_7L_4
12–11	+ 900	+ 820	+ 410	−6000	+5100	1, 3, 5	1 & 4	+ 6410	− 5100	+ 2050	U_6L_4
11–10	−1620	−1480	− 740	+2700	−3700	1 & 4	1, 3, 5	+ 1080	− 6060	− 3680	U_6L_3
10–9	+ 900	+ 820	+ 410	0	+1100	1, 3, 5		+ 2410		+ 2050	U_6M_2
9–8	− 810	− 740	− 370	0	− 960		1, 3, 5		− 2140	− 1840	U_5M_2
8–7	+2700	+2460	+1230	−3000	+5200	1, 3, 5	1 & 4	+ 9130	− 300	+ 6130	U_4M_2
10–7	+1800	+1640	+ 820	−3000	+4200	1, 3, 5	1 & 4	+ 6820	− 1200	+ 4090	M_2L_3

PROBLEMS

321. Analyze for the wind stresses in the bent with the Pratt roof truss. The wind loads are shown on the truss diagram. These wind loads are obtained when bents are 15 ft. apart. $P = 20$ psf; $P_n = P\theta/45$.

Ans. Stress at middle of lower chord = −920 lb.

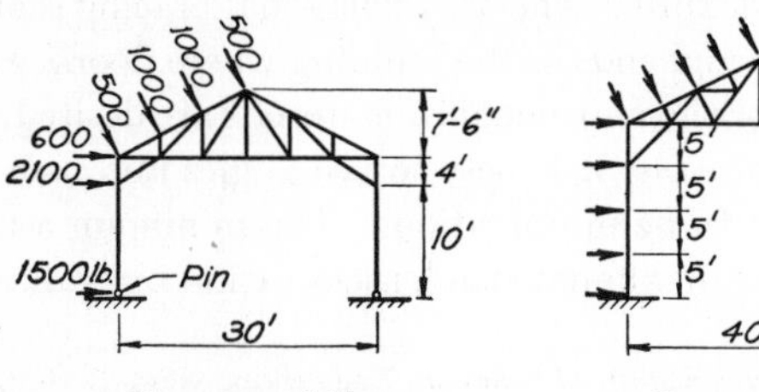

PROBLEM 321. PROBLEM 323.

322. Determine the maximum combined stresses for the members of the bent of Problem 321. The total dead load is 7000 lb. per truss and the total snow load is 11,000 lb. per truss. *Ans.* Stress at middle of lower chord = +9000 lb.

323. Determine the maximum combined stresses for this bent. The wind pressure is 25 psf on a vertical surface. Find the pressure normal to the roof by the *ASCE* formula. The columns are fixed at their bases. The dead load and the snow load are each 18 psf of roof surface. Bents are spaced 18 ft. apart. Neglect suction.

324. Fix the bases of the bent of Problem 321 and compute the wind stresses and the combined stresses including a dead load of 6000 lb. per truss and a snow load of 12,000 lb. per truss.

Diagonally Braced Building Frames

69. Bearing Walls vs. Steel Frame Construction. The examples of roof truss analysis in §55 and §56 are for roof trusses supported upon masonry walls or upon well-braced columns. Today, the high labor costs of brick masonry, the architect's desire for continuous window areas, and the costly foundations required to support heavy walls have led to the wide use of light steel construction with wall enclosures of glass and of prefabricated panels. The result is to place the entire burden of resisting wind forces upon the steel frame. This section will be restricted to consideration of building frames that are adequately braced with diagonal bracing in the sides, ends, and planes of the upper or lower chords of the roof trusses.

70. Diagonal Side and End Bracing. Full diagonal bracing is to be preferred to partial portal bracing in the side and end of the building because it removes the bending from the columns and produces a more rigid structure.[5] See Fig. 57. It is usually cheaper to resist loads by direct stress in diagonal

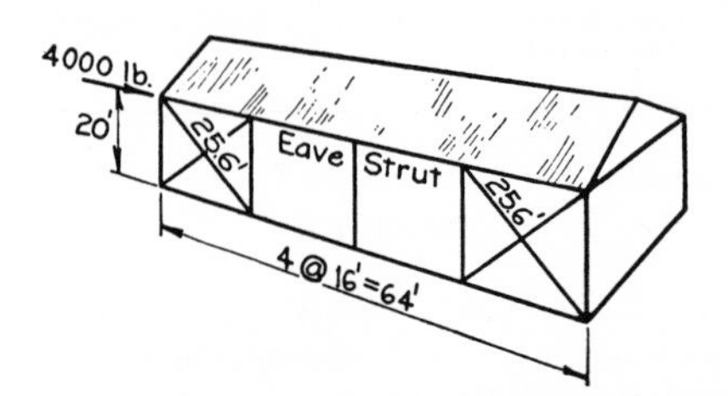

Fig. 57. Diagonal Side Bracing for Wind Resistance.

bracing than by column flexure. The use of diagonal bracing is objectionable in those bays of the sides and ends of the building where doors, windows, and unobstructed openings for the movement of materials are desired. Wherever diagonal bracing is permissible, it is best to use angles and usually only the tension angle is assumed to be in operation. The minimum angle that will meet the specification for maximum slenderness ratio (L/r value) frequently

[5] A. A. Weitzman, *Bracing of industrial buildings*, Engineering News-Record, Nov. 16, 1944, p. 91; also discussion by N. L. Ashton, Dec. 14, 1944, p. 77.

will be more than able to carry the stress. Nevertheless, the bracing of alternate bays is used for additional stiffness.

End Bracing. Usually, large doors must be placed in the ends of an industrial building, but even then two panels of diagonal bracing may possibly be used as shown in Fig. 58. A large central opening could be introduced in the end frame of Fig. 58. In some buildings the diagonal bracing may pass across windows since this is not always considered objectionable by modern architects.

Action of Double Diagonals. It is desirable to detail all diagonal-bracing angles about 0.02 in. short for each 10 ft. of length so that they will have to be *drifted*[6] into place and will carry about 5000 psi of *initial tension* $((30{,}000{,}000 \times 0.02)/(10 \times 12) = 5000)$. The advantage of this is that the structure is rigidly held together by these prestressed diagonals so that it does not wear loose at the joints. The action of the wind increases the tension in one angle and reduces it in the other instead of buckling one of the angles by the introduction of a compressive stress. Both diagonals will be in action under wind load when they are erected with sufficient initial tension. It would seem reasonable, then, to assume this condition as a basis for stress analysis except for the fact that *inaccuracies of fabrication* may result in certain angles being long enough to have only a slight amount of initial tension or even none at all. Hence it is usual to assume that only one diagonal is in action in each panel or bay.

Example. When diagonal bracing is used in several bays, all diagonals sloping in one direction may be taken as resisting the wind shear. For instance, the side bracing shown in Fig. 57 must resist a total horizontal shear of 4000 lb. Assuming that this shear is resisted by the two tension diagonals, we find the stress per diagonal to be $(4000/2)(25.6/16) = 3200$ lb. The maximum stress in the eave strut is equal to the load, or 4000 lb. compression.

71. Diagonal Chord Bracing. Each roof truss connected rigidly to its columns will form a transverse bent. For this type of construction the chord bracing serves merely to square the building during erection and to prevent collapse from the *twisting* action of a diagonal wind. Bracing must be used in at least two bays in the plane of one chord, but the bracing of alternate bays in the planes of both upper and lower chords is probably justified.

Horizontal Truss for Lateral Resistance. If the only lateral resistance in the building is furnished by end walls or braced end frames, the diagonal bracing in the plane of either the upper or the lower chord must form a horizontal or inclined truss which requires that the chord bracing be continuous from end to end of the building. This chord bracing forms a horizontal or inclined truss whose reactions are furnished by the end frames and which carries horizontal wind loads at its panel points. A panel concentration

[6] The members are stretched into place by the use of tapered pins called *drift bolts.*

is all of the horizontal component of the wind pressure acting on one bay of the roof and one half of the wind pressure on one bay of the sidewall. This panel concentration may be considered to be divided equally between the upper-chord and the lower-chord trusses if both are continuous from end to end of the building.

Longitudinal Struts. Whenever diagonal bracing is used, the panel points where the diagonals join the chord members must be separated by compressive struts. A longitudinal strut is always used along the tops of the columns, where it also serves as a member of the side bracing, and perhaps of both upper-chord and lower-chord bracing. This member is called the *eave strut*. The purlins and the *ridge strut* also serve as members of the upper-chord bracing. For buildings of ordinary widths, the lower-chord bracing usually consists of three pairs of diagonals per bay which makes necessary the use of two longitudinal interior struts. See Fig. 58(*a*). These struts are made continuous for the full length of the building to prevent vibration of the roof trusses, even though only a few panels may have diagonal bracing as may be seen in Fig. 34(*f*), where two longitudinal struts are shown.

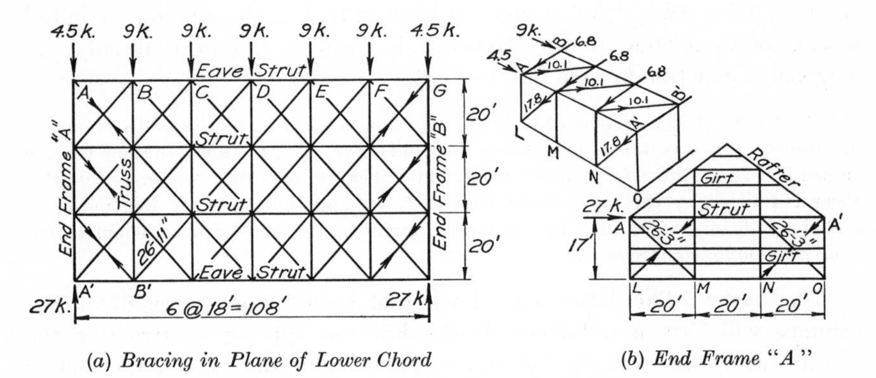

(*a*) *Bracing in Plane of Lower Chord* (*b*) *End Frame "A"*

FIG. 58. ROOF AND END BRACING.

The design of a strut is not always controlled by stress. Ordinarily the strut either transfers directly a determinable amount of wind force or else it receives a calculated stress as a member of a system of bracing. More commonly, however, the specification for the limiting slenderness ratio or L/r value will determine its size. Struts are unchanged in section from one end of the building to the other.

Diagonal Bracing Between Struts of Upper and Lower Chords. When roof trusses are being erected, some diagonal bracing in a vertical or nearly vertical plane is required. Hence, along the center line of the building or in two or three longitudinal vertical planes we find diagonal bracing either continuously or in alternate bays. The use of diagonal bracing in alternate bays permits erection of the roof trusses in pairs. Since there is no vertical shear between roof trusses such diagonals have no determinable stresses.

EXAMPLE. *Stresses in a Diagonally Braced Building.* A typical layout of continuous lower-chord bracing is shown in Fig. 58(a). The maximum panel shear is $27 - 4.5 = 22.5$ kips. This shear is resisted by the three tension diagonals in the end panel. The stress per diagonal is $(22{,}500/3)(26.9/20) = 10{,}100$ lb. The maximum stress in a strut is $10{,}100 \times (18/26.9) = 6800$ lb. The wind stress in the diagonals of panels nearer to the center of the building will be less, but even a center panel will not have a zero shear, because the wind force must be considered movable. Accordingly, for maximum shear in panel BC, the loads at A and B are removed, and for maximum shear in panel CD, the load at C is also removed. Counter diagonals have the same stresses as the main diagonals when the wind reverses its direction.

The End Frame. The diagonal bracing of the *end frame* is shown in Fig. 58(b). The end frame is loaded with the reaction of 27 kips from the horizontal truss shown in (a). Again, it is assumed that the horizontal shear is resisted by the two tension diagonals. The stress per diagonal is $(27{,}000/2)(26.3/20) = 17{,}800$ lb. The maximum stress in the strut placed at the level of the eaves in the end frame is $27{,}000/2 = 13{,}500$ lb. This will be evident when we observe in the perspective sketch that the reaction of 27 kips shown in Fig. 58(a) actually is produced by two separate diagonal forces of 17.8 kips in the vertical plane of the end frame whose horizontal components of 13.5 kips provide the 27-kip reaction. Hence the single load of 27 kips shown in Fig. 58(b) is really two loads of 13.5 kips each. The strut AA' in (b) and (c) is subjected to the components in the direction AA' of the stresses in the five diagonals shown in the perspective sketch in addition to the load of 4.5 kips at A.

PROBLEMS

325. Draw up neat sketches of the complete structural frame of a standard industrial building that has the following dimensions: width, 80 ft.; length 240 ft.; height to lower chords of roof truss, 20 ft.; truss to be of ⅕ pitch. All wind load is carried to the end frames. The wind pressure is 25 psf on the vertical. Determine the maximum wind stresses in all diagonals and struts. Many reasonable solutions are possible.

326. Repeat Problem 325 for a two-story building—30 ft. to the flat roof level.

327. Choose any one of the forms of roof trusses shown in Fig. 34 or Fig. 40 and use it in the layout of an appropriate building. Establish all dimensions. Place diagonal bracing as needed to provide stability without reliance upon masonry walls or the flexural resistance of columns. Show doors and windows with dimensions. Compute the stresses in all diagonals and struts (not in roof truss members) for a wind velocity of 90 mph. Use specifications of §49 as needed.

72. Standards of Accuracy in Building Analysis and Design. A common mistake made by young engineers is that of placing too much emphasis upon mathematical analysis and too little upon the other important features of analysis. The choice of basic assumptions and the estimate of the loads are fully as important as the mathematical calculation of stresses. Such features of the analysis involve the use of engineering judgment.

It should be evident that a preliminary estimate of the dead loads involves approximations while the probable snow load or wind load is a matter of opinion rather than of fact. In view of the uncertainties involved in the selection of the loads, it seems rather useless to attempt great precision in the calculation of stresses. A sure indication of lack of experience is shown by the engineer who records the dead-load stress in a certain member as 29,223 lb. The first four figures express the value of the stress more accurately than the dead load could possibly be estimated, and even more accurately than it is possible to read an ordinary slide rule. A recorded stress of 29,200 lb. would be proper. A stress ten times as large would be recorded as 292,000 lb. and not as 292,200 lb., unless it was obtained by direct addition of several smaller stresses. Even then, the fourth significant figure is of no real importance.

Computer Stresses. When computations are made by use of a digital computer stresses are usually furnished to six or more significant figures. This is because the machine retains all figures placed in its memory and does not drop insignificant figures. Hence machine results give the appearance of greater accuracy than is often justified. Usually, only the first three figures of a machine result can be used in the procedure of design.

CHAPTER 4

RIVETS, BOLTS, AND PINS

73. Types of Rivets. The usual rivet for structural work has a button head of rounded shape with a diameter of $1.5D + \frac{1}{8}$ in. (Fig. 59) where D is the nominal diameter of the rivet. The height of the head is 0.425 times its diameter, which makes it somewhat less than a hemisphere. These button heads can be flattened to ¼ or ⅜ in., countersunk for a projection of ⅛ in., or countersunk and chipped flush, as dictated by clearance requirements. Rivets countersunk and chipped flush do not have sufficient head to develop full strength. They should be discounted 50 per cent in design.

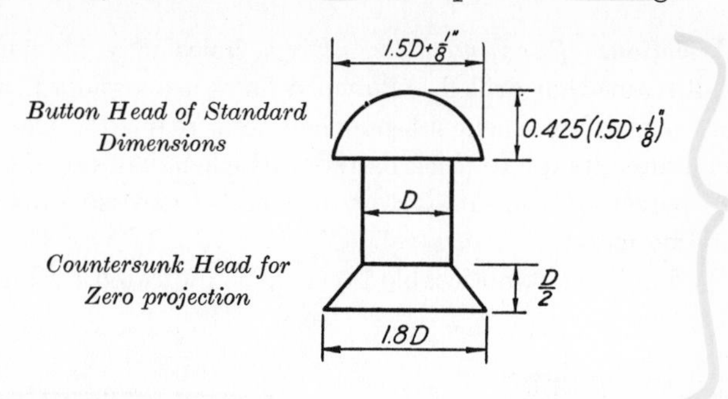

FIG. 59. RIVET HEADS MOST COMMONLY USED FOR STRUCTURES.

Conventional Signs for Riveting. The conventional symbols shown in Fig. 60 illustrate the method of indicating types of rivets on drawings.

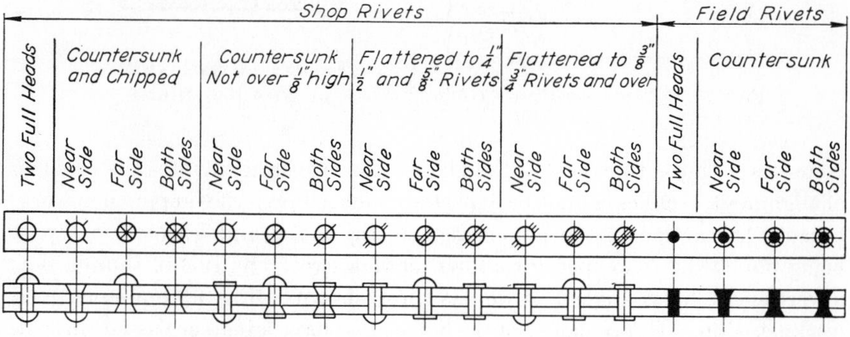

FIG. 60. CONVENTIONAL SYMBOLS FOR RIVETING.

Size and Weight of Rivets. The usual sizes of structural rivets are $\frac{3}{4}$ in. for industrial buildings and light structures and $\frac{7}{8}$ in. for ordinary bridges and office buildings. Tower structures and monumental bridges may require 1-in. or $1\frac{1}{8}$-in. rivets, while light frames, such as short-span roof trusses, electric sign supports, and power-line towers, may be made with $\frac{1}{2}$-in. or $\frac{5}{8}$-in. rivets. It is desirable to use one or not more than two sizes of rivets in a single member and as few sizes as possible in the entire structure. Nevertheless, even when the rivet size is standardized at $\frac{7}{8}$ in., it will be necessary to use smaller rivets through the flanges of channels and the legs of small angles where *proper edge distance* limits the size of a punched hole. Such limitations are given in all structural steel handbooks. (See Spec. 49 and Table S-5.)

The rivet heads add to the weight of the structure and must be estimated as a part of the dead load. The double heads (one manufactured and the other shop or field driven) for one hundred $\frac{3}{4}$-in. rivets weigh 24 lb. The corresponding weight is 36 lb. for $\frac{7}{8}$-in. rivets. The weight of the rivet heads is an appreciable factor for a structure containing many thousand rivets.

74. Fabrication. *Punching holes.* Rivet holes may be punched, sub-punched and reamed, or drilled. Punched holes are standard, but railway-bridge work has often been sub-punched and reamed. The expense of drilling has limited its use to thick material (thicker than the diameter of the hole) where punching is unsatisfactory because of excessive deformation of the surrounding metal.

A punched hole has a noticeable taper, as is indicated by Fig. 61, which

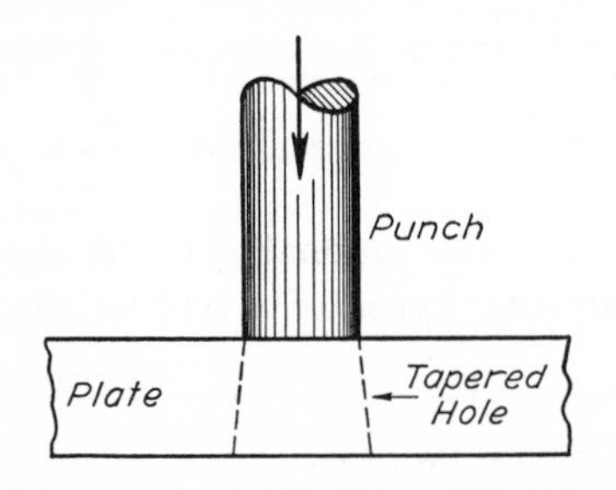

FIG. 61. TAPER OF RIVET HOLE.

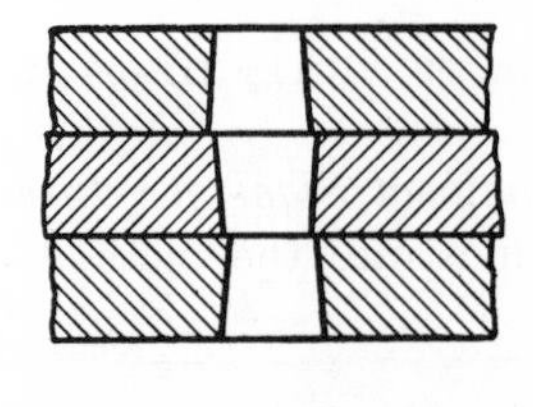

FIG. 62. MISALIGNMENT OF PUNCHED HOLES.

increases with the thickness of the plate. This taper aggravates the problem of alignment. Holes cannot be expected to match perfectly in punched work, because the action of the punch distorts the metal and *lengthens* the part being punched. The operator allows for this stretch by rule of thumb, but, nevertheless, holes aligned as well as those shown in Fig. 62 represent good workmanship. Hence, many of the holes must have a reamer passed through them before the rivet can be dropped in.

Driving Rivets. The rivet blank with one head already formed is heated until it glows and inserted in the hole. Then, either by direct pressure or by a series of blows, a second head is formed before the rivet becomes entirely black. The most satisfactory rivets are produced with direct pressure by use of a power or bull riveter employing pneumatic, hydraulic, or electric power. The riveter grips the rivet between its jaws and produces the head by direct pressure of perhaps 50 tons or even more. The head is formed by *squeezing* the rivet. Naturally, the plastic rivet steel is squeezed out to fill the hole adequately. In close work, or where the riveter cannot reach around the member, and for field connections, the rivet head usually is formed by the air hammer.

Problems of Fabrication. The entire process of cutting, bending, punching, and straightening structural steel shapes and plates is not one that can be carried out to exact dimensions. A variation of $1/16$ inch in a length of several feet represents good workmanship. The mere punching of a row of rivet holes in an angle will lengthen it and will usually curve it as well. Accordingly, fabricators have fixed tolerances that must be accepted by the designer.

Internal Action of Riveted Joints

75. Initial Tension. The self-evident fact that a cooling rivet develops initial tension has been long recognized, but the extent of this initial tension was seriously questioned. An occasional rivet would fail under a light blow by popping off the head, and this was taken to mean that the amount of initial tension was at least problematical. Finally, tests were made which showed that plate slip did not occur with proper fabrication until the stress in shear on the cross-sectional areas of the rivets reached about 11,500 psi. *Plate friction* was the only force that could prevent slight slippage, and even at an initial rivet tension of 35,000 psi the coefficient of friction would have to be approximately 0.33 to produce a frictional resistance equivalent to 11,500 psi per rivet. Later, tests[1] were made which showed conclusively that the initial tension could be expected to approach the elastic limit and might safely be taken at *90 per cent of the elastic limit as an average value.* Since the coefficient of friction for plates with rough mill scale in contact might be expected to be higher than the usual value of 0.33 given for steel on steel, it seems reasonable to state that most riveted joints properly designed and not overloaded act elastically without any slip between the parts joined by the rivets. Under such conditions the rivets themselves would be unstressed except for their initial tensions.

[1] W. M. Wilson and W. A. Oliver, *Tension tests of rivets*, Bulletin 210, University of Illinois Engineering Experiment Station.

C. R. Young and W. B. Dunbar, *Permissible stresses on rivets in tension*, Engineering Research Bulletin No. 8, University of Toronto.

76. Failures of Riveted Joints. *Rivet Shear.* A riveted joint will deform greatly before final failure. (See Fig. 63.) When slip occurs between the plates or structural shapes joined by the rivets, a shear is developed on the cross sections of the rivets. As shown in Fig. 63(*e*), the load may shear the rivet off along the plane of slip, but this is only one possible type of failure.

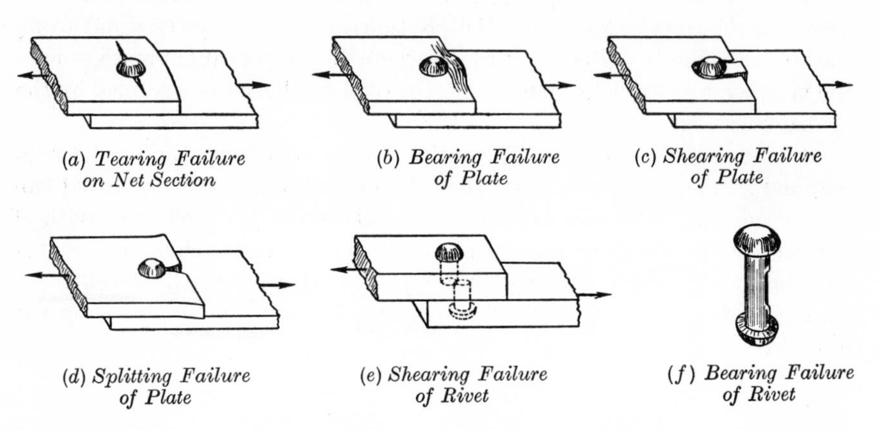

FIG. 63. FAILURES OF RIVETED JOINTS.

Net Section. A tearing failure, as illustrated in (*a*) of Fig. 63, may occur whenever the rivets are stronger than the plate. This possibility is enhanced not only by the fact that a hole reduces the effective section of the plate but also by the fact that a hole theoretically triples the maximum stress in a simple tension plate. Practically, the increase in elastic stress seems to be more nearly in the neighborhood of 100 per cent. In addition, it is known that plastic deformation beyond the yield point greatly reduces all stress concentrations, which are often largely neglected. Tension failure on the net section of the plate is considered in standard design simply by deduction of rivet holes from the gross section. Whenever fatigue failure is a possibility, this method will not be safe, because repeated stress concentrations around rivet holes may produce fatigue cracks before plastic flow occurs. Also, low temperatures, such as occur during the winter in the United States, produce an embrittling effect on most structural steels. Low temperature, along with stress concentrations, and other factors, can rob structural steel of a part of its ductility and possibly initiate brittle fracture. This matter will be discussed later when "plastic design" is considered.

Edge Distance. A plate failure may also occur at right angles to the main direction of stress, as illustrated in Fig. 63(*d*). Splitting failure may be caused by the internal pressure of an "overdriven" rivet where adequate edge distance has not been provided. Similarly, the double-shear failure of the plate, as shown in (*c*), will not occur when the proper edge distance is provided. The photograph (Fig. 64) illustrates such failures. The edge distance is measured from the center of the rivet. The required edge distance given in the specifications (Spec. 49 and Table S-5) varies with the diameter of the rivet, the direction of stress, and whether the edge is rolled, sheared, or flame cut.

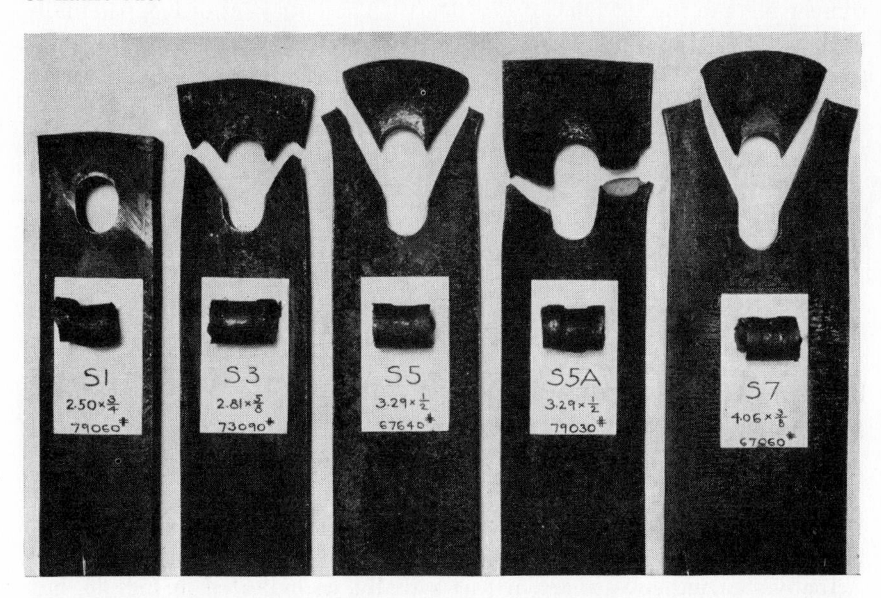

FIG. 64. FAILURES OF RIVETED TEST SPECIMENS.

Bearing between Rivet and Plate. Bearing failure is a crushing of the plate and rivet around the half circumference. The result for an edge rivet may appear externally as in (*b*) of Fig. 63. If a rivet that has failed in bearing is removed and examined, it will show a flattened face, as in (*f*), where the heaviest stressed plate pressed against it. The rivet shown in (*f*) joined three plates instead of two as for the other joints illustrated.

RIVET RESISTANCE

77. Lap and Butt Joints. Riveted connections are of all degrees of complexity, but basically they may be pictured and studied as being of two types, lap joints and butt joints. In order to understand the usual design procedure for riveted joints, it is necessary to visualize the rivet areas subjected to failure in these two types of joints.

Computation of Shear on Rivets. If failure occurs by shear *on the rivet*, the area subjected to shear failure is the cross section or *circular area* of the rivet. Failure occurs along one plane in the lap joint of Fig. 65(*a*), and the rivets are in *single shear*. The resistance of this joint in single shear would be the sum of the cross-sectional areas of the two rivets multiplied by the allowable shearing unit stress on the rivet, F_v. For ¾-in. rivets at 15,000 psi the value of the joint is

$$2AF_v = 2 \times 0.44 \times 15{,}000 = 13{,}200 \text{ lb.} \quad (1)$$

Bearing on Rivets. Bearing failure occurs between the rivets and the thinner plate in the lap joint of Fig. 65(*d*). The butt joint of Fig. 65(*e*) fails by bearing on the center plate, provided that it is thinner than the total thickness of the two outside plates which resist it. The bearing area used

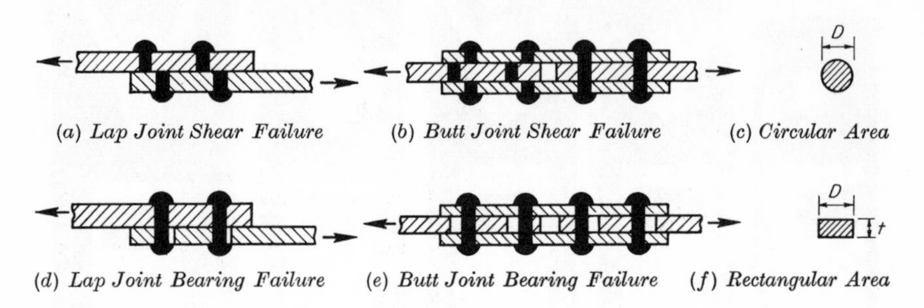

(*a*) *Lap Joint Shear Failure* (*b*) *Butt Joint Shear Failure* (*c*) *Circular Area*

(*d*) *Lap Joint Bearing Failure* (*e*) *Butt Joint Bearing Failure* (*f*) *Rectangular Area*

FIG. 65. FAILURES OF LAP AND BUTT JOINTS.

in design in either case is a *rectangular area* for each rivet equal to the diameter of the rivet times the thickness of the plate which fails by bearing or crushing. Actually, bearing stresses act in part radially, as indicated in Fig. 66, but such radial stresses are assumed to be equivalent to a uniform pressure on a diametral plane through the rivet. Since the bearing pressure is probably not hydrostatic, we cannot prove this assumption to be exactly true, but it is always used in design computations.

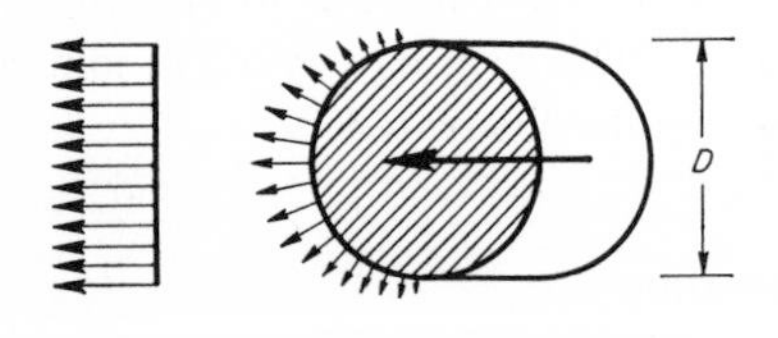

FIG. 66. BEARING STRESSES.

Computation for Bearing. The bearing value for either the lap joint, Fig. 65(*d*), or for the butt joint, (*e*) may be computed from the following data: $D = ¾$ in., $t = ½$ in. for the controlling plate; allowable bearing stress, $F_p = 45{,}000$ psi.

$$2 \times ¾ \times ½ \times 45{,}000 = 33{,}700 \text{ lb.}$$

Actually, the lap joint Fig. 65(*d*) is more likely to fail in bearing than the butt joint (*e*). The reason is that there is a tendency for the eccentric forces to bend the plates in a lap joint, as illustrated by Fig. 67(*a*), resulting in the *unequal bearing pressures* pictured in (*b*). Since this distribution of bearing pressure is far from uniform, the probability of bearing failure is increased. Some specifications have taken this fact into consideration by allowing a considerably higher *unit* bearing stress for butt joints (double or symmetrical bearing) than for lap joints (single or unsymmetrical bearing). However, as may be noted from Spec. 16, modern codes do not make this distinction. The reason is that rivet failure by bearing has seldom been found in tests of riveted joints. High bearing stresses appear to be fully justified.

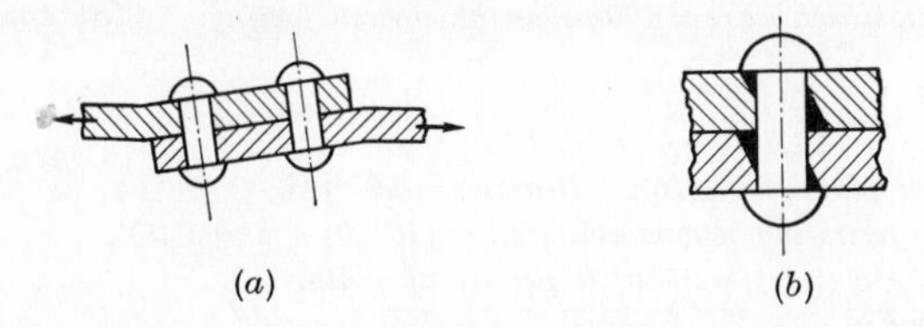

FIG. 67. NONUNIFORM BEARING.

78. Bending of Rivets. Since the forces acting on a rivet can never be in line (the plates must be side by side in order for the rivet to pass through them), it is inevitable as soon as friction is overcome that the rivet must resist flexure as well as shear and bearing. In Fig. 68 the flexural moment

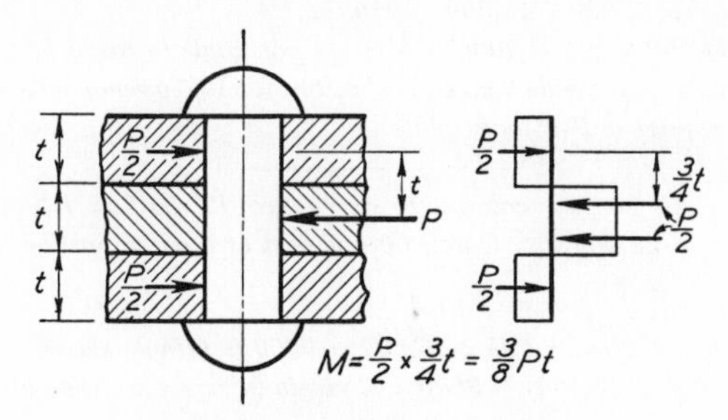

FIG. 68. RIVET FLEXURE.

will be $\frac{3}{8}Pt$ if the plates are of the same thickness. Bending in such standard cases is *not considered in design.* The allowable shearing and bearing values for rivets have been based upon tests of riveted joints in which the rivets tested must have had to resist flexure. Therefore, any weakening of a rivet of ordinary length from such bending moment is allowed for automatically by the standard working stresses in shear and bearing.

Filler Plates. A really serious condition of flexure may develop if filler plates are used improperly, as at the left of Fig. 69. Some specifications require that the number

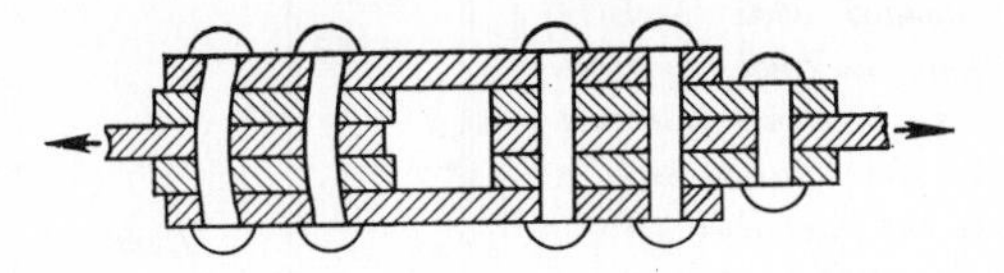

FIG. 69. RIVET ACTION WITH FILLER PLATES.

of rivets shall be increased as much as 25 to 33 per cent for the effect of each filler as a rule of thumb for allowing for rivet flexure. The extra rivets should be placed through an extension of the filler plate, as shown at the right of Fig. 69. This arrangement will effectively eliminate the excessive bending shown at the left of the illustration.

DP2a. *Design a column base for a 10WF49 column where the total load is 144,000#. One half of the load is transferred through the rivets, the remainder by bearing on a steel plate which bears at 600 psi on the concrete footing. AISC spec. A7 steel.*

Base Plate:

Area reqd. $= 144{,}000 \div 600 = 240$ *in.*^{2}

Try a base plate 16″ × 16″. Bearing = 563 psi.

Cantilever overhang beyond col. sect. $= (16\text{-}10) \div 2 = 3''$.

$M = 563 \times 3 \times 1.5 = 2530''\#$ *per in. of width.*

$t = \sqrt{6M/bF_b} = \sqrt{6 \times 2530/1.0 \times 22{,}000} = 0.83.$

Use pl. 16″ × ⅞″ × 1′-6″ to accommodate side angles.

Angles strengthen the plate where the overhang exceeds 3″. (See text.)

Side Angles:

Choose thickness to make single shear rather than bearing control.

$45{,}000 \times t \times 0.87 = 0.6 \times 15{,}000$ *(⅞″ rivets).*

$t = 0.23''$; *use ⅜″ angles for stiffness rather than strength.*

Rivet value $= 0.6 \times 15{,}000 = 9000\#$.

$n = 144{,}000 \times 0.5 \div 9000 = 8$ *rivets per angle to carry 50 per cent of load.*

Anchorage. Provide 2 holes 1¼″ diam. for 1⅛″ anchor bolts with 6 × 4 × ⅜″ ∠s which require a 1′-6″ base plate.

DP2b. *Design a cap for this column to carry two 12″-31.8# I-beams, each having a reaction of 22,500#. Carry 60 per cent of the load on the inside angle.*

Rivets:

Value of ⅞″ rivet $= 0.6 \times 15{,}000 = 9000\#$ *(single shear).*

$n = 0.60(2 \times 22{,}500) \div 9000 = 3$ *rivets (4 rivets are shown).*

Angles:

Use 6 × 4 × ¾″ ∠ to accommodate 2 rivet lines.

Cap Plate:

The function of this plate is similar to that of a bearing plate. For this load a 10¾″ × ½″ × 1′0″ pl. will be adequate.

Remarks: *A check upon the flexural stress in the ¾″ angle by the method used in DS8 shows that the angle is overstressed in bending unless it bears on the column section which is not intended. Rivet tension is within the allowable. The design should be improved by shortening the 4″ angle legs to 3″ to reduce bending.*

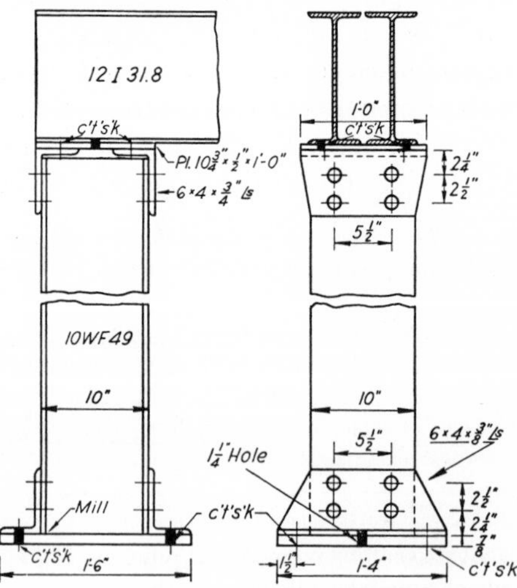

Long Rivets. Bending is more serious for long than for short rivets. A structural rivet (⅞ in.) is considered normal up to a length of 4 or 4½ in. Beyond that length its strength is reduced. For building frames it has been usual to increase the number of long rivets by 1 per cent for each 1/16 in. of grip above 5 diameters (Spec. 47).

Riveted Details

79. Riveted Column Details. Since compression members and details acting in compression need not have the rivet holes deducted, their design is usually simpler than that of tension member details. Columns must be furnished with a base at the bottom and also with a cap at the top if the load or a part of the load rests directly on the top of the column. A column splice is a common detail wherever the column is more than two stories high. Brackets and beam seats are attached to the sides of the columns, but these details usually involve flexure of rivet groups and hence must be studied separately. The design sheet marked *DS*2 illustrates a column base design, *DP*2*a*, and a column cap design, *DP*2*b*.

Column Base, *DP*2*a*. The base detail designed here is the simplest possible type for direct load without flexure. This detail would resist a small flexural moment about the major axis of the column section but almost no moment at 90 degrees to this direction because of the positions of the *anchor bolts*. It is common to design the rivets in such a base detail for from 25 per cent to 75 per cent of the column load. The fact is that the entire load is probably transferred through the *milled end* of the column. However, unless a definite load is specified for the design of the rivets, they may be entirely inadequate to hold the column in place against an accidental blow or against a jacking force applied during an alteration of the structure.

This design for riveting (*DP*2*a*) takes advantage of the side angles to reduce the overhang of the plate to 3 in. for moment computation. For welding, since no angles are used, it is suggested that the cantilever projection be measured from 80 per cent of the width of the flange, i.e.; overhang = $(16 - 0.8 \times 10) \div 2 = 4$ in. $M = 563 \times 4 \times 2 = 4500$ in-lb. per in. of width.

Hence $t = \sqrt{6M/bF_b} = \sqrt{6 \times 4500 \div 1.0 \times 22{,}000} = 1.10$ in.,

as compared to 0.83 in. when angle connections are used. To avoid material over 1.0 in. thick welded angles may be added.

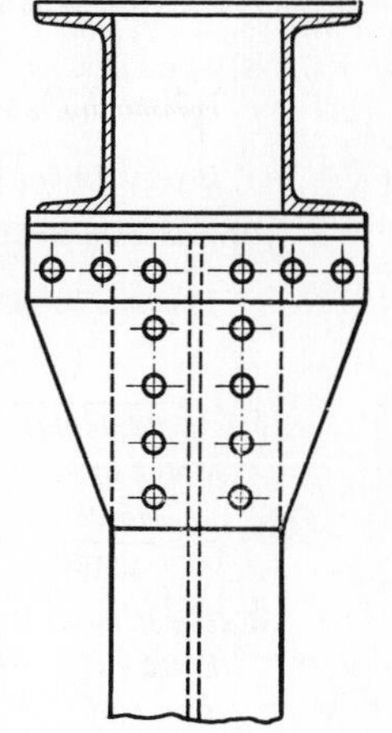

Fig. 70. Heavy Cap.

Column Cap, *DP*2*b*. The cap shown is adequate for the transfer of relatively light loads. Since the number of rivets cannot be increased without changing the type of detail, its capacity is limited to 8 times the value of a rivet in single shear. The critical factor in the design of such seat angles is usually flexure. This factor will be given consideration later in *DS*8. The rivets must be detailed so that the column top does not touch the fillet inside the angle. For narrow columns, the inside angle may be reversed so that its short leg extends further along the beam span. Heavier loads require a cap detail similar to Fig. 70.

DP3. *Design a bearing splice between a 10WF72 column section and a 12WF99 column section. The direct load is 315,000#. There is a shear of 25,000# and a moment of 700,000"#, both in the plane of the webs. AISC, A36 steel, $F_p = 32{,}500$ psi.*

Direct Bearing:

$A_p = 315{,}000/32{,}500$
$= 9.7 \text{ in.}^2$

A_p for web =
$0.51 \times 10.5 = 5.3.$

A_p on fill pls. = diff.
$= 4.4 \text{ in.}^2$

Load through rivets =
$4.4 \times 32{,}500.$

Single shear value for ⅞" rivet = 9000#.

$$n = \frac{4.4 \times 32{,}500}{2 \times 9000} = 8$$

(field rivets above splice).

Fill pls.; use two ½" and two ⁹⁄₁₆" pls.

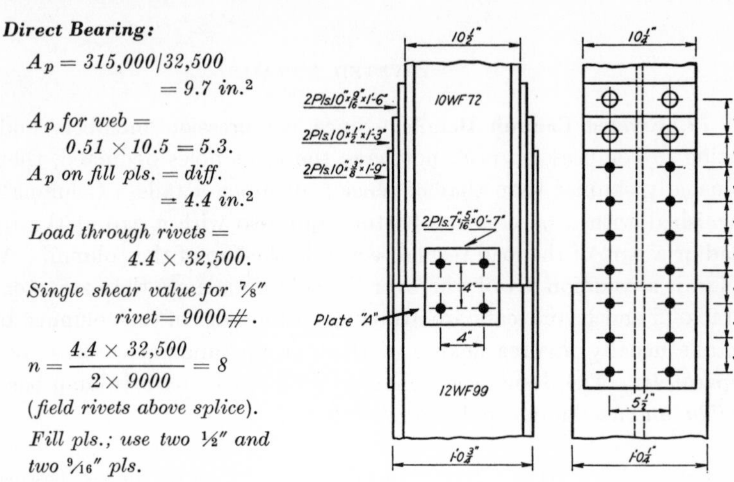

Transverse Shear Splice:

$$A_v = \frac{25{,}000}{14{,}500} = 1.73 \text{ in.}^2 \quad \textit{(Allowable unit shear = 14,500 psi.)}$$

2 pls. 7 × ⁵⁄₁₆" furnish 2.2 in.² each.

Value of ⅞" rivets in bearing on web = 48,500 × 0.87 × 0.51 = 21,500#.

$$n = \frac{25{,}000}{18{,}000} = 2 \text{ rivets approx. But for}$$

$$\Sigma M = 0,\ S_y = \frac{25{,}000 \times 4}{4 \times 2} = 12{,}500\#.$$

$$R = \sqrt{12{,}500^2 + 12{,}500^2} = 17{,}700\#.$$

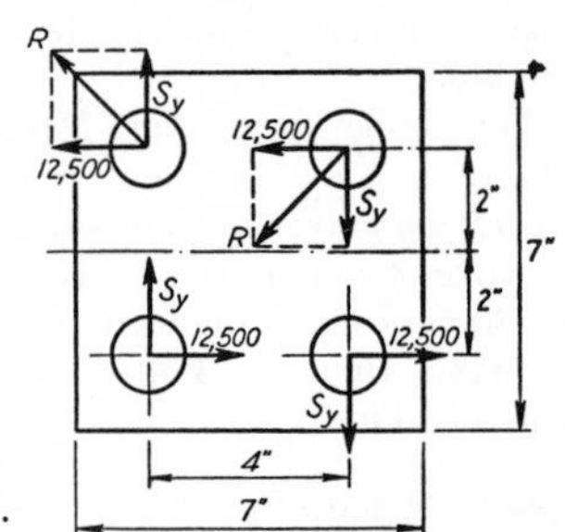

***Moment Splice:** Plate "A"*

$$\textit{Tension in plate} = \frac{700{,}000}{12.75} = 55{,}000\#.$$

$$t = \frac{55{,}000}{22{,}000(10.0 - 2)} = 0.32;\ \textit{use ⅜" pls.}$$

Value of ⅞" rivet in single shear = 9000#.

$$n = \frac{55{,}000}{9000} = 6.1;\ \textit{use 6 rivets below splice.}$$

***Extra Rivets:** Eight field rivets are shown above the splice in contrast to 6 below. Extra rivets are also placed through the ends of the fill plates. This is in accordance with specifications for fill plates which carry stress. Actually, if the full direct stress and bending moment occur simultaneously, 2 more rivets should be added above the splice. Since 6 rivets were needed for flexure and 8 for direct stress transfer, 14 would be needed in total. Only 12 are shown on the sketch above the splice.*

Column Splice, $DP3$. This splice is designed to resist direct load, shear, and moment. Some column splices are designed for direct load only. When the faces of the abutting sections of such columns are *milled to bear* over the entire area, the splice plates serve only the functions of aligning the sections for erection and of resisting an accidental lateral force or a blow. Such a splice in a tier building often has riveted splice plates designed to transfer only 25 per cent of the direct column load.

In the problem analyzed as $DP3$ the sections do not bear over the entire column area. The design is arranged to provide fill plates which enlarge the area of the upper column section and thus provide a larger area in direct bearing. These fill plates are "feathered out" to provide end rivets that are of shorter length than the rivets passing through all plates. This arrangement reduces the tendency for the rivets to bend, as illustrated by Fig. 69.

The *transverse shear splice* for the web is analyzed to illustrate the real action of such rivets. Since the rivets are spaced 2 in. away from the splice line, a pure shear on this line produces both shear and moment on the line of the rivets. The total moment of rotation is equal to the shear times the 4-in. vertical distance between rivet lines. This moment may be divided by the horizontal distance between the two rivet lines to obtain the vertical component of the rivet shear which develops to provide rotational equilibrium. This vertical force is combined with the horizontal component of rivet shear to obtain the resultant which controls the size of the rivet. The splice plate must be and is in equilibrium.

The *moment splice* is designed very simply. The number of field rivets shown in the splice plate is 33 per cent greater above than below the splice. This tends to allow for the fact that the upper rivets pass through fill plates. The fill plates also have *extra* rivets (shop) beyond the 8 (field) computed as necessary. Stressed fill plates should always be carried beyond the connection and riveted to the main part of the section with *extra* rivets. Some specifications require a large increase in the number of rivets. Since 8 rivets were required, this design provides 25 per cent excess rivets placed in the end of each fill plate. This provision seems adequate in this particular connection since the outside splice plates have not been considered to be available for transferring axial load. Where the splice plates must transfer a part of the axial load, the proper design will be to develop the fill plates beyond the limits of the splice plates for their full calculated stress.

Rivet Values

80. Working Stresses in Rivets. There is considerable variation in the unit stresses permitted by different specifications. The allowable stresses of importance for consideration here are the unit stresses in shear, bearing, and tension. The current values of allowable unit stresses for power driven rivets are compared in Table 4. These values are taken from the specifications given in Chapter 17.

It will be observed in Table 4 that the unit stresses of the American Institute of Steel Construction are more liberal than those of the American Association of State Highway Officials or those of the American Railway Engineering Association. It is true that the attitude of the building designer has always been more liberal than the attitude of the bridge designer. An explanation of this difference of opinion may be found in the severe conditions of impact, fatigue, reversal, corrosion, and even collision to which bridge members are subjected. Design specifications attempt to provide for each of these conditions, but their possible individual or combined severity in bridges, as contrasted with their negligible importance in building construction, justifies a difference in allowable unit stresses.

TABLE 4

ALLOWABLE UNIT STRESSES FOR POWER DRIVEN RIVETS

SPEC.	RIVET STEEL	SHEAR F_v PSI	TENSION F_t, PSI	BEARING F_p, PSI
AISC	*A*141	15,000	$28{,}000 - 1.6F_v \leq 20{,}000$	45,000 in *A*7 and 48,500 in *A*36
	*A*195*	20,000	$38{,}000 - 1.6F_v \leq 27{,}000$	Ditto—i.e., 1.35 F_y for base metal
AASHO	*A*141	13,500	$(\frac{3}{4}F_t)^2 = 13{,}500^2 - F_v^2$	27,000 in any base metal
	*A*195	20,000		40,000 in any base metal
AREA	*A*141	13,500		27,000 with single shear 36,000 with double shear

* Rivet steel *A*406 has the same allowable stresses as *A*195 under *AISC* specifications.

81. Tension Resistance of Rivets. Tension rivets have been used for a generation to furnish wind resistance in building construction. During this time nearly all bridge design specifications outlawed tension rivets, and some still do. However, by 1930, two sets of tests had been reported that eliminated most of the argument against the use of rivets in tension. These tests in reality justified the use of rivets at a tensile working stress fully equal to the working stress *in single shear,* since the rivets were shown to have an initial tensile stress equal, on the average, to about 90 per cent of their elastic limit in tension. Because externally applied tension does not increase initial tension until the external force is greater than the initial tension force, no possible harm could come to the rivet from substituting a given amount of externally applied tension for an equal amount of initial tension.

Combined Tension and Shear. By *AISC* specifications the allowable tensile stress applied to a rivet is to be reduced to take account of the *applied shear stress* f_v (Spec. 21). For *A*141 rivets, which are used for *A*7 and *A*36 steel, the following formula applies

$$F_t = 28{,}000 - 1.6f_v \leq 20{,}000 \text{ psi,} \tag{2}$$

and for *A*195 and *A*406 rivets

$$F_t = 38{,}000 - 1.6f_v \leq 27{,}000 \text{ psi.} \tag{3}$$

This simplified procedure replaces the computation of maximum stresses by the procedures given in §38 and Table 1. An important point illustrated by Fig. 71 is that initial rivet tension produced by shrinkage is merely replaced by applied tension with no increase in the critical rivet stresses.

It is difficult to reconcile all points of view regarding combined stress in rivets. As failure is approached, initial tension disappears because of rivet distortion. Then the rivet stress is dependent upon applied shear and applied tension, which do combine into a resultant shear and a resultant tension. It is therefore safe to design upon the basis of this resultant stress and to allow *full working stresses in tension and shear*. If, however, the allowable stress in tension is set at considerably less than the allowable stress in shear, it would seem that combined tension stress had been allowed for adequately, and there would be no need to combine tension with shear to obtain a resultant stress.

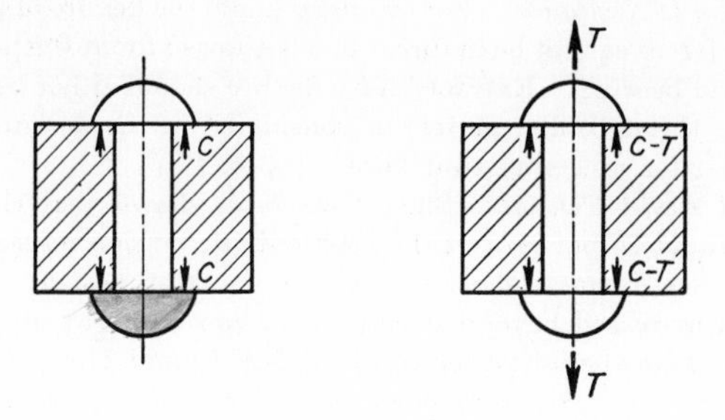

FIG. 71. INITIAL TENSION IN RIVET OR BOLT.

SPECIAL FEATURES OF DESIGN

82. Assumptions for the Design of Riveted Joints. The action of riveted joints from first load to failure has been discussed, and many complications have been mentioned. The design of a riveted joint is a procedure that must be performed literally hundreds of times in the design of any major structure. Therefore, it is desirable to simplify this procedure although the safety of the structure must not be endangered.

1. *Friction Is Neglected.* In other words, joints are designed for the kind of action that occurs near failure rather than for elastic conditions. Of course, an adequate factor of safety is introduced through the choice of working stresses for shear and bearing on rivets. Riveted joints might be designed on the basis of a *friction theory*, but this is reserved for bolted joints for which the friction can be controlled.

2. *Rivets Fill the Holes.* The gross section can therefore be used for a structural member acting in compression (column) or shear (web of a beam or girder), but holes must be deducted to obtain the net section that will resist the pull in a tension member.

3. *All Rivets Are Stressed Equally.* Each rivet of a riveted joint (centric load) is assumed to resist the same shear. Analysis shows that this cannot be true, even when friction does not exist, until after plastic flow above the yield point in rivets and plates has equalized the rivet deformations. At failure, test joints seem to have acted in this manner (static loading). Nevertheless, good design evidently opposes the use of long rows of rivets in line with the plate stress.

4. *Plate Stress Is Distributed Uniformly.* It is assumed that a plate reduced 25 per cent in cross-sectional area by rivet holes will still retain 75 per cent of its full tensile strength. This assumption neglects high concentrated stresses around rivet holes that are known to exist but which are of minor consequence after the average plate stress passes the elastic limit.

5. *Fatigue and Brittle Fracture Are Not Considered.* Assumptions (3) and (4) may be summarized by saying that fatigue failure or brittle fracture is not considered to be probable in the standard design of riveted joints. The most effective method of design of riveted joints for fatigue would seem to be to reduce the maximum load on the joint to less than the minimum friction value; that is, $0.33 \times 0.9nAF_y$ where n is the number of rivets, A is the cross-sectional area of a rivet, F_y is the elastic limit of the rivet material in tension, $0.9F_y$ is the residual tensile stress, and 0.33 is the coefficient of friction. Allowance should also be made for fatigue failure on the net section through the plate. *AISC* requirements are covered by Spec. 22 and Table S-3.

6. *Rivet Flexure Is Negligible.* For ordinary joints the flexure of the rivet caused by the fact that plate forces cannot be in direct line is allowed for in the permissible working stresses in shear and bearing. Extraordinary flexure should either be eliminated (as by use of extra rivets through filler plates) or considered in the design. Long rivets are increased in number for resistance to flexure. (Spec. 47.)

7. *Rivets Will Resist Tension.* Since tests have shown that rivets act under an initial tension of about 90 per cent of the elastic limit, tension resistance equal at least to the rivet resistance in single shear seems permissible in design. The tension stress in the rivet is not increased beyond its initial tension stress by an externally applied tensile force of less than the initial tension. (Specs. 16 and 21.)

8. *Reversal Is Serious.* Stress reversal tends to break down the frictional resistance of a joint and to wear the rivets loose in their holes. The proper design procedure is the one recommended for fatigue; that is, reduce the allowable load well below the friction value of the joint. This is often accomplished by designing the joint for the sum of the tension and compression forces acting on the member. (Spec. 22 and Table S-3.)

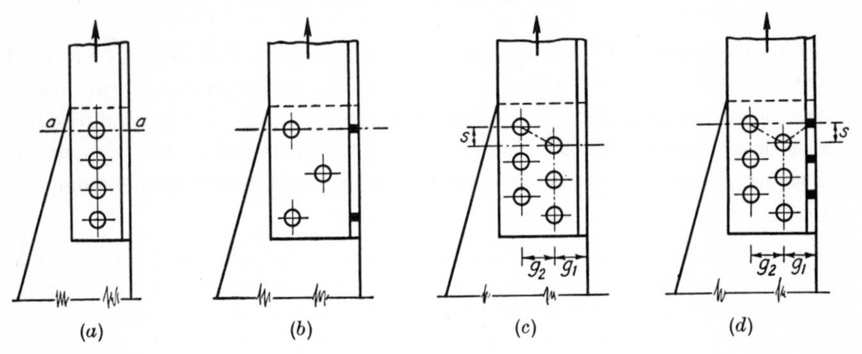

FIG. 72. NET SECTION OF TENSION MEMBERS.

83. Net Section Through Rivet Holes. The design of the rivets for the end connection of a tension member usually is made for the net value of the member, which is taken as the minimum cross-sectional area (with rivet holes deducted) times the allowable working stress in tension. The deduction for a rivet hole is a *rectangular area* equal to the thickness of the plate times the diameter of the hole, which is taken as ⅛ in. greater than the nominal diameter of the rivet; for example, we deduct ⅞-in. holes for ¾-in. rivets. (Spec. 37.)

Line of Fracture. The number of holes to be deducted is determined by an empirical formula set up to agree with observations and tests on the actual manner of fracture of riveted members. It is reasonably evident in Fig. 72 that the joint (*a*) would fail on a net section through one rivet hole while the joint (*b*) would fail through two rivet holes. (It is assumed that the rivets are stronger than the angle.) There is some question whether the joint (*c*) would fail on a net section perpendicular to the member through one rivet or on a net section as indicated through two rivets. If the rivet pitch or spacing s is small, the line of fracture will be along the diagonal section. Likewise, in (*d*) there is a possible choice of paths, either perpendicular to the member through two rivet holes or along the zig-zag line through three rivet holes.

84. Formulas for Deduction of Rivet Holes. *Formula Based upon Pitch.* The simplest possible formula was in use for many years and is still found in some specifications. It is based upon the assumption that fracture will occur along a diagonal line in (*c*) or (*d*) of Fig. 72 if the pitch or stagger s between successive rivets in the chain is less than 4 in. Expressed as a formula, this linear relationship becomes

$$A_{\text{deduct}} = A_{\text{hole}}\left(1 - \frac{s}{4}\right). \tag{4}$$

To apply this formula, we draw any line perpendicular to the member and deduct the areas of all holes along this line and fractional areas of all holes within 4 in. of the line as controlled by the formula. The stagger s is usually the pitch, but it would be the gage if the lines of rivets were perpendicular to the direction of stress, as may occur in tank work.

Formula Based upon Pitch, Gage, and Size of Hole. The most comprehensive empirical formula involves three variables, the pitch s, the gage g and the diameter of the rivet hole h which is taken as ⅛ in. larger than the nominal size of the rivet.[2]

$$A_{\text{deduct}} = A_{\text{hole}}\left(1 - \frac{s^2}{4gh}\right) \qquad \left(\frac{s^2}{4gh} < 1\right). \tag{5}$$

This formula usually is modified first by letting h equal unity and second by using the negative terms

$$\frac{s^2}{4g} \quad (\textit{AISC, AASHO, AREA}\ \text{Spec.}). \tag{6}$$

as additions to the net section after all holes in a chain along an assumed zigzag line of fracture have first been deducted. There will be as many terms $s^2/4g$ as there are spaces in the chain. Formula (6) appears in Spec. 35.

85. Net Section of an Angle. Spacing formulas (5) and (6) involve the gage of the angle. In Fig. 72(*c*) the gage that controls rivet deduction evidently is the gage g_2 along with the pitch or offset spacing s. The same statement applies to deduction for the second rivet hole in Fig. 72(*d*) (starting from the left with a deduction of the full value of the first rivet hole on the transverse section). However, the third rivet hole is in the outstanding

[2] D. B. Steinman, Proceedings, ASCE, April, 1922 $(1 - s^2/4gh)$.

DP4a. *Arrange the riveting in a 6 × 4 × ½″ tension angle for three gage lines so that only 2 holes for ¾″ rivets need be deducted. First use equation (5), and then check by AISC Spec. 35.* (5) $A_{\text{deduct}} = A_{\text{hole}}(1 - s^2/4gh)$.

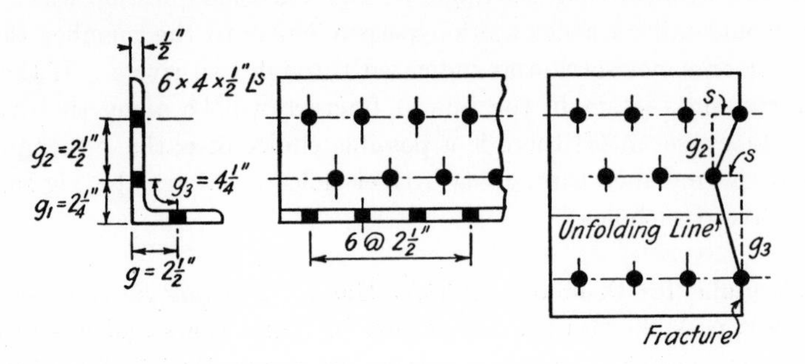

g = 2½″ or 4¼″ (where 2¼ + 2½ − ½ = 4¼″).

$$\text{Hence; } 1 + \left[1 - \frac{s^2}{4 \times 2\frac{1}{2} \times \frac{7}{8}}\right] + \left[1 - \frac{s^2}{4 \times 4\frac{1}{4} \times \frac{7}{8}}\right] = 2,$$

or $\qquad s^2(0.114 + 0.067) = 3 - 2 = 1;$

hence, $\qquad s = \sqrt{\dfrac{1}{0.18}} = 2.4.$

By AISC Spec. 35 we deduct 3 rivet holes and add

$$\frac{s^2}{4 \times 2\frac{1}{2}} + \frac{s^2}{4 \times 4\frac{1}{4}} = 0.16s^2.$$

Hence, for only 2 holes out

$$3 - 0.16s^2 = 2, \text{ or } s = \sqrt{\frac{1}{0.16}} = 2.5''.$$

DP4b. *Arrange the riveting for a wide plate in two gage lines so that the gross section is reduced by only 33 per cent more than by the rivet holes on a single line. Deduct for 1″ holes at 3″ centers. Make s the spacing in the direction of stress.*

Use the AISC formula ($s^2/4g$).

For a single line of rivets

Net width = $W - (5 \times 1.0) = W - 5$.

For a double line of rivets

Net width = $W - (10 \times 1.0) + 9(s^2/4g)$.

For a limiting factor of 1.33

$10 - 9(s^2/4g) = 5 \times 1.33$.

When $g = 3''$, $s = \sqrt{\dfrac{3.33 \times 12}{9}} = 2.1''$.

Use $g = 3''$, $s \geq 2.1''$; use $s = 2\frac{1}{4}''$.

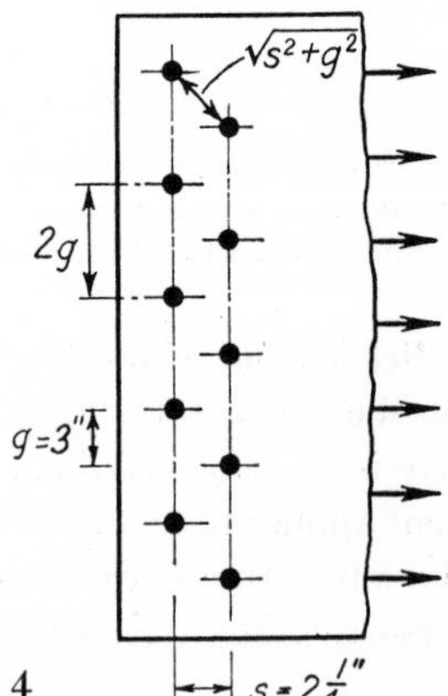

leg of the angle. Obviously, the spacing back to the transverse section is still s which will now be used along with the gage g_3 (Fig. 73) to obtain the reduced deduction for the third rivet hole. Several points may be repeated: first, the gage and the pitch are always measured from the rivet just deducted to the next rivet on the assumed line of fracture; second, the gage is along the center line of the metal; third, the pitch may be either away from or back toward the transverse section; and fourth, the rivets must be treated successively like the links of a chain. For clarity an angle may be considered to be unfolded into a flat plate.

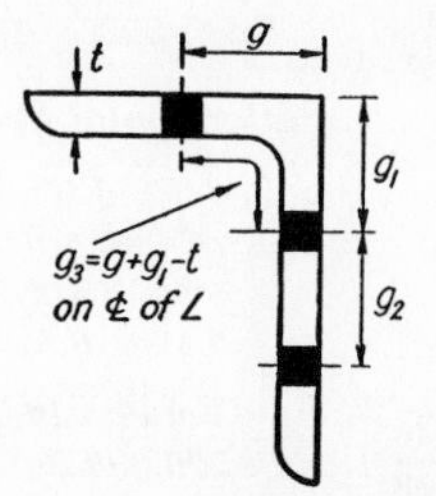

FIG. 73. ANGLE GAGES.

NET SECTION BY AASHO FORMULA, *DP4a*. This example illustrates the use of a standard formula for rivet hole deduction to determine the rivet spacing consistent with *a permissible deduction* of a certain number of rivet holes. This is a common problem in design. As the design of a tension member proceeds, it is necessary to estimate the net section that will be furnished by a given angle. Since the rivet details have not been made as yet, the designer must use his best judgment as to the proper deduction. Then, later, when the rivet details are drawn, it is necessary for the detailer to arrange the rivets so that the required deduction will be no greater than the deduction assumed by the designer. In *DP4b* a similar study is made by *AISC* Spec. 35 for lines of rivets resisting a lateral shear. The term s represents the spacing in the direction of stress.

86. Tension Member Splices. The function of a tension member splice by some specifications is to replace the *net effective area* of the member. This requirement results in the fact that the connection must develop any *excess area* put into the member over and above that needed to carry the design stress. The reason is traditional. If money is expended on excess area, it was considered good judgment from an economic point of view to expend the small additional cost of extra rivets to develop this excess area which at some time in the life of the structure may prove useful. However, under *AISC* specifications it is considered permissible to design a connection or splice for the calculated total stress which may be less than the value of the member.

In general, modern specifications tend to permit lighter connections than those of earlier years. For example, a very long tension member might sag if it were not made much heavier than would be required to carry the applied axial load. It would be foolish to require that its end connections or a splice be designed for the net tensile value of the member.

Some details of riveted splices for tension members are illustrated in Fig. 74. A single angle can be spliced by a slightly thicker angle with shorter or shortened legs. This detail, shown in (*a*), is the most satisfactory type of splice. Each part of the section is in contact with splice material, and rivets pass through each part of the section. This cannot be true in

DP5. *Arrange a joint splice for the value of a tension member that consists of four 6 × 4 × ½″ angles forming the lower chord of a highway bridge truss. AASHO, Spec. 202. Angles will be detailed for deduction of 2.25 holes per angle.*

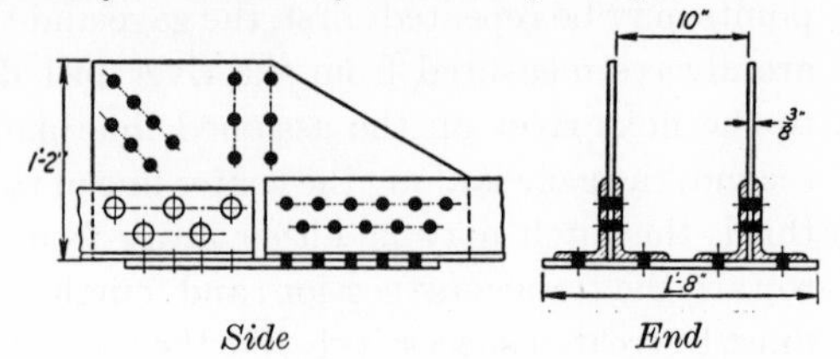

Horizontal Splice Plate:

Area of angles with 2.25 ⅞″ holes deducted from each $= 4(4.75 - 2.25 \times 0.87 \times 0.5) = 15.0$ *in.*^{2}.

Value $= 18{,}000 \times 15.0 = 270{,}000\#$.

Value of 4″ legs $= 270{,}000 \times 0.4 = 108{,}000\#$.

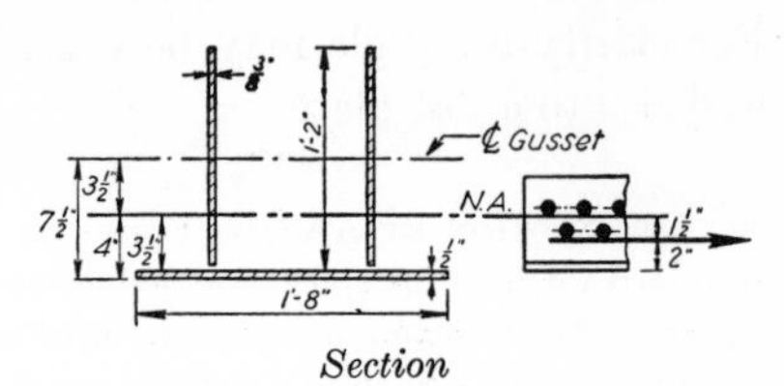

Area of splice pl. $= \dfrac{108{,}000}{18{,}000} = 6.0$ *in.*^{2}.

Pl. 20″ × ½″ gives 8.25 in.^{2} *net.*

Value of ¾″ rivet in single shear $= 0.44 \times 13{,}500 = 5940\#$.

$$n = \frac{108{,}000}{5940} = 18.2 \text{ rivets.} \quad \text{Use 20 field rivets.}$$

Rivets Through the Gusset Plate:

Value of a ¾″ rivet in bearing on a ⅜″ pl. $= 27{,}000 \times 0.37 \times 0.75 = 7600\#$.

Number of field rivets to attach vert. legs; $n = \dfrac{0.6 \times 270{,}000}{7600} = 21.4$*; use 22 rivets.*

Stresses Due to Gusset Flexure:

Height to N. A. of gusset-splice U-section $= \dfrac{2 \times 14 \times 0.37 \times 7.25}{2 \times 14 \times 0.37 + 20 \times 0.5} = 3¾''$.

Moment $= 270{,}000 \times 1.50 = 405{,}000''\#$.

$$\text{Moment of Inertia} = 20.0 \times \tfrac{1}{2} \times 3.75^2 + 2\left[\frac{1}{12} \times \frac{3}{8} \times 14^3 + \frac{3}{8} \times 14 \times 3.5^2\right]$$
$$= 141 + 172 + 129 = 442.$$

Fiber stress (increased 25 per cent for net section)

$$= 1.25\left[\frac{270{,}000}{20.5} + \frac{405{,}000 \times 4.0}{442}\right] = 16{,}400 + 4600 = 21{,}000 \text{ psi } T;$$

$$= 1.25\left[\frac{270{,}000}{20.5} - \frac{405{,}000 \times 10.5}{442}\right] = 16{,}400 - 12{,}000 = 4400 \text{ psi } T.$$

Redesign: *In order to reduce the tension fiber stress from 21,000 to less than 18,000 psi, the horizontal splice plate will be increased to ⅝″ in thickness. Then the P/A term will reduce to 14,600 and the Mc/I term will reduce also. It is evident that the design will then be adequate and a recalculation of fiber stress is not considered necessary.*

(*b*), where plates are attached only to the web of the channel. In (*c*) and (*d*) the splice rivets pass through each part of the section. Note that the splices (*a*), (*c*), and (*d*) have rivets in single shear, while the channel splice (*b*) has rivets in double shear. This device of double splice plates can be used in other instances to reduce the number of rivets needed.

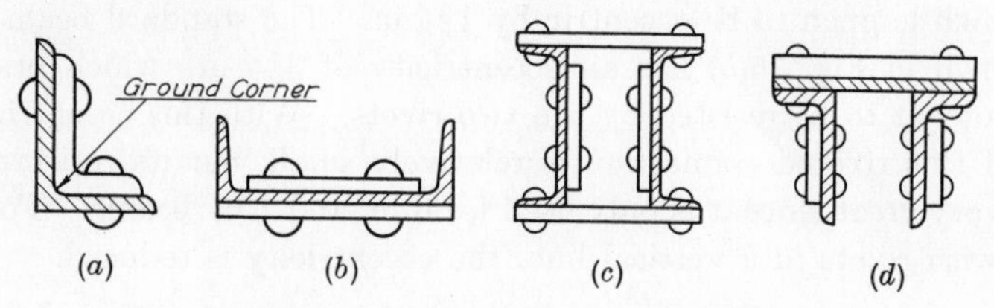

FIG. 74. SPLICES OF RIVETED TENSION MEMBERS.

Indirect Splices. The top splice plate of Fig. 74(*d*) is a direct splice for the horizontal plate of the tension member, but it is an indirect splice for any part of the angle area that it may be used to splice. Specifications commonly require the use of *excess rivets* where the splice is indirect (intermediate plate). The requirement may be an increase of as much as 25 or 33 per cent in the number of rivets for the effect of *each intermediate plate*.

CHORD MEMBER SPLICED AT A CHORD JOINT, *DP*5. Some specifications warn the designer against arranging a chord member splice that involves the use of the gusset plates as splice plates. However, it is sometimes desirable to use the gusset plates in this manner, and there can be no objection raised if the gusset plates are analyzed properly as splice plates. The trouble has been that gusset plates were simply chosen for their function as gussets and were then called upon to withstand the *extra duty* of splice plates for which they had not been designed.

In the design problem *DP*5, the angles of the chord are spliced for the value of their outstanding legs by the horizontal splice plates. The vertical legs are simply attached to the vertical gusset plates. On a vertical line through the center of the joint between the angles to be spliced, the cross section resisting stress consists of the two 14 × ⅜-in. gussets and the 20 × ½-in. horizontal splice plate. These plates, joined together through the medium of the chord angles, form a U-section. Since the pull in the angles to the right is eccentric by 1.5 in. from the neutral axis of the U-section, there is not only a direct stress but also a *flexural moment* resisted by this section. The fiber stresses are computed, and a proper design is suggested.

Although in this design problem a solution is reached, it is not always feasible to obtain such a satisfactory design for a joint splice. For instance, in *DP*5 the problem will be found to be seriously complicated by an extension of the height of the gussets to 15 in., 16 in., or more, which will increase the eccentricity. A similar effect is obtained by the use of thicker gussets or a thinner or narrower splice plate. Naturally, the problem will be more difficult to solve if the chord angles are thicker. A *splice between joints* is usually the better solution.

ECCENTRICITY IN RIVETED CONNECTIONS

87. Eccentrically Riveted Connections. The ideal riveted connection for a tension or compression member has the center of gravity of the rivet group comprising the connection lined up exactly with the center of gravity of the member or with the line of the applied load. This ideal is seldom attained, and it is not uncommon to find considerable eccentricity even in *standard connections*. For example, the double angle tension member of Fig. 75(*a*) has two lines indicated on the figure, the gage line, and the gravity axis, which happen to be eccentric by 1⅜ in. The standard beam connection shown in Fig. 75(*b*) has an eccentricity of 3½ in., which produces a large moment to be resisted by the two rivets. With this eccentricity, the value of this riveted connection is relatively small, but its resistance need not be very great since it is only used for 6-in. and 7-in. beams. For deeper beams with rivets in a vertical line, the eccentricity is reduced.

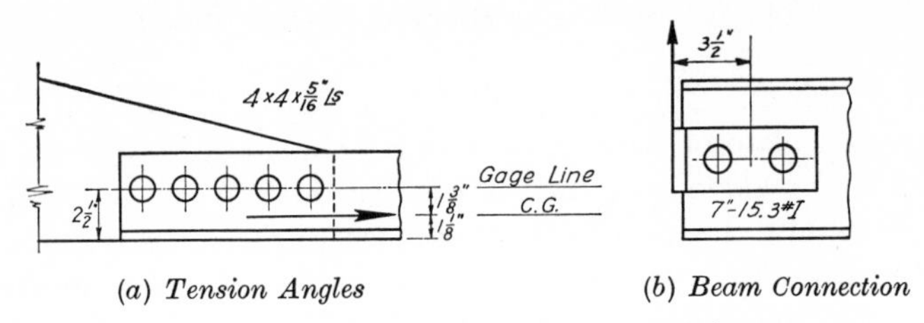

(*a*) *Tension Angles* (*b*) *Beam Connection*

FIG. 75. ECCENTRICITY IN STANDARD CONNECTIONS.

Some connections are actually designed for moment resistance. In the tie-rod connection of Fig. 76(*a*) the tensile force is intended to intersect with the center line of the post at the base plate. The force does not pass through the center of the rivet group. Therefore, it produces both a direct shear and a twisting moment to be resisted by the rivets. The side bracket shown on

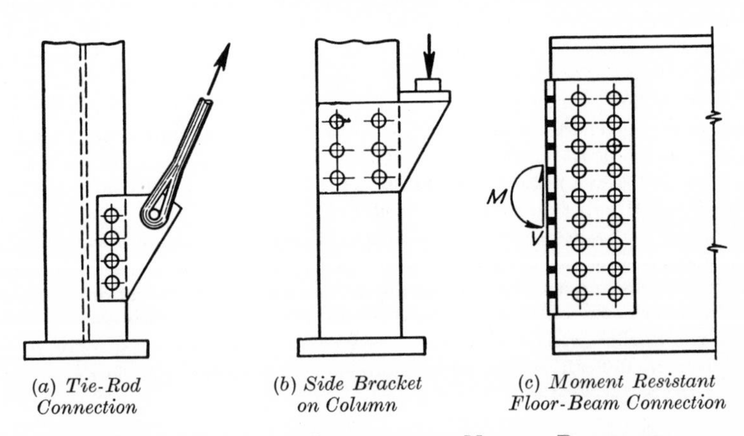

(*a*) *Tie-Rod Connection* (*b*) *Side Bracket on Column* (*c*) *Moment Resistant Floor-Beam Connection*

FIG. 76. CONNECTIONS DESIGNED FOR MOMENT RESISTANCE.

the column in Fig. 76(*b*) acts in about the same manner as the connection (*a*), but the eccentricity is greater, and two rows of rivets are desirable for this reason. The heavy end connection shown in (*c*) is for a floor beam of a low-truss bridge where lateral stability is dependent upon a moment resistant connection from the floor beam to the vertical post. The connection is designed to resist both the end shear of the beam and the moment caused by a lateral wind force on the truss.

88. Analysis of Eccentric Riveted Connections. The extent of the printed matter on the analysis of eccentric riveted connections would lead one to believe that the subject is very complex. Actually, it is rather simple. The theory in one of its special applications may be compared to the formula for the fiber stress on any section carrying a normal load P eccentric from the center of gravity of the cross-section by the distance e.

$$f = \frac{P}{A} \pm \frac{Pec}{I}. \tag{7}$$

Rivets in a Single Line. The revised formula for application to a *line of rivets* (n rivets of *unit area* at distances y from the center of gravity of the group, c being the maximum value of y) becomes

$$V = \frac{P}{n} + \frac{Pec}{\Sigma y^2}. \tag{8}$$

In this formula, V is the maximum shear per rivet, since each rivet area is treated as unity. The use of this equation assumes that the direct shear on the most highly stressed rivet and the shear caused by the moment of eccentricity are in line, as in Fig. 75(*b*). In case they are 90 degrees apart, as in Fig. 75(*a*), the expression for R, the resultant shear per rivet, becomes

$$R = \sqrt{\left(\frac{P}{n}\right)^2 + \left(\frac{Pec}{\Sigma y^2}\right)^2}. \tag{9}$$

The direction of the shear represented by the term P/n may be oblique to the direction of the shear represented by the term $Pec/\Sigma y^2$, as in Fig. 76(*a*) and Fig. 77. Here the term P/n represents a shear acting in line with

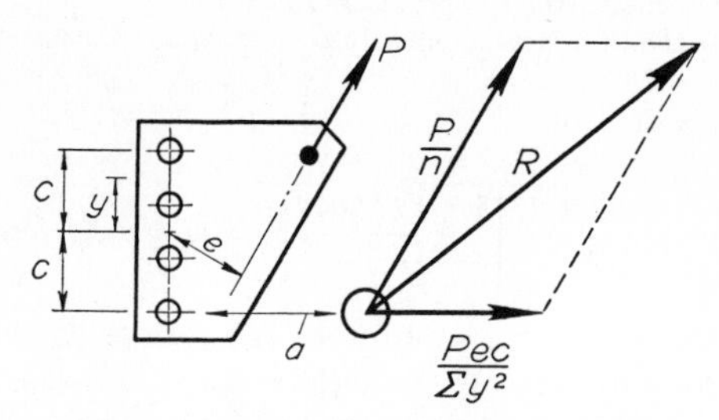

FIG. 77. RESULTANT RIVET SHEAR.

the load, while the term $Pec/\Sigma y^2$ represents a horizontal shear caused by the moment of eccentricity. The design shear for the most highly stressed

DP6. *Design the connection for two $6 \times 4 \times \frac{1}{2}''$ angles attached back to back to a $\frac{1}{2}''$ plate. Take account of eccentricity in the connection. AASHO Spec. 202.*

Standard Design Procedure:

$$\text{Holes to deduct (1'' holes)} = 2 - \frac{s^2}{4g}$$

$$= 2 - \frac{2^2}{4 \times 2\frac{1}{2}} = 1.6.$$

Net area of 2 angles $= 2(4.75 - 1.6 \times 1 \times \frac{1}{2}) = 7.9$ in.^{2}
Value of angles $= 7.9 \times 18{,}000 = 142{,}000\#$.
Value of $\frac{7}{8}''$ *rivet for bearing on* $\frac{1}{2}''$ *plate;* $0.875 \times 0.5 \times 27{,}000 = 11{,}800\#$.
Number of rivets (neglecting eccentricity) $= 142{,}000 \div 11{,}800 = 12.0$

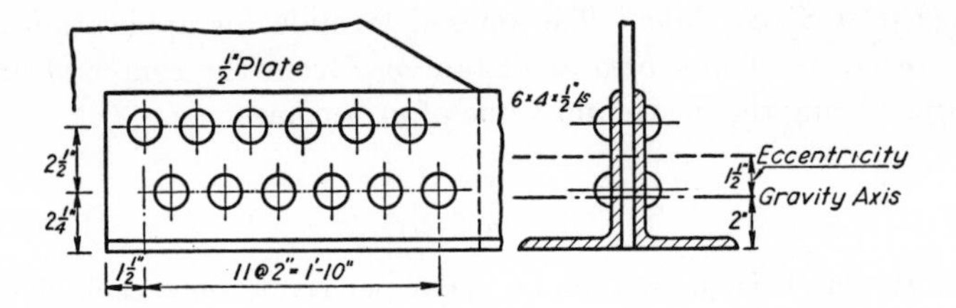

Allowance for Eccentricity:

Moment of eccentricity $= 142{,}000 \times 1.5 = 213{,}000''\#$.
I of rivet group $= 2[1^2 + 3^2 + 5^2 + 7^2 + 9^2 + 11^2] = 572$.
Note that Σy^2 *is neglected since it is relatively small.*

$$\text{Shear due to flexure} = \frac{213{,}000 \times 11}{572} = 4100\#/\text{rivet}.$$

$$\text{Resultant rivet shear} = \sqrt{4100^2 + 11{,}800^2} = 12{,}500\#/\text{rivet (excessive)}.$$

Try a connection with 1 extra rivet, 13 in all.
$I = 2[2^2 + 4^2 + 6^2 + 8^2 + 10^2 + 12^2] = 728$.

Resultant rivet shear

$$= \sqrt{\left[\frac{213{,}000 \times 12}{728}\right]^2 + \left[\frac{142{,}000}{13}\right]^2} = 11{,}500\#/\text{rivet} \ (<11{,}800).$$

Redesign: *Use 13 rivets in place of the 12 shown in the illustration. Actually this allowance for eccentricity is seldom made in design although it is fully justified. It will be more serious in connections with fewer rivets.*

rivet (the lower one of the group in Fig. 77) is the resultant of these two shears, and it may be obtained graphically as illustrated. The same general procedure may be followed irrespective of the directions of the two components of shear.

ECCENTRICITY IN ANGLE CONNECTIONS, *DP*6. Where two lines of rivets are used in a 5-in. or 6-in. angle leg, there is always considerable eccentricity. This eccentricity for the example *DP*6 is 1½ in. The resultant moment produces a cross shear perpendicular to the direct shear on the rivets. The result obtained by equation (9) is shown on Design Sheet 6 to be an increased rivet stress that will be resisted adequately by the addition of an extra rivet to the 12 required for direct load.

89. Torsion Formula for Rivet Groups. The revised flexure formula (8) or (9) applies only to rivets in a single line or for two or more lines that are close enough together so that the *length of the group is several times the width.* Actually, the action of a rivet group in resisting the moment of an eccentric load is comparable to the action of a shaft in resisting a torque moment. If it is assumed that the rivets are forced by the plate to deform so that rivet shears are proportional to radii from the center of rotation, the most important requirement of the torsion formula is met. Hence, we may write the expression for unit torsional shear stress τ.

$$\tau = \frac{Tr}{J} \tag{10}$$

or, for rivets of unit cross-sectional area, by substitution of Σr^2 for J and Pe for T, we obtain the rivet shear in pounds

$$R' = \frac{(Pe)r}{\Sigma r^2} = \frac{Per}{\Sigma(x^2 + y^2)} = \frac{Per}{\Sigma x^2 + \Sigma y^2}. \tag{11}$$

The factors x and y are the coordinates of the rivets measured from the center of gravity of the rivet group from which point the radii (r) also are measured. R' is the shear per rivet due to the torque moment when each rivet area is treated as unity.

Bracket Connection. An analysis of the side-bracket connection of Fig. 76(*b*) is indicated in Fig. 78. There is a vertical shear on each rivet equal to P/n, and the rivet a (upper right-hand rivet) also resists a shear acting downward and to the right caused by rotation about the center of gravity of the rivet group. The *resultant shear* is obtained graphically as the vector R. The other rivet shears may be found likewise. Alternately, R may be found from x and y components as shown in the right-hand vector diagram of Fig. 78.

ASSUMPTIONS. There were several assumptions involved in the theory presented in this section for the analysis of riveted connections acting under eccentric loading. It will be well to review them here in order that the methods presented shall not be extended beyond their legitimate fields of use.

1. Direct load produces an equal shear P/n on each rivet.

2. Rotation about the center of gravity of the rivet group produces a shear on each rivet proportional to its radius from the c.g. and *normal* to that radius.

3. Friction is neglected.

4. Long rivet lines resisting moment may be treated by a simplification based upon the flexure formula, equations (8) and (9).

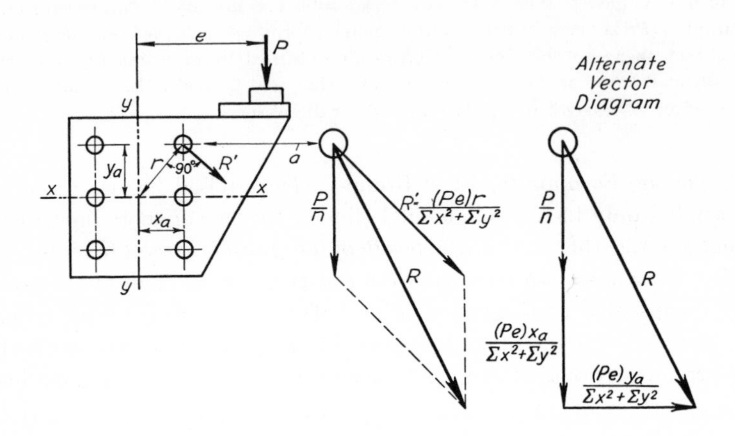

FIG. 78. ACTION OF A RIVET GROUP.

90. Design of Rivet Lines to Resist Moment. The use of equations such as (8) and (9) which involve the term Σy^2 is convenient for the analysis but not for the design of a riveted joint for moment resistance. If we consider a line of rivets n in number at spacing s or $(n - 1)s$ in length as equivalent in moment resistance to a long narrow rectangular cross-section ns in length, the total force *due to moment only* resisted by the farthest rivet V can be obtained approximately as the extreme fiber stress of the rectangular section times s, the rivet spacing. For a section modulus of $(ns)^2/6$, this expression becomes

$$V = \frac{6Ms}{(ns)^2} = \frac{6M}{n^2 s}. \tag{12}$$

This equation may be solved for the number of rivets n which gives the relation

$$n = \sqrt{\frac{6M}{Vs}}. \tag{13}$$

The use of equation (13) is convenient as a *design procedure.* First, a choice of rivet spacing s is made to agree with standard rivet spacing for other parts of the structure. Then, the moment M in inch pounds is computed and V is taken as the limiting shear on the rivet in pounds. The computed value of n is the number of rivets (not the number of rivet spaces) needed on the line.

DESIGN OF HEAVY COLUMN BRACKET, *DP*7. The rivets are shown arranged in four lines, the outside rows spaced 12 in. apart. This group of rivets will possess considerable moment of inertia about each axis; in other words, its polar moment of inertia will be considerably greater than the moment of inertia about its horizontal axis. As an initial estimate, the use of equation (13) will aid us in obtaining the approximate number of rivets needed in each line.

The important point to consider in applying equation (13) to any such problem is the estimated value of V. For a single row of rivets resisting pure flexure, V is the value in pounds of one rivet. In case there is a direct load as well, V must be *reduced* to compensate for this effect. On the other hand, if there is more than one line of rivets, the value of V should be *increased* in order to allow for the moment of inertia about the second principal axis. These two influences tend to cancel each other. Therefore, in the example $DP7$, V is estimated as the actual value of the rivet. The check analysis shows that the resultant rivet stress is almost exactly the allowable shear. Hence, our guess at the proper value of V to use in equation (13) was a good one.

91. Moment Resistance with Tension Rivets. Beam connections and brackets attached to the face of a column offer moment resistance because of the tension values of the rivets. We will treat the cross-section shown in Fig. 79 as a beam section and compute its resistance to moment by the beam flexure formula.

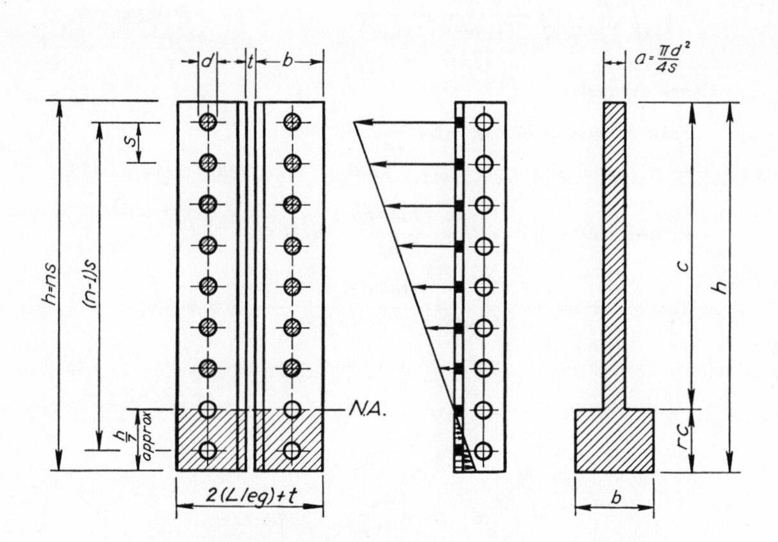

Fig. 79. Action of a Beam Web Connection.

Assumption. *Neglect consideration of initial rivet tension* and assume that the neutral axis is at the center of gravity of the effective cross-section, which consists of the *circular rivet areas* above the neutral axis and the *rectangular bearing area* of clip angles against the column face below the neutral axis. This procedure agrees with the method of analyzing direct riveted connections and eccentric riveted connections as discussed above in that friction and the initial rivet tension that produces friction are being neglected.

DP7. *Design a heavy riveted bracket connection to the faces of a 14 × 16 WF287 column to resist a girder reaction of 165k. as shown. Use 4 lines of rivets in each face of the column. AISC spec. A36 steel and A141 rivets.*

Standard Design Method:

Value of a ¾″ rivet in single shear = 15,000 × 0.44 = 6600#.

Approx. number of rivets per row can be estimated by use of equation (13). In making this estimate, V should be decreased to allow for direct shear and increased because the rivet lines are spread laterally. Hence, it will be used as 6600. Let M = moment per rivet line.

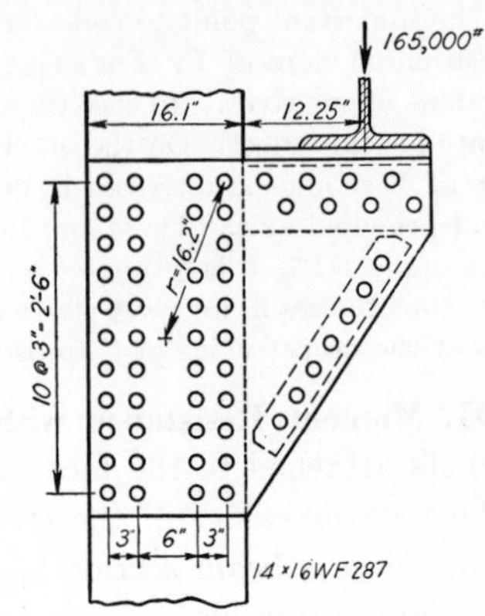

$$n = \sqrt{\frac{6M}{Vs}} = \sqrt{\frac{6(165,000 \times 20.3)/8}{6600 \times 3}} = 11.2; \text{ try 11 rivets per row.}$$

Check Analysis:

Polar moment of inertia $= \Sigma y^2 + \Sigma x^2;$

$$16[3^2 + 6^2 + 9^2 + 12^2 + 15^2] + 44[3^2 + 6^2] = 7920 + 1980 = 9900.$$

$$\text{Vertical rivet shear} = P/n = \frac{165,000}{88} = 1880\#.$$

$$\text{Torsional rivet shear} = \frac{Tr}{J} = \frac{(165,000 \times 20.3)16.2}{9900} = 5500\#.$$

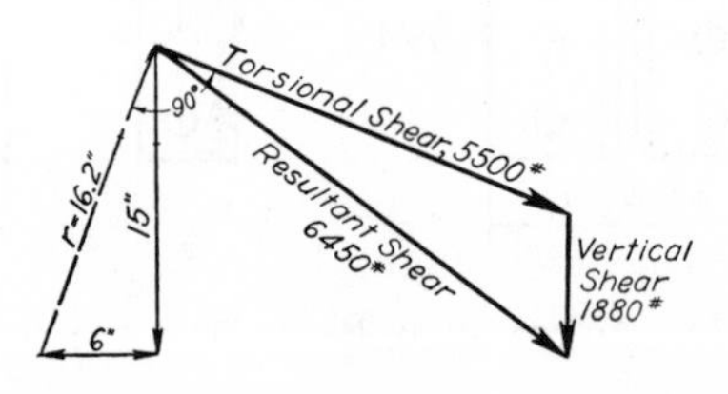

Graphical Determination of Resultant Rivet Shear:

Value of resultant shear = 6450# per rivet (<6600).
The estimate of 11 rivets per row for 8 rows was satisfactory.

DESIGN SHEET 7

This concept is consistent also with ultimate load design which will be discussed later.

The method of analysis for such a connection is reasonably direct. The neutral axis will lie somewhere near $\frac{1}{7}$ *of the length of the clip angles above their lower ends.* It may be taken at this position, and the statical moment of the rivet areas above this line can be compared with the statical moment of the bearing area below. An adjustment in the neutral axis should then be made to obtain an approximate balance of these statical moments. An exact location is not needed; an adjustment to the nearest half inch is acceptable. Then the moment of inertia is determined and the tension stress in the upper rivets is computed from the flexure formula. Since actual cross-sectional areas of rivets must be used, the stress will be obtained in pounds per square inch. The illustration, Fig. 80 shows both web angle and seat angle connections of beams and girders to a column.

Courtesy Eng. News-Record.

FIG. 80. BEAM AND GIRDER FRAMING.

SEAT-ANGLE CONNECTION, *DP*8. The design of this seat angle or unstiffened bracket involves the design of the angle leg for flexure and the design of the rivets for tension and shear. A triangular bearing pressure is assumed on the outstanding leg to account for the fact that this leg deflects downward and therefore resists less bearing at the toe than at the heel of the angle. The length and thickness of the leg are then selected to keep the flexural fiber stress under 24,000 psi *at the net section of the vertical leg.*

The neutral axis for flexure is assumed to be ⅞ in. above the bottom of the angle. A comparison of statical moments of rivet areas (circular areas) above the axis with bearing area (rectangular area) below the axis shows a statical moment of 3.2 against one of 2.9, a satisfactory balance for locating the neutral axis. Then, the moment of inertia is determined for this effective section and the rivet tension is computed by an application of the Mc/I formula. The rivet tension of 5600 psi is very low and the vertical shear of 6900 psi is not critical. However, fewer rivets would not ordinarily be used because of the danger of loosening the seat angle in shipment.

DP8. *Design a seat angle for a column to support an 8″ I-beam with an end reaction of 12,000#. The angle legs are 6″ and 3½″. AISC spec. A36 steel, A141 rivets.*

Flexure of Vertical Angle Leg at Net Section on Upper Rivet Line:

Assume thickness of angle leg to be ¾″.
Assume triangular variation of bearing pressure.

$M = 12{,}000 \times (1.5 - 0.375) = 13{,}500''\#$. (*About N.A. of vert. leg*).

$$\text{Length of angle for flexure only} = \frac{6M}{t^2 F_b} = \frac{6 \times 13{,}500}{0.75^2 \times 24{,}000} = 6.0''.$$

$$\text{Max. fiber stress} = \frac{12{,}000}{6.0 \times 0.75} + 24{,}000 = 26{,}600 \text{ psi} \quad (11\% \text{ overstressed}).$$

Set gross length at 8½″ to allow for 2 rivet holes and a 11% increased length of cross section.

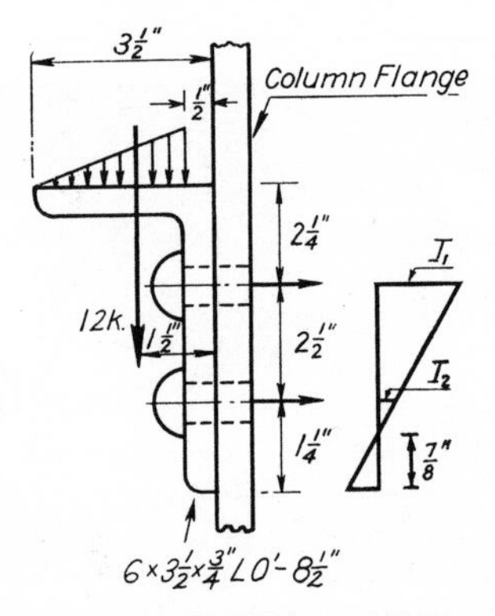

Shear and Tension in Rivets: (*assume 4 rivets, ¾″ diam.*)

Unit shear $= 12{,}000 \div (4 \times 0.44) = 6900$ *psi.*

Guess location of N.A. at ⅞″ above bottom. (*This approaches ⅐ of depth.*)

Stat. mom. of comp. area $= 8.5 \times 0.87 \times 0.87/2 = 3.2.$

Stat. mom. of rivet areas $= 2 \times 0.44(0.37 + 2.87) = 2.9.$

This balance of statical moments is satisfactory for locating the N.A.

$$\text{Moment of inertia} = 2 \times 0.44(0.37^2 + 2.87^2) + \frac{1}{3} \times 8.5 \times 0.87^3 = 9.3.$$

$$\text{Rivet tension} = \frac{12{,}000 \times 1.5 \times 2.87}{9.3} = 5600 \text{ psi} < F_t \text{ by equation (2)}.$$

Remarks: *Two rivets would have been adequate for stress, but a connection with two rivets is likely to be loosened in shipment. Four rivets are common in seat angles.*

DESIGN SHEET 8

92. Design of Tension Rivets for Moment Resistant Connections. The problem of design is complicated here by the fact that several widths of clip-angle legs may be used. However, a convenient procedure will be obtained by use of standard clip angles ($3\frac{1}{2}$-in. or 4-in. bearing legs) with the rivets spaced 3 in. apart, as in standard beam connections.

In Fig. 79 we can let b be 7 in. for $3\frac{1}{2}$-in. clip angles. With $\frac{7}{8}$-in. rivets, the width a, which is $\pi d^2/4s$, will be 0.20 when rivets are spaced 3 in. apart. The value of h will be $3n$, where n is the number of rivets in a single line. It is possible then to compute the location of the center of gravity of the T-section and to determine the section modulus S in terms of n. Thus, we find approximately for *Standard Beam Connections*:

(14) $$S = 0.5n^2,$$

(15) $$n = \sqrt{2S} \quad (\tfrac{7}{8}\text{-in. rivets}).$$

Similarly, we find

(16) $$n = \sqrt{3S} \quad (\tfrac{3}{4}\text{-in. rivets}).$$

In each of these equations S represents the required section modulus obtained by dividing the flexural moment per rivet line in inch pounds by the allowable tension stress on a rivet in pounds per square inch. The value of n is relatively independent of the size of angle leg used.

Design of a Moment Resistant Connection to a Beam Web, *DP9a*. This connection is the standard end connection for a rolled beam. Its moment resistance is in no sense equal to that of the beam, but it is of importance in several usages, as, for example, to form a moment resistant connection between a column and girder to resist a small wind moment. Use is made of equation (15) which applies to standard beam connections ($\frac{7}{8}$-in. rivets at 3-in. spacing). It should be noted that no attempt is made in this problem to *combine* tension and shearing unit stresses for the tension rivets. However, as a matter of interest, the *combined stresses* would be as follows. [Equations (25*a*) and (26*a*) from §38 and Table 1.]

$$\text{Max. } \tau = \sqrt{\frac{\sigma_y{}^2}{4} + \tau_{xy}{}^2} = \sqrt{\left(\frac{15{,}000}{2}\right)^2 + 7750^2} = 10{,}800 \text{ psi for shear.}$$

$$\text{Max. } \sigma = \frac{\sigma_y}{2} + \text{Max. } \tau = \frac{15{,}000}{4} + 10{,}800 = 18{,}300 \text{ psi for tension.}$$

In these formulas, σ_y represents the unit *axial* tensile stress in the rivet; τ is the unit average shearing stress on its circular cross-section. These unit stresses are considerably under the allowable shear and tension values by *AISC* specifications. The maximum combined stresses of 10,800 psi for τ and 18,300 psi for σ are acceptable.

Design of Connection Angles

93. Design of Connection Angles with Tension Rivets. Contrasting assumptions regarding the structural action of connection angles are illustrated by Fig. 81. These assumptions form the bases of common design

DP9a. *Design a clip-angle connection to the face of a column for a 24WF94 beam to develop a moment resistance of 50,000′# and on end reaction of 65,000#. Use AISC spec. for A36 steel and A141 rivets. Restrict rivet tension to 15,000 psi. Check by equation (2).*

Tension Rivet Connection to Column Face: *For a standard rivet spacing of 3″ and for ⅞″ rivets, we may use equation (15) to determine n.*

Sect. mod., $S = \frac{50{,}000 \times 12}{2 \times 15{,}000} = 20$ *(per rivet line).*

$n = \sqrt{2S} = \sqrt{40} = 6.3$ *rivets.* [*Equation (15) for 3″ spacing.*]

Try a standard A7 connection (7 — ⅞″ rivets @ 3″ spacing).

Unit rivet shear $= \frac{65{,}000}{14 \times 0.6} = 7750$ *psi.*

Allowable F_t *by equation (2)* $= 28{,}000 - 1.6 \times 7750 = 15{,}600$ *psi. OK.*

Check on Rivets through Beam Web:

I of rivet group $= 2(3^2 + 6^2 + 9^2) = 252$. *(Rivet area treated as unity.)*

Resultant rivet shear $= \sqrt{\left(\frac{65{,}000}{7}\right)^2 + \left(\frac{600{,}000 \times 9}{252}\right)^2} = 23{,}200\#/$*rivet.*

This is satisfactory for double shear or bearing on web for 1″ rivets (Spec. 16).

DP9b. *Design the connection angles (Try 5 × 3½ × ⅝″ ∠s).*

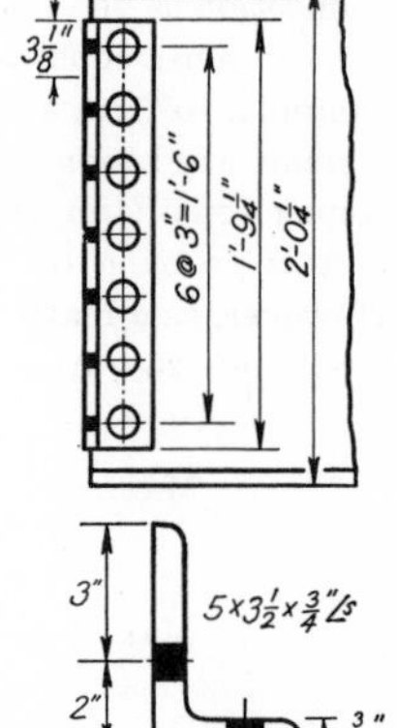

Double Flexure of Angle Leg:

Pull on upper rivet $= 15{,}000 \times 0.6 = 9000\#$.
Length of angle resisting this pull = 3⅛″.
Lever arm, equation (19) $= 0.6(g - t) = 0.6(2 - 0.62) = 0.82''$.
Bending moment on one angle leg $= 9000 \times 0.82 = 7400''\#$.
Thickness of angle leg, $t = \sqrt{6M/bF_b}$.

$$t = \sqrt{\frac{6 \times 7400}{3.12 \times 24{,}000}} = 0.77'', \text{ use } \tfrac{3}{4}'' \text{ angles.}$$

Extra rivet stress in tension [equation (21)];

$$1 + \frac{3}{4}\left(\frac{g-t}{q}\right) = 1 + \frac{3}{4}\left(\frac{1.25}{3}\right) = 1.32 \text{ or 32 per cent increase.}$$

Remarks: *A satisfactory solution would be to increase the tension rivets to 1″ diameter, a 31 per cent increase in area. Note that no allowance was made for the weakening of the angle leg by holes. Since equation (19) rather than (18) was used, the maximum moment as failure approaches is expected to occur near the inside corner of the angle on a gross section. The increase in angle leg facing the column to 5″ reduces the increment of rivet tension by equation (21) without significantly changing n in DP9a.*

DESIGN SHEET 9

methods. In (*a*) the rivets are assumed to have elongated due to tension stress above the yield point, and the outstanding legs of the angles curve in *simple flexure*. In (*b*) the angle legs are held flat against the column by the initial tension in the rivets, and each outstanding leg bends into a *reversed curve*. The analysis of these two types of flexure is indicated in Fig. 82.

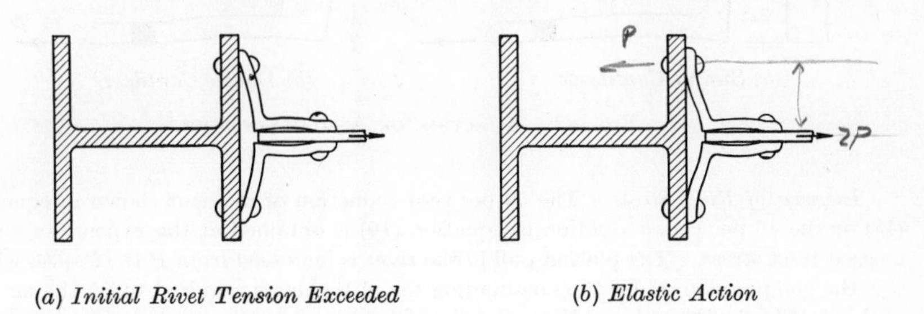

(*a*) *Initial Rivet Tension Exceeded* (*b*) *Elastic Action*

FIG. 81. ASSUMPTIONS AS TO THE ACTION OF CONNECTION ANGLES.

Simple Cantilever Flexure. In (*a*) of Fig. 82 the outstanding angle leg acts as a simple cantilever; the pull on the rivet is the total applied tension load P on a length of angle equal to the spacing or pitch of the rivets. The bending moment to be resisted by the angle leg is

$$M = P(g - t). \tag{17}$$

The moment represented by this expression, where g is the gage and t is the thickness of the angle, must be resisted by a length of angle leg equal to the rivet spacing.

Double Cantilever Flexure. The moment to be resisted by the angle in Fig. 82(*b*) is computed as the bending moment of a double cantilever. There is a point of *contraflexure* or of zero moment midway between the rivet and the face of the angle. This bending moment is

$$M = P\left(\frac{g - t}{2}\right). \tag{18}$$

This is but one half of the moment that had to be resisted by simple cantilever action as expressed by equation (17). It has been assumed that any angle change at the heel of the angle in Fig. 82(*b*) will be balanced by an equal angle change at the outer rivet and that the point of contraflexure will therefore be as indicated by Fig. 82(*b*). For safety, some shift in the point of contraflexure away from the mid-point *toward the rivet* should be assumed; and, therefore, equation (19) is recommended for reasonably conservative design of clip angles and split-beam connections.

$$M = 0.6P(g - t). \tag{19}$$

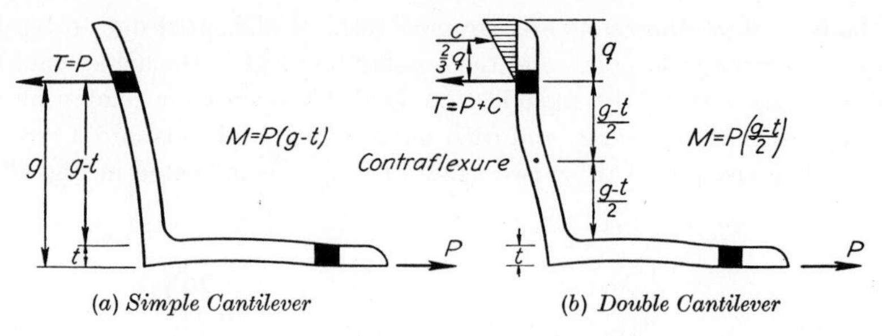

(*a*) *Simple Cantilever* (*b*) *Double Cantilever*

FIG. 82. ANALYSIS OF ANGLE FLEXURE.

Increase of Rivet Stress. The 50 per cent reduction of moment shown in equation (18) or the 40 per cent reduction in equation (19) is obtained at the expense of an increased rivet stress. The tension pull in the rivet is increased from P to $(P + C)$ where C is the compression under the outstanding toe of the angle required to fix the far end of the double cantilever leg. We will call the distance from the tension rivet to the toe of the angle leg q. Then, upon the assumption of triangular variation of toe pressure, the arm of the couple formed by the two forces C [Fig. 82(*b*)] is $(2/3)q$. Hence, we may equate the expression $C(2/3)q$ and the moment expressed by equation (18).

$$C\left(\frac{2}{3}q\right) = P\left(\frac{g - t}{2}\right),$$

or

$$C = \frac{3}{4}P\left(\frac{g - t}{q}\right), \tag{20}$$

The tension pull on the rivet becomes

$$T = P + C = P\left[1 + \frac{3}{4}\left(\frac{g - t}{q}\right)\right]. \tag{21}$$

This is the tensile force for which the rivet in Fig. 82(*b*) should be designed. If M is reduced to $0.4P(g - t)$ at the rivet to agree with equation (19), the factor ¾ will be reduced to 0.6 in equation (21). However, for conservative design, equations (19) and (21) may be used together as in *DP*9*b*.

94. Choice of a Design Method. For consistency with design methods used for other types of riveted joints, where initial rivet tension is always neglected, we would design connection angles for simple cantilever flexure as shown in Fig. 81(*a*) and Fig. 82(*a*). The design of large beam or girder connections by these equations results in angles that are too thick to punch. They add materially to the weight and cost of the structure. It is permissible to reduce the bending moment according to equation (18) or preferably equation (19), but there is the *absolute necessity then of increasing the number or size of rivets* to meet the requirements of equation (21). This has often been overlooked. The result is a serious error.

For 4-in. clip angles, g is 2½ in. and we will take t at ⅜ in. Then

$$C = \frac{3}{4}P\left(\frac{2.5 - 0.37}{1.5}\right) = 1.06P.$$

Thus the total force to be resisted by rivet tension is increased from P to $2.06P$. Either the number or the cross-sectional areas of the rivets must be doubled.

For 6-in. clip angles, g is 3½ in. and we will take t at ½ in. Then

$$C = \frac{3}{4}P\left(\frac{3.5 - 0.5}{2.5}\right) = 0.90P.$$

The total rivet tension has been increased by double cantilever flexure from P to $1.90P$. The increment of rivet tension can be reduced by using a small gage g in a large angle leg.

Clip Angles to the Web of a Beam, *DP9b*. These connection angles have been estimated as ⅝ in. thick. It is assumed that double cantilever flexure can be depended upon. The angle leg outstanding is set at 5 in. in order to increase the quantity q (projection beyond the rivet) which helps to hold down the increase in rivet stress that accompanies *double cantilever flexure.* It is found that the required thickness of the angle leg is ¾ in. (it would be more for simple cantilever flexure). However, it is important to note that there is also an increase in rivet tension $(\frac{3}{4}(g - t)/q)$ which amounts to 32 per cent. The proper solution would be to increase the tension rivets to 1-in. diameter (a 31 per cent increase of area) or to use high strength bolts as will be discussed later.

Clip Angles as Tension-Plate Connection, *DP10*. Here the connection angles are first designed as simple cantilevers and found to be 1⅛ in. thick. Such thickness of metal requires drilling. Hence, the use of extra rivets to permit the assumption of double cantilever flexure may be more economical. It is found that the angles can then be reduced to a thickness of ¾ in. but that they must be increased in length from 6 to 9 in. to hold three tension rivets in each angle leg instead of two rivets. Probably the cost is not actually reduced, but the design with ¾-in. metal seems a more practical solution to the problem. This is true because there are no angles rolled of 1⅛-in. thickness with 4-in. legs. It would be necessary to reduce 8-in. angles to 4 in.

Repeated Stresses

95. Fatigue Tests of Riveted Joints. Results of fatigue tests of practical riveted joints[3] have led to the following information.

Failure in the Rivets. Those specimens designed to fail by rivet shear indicate that the *fatigue limit of ordinary rivets* is 30,000 psi. This figure signifies that a fatigue shear failure can be expected at 2,000,000 repetitions whenever the rivet shear varies from 0 to 30,000 psi for a non-reversing load. Results with a reversing load (direction of shear on rivet reversed) are not very consistent, since they show a variation of fatigue limit from as little as 15,000 psi to as great as 30,000 psi. So many variables seemed to be involved in the case of full reversal, that further tests were considered necessary.

[3] W. M. Wilson, *Fatigue tests of riveted joints*, Bulletin 302, University of Illinois Engineering Experiment Station.

DP10. *Design a pair of clip angles not over 9″ long to resist a pull of 30,000# in a plate 9″ × ⅝″. A7 steel and standard A141 rivets. AISC spec.*

Shear Rivets: *On ⅝″ metal, double shear controls.*

Allowable shear = 15,000 psi. (Spec. 16.)

$$n = \frac{30,000}{2 \times 0.6 \times 15,000} = 2 \text{ rivets } (⅞″).$$

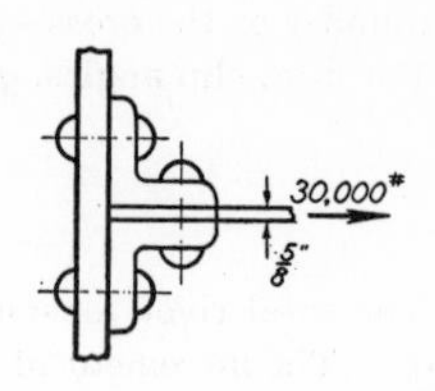

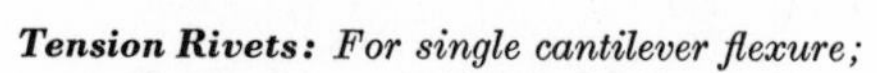

Tension Rivets: *For single cantilever flexure;*

$n = 30,000 \div 0.6 \times 20,000 = 2.5$ *rivets.*

Use 4 tension rivets for symmetry.

Thickness of Connection Angles: *(Use 4″ × 4″ angles.)*

Length = 6″ to hold rivets at 3″ spacing.

(Assume t = ¾″.) Gage = 2½″.

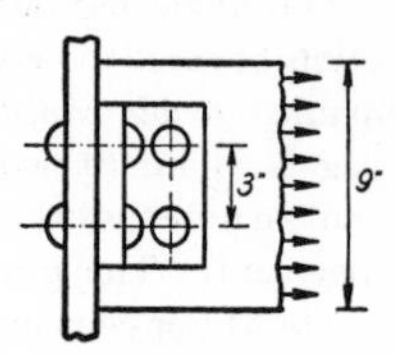

$$M = \frac{30,000}{2} \times (2.5 - 0.75) = 26,200''\#.$$

$S = 26,200 \div 22,000 = 1.19$ *in.*^{3}

Hence, $\frac{1}{6} \times 6 \times t^2 = 1.19$, *or* $t = \sqrt{1.19} = 1\frac{1}{8}''$.

Metal 1⅛″ thick must be drilled. Design will be revised for double cantilever flexure. Extra rivets will require longer angles. Assume angles to be 9″ long and ¾″ thick.

Double Flexure:

$$M = \frac{30,000}{2} \times 0.6(2.5 - 0.75) = 15,700''\#.$$

[Equation (19).]

$$S = \frac{15,700}{22,000} = 0.72 \text{ in.}^3 \quad \text{Hence, } \frac{1}{6} \times 9 \times t^2 = 0.72,$$

or $t = \sqrt{0.48} = 0.70''$.

Use angles 4 × 4 × ¾″ × 0′ − 9″ long.

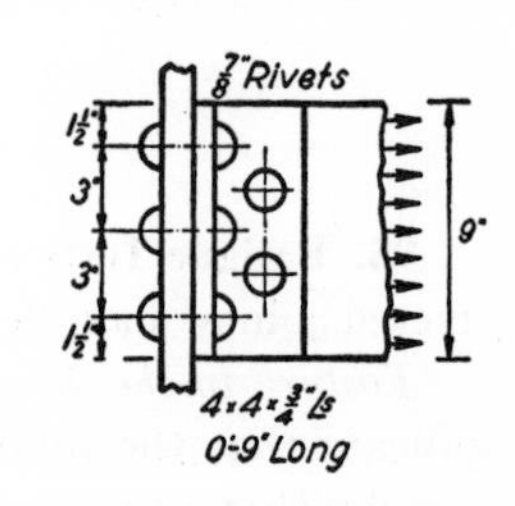

Rivet Tension: *Equation (21).*

For each line of rivets,

$$T = P\left(1 + \frac{3}{4}\left(\frac{g-t}{q}\right)\right) = \frac{30,000}{2}\left[1.0 + 0.75\left(\frac{2.5 - 0.75}{1.5}\right)\right] = 28,000\#.$$

Tension value of a ⅞″ rivet $= 0.6 \times 20,000 = 12,000\#$.

$n = 28,000 \div 12,000 = 2.4$; *use three ⅞″ rivets in each vertical line.*

Failure Through the Plates. Plate failure always started at a rivet hole and developed as indicated in Fig. 83. These tests show quite conclusively that the average stress on the net section which will produce failure at 2,000,000 repetitions is approximately 26,000 psi. Strangely enough, this value seems to be independent of the kind of steel used or of its ultimate strength, since it held constant for carbon, silicon, and nickel steels (ultimate strengths varying from 63,000 to 99,000 psi). Furthermore, the method of making rivet holes—punching, sub-punching and reaming, or drilling—had no measurable effect upon the fatigue strength of the plates.

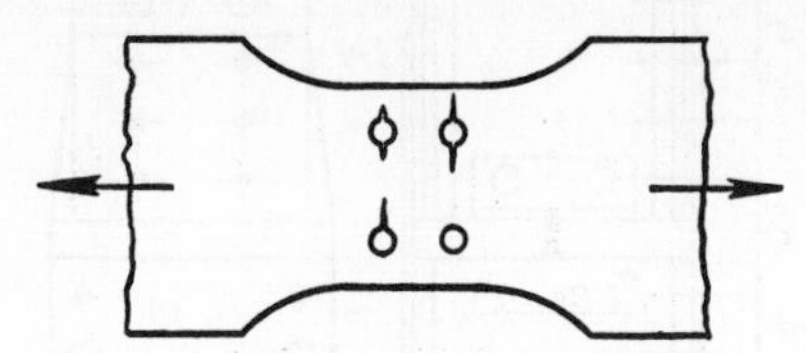

FIG. 83. FATIGUE CRACKS.

Design Specifications for Repeated Stresses. As will be clarified by reference to the allowable stress (Spec. 22, Table S-3), *AISC* requires that the maximum stress be increased by a fraction of the minimum stress for stress repetitions from 10,000 to 2,000,000; and for stress repetitions above 2,000,000 the allowable stresses are also reduced by one third. It requires about 200 applications of load each day for 25 years to produce 2,000,000 repetitions of stress.

PROBLEMS

401. Determine the edge distance in terms of plate thickness so that a shearing failure as shown in Fig. 63(*c*) would be no more probable than (*e*) which is a shear failure of the rivet. *Ans.* Edge dist. $= \pi d^2/8t$.

402. Determine the initial tension that would be set up by the cooling of a rivet from below the softening temperature (600° F.) to room temperature (70° F.) if the rivet can stretch under stress but the plates gripped cannot be compressed. Use grips of 1 in., 2 in., and 3 in. *Ans.* Stress exceeds yield point.

403. Connect a 6 × ⅜-in. plate directly to the face of a heavy column to resist 35,000 lb. of plate tension. Select size and number of rivets for *AISC* spec. No clip angles. *A*7 steel and *A*141 rivets. *Ans.* One solution is 4 ⅞-in. rivets.

404. A lap joint in a tank carries a stress of 2000 lb. per lineal in. The plates are ¼ in. thick. Find the spacing for ¾-in. rivets. Use *AISC* spec. *A*141 rivets. *Ans.* Rivets at 3¼-in. spacing.

405. Revise Problem 404 to allow for the changed conditions of a double butt strap joint with ¼-in. straps. *Ans.* Rivets at 4-in. spacing.

406. Revise the example *DP*3 for a 20 per cent reduction of load, shear, and moment. Use *AASHO* spec.

407. Design a column base for an 8*WF*48 section carrying a 160,000-lb. central load. Transfer 50 per cent of the load through the riveted detail with ¾-in. rivets. *AASHO* spec.

408. Design a column cap for the column of Problem 407 to seat a 20-in., 65.4-lb. I-beam whose end reaction is 39,000 lb. Turn the web of the column parallel to the web of the beam. *Ans.* Use 6 × 3½ × ½-in. angles.

409. Design a column splice between a 10*WF*66 section and a 12*WF*92 section to transfer 250,000 lb. Splice plates must transfer 25 per cent of the load. Choose spec.

410. Revise Problem 409 to allow for a shear of 30,000 lb. and a bending moment of 500,000 in-lb. (at the splice) acting simultaneously with the direct load.

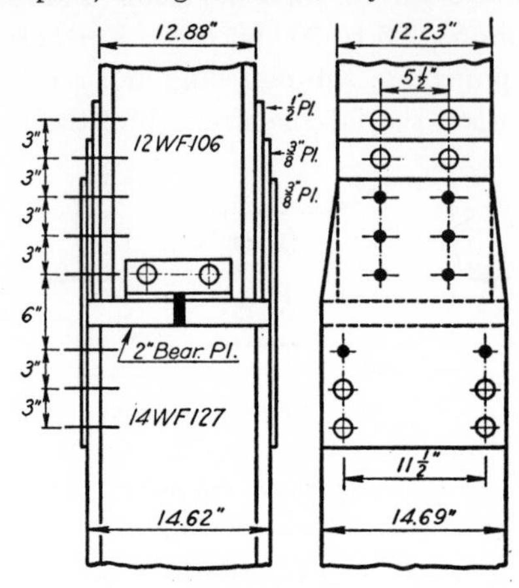

PROBLEM 411.

411. Check the column-splice detail illustrated to find what percentage of the total allowable column load could be transferred by the riveted detail. This is a typical column splice arranged with a 2-in. bearing plate which actually transfers nearly all of the load. Use ⅞-in. rivets, *AISC* and *A*7 steel. Neglect L/r factor and use 17,000 psi for allowable compression. First, assume that the fill plates bear on the 2-in. plate, and then decide whether this is necessary or desirable.

Ans. 20 per cent by splice plates and 34 per cent through bearing of fill plates.

412. Design a splice between a 12*WF*99 column section and a 14*WF*127 column section to transfer 70 per cent of the value in direct compression (short column), 35 per cent of the value in flexure, and 25 per cent of the shear value (web) of the smaller section. *AISC* spec., *A*36 steel, and *A*141 rivets.

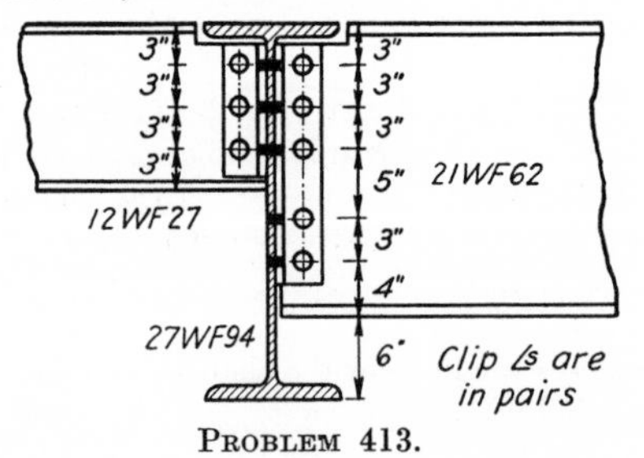

PROBLEM 413.

413. Determine the allowable end reaction of each beam connection shown. Consider the fact that these reactions may occur separately or together. Use ⅞-in. rivets, *AISC* spec. Use *A*7 steel and *A*141 rivets. Do not allow for eccentricity of the rivets through the beam webs. *Ans.* 25 kips and 70 kips.

414. Design a riveted connection to attach two $5 \times 3 \times \frac{3}{8}$-in. angles by the long legs on opposite sides of a $\frac{5}{16}$-in. gusset plate for the net value of the angles in tension. Revise the design to allow for eccentricity. Use $\frac{3}{4}$-in. rivets and *AASHO* Spec. 202.

415. Design a riveted connection to attach two $4 \times 4 \times \frac{7}{16}$-in. angles on opposite sides of a $\frac{3}{8}$-in. gusset plate for the net value of the angles in tension. Revise the design to allow for eccentricity. Use $\frac{7}{8}$-in. rivets and *AISC* spec. for low elastic limit materials.

Ans. 9 rivets at 3-in. spacing are acceptable.

416. Revise the example *DP*5 for $5 \times 3 \times \frac{1}{2}$-in. angles and $\frac{5}{16}$-in. gussets.

417. Revise the example *DP*5 for $6 \times 4 \times \frac{9}{16}$-in. angles and $\frac{7}{16}$-in. gussets and choose specifications.

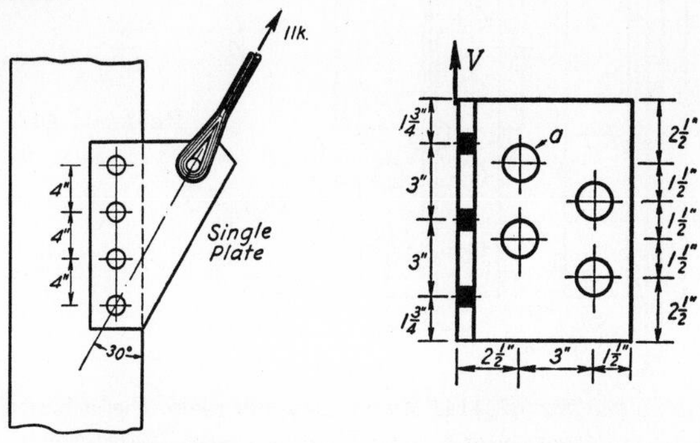

PROBLEM 418. PROBLEM 422.

418. Find the size of rivet necessary to resist a pull of 11,000 lb. in the tie rod for the detail illustrated. Allow 15,000 psi for rivet shear which controls the design.

Ans. $\frac{5}{8}$-in. rivets.

419. Extend the rivet line of Problem 418 upward to hold a total of 6 rivets at 4-in. spacing. Find the allowable rod stress for $\frac{3}{4}$-in. rivets at 20,000 psi for single shear.

Ans. 30 kips.

420. Revise the example *DP*6 for $5 \times 3 \times \frac{3}{8}$-in. angles and *AASHO* spec.

421. Revise the example *DP*6 for $6 \times 4 \times \frac{3}{4}$-in. angles.

422. Find the allowable shear V for the connection shown in order to stress the extreme rivet a to its value of 15,000 psi (1-in. rivets) in double shear. This stress is assumed to control the design. *Ans.* $V = 33$ kips.

423. Revise the example *DP*7 for a load of 180,000 lb. at 10 in. from the edge of the column.

424. Revise the example *DP*7 for a load of 298,000 lb. and *A*195 $\frac{7}{8}$-in. rivets.

425. Revise example *DP*8 for a 6×4-in. angle and a load of 15,000 lb. Limit the seat angle to 12 in. long.

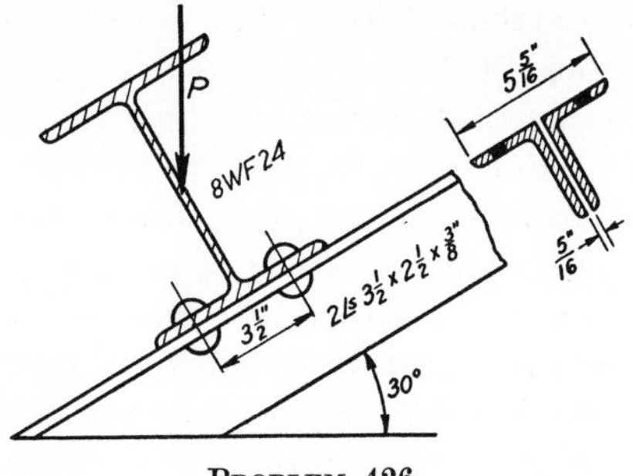

PROBLEM 426.

426. Determine the rivet size required by a vertical load P of 25,000 lb., acting through the center of gravity of the purlin section, that will stress the two upper rivets to the allowable stress in tension. Assume the rivet gage, or 3.5 in., to equal the lever arm for computing the rivet tension. Restrict shear and tension as specified in the *AISC* code (Spec. 21). Use *A*141 rivets. *Ans.* ¾ in.

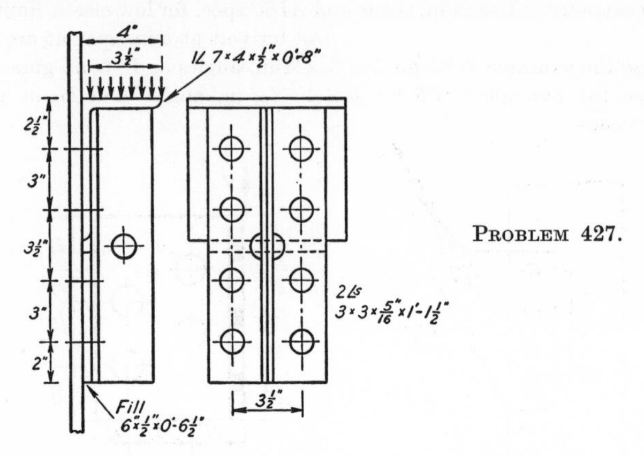

PROBLEM 427.

427. Determine the size of *A*141 rivets that will make the stiffened bracket shown carry a 40,000-lb. end reaction of a beam, distributed uniformly over 3½ in. Restrict shear and tension as specified in the *AISC* code. (Spec. 21.) Compare your answer with the *AISC* table of Stiffened Beam Seats.

428. Revise the design of the stiffened bracket of Problem 427 in any desirable manner to increase its capacity to 50,000 lb. of vertical load.

429. Revise *DP*9*a* and *DP*9*b* to meet *AASHO* code requirements.

430. Revise *DP*10 for a pull of 40,000 lb. in a plate 12 × ⅝ in. Choose materials and specifications.

HIGH-STRENGTH BOLTS

96. Bolts Used to Replace Rivets. Bolts may be used in place of rivets under most specifications, but they may be given changed working stresses. Low carbon bolts designated as *A*307, used in punched holes, are given lower allowable values in both shear and tension than power driven rivets of *A*141 steel. Such bolts are used mainly for light structures. Two qualities of high strength bolts, *ASTM A*325 and *A*354 Grade *BC*, are widely used and are often more economical than rivets. These bolts provide allowable stresses respectively of 40,000 and 50,000 psi for tension (on gross section) by *AISC* specifications. All *A*325 and *A*354 bolts shall be tightened to a bolt tension about 90 per cent of their elastic limit capacity as specified by the American Society for Testing Materials. Tightening shall be done by properly calibrated wrenches (Fig. 84) or by a specified ½ to ¾ turn of the nut after full (snug) bearing is obtained. A hardened washer is used under the nut or head when it is turned by a calibrated wrench. Hardened washers are not required, however, if the bolts are tightened by the "turn-of-nut" method. A beveled washer is used if the face on which the bolt head or nut bears has a slope of more than 1 to 20 with respect to a plane perpendicular to the axis of the bolt.

Special alloy steel bolts *A*409 are available where exceptional strength is needed. These bolts have tensile, shear and bearing strengths nearly 50 per cent greater than *A*325 bolts.

Courtesy Peter Kiewit Son's Co.

FIG. 84. IMPACT WRENCH AND TORQUE WRENCH FOR CONTROLLING BOLT TENSION.

Friction Versus Bearing Connections. Bolted joints may be designed to act as friction joints for which the initial slip is so small that the bolts do not come into bearing on the sides of the holes. High strength bolt steels, *ASTM A*325 and *A*354, may be used in this manner when tightened in tension to at least 90 per cent of the elastic limit tension of the bolt material. The tests upon which specifications for allowable stresses for such friction-type joints were made used bolts $\frac{1}{16}$ in. smaller than the holes. When such bolted joints are properly tightened the plates develop a high frictional resistance so that sufficient slip to bring the bolts into bearing on the plates does not occur under working loads. Tests have shown that the first major slip of a joint made with high strength bolts will occur at a calculated bolt shear of about 50 per cent of the actual bolt tension. When the calculated shear is reduced to 33 per cent of the bolt tension any significant slip will be eliminated. Hence, for *A*325 bolts the allowable bolt shear for a friction-type connection of 15,000 psi requires a bolt tension of 45,000 psi, which is only 70 per cent of the elastic limit strength of *A*325 steel, while the required initial tension is 90 per cent. No damage to bolts or joints occurs if bolts are overtensioned by turning the nuts up $1\frac{1}{2}$ turns although only $\frac{3}{4}$ turn is required to develop the full elastic limit stress of a typical bolt.

Threads at Shear Planes. For friction-type joints it is not important whether a shear plane between the plates of the joint crosses the shank or the threads of the bolt because the bolt never acts in shear, only in tension. However, if the bolts are made nearly the same size as the holes and are tightened less fully, a slight slip can occur followed by bearing. In such a joint the resistance is greatly increased by selecting the length of bolt and of unthreaded shank so that threads are eliminated from all shear planes. The highest working stresses for bolt shear in Table 5 are applicable to bearing type connections when threading is excluded from the shear planes. This type of bolted construction is growing in use because of its economy. Increased allowable stresses for bearing of 1.35 times the elastic limit strength in tension of the plate material have encouraged the use of bolts in bearing with threading excluded from the shear planes.

TABLE 5

ALLOWABLE STRESSES FOR BOLTS ON GROSS AREA, *AISC* SPECIFICATIONS

Description	Tension (F_t)	Friction Connections Shear (F_v)	Bearing Connections Shear (F_v)
Threaded parts of *A*7 and other steels	$0.40F_y$		$0.30F_y$
*A*307 bolts	14,000 psi		10,000 psi
*A*325 bolts when threads are *not* excluded from shear planes	40,000	15,000 psi	15,000
*A*325 bolts when threads are excluded from shear planes	40,000	15,000	22,000
*A*354, Grade *BC*, bolts when threads are *not* excluded from shear planes	50,000	20,000	20,000
*A*354, Grade *BC*, when threads are excluded from shear planes	50,000	20,000	24,000

Fatigue Resistance of Bolted Joints. Generally the fatigue strength of a bolted joint is somewhat greater than that of a comparable riveted joint. Tests by Frank Baron and E. W. Larson on joints with bolts tensioned to only 78 per cent of their elastic limit showed a fatigue strength on the net section of the plate of 28,000 psi for 2,000,000 cycles of a zero to tension loading. This is comparable to well-riveted joints, but it is to be noted that rivets may fail under fatigue loading, while joints with high strength bolts develop no bolt failures from fatigue. This would be anticipated, because the joint is held together by friction rather than bolt shear.

TORQUE REQUIRED TO TENSION *A*-325 HIGH-STRENGTH BOLTS

Bolt Size	*Minimum Bolt Tension*	*Torque Required*
⅝	17,250 lb.	180 lb-ft.
¾	25,600 lb.	320 lb-ft.
⅞	32,400 lb.	470 lb-ft.
1.0	42,500 lb.	710 lb-ft.

Tension Loads on Bolts. High-strength bolts have been particularly effective in providing safe connections for tension members and members undergoing flexure. The amount of initial stress in the bolt has no particular influence upon the capacity of a bolt for ultimate tension resistance. Therefore, since their capacity to resist shear is dependent upon the amount of initial bolt tension, all bolts should be tensioned to about 90 per cent of their elastic limit capacity.

Structural Pins

97. Structural Uses for Pins. A pin functions essentially as a single rivet or bolt. Its size may range from the common cotter pin of $\frac{3}{8}$-in. or $\frac{1}{2}$-in. diameter, used for connecting strap-iron bars, to the railway bridge pin 12 in. or more in diameter. Fixed shafts or trunnions for bascule bridges are also pins, and they may be of much larger size. Pins of more than the 9-in. diameter have a 2-in. hole drilled longitudinally on the center line to aid in the relief of locked-up stresses. This hole may be used to carry a 2-in. bolt for clamping circular caps on the ends of the pin to take the place of large lock nuts.

Building Structures. Light diagonals can often be connected to column or beam flanges by pins, thus permitting the use of tie rods at less expense than diagonal angle bracing. An end clevis, as shown in Fig. 85, may be

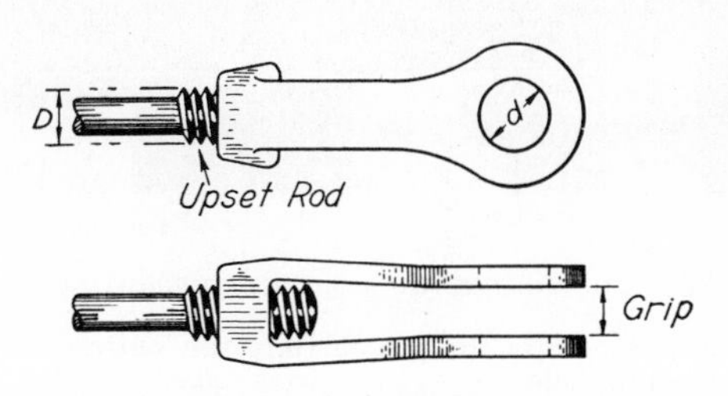

Fig. 85. Clevis.

used for such connections. Pin-connected tension rods, with adjustable turnbuckles to introduce initial tension, form excellent diagonals for water towers, elevated bins, etc. Hinged arches are used for coliseums and for other large open buildings. Since a pin is considered to be a *point of zero moment*, the introduction of each pin simplifies the analysis of an indeterminate structure.

Bridge Structures. In light bridge trusses it is permissible to use pin-connected tie rods for diagonal bracing, although angle bracing is usually specified for stiffness. End pins and end rollers are provided in all except the smallest bridge trusses to allow for expansion and to permit the end rotation that accompanies deflection. Viaduct columns, as shown by Fig. 86; may be pin connected at both top and bottom to provide for the *expansion of great lengths of roadway.* Suspension bridge towers have even been hinged at the base (requiring very large pins) to provide for change in length of the straight back-stay cables under stress. Perhaps, however, the most extensive use for pins in bridge structures has been for large pin-connected railway truss bridges where a pin occurs at each panel point of each chord. The advantages of using pins are the reduction of secondary stresses that

Courtesy C. M. St. P. & P. R.R. Co.

FIG. 86. PIN CONNECTED COLUMN SUPPORTING GIRDER.

Observe in the photograph the pin casting, the pin nut, girder stiffeners, floor stringers, and open drain hole.

should accompany freedom of pin rotation and the common use of heat treated eye bars of high strength as tension members. At present, eye bars and pin connections are being used only on an occasional truss of long span where the disadvantages of pin connections are overbalanced by the possible reduction in dead load.

PIN DESIGN

98. Factors in Pin Design. The design of a pin follows essentially the same procedure as the design of a rivet. The process will be simplified if we think of a pin as a single large rivet. *Shear*, *bearing*, and *flexure* must be investigated. However, there is no initial tension.

Shear may determine the diameter of the pin, and since the pin is a very important part of the structure, we should investigate the shear properly by use of the beam-shear formula. The pin is, in fact, a deep beam for which the shear stress is often critical. For a circular section this formula reduces to

$$\frac{VQ}{Ib} = \frac{4}{3}\frac{V}{A} = \frac{16V}{3\pi d^2} \geq F_v. \tag{22}$$

The unit shear allowance for pins (F_v) is usually found to be the same as the shear value permitted for beams, i.e., $0.40F_y$.

Bearing need not be treated any differently for pins than for rivets, although the allowable unit bearing value may be changed. It is usually possible to increase the bearing area by riveting or welding extra pin plates to the end of the member instead of increasing the diameter of the pin. *Bearing on eye bars determines the minimum pin diameter* which becomes the width of the widest bar (b) times the ratio of the allowable stress in tension to the allowable stress in bearing, that is, $d = b(F_t/F_p)$. Bridge specifications further limit the minimum pin diameter to $\frac{8}{10}$ of the width of the widest bar attached to it. Compare with *AISC* Spec. 38. Allowable bearing values between rocker pins and cast steel rockers should be reduced to resist wear. This reduction is 50 per cent in bridge specifications.

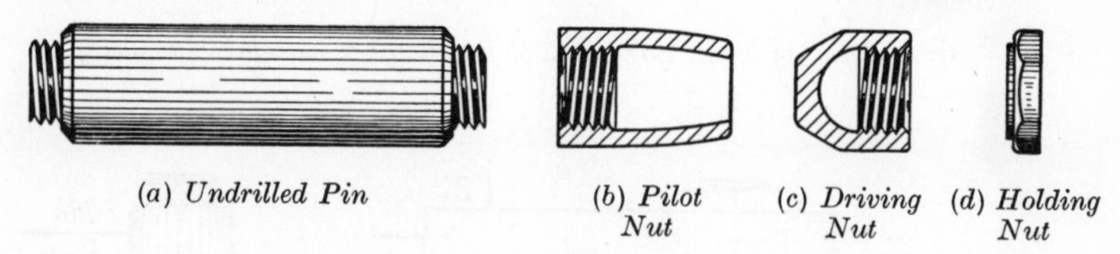

(*a*) *Undrilled Pin* (*b*) *Pilot Nut* (*c*) *Driving Nut* (*d*) *Holding Nut*

FIG. 87. LARGE DIAMETER PIN AND NUTS.

Flexure is more serious in pins than in rivets or bolts, since the bearing plates on a pin are separated to permit clearance for free rotation. If two built-up riveted members bear on a pin, the adjacent faces of these two members may have to be separated as much as $1\frac{5}{8}$ in. This will be the case if the 1-inch rivet heads are not flattened or countersunk and are separated the required distance of $\frac{1}{4}$ in. Evidently, the bending moment in the pin will be increased greatly by such separation of members and the pin diameter may therefore be controlled by flexure. The allowable flexural stress in a pin is usually 50 per cent greater than the allowable tension in a truss member. The facts that (1) secondary stresses do not occur in pins, (2) large pins (over 7 in.) are forged and annealed, and (3) there are fewer possibilities of introducing fabrication and erection stresses in pins than in truss members are justifications for a higher working stress. For the purpose of computing bending moments, it is usual to assume that each plate or united group of plates which bears on the pin will produce a concentrated bearing load.

The moment of inertia of a circular area is $\pi r^4/4$ or $0.049d^4$. The section modulus for a cylindrical pin becomes $I/c = 0.049d^2 \div d/2 = 0.098d^3$. Hence, for a circular pin, we may write by use of the flexure formula

$$d = \sqrt[3]{\frac{M}{0.1F_b}} = \sqrt[3]{\frac{10M}{F_b}}. \tag{23}$$

DP11. *Design a pin to connect two pairs of parallel eye bars of size 8″ × 2″. The eye bars of a single member are spaced at least 4″ apart and those of adjacent members at least ⅛″ apart. Allowable pin shear is 13,500 psi and bearing is 27,000 psi.*

Minimum Pin Diameter:

Minimum diameter is ¾ of the width of the widest bar or 6″.

Bar tension. $8 \times 2.0 \times 18{,}000 = 288{,}000\#$.

Bearing unit stress. $288{,}000 \div 6 \times 2.0 = 24{,}000$ psi ($<27{,}000$).

Average shear stress. $288{,}000 \div (\pi \times 6^2/4) = 10{,}200$ psi.

Max. shear stress [equation (22)] = 1.33 × 10,200 = 13,600 psi. This unit shear is slightly greater than the specification stress of 13,500 psi but is acceptable.

Arrangement of bars. Bars must be alternated to maintain symmetry.

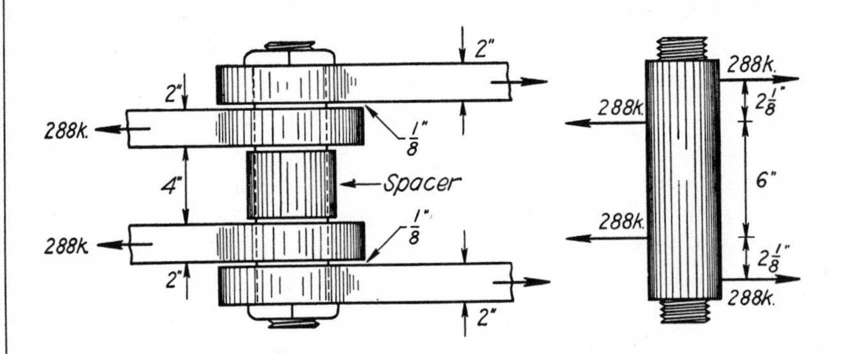

Bending moment. $M = 288{,}000 \times 2.125 = 613{,}000''\#$.

Diameter for flexure. $d = \sqrt[3]{\dfrac{613{,}000}{0.1 \times 27{,}000}} = 6.1''$ [*Equation 23.*]

Remarks: *The minimum pin diameter of 6″ would be adequate for shear and bearing but it must be increased to 6¼″ for flexure.*

Specification: *By AASHO specifications it is required that the pin be eight-tenths of the width of the widest bar attached thereto. To meet this specification a pin of 6½-in. diameter would be required. The same requirement is covered by AREA specifications.*

99. Chain-Link Pin. Suspension bridges may be supported either by parallel wire cables, by wire rope strands, or by chain-link cables. The latter are used for spans of medium length. Such chain links are connected by pins that are subject to bearing, shear, and flexural stresses.

EXAMPLE *DP*11. The example *DP*11 illustrates the design of a pin to develop the strength of a pair of 8-in. by 2-in. eye bars. Two procedures are always possible in such design problems. (1) We can calculate the actual stresses for an assumed size of pin and compare them with the allowable stresses, thus determining whether a revision of size is necessary. This is the procedure used in the example *DP*11 for checking the minimum pin diameter for shearing and bearing stresses. (2) We can use the allowable unit stresses in bearing, shear, and flexure to determine the pin size to resist each stress, and then we must choose the largest pin required by any type of stress. This method is used to select the pin diameter for flexure in the example *DP*11. Some designers prefer the first procedure and some prefer the second. The author usually attempts to select any structural member or part according to his best judgment as to the probable controlling stress. Then this tentative design is checked to determine its resistance to the other stresses involved. A revision of the initial cross-section is usually required.

Capacity to Resist Load. A third procedure in design is to determine the capacity of a part tentatively selected and to compare it with the applied load. *This seems the least convenient procedure of all.* It would be exemplified by the following calculation relative to the problem *DP*11. These calculations are for a 6-in. pin.

$$\text{Bearing resistance} = 27{,}000 \times 6 \times 2 = 324{,}000 \text{ lb.}$$

$$\text{Shearing resistance} = 13{,}500 \times 0.75 \times \pi \times 6^2/4 = 287{,}000 \text{ lb.}$$

$$\text{Flexural resistance} = 0.1 \times 6^2 \times 27{,}000/2.125 = 274{,}000 \text{ lb.}$$

Since the load is 288,000 lb. per bar, it is evident that the 6-in. pin is adequate for bearing and shear resistance but not for flexure.

PROBLEMS

431. Revise Problem 403 for use of *A*325 bolts for a bearing-type connection with threads excluded from the shear planes. *Ans.* 3 ⅞-in. bolts.

432. Revise Problem 404 for use of *A*325 bolts for a bearing-type connection with threads not excluded from the shear planes. *A*7 steel plates.

Ans. ¾-in. bolts at 3¼ in.

433. Revise Problem 418 for use of *A*354 bolts and *A*36 steel for a bearing-type connection with threads excluded from the shear planes. *Ans.* ½-in. bolts.

434. Use bolts chosen from *AISC* specifications to increase the capacity of the bracket seat of Problem 427 from 40,000 to 55,000 lb.

435. Determine whether ⅞-in. *A*325 bolts could be used in the outer rows of holes for the column connection of *DS*7 for a bearing type connection if threads are excluded from the shear planes. The objective is to reduce the four lines of rivets to two lines of bolts for economy.

436. Substitute ¾-in. *A*354 bolts for rivets in the four lines through the column flange in *DS*7. Determine the maximum value of the load if a bearing type connection is permitted but threads are not excluded from the shear planes. *Ans.* $P = 225$ kips.

437. Design a chain-link pin to connect two pairs of parallel eye bars of size 6 in. by 1¾ in. Other details and working stresses are obtained from *DP*11.

438. Revise $DP11$ for allowable stresses of $0.90F_y$ in flexure and bearing and $0.40F_y$ for the maximum shear on a circular section. Let the allowable eye-bar tension be $0.60F_y$ on section of bar. $F_y = 40{,}000$ psi.

100. Yielding as a Basis for Design. The structural engineer cannot set a fixed rule as to whether all structural parts should be designed for normal elastic conditions or for conditions near failure. It seems reasonably clear that the proper criterion is whether the structural part adjusts its action to become *relatively stronger* or *relatively weaker* as the yield point is reached. If the structural part becomes relatively weaker, plastic conditions *should* be considered; if it becomes relatively stronger, plastic conditions *may* be used with a proper factor of safety, and a conservative design for static loads will be obtained. This criterion of design may be illustrated by a comparison of tension and compression members. Tension members become relatively stronger beyond the yield point (stress concentrations disappear and the tensile strength increases); compression members become relatively weaker and buckle. We are always willing to stress tension members more heavily than compression members, and, as working stresses have been raised, allowable tension stresses have been increased more rapidly than allowable column stresses.

Riveted and bolted joints seem to fall into the category of structural parts that become relatively stronger as the yield point is passed. Shear variations between rivets reduce or disappear whether caused by plate distortion, member eccentricity, or merely by irregularities in fabrication. A bracket connection undergoes a shift in the neutral axis that increases its moment resistance. Rivets highly stressed in tension stretch and pass their loads on to rivets of lower stress. Applied tension, which weakens a shear rivet near failure, may be taken into consideration by use of a combined stress. With these points in review, we reach the conclusion that conditions beyond yield may properly and consistently be used to direct the design of riveted or bolted joints *acting under static loading*.

Reversal, Fatigue, and Brittle Fracture. The study of plasticity as a basis for design must be limited to members and details that do not undergo reversal or fatigue. Reversal is a very severe test upon a riveted joint in that a slight slip repeated in two directions may eventually wear the joint out and loosen all the rivets. Reversal is covered in most specifications by a reduction of working stresses or by an increase of the effective design loading. Fatigue is important where the number of repetitions approaches two million. Both in the design of members and in the design of joints, stress concentrations as found by the theory of elasticity should govern the design of parts subjected to fatigue loading. The reason is that a fatigue crack can develop with applied stresses below the elastic limit. Under these conditions the stress-leveling influence of plastic deformation is inoperative.

Brittle fracture has also occurred occasionally under static loading. One embrittling factor usually present is winter temperature. Another is triaxiality of tensile stress which may be produced by internal corners, flaws, residual stresses from welding, straightening, etc. When Charpy or other tests on the steel to be used show less than full, normal ductility at the minimum operating temperature, the assumptions of design should be reviewed. In particular, the neglect of stress concentrations on rivets or around holes is dangerous in any case where brittle fracture might occur. And it should be recognized that brittle fracture will often propagate itself into plates of relatively low stress once it is initiated by a severe condition of stress concentration and temperature. Such cracks travel at several thousand feet per minute and have produced catastrophic fractures of ships, tanks, steel stacks, girder bridges, and other types of plate structures. Brittle fracture and fatigue must be eliminated as possibilities before full advantage can be taken of the economy of design inherent in plastic action of the structure and its connections. These matters will receive further consideration in Chapter 10.

CHAPTER 5

WELDED CONNECTIONS

101. Arc Welding Process. Structural welding may be either gas welding or electric arc welding. However, the electric arc process is now so widely used that its name has become almost synonymous with the term *structural welding*. The basic procedure in electric arc welding is very simple. Electric current, usually direct current, provides the welding heat through the medium of an electric arc. One terminal of the direct current generator is connected to the base metal and the other terminal is connected to the electrode or welding rod through an insulated electrode clamp or holder which the welder grips in his hand. (See Fig. 88.) Depending upon the choice of

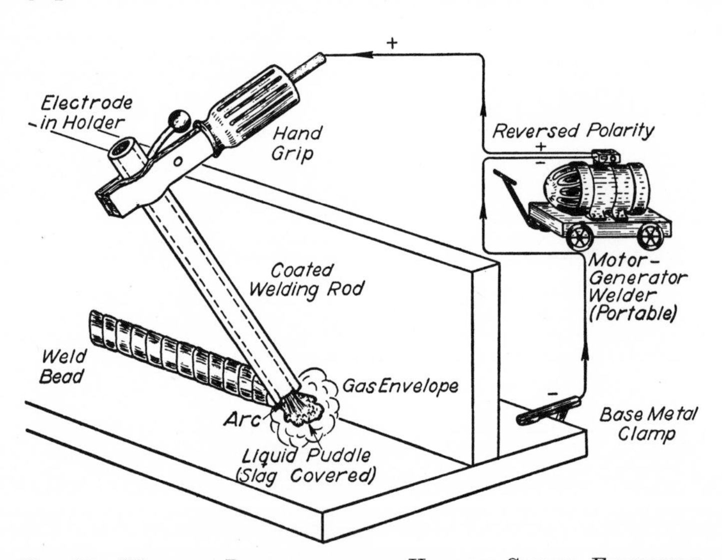

FIG. 88. WELDING PROCEDURE WITH HEAVILY COATED ELECTRODE.

type of electrode and other factors, the positive terminal of the generator may be attached either to the base metal or to the electrode, producing respectively *straight* or *reversed polarity*. The type of work to be done, the required welding speed, the penetration of the weld metal into the base metal, and the physical characteristics of the weld determine the choice of such factors as size of electrode, type of electrode coating, voltage, and current. These matters are usually left to the welder or to the welding superintendent. The designer is interested primarily in the results obtained rather than in the devices used to obtain them.

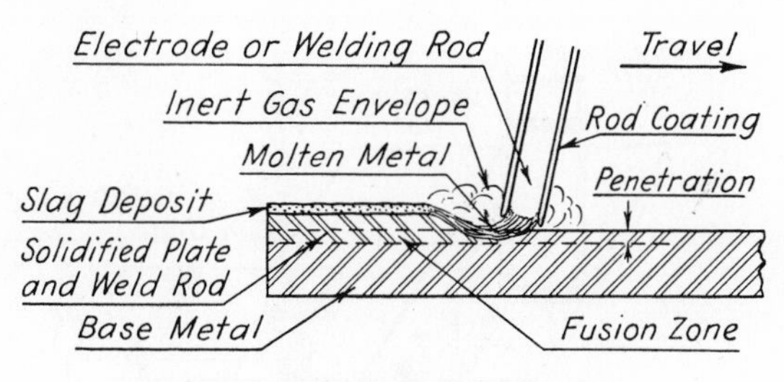

Fig. 89. The Welding Process.

As indicated by Fig. 88 and Fig. 89, the weld rod must be fed into the weld, but the weld is really composed of a mixture of the base metal and the electrode metal. Since the temperature of the arc is 6500° F., it is evident that the weld can be made to penetrate a considerable distance into the base metal—this *penetration* being controlled by the current consumed. Incidentally, the electrode metal is carried across the arc in minute droplets or as a metallic vapor. This metal acquires a velocity that is used by the welder to penetrate the base metal and to stick the weld metal in position when he is doing *overhead welding*. Such welds are slower to produce and more expensive, but they are as strong as ordinary welds. Flat welds may be made by automatic machines, but most structural welding is so placed that it must be done by hand. The rod coating fuses, gives off an inert gas and floats on top of the weld. The gas and slag protect liquid weld metal from the atmosphere which is desirable because oxygen and nitrogen gas act to embrittle the weld metal.

Arrangement of Structural Welds

102. Kinds of Welds. Besides overhead welds mentioned in the paragraph above, there are *flat*, *horizontal*, and *vertical welds*. These are all illustrated in the composite picture, Fig. 90. For economy we would choose the flat weld first, the horizontal weld second, the vertical weld third, and the overhead weld last. Good design will avoid overhead welding in almost all instances.

Butt and Fillet Welds. Another distinction between types of welds refers to fillet welds and butt welds. Specifications 39 and 51 define these terms. Several of each are shown in Fig. 90. A butt weld may be acting only in direct tension or compression while a fillet weld, being placed on the side or edge of the base metal, is undergoing shear as well as tension or compression and usually flexure besides. Structural fillet welds are nearly all of one type or shape, since they are usually placed in a right angle formed

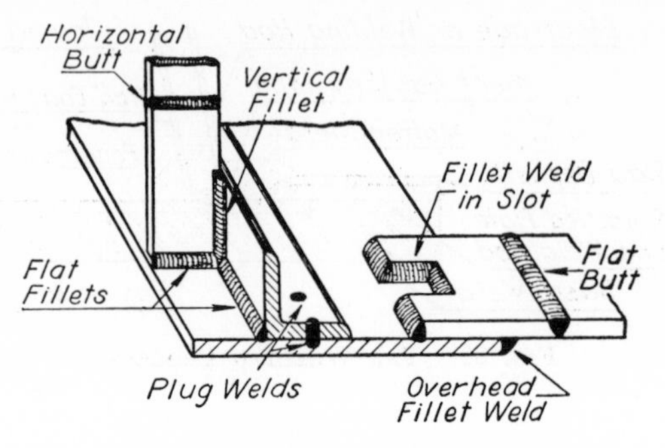

FIG. 90. TYPES AND POSITIONS OF WELDS.

by two plates or two structural members. The double tee shown in Fig. 91 is actually formed by two fillet welds. The other welds shown in Fig. 91 are butt welds. The single vee is produced by burning the edge of the plates away with a torch after which the weld bead is placed in one or more passes. For thicker plates the volume of weld metal becomes too great for the use of a single vee, and it is progressively reduced by changing to the single *U*, the double vee, and the double *U*. Each of these joints can now be prepared for welding largely by use of an automatic torch, but, of course, the single vee is prepared most simply and cheaply.

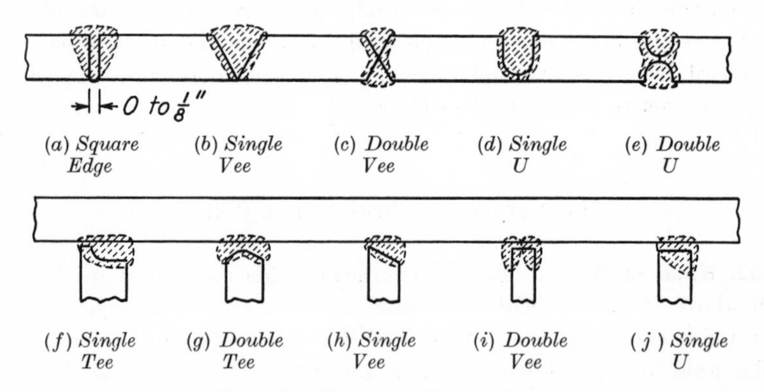

FIG. 91. KINDS OF BUTT WELDS.

103. Direct Structural Connections. Although the butt weld shows consistently greater strength than the fillet weld, structural connections are produced largely by fillet welding. Even direct connections of structural shapes, as illustrated by Fig. 93, are most likely to be produced by the use of fillets, since this saves the operation of scarfing or vee-ing the ends of the members. Direct connections, such as those of Fig. 93, are not particularly common in structural frames. The butting of sections directly together, as in Fig. 93, necessitates the cutting of the members to *exact length* and presupposes that the other parts of the frame will be fitted together so perfectly that the length of each member will be found to be exact in the field. Field engineers know that this is seldom true even in riveted structures where it is common practice to pull the structure together with *drift pins*. A direct connection can sometimes be used at one end of a beam and the necessary "play" can be provided at the other end by the use of extension plates or other devices.

Courtesy Bethlehem Steel Co.

Fig. 92. Erection of a Welded Frame.

104. Beam Connections Permitting Adjustment of Length. The connections of Fig. 94 are for attaching beams to columns by resting the beams on welded seats. The actual connection of the beam to the seat is by two location bolts, but the seat is structurally welded to the column to resist the end reaction of the beam. If desired, the bolt holes can be slotted in one member for easy alignment of the columns, and the beams can be field welded to the brackets after alignment. This would increase the stiffness of these connections greatly.

105. Column Splices and Bases. A welded column splice, like a riveted splice, is not expected to be designed for the full compressive value of the member. A large part of the compression should be transferred by *direct bearing*. (Spec. 44.) Where all of the stress could be transferred by direct

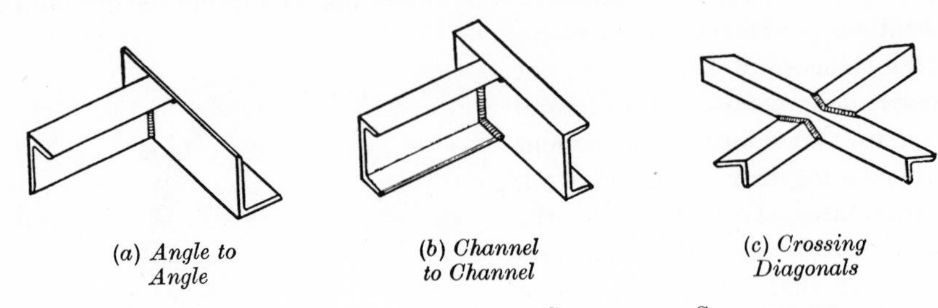

(*a*) *Angle to Angle* (*b*) *Channel to Channel* (*c*) *Crossing Diagonals*

FIG. 93. DIRECT CONNECTIONS OF STRUCTURAL SECTIONS BY WELDING.

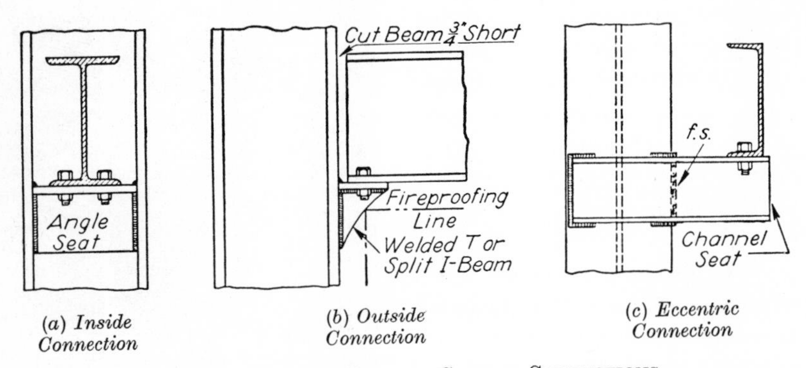

(*a*) *Inside Connection* (*b*) *Outside Connection* (*c*) *Eccentric Connection*

FIG. 94. WELDED BEAM-TO-COLUMN CONNECTIONS.

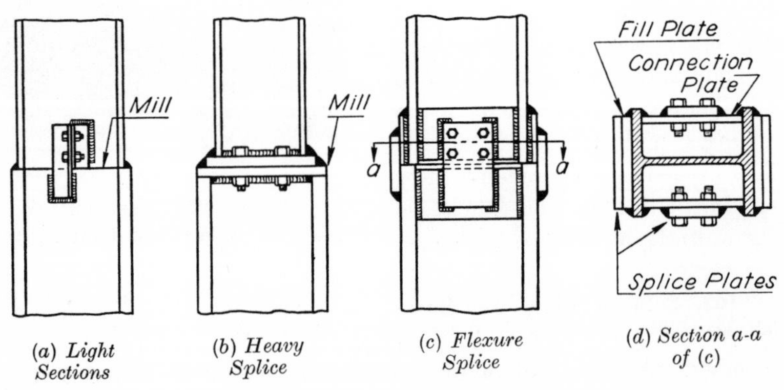

(*a*) *Light Sections* (*b*) *Heavy Splice* (*c*) *Flexure Splice* (*d*) *Section a-a of* (*c*)

FIG. 95. WELDED COLUMN SPLICES.

bearing of milled ends, the requirements of a satisfactory splice are a pair of connection angles for aligning the columns during erection and sufficient weld to produce a stiff connection. As a rule of thumb for producing adequate stiffness, the welds may be designed to transfer 25 per cent of the direct column load. This type of connection is illustrated in Fig. 95(*a*).

In many splices the entire load cannot be transferred by bearing of the upper section upon the lower one. In such instances there is use for horizontal bearing plates as shown in Fig. 95(*b*). A column that undergoes severe flexure must be spliced to resist tension as well as compression. Either of the splices of Fig. 95(*a*) or (*b*) could be designed to resist some flexure, but Fig. 95(*c*) shows a splice that will resist heavy flexural moments about *either axis* of the column. By care in choosing the welds that are to be produced in the field, it is possible to attach each splice plate to one member or the other in the shop. Loose plates are always to be avoided by preference.

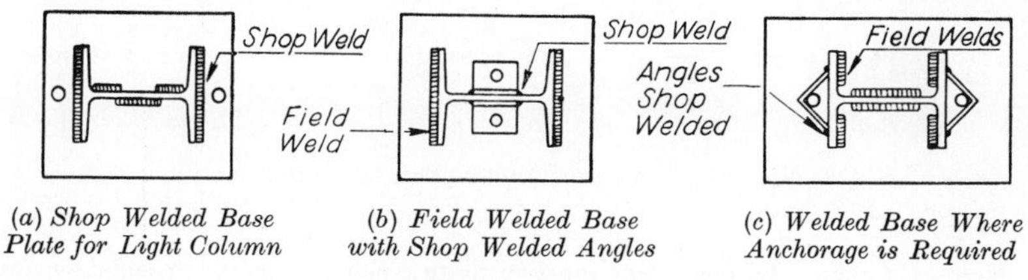

(*a*) *Shop Welded Base Plate for Light Column* (*b*) *Field Welded Base with Shop Welded Angles* (*c*) *Welded Base Where Anchorage is Required*

FIG. 96. WELDED COLUMN BASES.

Column Bases. The cheapest column base for light construction is a welded plate of the type shown in Fig. 96(*a*). Such rolled plates may become damaged in shipment and would not then present a satisfactory flat bearing surface for heavy loads. If *loose base plates* (usually milled for bearing) are desired for this reason, a connection such as Fig. 96(*b*) may be used where clip angles are shop welded to the column but where the column is welded to the base plate after erection in the field. The base plate may or may not have additional bolts anchoring it to the foundation. The detail Fig. 96(*c*) provides moment resistance.

STRESS ANALYSIS OF WELDS

106. Analysis of Stresses in Welds.[1] The actual analysis of internal stresses in unsymmetrical welds would be a very complicated procedure involving the mathematical theory of elasticity. However, for purposes of design, much simpler analyses based upon the usual direct stress formula $f = P/A$, the flexure formula $f = Mc/I$, the torsion formula $f_v = Tr/J$, and the beam-shear formula $f_v = VQ/It$ are considered adequate.

[1] Also see C. H. Jennings, *Welding design*, Transactions ASME, Oct., 1936, pp. 497–509.

Use of the Direct Stress Formula P/A. The assumption is made for all butt welds under direct tension or compression that the unit stress in the weld is equal to the total load divided by the net effective area, which is the length of the weld times the minimum or *throat* dimension. Although variation in the amount of heat applied, or variation in rate of cooling because of change of thickness of the metal may partially invalidate this assumption, it is useful in the analysis of a large majority of direct stress welds. *Ductility of the weld* will permit equalization of such stresses before failure.

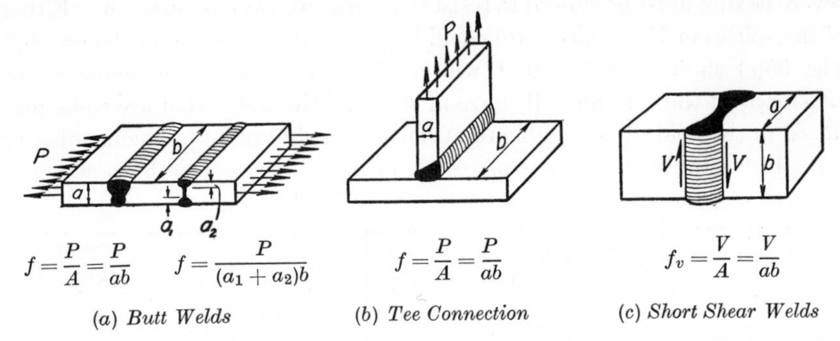

$f = \frac{P}{A} = \frac{P}{ab}$ $f = \frac{P}{(a_1 + a_2)b}$ $f = \frac{P}{A} = \frac{P}{ab}$ $f_v = \frac{V}{A} = \frac{V}{ab}$

(*a*) *Butt Welds* (*b*) *Tee Connection* (*c*) *Short Shear Welds*

FIG. 97. USE OF DIRECT STRESS FORMULA.

SPECIAL CASES. In Fig. 97(*a*) the two plate welds are placed in single-vee and double-vee notches. In either case the unit stress is the total load P divided by the net area, which is ab for the single-vee weld and $(a_1 + a_2)b$ for the double-vee weld. No allowance is made for the bulge of the weld in producing excess throat area, and, in fact, it would be better to avoid such a bulge entirely, since the result is a change of cross section which produces an inevitable concentration of stress. In work of high grade, such welds are often *chipped* or *ground* flat after welding. The expense precludes this refinement in structural work, but good welding will show little bulge beyond the plate. *Chipping* must not leave indentations or it will produce stress concentrations that weakens the weld.

There is no particular difference in the action of the weld of Fig. 97(*b*) from the similar weld in (*a*). Naturally, the weld is of a different shape since only one plate can be beveled. This is known as a *bevel groove* weld. Again the tension stress is taken as the load divided by the net area of the throat without allowance for any convexity of the weld surface.

The short shear welds of Fig. 97(*c*) are assumed to act under uniform shear. Hence, the unit shearing stress in this bar would be V/ab, or the shear divided by the net throat area. This is a double-vee weld where penetration joins the two parts. This arrangement is in contrast to the right-hand weld of Fig. 97(*a*) where the vees are not joined together. If the shear welds of Fig. 97(*c*) are considerably longer, the shear formula will need to be applied, as for the cross-section of a beam.

Direct Loads on Fillet Welds. The same relationship is used for computing the critical stresses in butt and fillet welds, that is, the total load is divided by the net area at the throat or smallest section of the weld. Evidently, for the standard 45-degree fillet of Fig. 98(*a*), the throat is 0.707

times the length of the side or leg of the weld. *The throat is the minimum dimension.* Convexity of the weld, as illustrated in Fig. 98, does not add

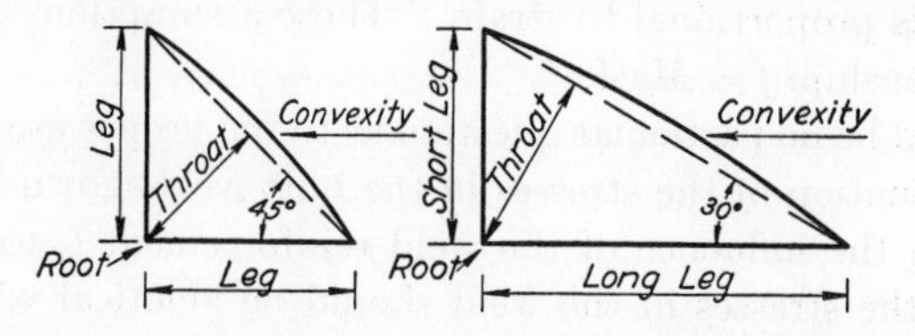

(a) *Standard Fillet Weld* (b) *Special Fillet Weld*

FIG. 98. THROAT OR CONTROLLING DIMENSION OF FILLET WELDS.

strength and, therefore, should be reduced to a minimum. Parts (*a*), (*b*), and (*c*) of Fig. 99 illustrate the usual action of fillet welds. Clearly, the lap welded plates in (*a*) undergo flexure and shear as well as direct stress, since the two loads P are eccentric by the amount of the thickness a, but the welds are probably no more heavily stressed than those in (*b*), where the resisting forces $P/2$ are also eccentric by the distance $a/2$ on each side of the plate. Such eccentricity does not produce crossflexure in (*c*), where the welds have been turned through 90 degrees with respect to the load. However, tests as well as theory indicate that the shear distribution along welds in line with the load is far from uniform, so that the common practice is to treat all welds of Fig. 99 as if they were stressed equally. The con-

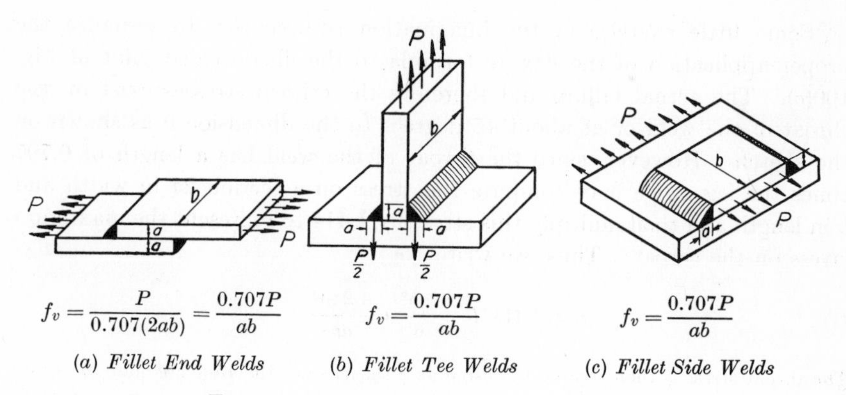

$$f_v = \frac{P}{0.707(2ab)} = \frac{0.707P}{ab} \qquad f_v = \frac{0.707P}{ab} \qquad f_v = \frac{0.707P}{ab}$$

(a) *Fillet End Welds* (b) *Fillet Tee Welds* (c) *Fillet Side Welds*

FIG. 99. DIRECT LOAD ON FILLET WELDS.

trolling stress in a fillet weld usually is *shear* instead of tension or compression. The three stresses may occur in about equal intensities, but since the allowable stress in shear is always less, it usually controls the design. Failure seems to occur by shear at 45 degrees along the throat section. It is common to assume that this shear is uniformly distributed over the area of the throat.

107. Use of the Flexure Formula. All calculations based upon the flexure formula partake of its *fundamental assumptions* which are : (1) that strain has a straight-line variation increasing from the neutral axis outward and (2) that stress is proportional to strain. These assumptions give rise to the common relationship, $f = Mc/I$.

There should be no particular question as to the proper use of this formula for the determination of the stresses in the butt weld shown in Fig. 100 (*a*). By discounting the influence of the weld reinforcement (surface bulge), we conclude that the stresses in the weld should be identical with the stresses in the plate, which are known to be represented quite closely (below the elastic limit) by the flexure formula.

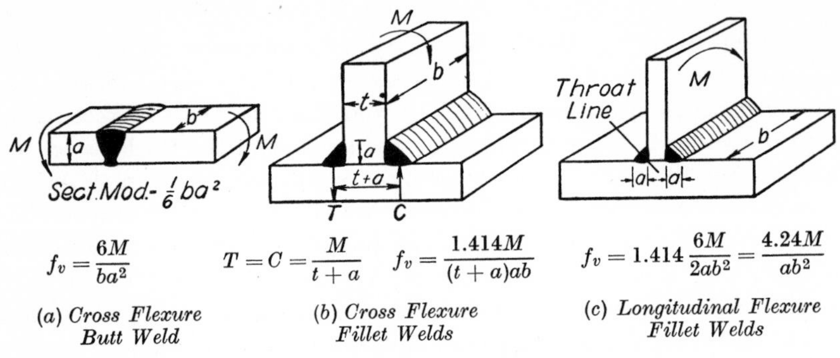

$f_v = \dfrac{6M}{ba^2}$ $\qquad T = C = \dfrac{M}{t+a} \quad f_v = \dfrac{1.414M}{(t+a)ab}$ $\qquad f_v = 1.414\dfrac{6M}{2ab^2} = \dfrac{4.24M}{ab^2}$

(*a*) *Cross Flexure Butt Weld* (*b*) *Cross Flexure Fillet Welds* (*c*) *Longitudinal Flexure Fillet Welds*

Fig. 100. Flexure Resisted by Structural Welds.

Some little exercise of the imagination is necessary to visualize the proper application of the flexure formula to the fillet welded joint of Fig. 100(*c*). The actual failure and therefore the critical stresses exist on the throat of the weld or at about 45 degrees to the dimension a as shown on the sketch. However, since the throat of the weld has a length of 0.707 times the leg a, we may compute the stress on a section $2a$ in width and b in length and then multiply this stress by 1.414 to represent the maximum stress on the throat. Thus, we write

$$f_v = 1.414M \div \frac{2ab^2}{6} = \frac{4.24M}{ab^2}. \tag{1}$$

The throat stress is then treated in design as a shear, since the 45-degree line of failure is indicative of a shear fracture and because the throat is a line of high shearing stress.

Discontinuous Cross Sections. The analysis for the tee connection of Fig. 100(*b*) might be based upon the flexure formula by use of the section modulus for a discontinuous cross section, but this would indicate a maximum stress at the toe of the weld (extreme fiber), while actually the maximum shearing stress as well as the maximum tensile stress seem to occur at the root or inside corner of the weld. Accordingly, the approximate method indicated by Fig. 100(*b*) is more used. This procedure is to represent the weld stresses as a couple with an arm equal to the clear distance between the welds plus the length of one leg, or $t + a$. The applied moment M on the length b, divided by the arm $t + a$, is the force on one weld for the length b. This force divided by the nominal area ab of the weld may be multiplied by 1.414 to represent the design shear on the throat. Hence, we write

$$f_v = 1.414 \frac{M}{t+a} \div ab = \frac{1.414M}{(t+a)ab}. \tag{2}$$

108. Use of the Torsion Formula. The flexure formula may be looked upon as a special case of the torsion formula in certain of its applications; that is, when the cross-section is long and narrow so that the polar moment of inertia reduces essentially to the moment of inertia. For instance, in Fig. 101(*c*) the torsional shearing stress is computed by the flexure formula, while, for the circular weld of Fig. 101(*a*) the torsion formula is used. It

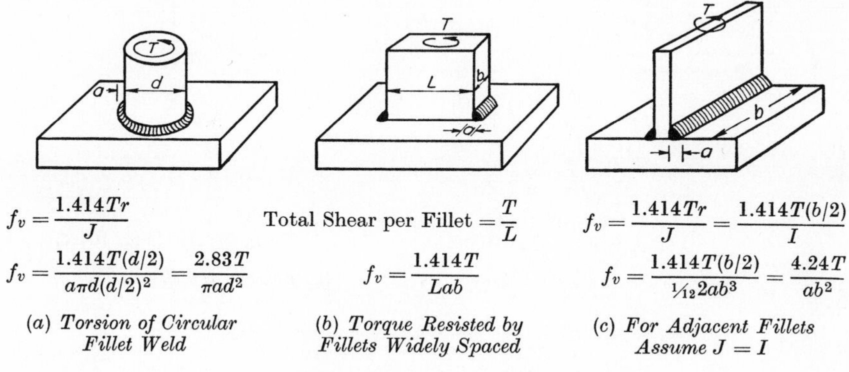

$$f_v = \frac{1.414Tr}{J}$$

$$f_v = \frac{1.414T(d/2)}{a\pi d(d/2)^2} = \frac{2.83T}{\pi a d^2}$$

(*a*) *Torsion of Circular Fillet Weld*

$$\text{Total Shear per Fillet} = \frac{T}{L}$$

$$f_v = \frac{1.414T}{Lab}$$

(*b*) *Torque Resisted by Fillets Widely Spaced*

$$f_v = \frac{1.414Tr}{J} = \frac{1.414T(b/2)}{I}$$

$$f_v = \frac{1.414T(b/2)}{\frac{1}{12}2ab^3} = \frac{4.24T}{ab^2}$$

(*c*) *For Adjacent Fillets Assume* $J = I$

FIG. 101. TORSION RESISTED BY FILLET WELDS.

should be realized that only in these two cases—that is, (1) the circular cross-section and (2) the long narrow cross-section—can torsional stresses be computed in a simple manner with reasonably accurate results. The torsion of square, rectangular, angle, channel, and I-beam cross-sections has undergone individual study, the results of which would have to be investigated for such special cases. The important thing to realize is that the ordinary torsion formula is exact *only for circular cross-sections* and that it becomes equivalent to the flexure formula for *long narrow cross-sections*.

109. Combined Stresses in Fillet Welds. Two studies of combined stresses will be made:

1. Where two load systems produce collinear stresses that add directly.
2. Where two load systems produce stresses 90 degrees apart that combine into a resultant.

Discontinuous Cross Sections. Short fillet welds widely separated may be analyzed with reasonable accuracy as illustrated by Fig. 101(*b*).

The classification (1) is always important, and the addition or subtraction of such stresses is always proper. A few cases are illustrated in Fig. 102. In (*a*) we find the common superposition of *direct stress and flexure.* The computed throat shears must add at one extreme fiber, the upper or tension fiber for the cantilever bar pictured. They are of opposite signs at the lower fiber. In (*b*) is illustrated a similar arrangement where *flexure and*

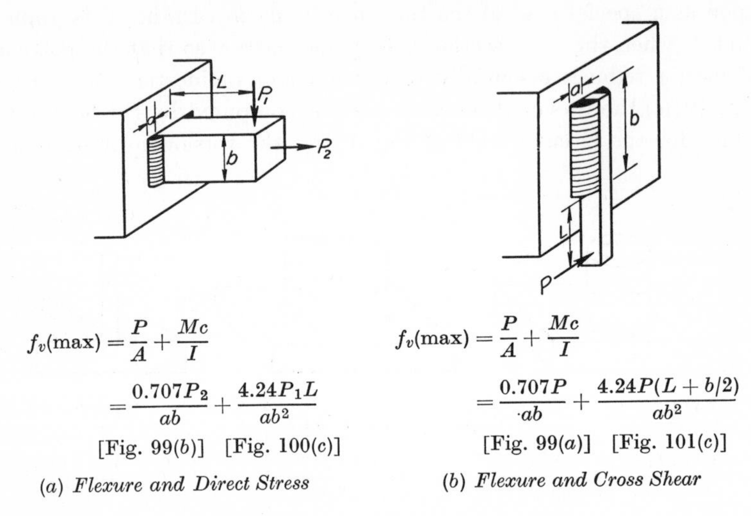

$$f_v(\text{max}) = \frac{P}{A} + \frac{Mc}{I}$$

$$= \frac{0.707P_2}{ab} + \frac{4.24P_1L}{ab^2}$$

[Fig. 99(*b*)] [Fig. 100(*c*)]

(*a*) *Flexure and Direct Stress*

$$f_v(\text{max}) = \frac{P}{A} + \frac{Mc}{I}$$

$$= \frac{0.707P}{ab} + \frac{4.24P(L + b/2)}{ab^2}$$

[Fig. 99(*a*)] [Fig. 101(*c*)]

(*b*) *Flexure and Cross Shear*

FIG. 102. COMBINED OR MAXIMUM SHEARS IN WELDS.

cross shear combine. The flexure partakes of the nature of torsion, but since the cross section consists of two long narrow welds placed adjacent to each other, their end shears are computed properly by the flexure formula. The maximum shear occurs at the lower end of the weld.

Resultant of Cross Shears in Welds. The second classification of combined stresses in fillet welds relates to the computation of a resultant throat shear as caused by two load systems. This action is illustrated by Fig. 103. Each of the forces P_1 and P_2 produces a shear on the throat section, but one shear, P_1, is across the weld, while the other shear, P_2, is along the weld. The *diagonal resultant shear* R is also acting on the throat section and since it is larger than either P_1 or P_2, it must be taken as the critical shear in design. This action is not unusual in structural welding and should not fail to be considered properly in the design. In all respects this analysis is consistent with the usual procedure of computation of the resultant shear on a rivet when a rivet group resists shears in two or more directions. The use of a resultant has been common in rivet calculations for many years, but it has been neglected in weld calculations.

Resultant Stress on Throat. In (*c*) of Fig. 103 there is shown a common situation where shear and tension are applied to one face of a fillet weld.

Evidently, each of the applied forces gives rise to a tension stress on the throat of the weld, although for the particular case shown the two shearing stresses on the throat tend to cancel each other. If the direction of either applied force is reversed, the critical throat stress will become a shear. As a practical design method, we may always feel safe in treating the *resultant applied force on the throat section as a shearing force.*

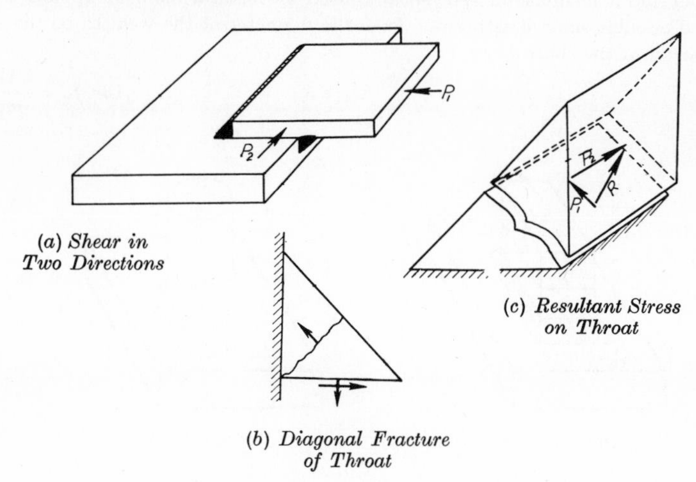

(*a*) *Shear in Two Directions*

(*b*) *Diagonal Fracture of Throat*

(*c*) *Resultant Stress on Throat*

FIG. 103. RESULTANT THROAT STRESS ON WELD.

PROBLEMS

501. Derive an expression to represent the maximum tensile fiber stress in this double-vee butt weld caused by the applied moment M. Assume that the stresses in the welds at the extreme fiber are controlled by the beam-flexure formula. Consider the weld faces to be flush with the vertical faces of the plate, so that $t/2$ is the distance to the extreme fiber.

$$Ans.\ f = \frac{3Mt}{ab(3t^2 + 4a^2 - 6at)}.$$

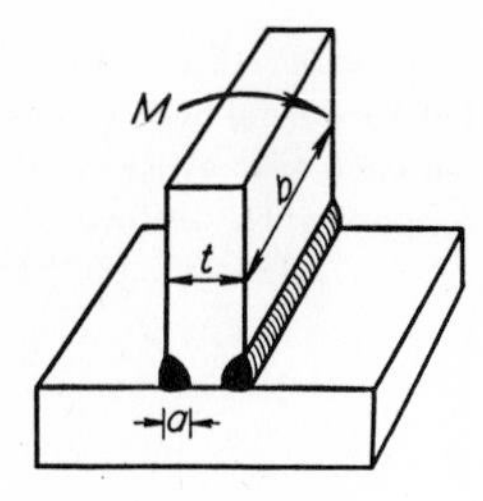

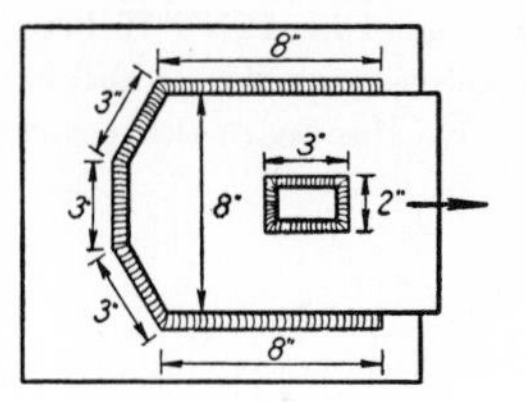

PROBLEM 501. PROBLEM 502.

502. A plate 8 × ¾ in. as illustrated is to be developed by fillet welding for a tensile working stress of 24,000 psi. The weld along the outside of the plate is a ½-in. fillet, and the weld placed around the slot is a ¼-in. fillet. Compute the average throat shear in each weld. *Ans.* 13,600 psi.

503. Develop a formula to express the throat shear caused by flexure of the bar shown welded all around. Assume that the dimensions b and t are large as compared to a. The extreme fiber distance may appropriately be taken as $t/2$ to the root of the weld where failure starts.

$$\textit{Ans. } f_v = \frac{1.414M}{abt + at^2/3}$$

504. Develop a formula for root shear caused by flexural moment applied to the fillet welded circular shaft illustrated. Take the diameter of the weld to be the same as the diameter of the shaft d.

$$\textit{Ans. } f_v = \frac{1.414M.}{\pi a d^2/4}$$

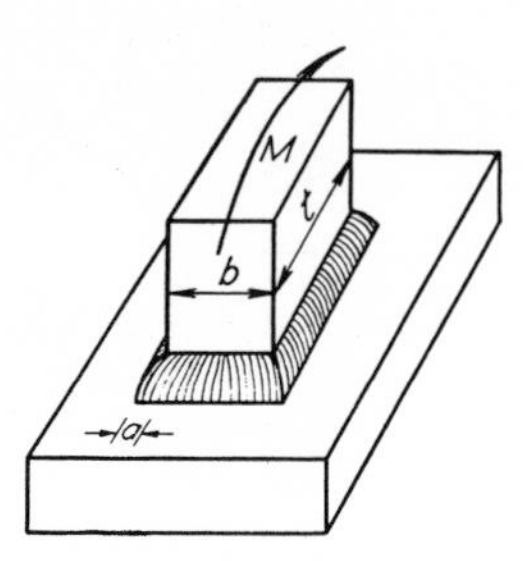

PROBLEM 503.

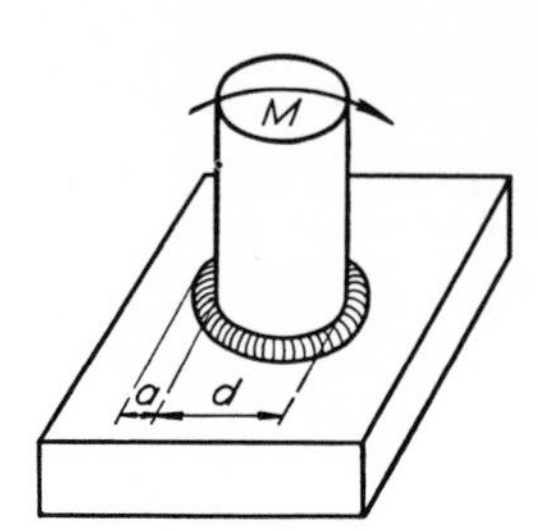

PROBLEM 504.

505. In Fig. 100(c) the data are as follows: $b = 6$ in., $a = \frac{1}{2}$ in., and $M = 30{,}000$ in-lb. The plates are 1 in. thick. (a) Compute the controlling shear on the throat by application of the beam-flexure formula and check by use of the formula given on the figure. (b) What is the resultant shear if the plate carried a direct tension (vertical) of 4500 psi?

Ans. (a) 7070; (b) 13,400 psi.

506. Same data as Problem 505 except that the moment acts as a torque as illustrated by Fig. 101(c). Do the shears produced by the torque and the direct stress combine?

Ans. (a) 7070; (b) 13,400 psi.

507. In Fig. 101(b) the data are as follows: $b = 4$ in., $a = \frac{3}{8}$ in., $L = 10$ in., $T = 120{,}000$ in-lb. which is caused by a force of 12,000 lb. parallel to the dimension L but located 10 in. out from the centre of the block. Find the resultant shear on the throat caused by this eccentric force.

Ans. 12,700 psi.

508. Compute the maximum allowable end reaction at 13,600 psi of throat area for the connection of an 18WF70 beam fillet welded to the face of a heavy column by an 8-in. weld across each flange and a 15-in. weld on each side of the web: these are all $\frac{3}{8}$-in. fillets. Use the beam-shear formula, and compare with uniform distribution.

Ans. 108,000 lb; 65 per cent.

DETAILING STRUCTURAL WELDS

110. Standard Welding Symbols. As welding developed both in usefulness and in complexity, it became necessary to adopt symbols to distinguish between *butt* welding and *fillet* welding, *shop* welding and *field* welding, welding on *far* side, *near* side, or *both* sides. Symbols were also needed to designate the type of notch to be prepared for the welder and the extent to which the welder was expected to add extra metal beyond the amount needed to fill the notch.

The system of symbols devised is explained by Fig. 104. The system eliminates entirely any actual need for picturing the welds on the drawing. Instead, all information is contained on an arrow which points to the position of the weld.

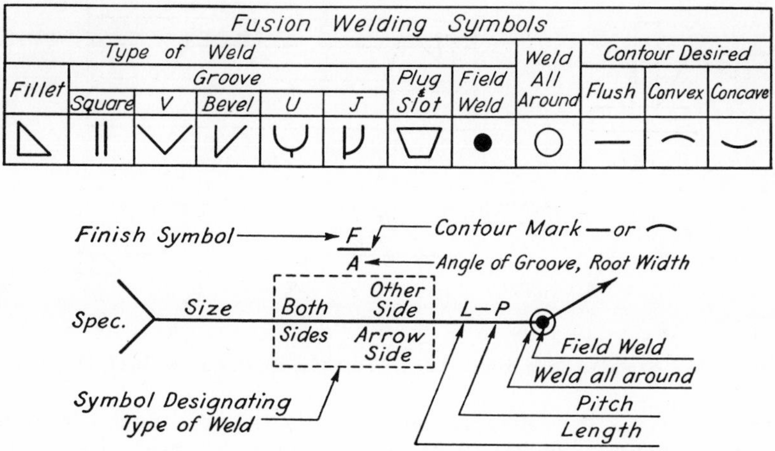

Fusion Welding Symbols											
Type of Weld								Weld All Around	Contour Desired		
Fillet	Groove					Plug & Slot	Field Weld		Flush	Convex	Concave
	Square	V	Bevel	U	J						

Finish Symbol
F
Contour Mark — or
A
Angle of Groove, Root Width
Spec.
Size
Both Sides
Other Side
Arrow Side
L—P
Field Weld
Weld all around
Pitch
Length
Symbol Designating Type of Weld

FIG. 104. WELD SYMBOLS — AMERICAN WELDING SOCIETY.

American Welding Society Symbols. In Fig. 105 the arrow for illustration (*a*) indicates that a fillet weld of ⅜-in. leg and 6-in. length is to be placed on the "arrow side" of the joint or the side to which the arrow points. The relative position along the joint, if important, would be designated on the elevation of the joint as indicated in (*f*). The designation of "near side," if needed, may be found in the fact that the right-angle triangle (45-degree fillet) is placed on the lower side of the arrow nearest to the reader in (*a*). In (*b*) the use of two such triangles is intended to signify that fillet welds (⅜ in. and 12 in. long) are placed both "arrow side and other side" or "near side and far side." Other common symbols are indicated in Fig. 105, such as the dot at the break in the arrow for designating field welding and the use of the symbol *V* in (*g*) to illustrate the kind of scarfing used for preparing the plates for welding. Finish marks such as *C* (chip), *G* (grind), *M* (machine), or *f* (finish) are placed above or below the mark indicating rounded bead (⌒) or the flush mark (—), see Fig. 105(*i*). Note in (*h*) that the root width ⅛ in. is indicated above the contour mark. The specification controlling the type of weld rod, and other welders' specifications, or instructions to the welder from the designer, may be placed in the tail of the arrow as shown on (*e*) and (*g*) of Fig. 105. Otherwise, the arrow tail may be omitted.

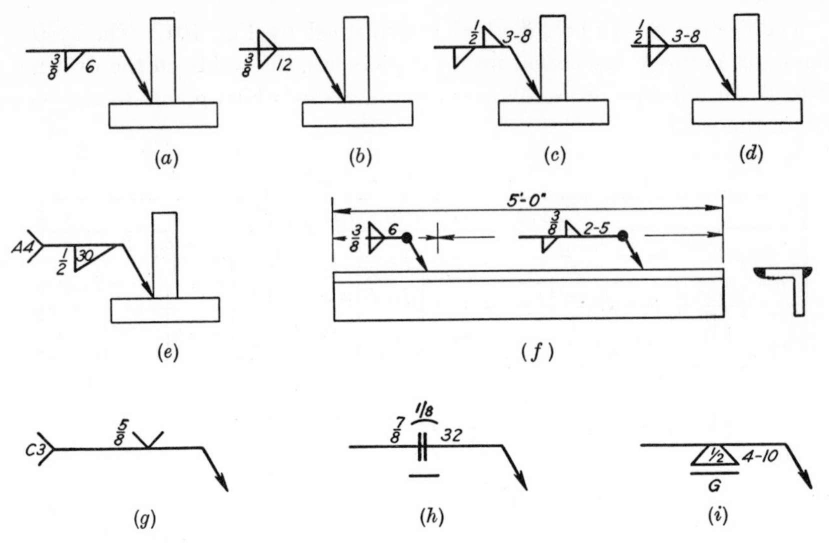

FIG. 105. SYMBOLS FOR STRUCTURAL WELDING AS USED ON SHOP DRAWINGS.

Special Symbols. If the designer wishes to place a distinctive marking on the plan or elevation showing the line of weld, he may use the marks employed originally in the *AWS* specifications. (See Fig. 106). The series of small x marks placed along the line on which welding is done indicates "near side," while the other symbols are for "far side" and "both sides." These marks can be used to show where the weld starts and stops, although exact dimensions should also be given. These supplementary marks should never be used alone, but they may be used along with the arrow designation.

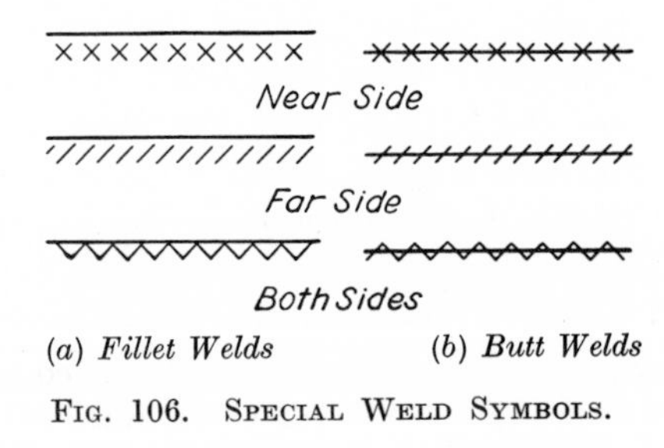

(*a*) *Fillet Welds* (*b*) *Butt Welds*

FIG. 106. SPECIAL WELD SYMBOLS.

DESIGN OF STRUCTURAL WELDS

111. Working Stresses. Standard allowable stresses for structural welds as specified by *AISC* are given in Spec. 17 as follows.

Fillet, plug, slot, and partial penetration groove welds (on throat of fillet or faying surface of plug weld.)

Made with Class $E60$ electrodes or submerged arc welding Grade SAW-1, 13,600 psi.
Made with Class $E70$ electrodes or submerged arc welding Grade SAW-2, 15,800 psi.
Butt welds, or complete penetration groove welds.
Same as allowed for connected material for tension, compression, shear, or bearing.

Allowable unit stresses for *Welded Highway and Railway Bridges* as specified by *AWS* and *AASHO* are as follows:

Shear = 12,400 psi on throat of fillet or faying surface of plug weld.
Shear = 13,000 psi on throat of butt weld.
Tension = 18,000 psi
Compression = 18,000 psi } or same as base metal.

Fillet Welds. The working stresses of 13,600 and 15,800 psi on the throat section of a fillet weld may be transferred into very convenient units for purposes of design. For a ⅛-in. fillet (leg = 0.125 in.) these working stresses give rise to an allowable shear on each lineal inch of weld of

$$V = 0.125 \times 0.707 \times 13{,}600 = 1200 \text{ lb.}$$

and

$$V = 0.125 \times 0.707 \times 15{,}800 = 1400 \text{ lb.}$$

Hence, for standard structural welds for buildings (*AISC*) we conclude that the allowable shear on a fillet weld is either 1200 or 1400 *lb. per lineal inch per eighth inch of fillet leg, or*

	At 13,600 psi	At 15,800 psi
For a ¼-in. fillet,	$V = 2400$ lb.	2800 lb.
For a 5⁄16-in. fillet,	$V = 3000$ lb.	3500 lb.
For a ⅜-in. fillet,	$V = 3600$ lb.	4200 lb.
For a ½-in. fillet, etc.	$V = 4800$ lb.	5600 lb.

It is evident from these results that the allowable shearing stresses of 13,600 and 15,800 psi were chosen to produce simple design calculations. Such simplification is commendable and justifies the slight variation in the desired working stress that it may necessitate.

Fatigue. Tests reported by W. M. Wilson and A. B. Wilder show unexpectedly low failure stresses for butt welded joints under fatigue loading. "The specimens, consisting of single-vee butt welds in ⅞-in. structural carbon steel and low alloy (manganese-vanadium) steel plates, were subjected to three repetitions of minimum to maximum stress: (1) from tension to an equal compression; that is, complete reversal; (2) from zero to tension; (3) from tension to tension one half as great. The maximum stresses in the stress cycle were chosen to cause failure at 100,000 cycles and at 2,000,000 cycles. The specimens were tested (1) in the condition as welded, (2) with the welds planed flush with the base plate, (3) after stress relief at 1200°F. for one hour and cooling in the furnace. The effect of frequent periods of rest upon the fatigue strength of the butt welds in the carbon steel plates was also investigated. A summary of the results follows.

(1) In the condition as welded, the values of fatigue strengths for the complete stress reversal cycle were 21,600 psi for failure at 100,000 cycles and 14,800 psi for failure at 2,000,000 cycles; for the cycle from zero to tension, strengths were 32,600 psi (100,000 cycles), and 23,100 psi (2,000,000 cycles).

DP12. *Design a splice between two tension members one of which is a 14WF48 split beam and the other consists of two angles 5 × 3½ × ⅜″. AISC spec. for A7.*

Value of Angle Legs:

Angles were designed for 80 per cent of their gross area. (∠ area = 3.05 in.^{2})
Net value = 2 × 3.05 × 0.80 × 20,000 = 97,500#.

Burn 5″ angle leg as indicated to keep c. g. of angles in line with c. g. of split beam.

$$\text{Value of remaining 3.5'' legs} = \frac{3.5 \times 0.375}{3.05} \times 97{,}500 = 42{,}000\#.$$

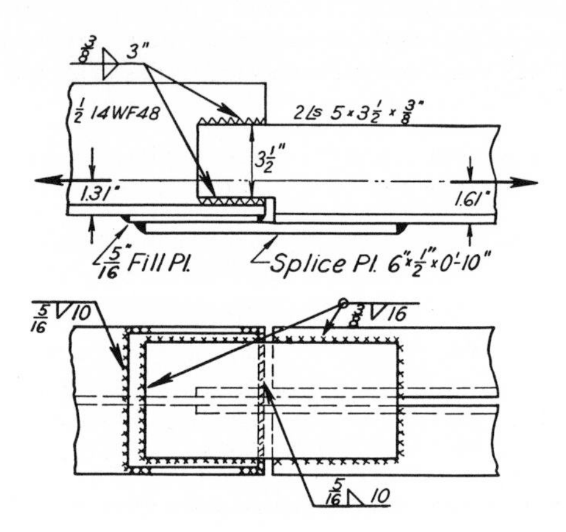

Weld Lengths: *Allowable shear = 13,600 psi.*

$$\text{Length of } \tfrac{3}{8}'' \text{ fillet} = \frac{42{,}000}{3600} = 11.7''.$$

Use 4 fillets 3″ long.

$$\text{The remaining } 55{,}500\# \text{ requires } \frac{55{,}500}{3600} = 15.5'' \text{ of } \tfrac{3}{8}'' \text{ fillet.}$$

Place 16″ of ⅜″ fillet around each end of the 6″ × 10″ splice pl.

Splice Plates:

$$\text{Thickness of splice pl.} = \frac{55{,}500}{6 \times 20{,}000} = 0.46''. \text{ Use } \tfrac{1}{2}''.$$

Fill pl. 5/16″ thick must be connected with 18½″ of 5/16″ weld for 55,500#. Size of fill pl. is 7″ × 8″.

Remarks: *If no fill plate is used here, the eccentricity between the two members will be 3/10″. The corresponding moment of nearly 30,000″# would be serious.*

(2) For specimens with welds machined flush with the base plate, fatigue strengths for the stress reversal cycle were 29,400 psi (100,000 cycles), and 19,800 psi (2,000,000 cycles); for the zero to tension cycle, fatigue strengths were 47,000 psi (100,000 cycles) and 30,100 psi (2,000,000 cycles). That is, removing the stress raiser caused by the change in section at the edge of the weld reinforcing increased the fatigue strength 43 per cent. Moreover, the fatigue strengths of these welded specimens were equal to the fatigue strengths of the plates without welds.

(3) Stress relieving by heating had no effect upon fatigue strength, nor did frequent *rest periods* between applications of loads.

(4) For all specimens in the stress cycle from tension to tension one half as great, the yield point of the material was exceeded, so that such a cycle is not important to the structural designer.

(5) Fatigue strengths on complete reversal for welded specimens of low alloy steel plate with a static strength of 83,000 psi were 24,000 psi (100,000 cycles) and 16,100 psi (2,000,000 cycles)."

Allowable Repeated Stresses. Such tests as those summarized above have led to reduced allowable stresses for welds where repeated loads are a serious factor. This is covered by *AISC* Spec. 22 and *AWS* Specifications for Welded Highway and Railway Bridges, to which reference is made.

112. Design for Direct Loads. This is a particularly simple problem as long as symmetry can be maintained. The total load is merely divided by the value of the weld in pounds per lineal inch to determine the required number of inches of weld. This length of weld is then placed on the member to maintain symmetry in the welded joint.

EXAMPLE. Design a lap-welded vertical seam for a tank of 20′ diam., 55′ head of water, plates ¼″ thick, *AISC* spec. Weld value = 13,600 psi in shear.

$$\text{Pl. tension} = \frac{55 \times 62.5}{144} \times \frac{20 \times 12}{2}$$
$$= 2860\,\#\,|'' \text{ of height.}$$
$$\text{Weld leg} = \frac{2860}{2} \times \frac{1.414}{13{,}600}$$
$$= 0.15''.$$

Use ¼″ fillet welds which provide 1/10″ for corrosion.

SPLICE IN A TENSION MEMBER, *DP*12. The design sheet *DS*12 illustrates a connection of a two-angle tension member to a split-beam or *T-section* tension member. The important detail to arrange is for the gravity axes of the two members to be placed in line. This is accomplished by burning away the outstanding legs of the angles and by adding a fill plate to the bottom of the split-beam section. The welds attached to the remaining 3.5-in. legs of the angles are then designed to develop the part of the total stress that these 3.5-in. legs will carry. The remainder is transferred through the lower splice plate, and thence through the fill plate to the split beam. The splice is very compact and inexpensive.

An even cheaper alternative would be to slot the angle as indicated in Fig. 107 and to weld the juncture so completely that the full section of the angle would be available at the end of the slot. The only difficulty involved is that it will not ordinarily be possible by this means to eliminate all eccentricity (*e* of Fig. 107) between the gravity lines of the two members.

113. End Connections for Channels and Angles. The problem of forming a welded end connection to develop a heavy channel or angle is usually complicated by the fact that the space available is quite limited. Frequently the length along the section available for welding is no greater than the width of the section. Slots are used in *DP13a* to provide extra weld length. Note by Spec. 41 that *AISC* permits neglect of a small eccentricity at a connection.

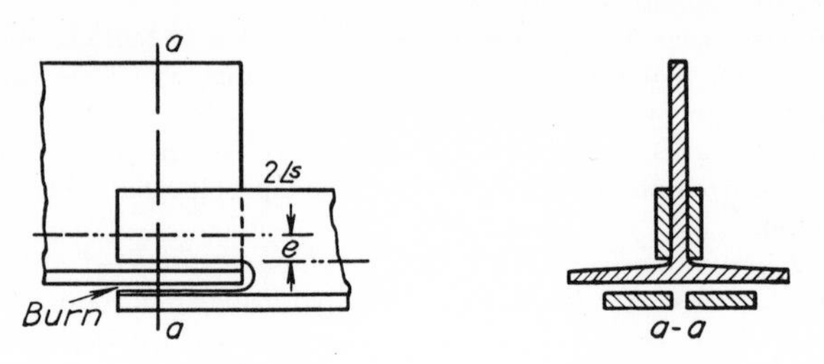

FIG. 107. SPLICE OF TENSION MEMBERS.

Balancing Welds on an Angle. The problem of connecting an angle to another member by welding is properly solved when the total length of weld required to resist the pull is so placed that the center of resistance of the weld is in line with the applied load. In Fig. 108 is shown an end connection formed by three welds of lengths a, b, and c. If only the welds a and b are used to produce a total length of L, then the center of resistance will be in line with the load when the following relationship is satisfied.

$$\frac{a}{a+b} = \frac{x_2}{x_1 + x_2},$$

or

$$a = \frac{Lx_2}{c} \quad \text{and} \quad b = \frac{Lx_1}{c} \text{ (two welds).} \tag{3}$$

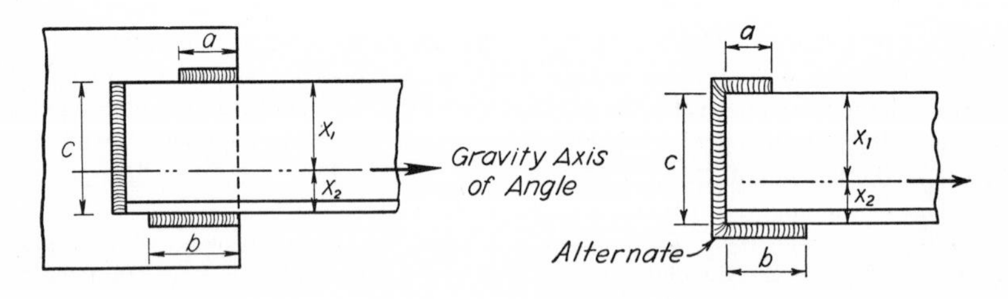

FIG. 108. BALANCING WELDS ON AN ANGLE.

But if three welds a, b, and c are used to make up the required length of weld L, the result will be more complex. We will have to make use of an equation of moments about the lower edge of the angle or about the weld line b in Fig. 108. Thus we obtain

$$ac + \frac{c^2}{2} = Lx_2,$$

or

$$a = \frac{Lx_2}{c} - \frac{c}{2} \text{ (three welds)}, \tag{4}$$

and

$$b = \frac{Lx_1}{c} - \frac{c}{2} \text{ (three welds)}. \tag{5}$$

Channel Connection, *DP*13*a*. In the example *DP*13*a* it is found necessary to slot the channel in order to obtain a sufficient length of standard ⅜-in. weld. Such slot welds are in reality merely additional lengths of fillet welds. Slots or round holes are sometimes made smaller and are completely filled with weld. They then become the equivalent of weld rivets, but their use is not common. The strength of the tongue at c between slots is found to be adequate on *DP*13*a*. This arrangement also meets Spec. 57.

Example *DP*13*b*. Here we have a case in which the application of equation (3) gave rise to an excessive length of weld b. A solution was then obtained by the use of three welds a, b, and c, with equations (4) and (5).

114. Long Longitudinal Welds. In designing for direct loads it is often convenient to use long welds in line with the load in place of cross or transverse welds. Theory indicates that such welds have very high concentrations of stress at the ends (Fig. 109), but tests have not borne out the seriousness of these stress concentrations for *static loads*. Nevertheless, certain rules of thumb have developed such as to discount the length of a longitudinal weld by 25 per cent, or to credit it with the first 6 in. plus one half of the length over 6 in. If fatigue failure is a possibility, specifications for welding of machines should be consulted.

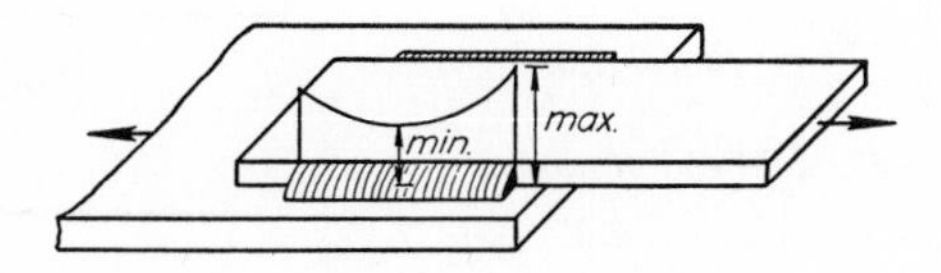

Fig. 109. Distribution of Longitudinal Shear.

Moment Resistance

115. Weld Design for Flexure. Transverse flexure should certainly never be permitted on a single line of weld, and even two lines of weld separated by a plate or an angle leg of ⅜-in. or ½-in. thickness have relatively little flexural resistance. Two lines of weld separated by several inches may be

DP13a. *Design end welds to reproduce the tensile value of a 10″-30# channel. Use ⅜″ welds. Weld value = 1250#/″ per ⅛″ of fillet leg.*

Value of channel = 8.8 × 20,000 = 176,000#.

Max. length of fillet = 8 + 8 + 10 + 10 = 36″.

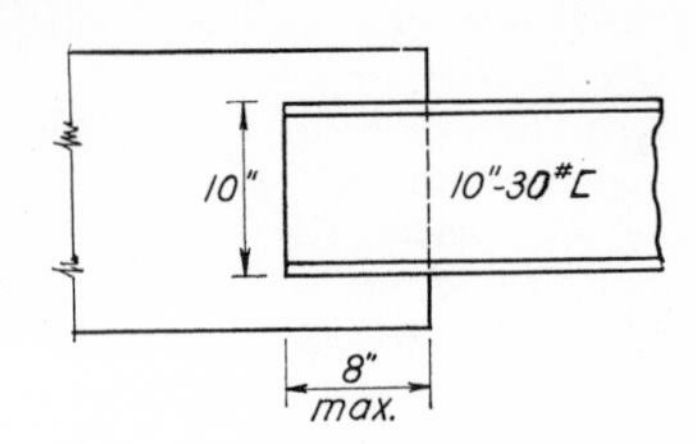

Weld value = 176,000 ÷ 36 = 4900#/″.

This is too great for a ⅜″ weld which has a maximum value of 3750#/″.

Try Use of Slot Welds: (*Spec.* 57).

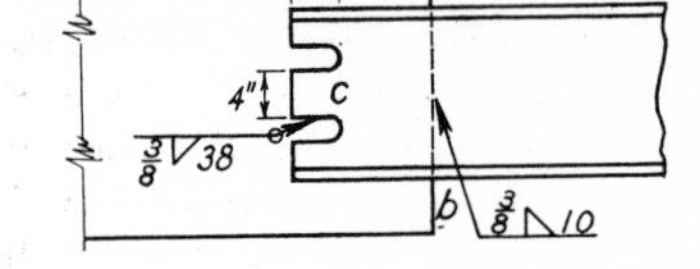

$$\text{Total fillet length} = \frac{176{,}000}{3750} = 47''.$$

Slots must provide 47 − 36 = 11″.

Use two 3″ slots ⅞″ wide providing 12″ length of fillet which allows 1″ for craters at a and b. Also note Spec. 57.

Stress at c. For a 4″ width at c, tensile area = 4 × 0.673 = 2.7 in.² *Shear from 10″ weld* = 3750 × 10. *Tension at c* = 37,500 ÷ 2.7 = 13,900 *psi.*

DP13b. *Design end welds to produce a value of 29,000# for a 4 × 4 × ¼″ angle. Use allowable unit shear for high strength welds of 15,800 psi on throat.*

Value of ¼″ weld = 2800#/″.

Weld length = 29,000 ÷ 2800 = 10.3″.

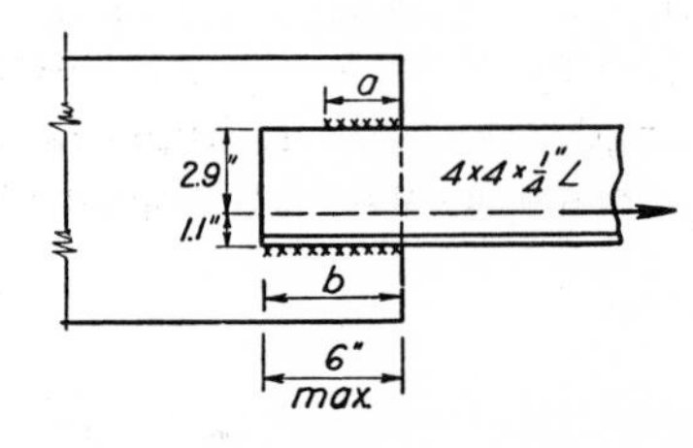

Balancing Welds:

$$\text{Length } a = \frac{1.1}{4} \times 10.3 = 2.8''.$$

$$\text{Length } b = \frac{2.9}{4} \times 10.3 = 7.5''.$$

Max. $b = 6''$; *weld end of angle.*

$L = 10.3''$, $c = 4''$, $x_1 = 2.9''$.

See Fig. 108, *and equation* (5).

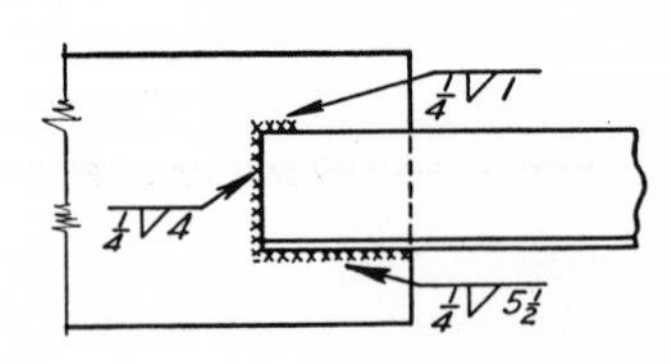

$$b = \frac{Lx_1}{c} - \frac{c}{2} = \frac{10.3 \times 2.9}{4} - 2$$

$$= 5.5''.$$

$$a = \frac{Lx_2}{c} - \frac{c}{2} = \frac{10.3 \times 1.1}{4} - 2 = 0.9''. \text{ Use } 1''.$$

Total length = 5.5 + 4 + 1 = 10.5″. *Check.*

designed to resist transverse flexure. Relatively long lines of weld furnish good flexural resistance when subjected to longitudinal flexure.

Example *DP*14. We will investigate on design sheet *DS*14 the action of longitudinal flexure on a set of welds which are shaped like the Greek letter π. Calculations are based upon the flexure formula, and only the weld section is taken into consideration. Actually, the lower stem of the split-beam section will *bear* against the column and will resist some compression. If the split-beam section had been faced for bearing, we could properly take its area into consideration below the neutral axis, but, since it is commonly burned to shape, the bearing area in contact is likely to be so small that it should be neglected, as was done in this example. Note that the moment resistance could be increased by lowering the vertical welds about one inch.

Beam Continuity, Example *DP*15. Continuity is to be produced between two beams which frame into a girder. These beams might be stringers of a bridge floor or joists in a building. The device of using a channel to produce a tie spaced 2¼ in. above the top of the beam is an excellent design in that it saves the cost of *coping the beam* to raise it to the level of the girder. The channel welds must resist not only the pull across the top of the connection but also the eccentric moment caused by the 2¼-in. lift of the tie plate. Because of a modern device, the burning torch, this channel can be shaped at little cost. Other possible connections could be made by slotting the web of the girder for a tie plate or by raising the tie plate on welded leg plates. The latter would be used if the heavy channel section needed should not be available.

PROBLEMS

(Use *AISC* working stresses except as noted.)

509. Design a lap-welded circular girt seam for a water tank where the ⅜-in. plates must carry a stress of 22,000 psi across the joint.

510. Design a splice joining two tension members one of which is one half of a 12*WF*36 beam and the other is composed of two angles 3 × 3 × ⅜ in. back-to-back with the legs turned out. The connection is to develop the full value of the angles for *A*36 steel.

511. Repeat Problem 510 for a split-beam section obtained from a 21*WF*112 beam and two 6 × 6 × ⅝-in. angles. Design the splice for the value of angles of 50,000 psi yield.

512. Design an end connection to develop the full tensile value of an 8-in., 13.75-lb. channel in a length of 5 in. The back of the channel is connected to a 5/16-in. plate and welds are limited to 5/16 in. *A*36 steel.

513. Repeat Problem 512 for an 18-in., 58-lb. channel with ½-in. welds limited to a 10-in. length along the member.

514. Design an end connection to develop the full tensile value of two 6 × 4 × ½-in. angles connected back-to-back to a ⅝-in. plate by their 6-in. legs. The length of the connection is limited to 8 in. *AISC* specifications for *A*36 steel. Specify weld rods.

515. Design a connection for the angle of Problem 514 with no weld more than 6 in. long.

516. Design a welded bracket seat using one half of a 16*WF*58 beam to resist an end reaction of 46,000 lb. located 1⅞ in. from the face of a column. The welds are designed to provide all resistance. Use *A*7 steel and *AISC* specifications.

517. Design an angle seat with stiffeners for an end reaction of 58,000 lb. acting 4 in. from the face of the column. Do not increase the welds beyond ½ in., but add

DP14. *Design a welded bracket as a seat for an I-beam where the end reaction of 43,000# is located at 1¾″ out on the bracket. Weld value = 13,600 psi.*

Data:

$M = 43{,}000 \times 1.75 = 75{,}000''\#.$
$V = 43{,}000\#.$

Length of ⅜″ welds for vertical shear $= 43{,}000 \div 3600 = 12''$.

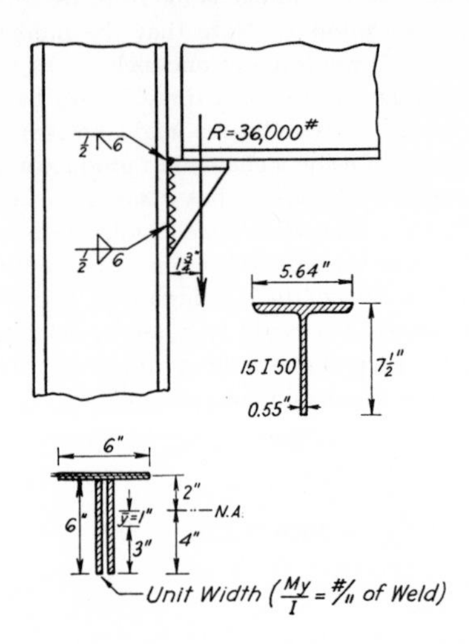

Trial Section:

Try a split beam 14WF38 with three 6″ lengths of weld of unknown size. Treat width as 1.0.

$$\bar{y} = \frac{6 \times 3 + 2 \times 6 \times 0}{(6 + 6 + 6)} = 1'' \text{ (above mid-height of vertical welds).}$$

$$\begin{aligned} I = 6 \times 2^2 \quad &= 24 \\ 2(6 \times 1^2) &= 12 \\ 2(\tfrac{1}{12} \times 6^3) &= \underline{36} \\ I \text{ (Weld)} &= 72 \end{aligned}$$

$$\text{Horizontal shear on weld from flexure} = \frac{75{,}000 \times 4}{72} = 4200\#/''$$

at bottom of Tee.

$$\text{Vertical shear on weld} = \frac{43{,}000}{18} = 2400\#/''.$$

$$\text{Resultant throat shear} = \sqrt{4200^2 + 2400^2} = 4830\#/''.$$

Use ½″ welds 6″ long.

Remarks: *A resultant throat shear is computed here which is in accordance with the appropriate theory explained in §109. Shears 90 degrees apart must be combined as vectors.*

welds on the edges of the angle if necessary. The column flange is 10 in. wide. Select specifications and material.

518. Design a welded seat angle to fit between the flanges of a 14*WF*314 column as in Fig. 94(*a*). This seat carries a 12-in. beam having an end reaction of 17,500 lb. eccentric 2 in. from the center line of the column (nearer to one flange than the other). The angle should be stiffened, since it is connected only by its vertical leg to the inside of the column flanges. The reaction line is 1½ in. outside of the center of the vertical leg. Hold weld shear to 15,800 psi.

519. Design a welded end connection to the web of a 12*WF*92 column for a 12-in., 31.8-lb. I-beam. Develop a moment resistance of 500,000 in-lb. and an end shear of 22,000 lb. Use minimum *AISC* working stresses.

520. Design a connection similar to the one illustrated by the example *DP*15 to replace the moment resistance of a 16*WF*45 beam and thus provide full continuity across the girder. The top of the girder is 2 in. above the beam.

521. Repeat Problem 520, but slot the girder to permit a splice plate to pass through and reweld. Use *AWS-AASHO* specifications and allowable stresses.

116. Weld Problems. A question that has been raised repeatedly concerns the impact resistance of weld metal. Charpy tests on weld metal placed by the bare electrode, made under the author's direction in 1930–31, showed consistently low values of impact resistance.[2] In contrast, weld metal placed by heavily coated electrodes proved to be very ductile and showed a high Charpy value; in fact, one even greater than that of structural steel. This is convincing proof that there need be little question as to the impact resistance of weld metal placed by use of proper electrodes adequately coated to shield the weld from the atmosphere.

Shrinkage and Plastic Deformation. Cooling stresses are serious in welded structures, since unequal shrinkage is inevitable. It is known, however, that equally high stresses occur from unequal cooling of structural sections after they have passed through the rolls in the mill. Furthermore, these sections often must be straightened in the fabrication shop, and this procedure leaves residual stresses. An occasional fracture of a rolled section from a light blow indicates that such residual stresses may approach the elastic limit of the material The property that protects good structural steel from injury by these internal stresses is its ductility. Standard welds of ductile metal will be equally safe.

Ductility versus Brittle Fracture. To the designer, ductility has another significance. Unequal stress distribution from welding or from other fabrication or erection methods will be ironed out by plastic deformation. Those fibers stressed to the yield point deform and do not resist additional load that may come on the structure. Less heavily stressed parts or particles must resist such load increments until they in turn reach the elastic limit. Near the ultimate load the result is a structure with stresses that approach those which would have existed if there had been no initial shrinkage stresses.

[2] H. C. Givens and B. W. Farquhar, Thesis Studies for the M.S. Degree, 1931, Texas A. and M. College.

DP15. *Design a connection for a continuous beam which is a 14WF30 section. The beams frame into a 24WF94 girder. Use AISC stresses. A7 steel.*

Channel Tie:

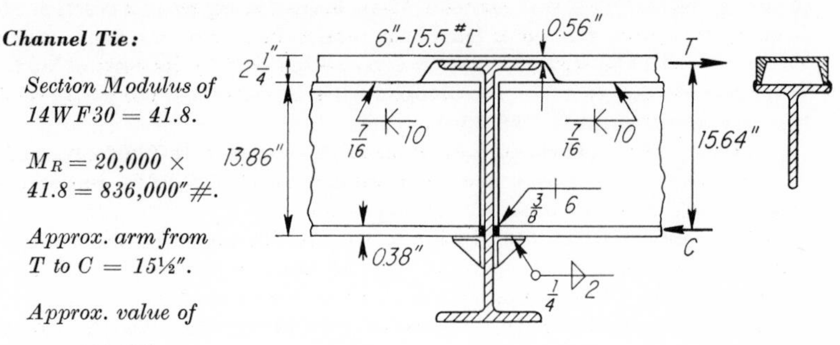

Section Modulus of 14WF30 = 41.8.

$M_R = 20{,}000 \times 41.8 = 836{,}000''\#$.

Approx. arm from T to C = 15½″.

Approx. value of

$$T = \frac{836{,}000}{15.5} = 54{,}000\#.$$

$$\text{Web area of tie channel} = \frac{54{,}000}{20{,}000} = 2.7 \text{ in.}^2$$

Select a 6″-15.5# [; $A_w = 3.3$ in.² or use 6″ × ⅝″ × 2′-6″ tie plate welded to vertical leg plates 10″ long at each end.

Welded Connection:

$$\text{True arm from } T \text{ to } C = 13.86 - \frac{0.38}{2} + 2.25 - \frac{0.56}{2} = 15.64''.$$

$$T = C = \frac{836{,}000}{15.64} = 53{,}400\#.$$

Compression weld has value of $0.38 \times 20{,}000 \times 6 = \underline{45{,}400\#}$.

$$\text{Diff.} = 8000\#$$

This force is resisted by ¼″ fillets to seat.

$$\text{Length of } \tfrac{1}{4}'' \text{ fillet} = \frac{8000}{2400} = 3.4''. \text{ Use } 4''.$$

The channel tie is connected to the beam by 10″ fillets that undergo longitudinal shear and longitudinal flexure.

$$\text{Unit longitudinal shear} = \frac{53{,}400}{20} = 2670\#/''.$$

$$\text{Unit shear from flexure} = \frac{53{,}400(2.25 - 0.028) \times 5}{\frac{1}{12} \times 2 \times 10^3} = 3150\#/''.$$

$$\text{Resultant shear on throat} = \sqrt{3150^2 + 2670^2} = 4120\#/''. \text{ Use } \tfrac{7}{16}'' \text{ fillets.}$$

Remarks: *A 7⁄16″ fillet weld has a value of 4200#/″. Also the flange of the 14WF30 is only 6¾″ wide. Hence the channel flange must be beveled to permit 7⁄16″ welds on each side.*

This favorable redistribution of stress will not have a chance to occur, however, if the material can fracture in a brittle manner. Such fractures have occurred most frequently in welded plate structures such as girders, tanks, steel stacks, and ships. Some of the reasons for such fractures have been determined to be loss of ductility due to low temperature, to excessive previous deformation, particularly compressive deformation, or to the effect of triaxial tension caused by severe notches, corners, or holes. However, some of the reasons for brittle fracture are metallurgical and are still to be clarified by research.

CHAPTER 6

TENSION AND COMPRESSION MEMBERS

117. Design of Tension Members and Connections. In the design of tension members it is usual to arrange the member and its connection in such a manner that there will be no bending in the member from eccentricity of the connection. When this arrangement can be made, the stress is considered to be distributed uniformly over the net section of the member; that is, at the root of a thread, across the section at a pin hole, or on a section taken through a group of rivet holes. The unit stress on the net section is the total force divided by the *net area*, and this stress must be kept within the allowable working stress in tension. Where an eccentric connection exists, the effect of the eccentricity may be provided for by specifications, or else the stress caused by the bending moment must be considered in the design. Only members where eccentricity is provided for by specification will be considered under the heading of simple tension members. For instance, a single-angle tension member connected by one leg has its net area reduced by specification to allow for eccentricity. Only 50 per cent of the unconnected leg is considered effective according to several specifications.

Bars and Rods

118. Welded Tension Bar. The welded tension bar is a satisfactory member for use in the design of light structures such as stairway framing around industrial plants, foot bridges, electric sign supports, power line towers, and in other cases where the general specification requiring tension members to be capable of resisting compression does not apply. Since no holes need be punched through the bar, the full gross area may be used for carrying stress. The welding at the end of the bar should be arranged symmetrically in order that there will be no bending stresses caused by an eccentric connection.

Example of a Tower Diagonal, *DP*16*a*. Probably the welded bar or *flat* is the most satisfactory tension diagonal for a light stairway tower such as the one illustrated. The gross area of the bar is effective, resulting in full efficiency. The member design to resist the direct stress is so simple that the calculations need no explanation. The joint detail is of some interest. The gravity axes of the four members meet at a point as shown in the illustration. The upper diagonal may be cut ¾ in. short of its line of contact with the lower diagonal to permit two 3/8-in. fillet welds to be placed between. Usually, however, the gap is made only 1/4 in. or 1/8 in. wide so that a single rectangular butt weld serves the double purpose as indicated on the detail of the joint. The lower diagonal is connected by 5 1/4 in. of weld (the minimum required amount). The upper diagonal has an end connection of 5 1/2 in. of weld which is necessary because the minimum length of the side welds is usually set at 1 1/2 in.

119. Tension Rods. Tension rods are used only as secondary structural members for which the design stress is relatively small. One common use for a tension rod is as a sag rod in industrial buildings with sloping roofs. The purpose is to support the purlins between trusses in a direction parallel to the roof or to support the girts vertically between columns. This support is particularly necessary where the purlin or girt is a channel, which has a low flexural resistance about its axis of least radius of gyration. The maximum stress in a sag rod occurs at the ridge of the roof and is computed as the sum of its purlin reactions from the eave to the ridge produced by the component of dead load and snow load taken parallel to the roof. Other uses for tension rods are as hangers and as tie rods to resist the thrust of a floor arch or bridge arch for which fixed abutments are not available. For this latter use, large tie rods may be needed.

End Connections. Tension rods can be obtained either in round or square sizes. Large rods (1 in. or larger) usually are upset before threading so that the area at the root of the thread is at least 20 per cent greater that the area of the bar. The cost of upsetting overbalances the saving for bars of smaller diameter. For non-upset bars the designer should increase the diameter at the *root of the thread* by 1/16 in. over the actual required diameter to allow for *localized stress* at this point.[1] Bent tension bars should be avoided, if possible, or else should be designed conservatively. Tension rods arranged for connecting to a pin are known as clevis rods or loop rods. These are shown in Fig. 110. Standard connections of these types are strong enough to develop the bar. They may be obtained with turnbuckles for the purpose of introducing initial tension.

Initial Tension in Rods. It is desirable to introduce initial tension into the diagonal wind bracing of towers and buildings, because sway is thereby reduced. Tension rods used for this purpose should have an initial tension of at least 5000 lb. (often 5000 psi for larger rods) introduced by turning up the end nuts or turnbuckles. As long as any initial tension exists, the

[1] Note that by AISC specifications the full gross area before threading is used for load resistance at 2/3 of the normal allowable stress in tension or 0.40 F_y. However, the engineer should know that one way to produce a brittle fracture in steel is to provide a circumferential notch or thread around a tension bar and to apply a direct stress with a light shock or impact. The reason is that the notch produces a state of triaxial tensile stress at its root which reduces ductile deformation. Impact and low temperature also reduce ductility. Hence, it is wise to make an allowance for stress concentration at the root of a thread if there is any possibility of shock, impact, or low temperature, because fractures under such conditions have been produced in the laboratory below the yield load for the net or root area.

DP16a. *Design and detail a welded bar as a tension diagonal CF of the stairway tower shown. Reduce thickness $\frac{1}{16}''$ for corrosion hazard; AISC spec. A7 steel.*

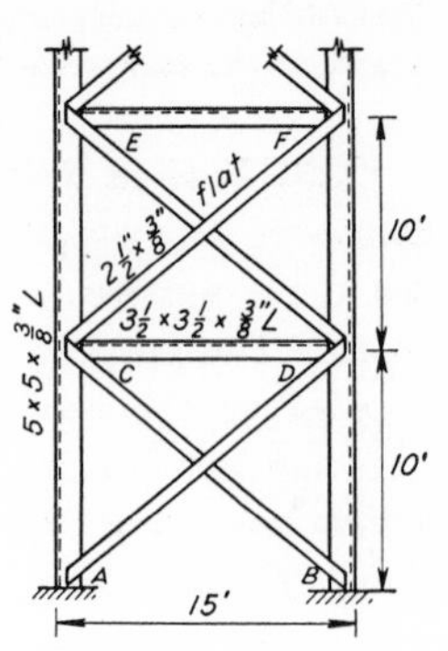

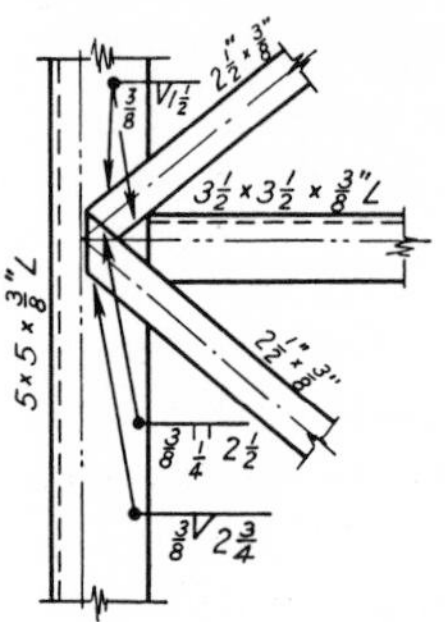

Data:

Design stress (wind) in diagonal = 20,200#T.

Member:

Allowable stress = $20{,}000 \times 1.33 = 26{,}700$ psi.

Area = $20{,}200 \div 26{,}700 = 0.76$ in.^{2}

Bar size. A $2\frac{1}{2}'' \times \frac{5}{16}''$ flat furnishes 0.78 in.^{2}

Corrosion. Choose a $2\frac{1}{2}'' \times \frac{3}{8}''$ bar to allow $\frac{1}{16}''$ for corrosion hazard.

Slenderness Ratio. Tension bars cannot meet AISC Spec. 23 for $L/r < 300$. Instead, bars are preheated locally to produce small initial tension after welding to avoid sagging.

Connection: *Increase weld leg $\frac{1}{16}''$ for corrosion.*

Value of member = $26{,}700 \times 0.78 = 20{,}800$#.

Value of $\frac{3}{8}''$ fillet weld (E60) reduced to $\frac{5}{16}''$ by corrosion = $3000 \times 1.33 = 4000$#/″.

Length of $\frac{3}{8}''$ weld = $20{,}800 \div 4000 = 5.2''$.

Remarks: *The arrangement of the welds is shown on the detail. The diagonals join together on the near face of the column. The horizontal strut is welded to the back face of the column angle with $4\frac{1}{2}''$ of $\frac{3}{8}''$ fillet weld which is adequate to care for the horizontal component of the stress in the diagonal. The connection is designed for the value of the member before its thickness is increased for corrosion since the $\frac{3}{8}''$ welds are reduced to the value of $\frac{5}{16}''$ welds to allow for $\frac{1}{16}''$ of corrosion. The diagonals may be tack welded at the point of crossing to reduce flexure in the vertical plane.*

DP16b. *Select an upset rod diagonal to serve in place of the flat bar of DP16a. Make no allowance for stress concentration at root of thread but add 20 per cent for corrosion.*

Net Area = $(20{,}200 \div 26{,}700)1.20 = 0.91$ in.^{2}

Net Area of a 1″ sq. rod = 1.0 in.^{2} (1.29 in.^{2} at root of thread).

Net Area of a $1\frac{1}{8}''$ round rod = 0.99 in.^{2} (1.29 in.^{2} at root of thread).

Remarks: *Economy would probably be met by the use of rod diagonals. However, the welded bars provide the simpler and more satisfactory connections.*

wind stress is divided equally between the crossing bars by reducing the tension in one and increasing the tension in the other. Accordingly, when the stress in one reduces from 5000 lb. to zero, the other will have a stress of 10,000 lb., which is the same stress that it would have if no initial tension had been introduced. It follows that *we should design heavy crossing diagonals with or without initial tension for exactly the same stress*. This assumes that the crossing diagonals have the same slope. Initial tension may be introduced into riveted diagonals by detailing the members $\frac{1}{16}$ in. short for each 20 ft. of length. The members are then pulled into place in the field with drift pins. Welded bars can be preheated over a part of the length to obtain the same result.

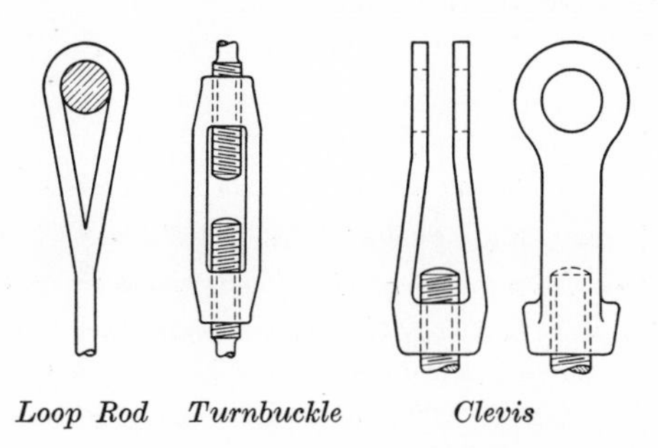

FIG. 110. PIN CONNECTED RODS.

120. Tension Rod Design. EXAMPLES *DP*16 and *DP*17. The first example on tension rods is the selection of an upset rod as a diagonal for a tower. An upset rod is proper for this member because the diameter is greater than 1 in. The second example is properly the choice of a non-upset rod since the diameter is small. Some specifications have limited the minimum diameter of a tie rod in a building or bridge structure to ⅝ in. The reason is that a smaller non-upset rod has so little effective area that it furnishes almost no factor of safety against possible increase of loading. A ⅝-in. rod is often considered a minimum structural size in the same manner that a 2-in. angle is taken as the minimum section for a tension diagonal.

121. Eye-Bar Tension Members. The pin connected truss bridge with eye-bar tension members was at one time almost universally used. This type of truss is used today for long span bridges only, since the large dead weight of a long span structure is necessary to prevent rattling and excessive vibration under heavy traffic. Eye bars are also used to make up the chains of some suspension bridges, and they may be used as floor-beam hangers for large suspension or through arch bridges. A special use of eye bars for an anchorage is illustrated by Fig. 111.

The use of eye bars offers the advantage that heat treated steel of high strength may be used with correspondingly high working stresses. For

DP17. *Design sag rods to support the purlins of an industrial building roof. Sag rods are placed midway between roof trusses which are spaced 16′ apart. Compare with AISC spec. A7 steel rods.*

Loads: *Roofing is corrugated asbestos at 3 psf and purlins weigh 3½ psf of roof surface. Snow load is 20 psf of horizontal projection or 18.1 psf of roof surface. Total vertical load is therefore 24.6 psf of roof surface.*

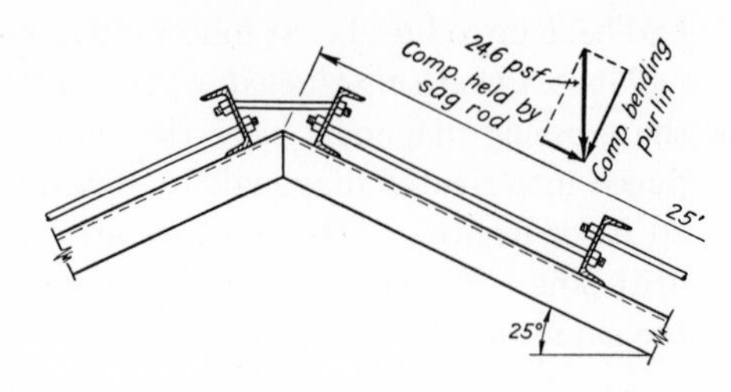

Load component parallel to roof $= 24.6 \times \sin 25°$

$= 24.6 \times 0.423 = 10.4$ *psf.*

Rod size:

Load carried by one sag rod $= 10.4 \times 25 \times 8 = 2080\#$.

Required area of rod $= 2080 \div 20{,}000 = 0.104$ *in.*^{2}

Net diameter. A net diameter of ⅜″ will furnish the required area.

Root diameter $=$ ⅜ $+$ ¹⁄₁₆ *(for stress concentration)* $=$ ⁷⁄₁₆″ *at root of thread. (Stress concentration factor not required by AISC, but recommended here.)*

Minimum diameter $=$ ⅝″ *which furnishes a root diameter of 0.507″.*

Bent rod. The use of slant washers avoids bending the ridge rod.

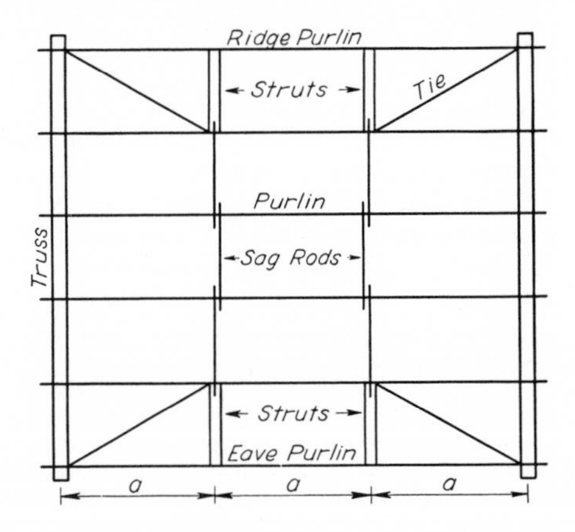

Remarks: *Multiple sag rods are required for very wide bays. Diagonal ties and short struts, as shown, provide three-panel trusses in the plane of the roof to resist snow covering one side only of a large roof. The truss at the eave is omitted for low-pitch roofs or light snow load. By AISC specifications a ½″ rod is obtained.*
$F_t = 0.4F_y = 13{,}200$ *psi for A7 rod.* $A = 2080 \div 13{,}200 = 0.158$ *in.*^{2}; $d =$ ½″.

instance, in a recent suspension bridge design, the eye bars for the chain were heat treated to produce an elastic limit of 75,000 psi and were stressed to nearly 50,000 psi. Even higher working stresses have been used.

Bridge specifications require that the eye bar have an excess net area of 35 per cent through the center of the pin over the body of the bar. The pin diameter is required to be not less than $\frac{8}{10}$ of the width of the widest bar attached. The thickness of the bar must be between 1 in. and 2 in., and it is commonly not less than $\frac{1}{8}$ of the width. To meet these specifications, it is frequently necessary for the designer to use several bars in parallel. Bars are required to be packed on the pin so that adjacent bars will not touch.

Courtesy Bethlehem Steel Co.

FIG. 111. EYE BARS 2¼-IN THICK FORM ANCHORAGE FOR SUSPENSION BRIDGE CABLE.

PROBLEMS

601. Redesign the welded bar of *DP*16*a* using a total stress of 28,000 lb. caused by wind. Detail the joint upon the assumption that the vertical members are 6 × 6 × ⅜-in angles. Use *AISC* allowable stresses for *A*36 steel and *E*60 weld electrodes.

602. Design a welded bar as a vertical hanger to carry a dead and live load stress of 75,000 lb. Detail its connection to the end of a 20-in., 65.4-lb. standard I-beam whose reaction it provides. Do not use overhead welds. *AISC* spec. *A*36 steel; choose weld.

603. Repeat Problem 602 by using two tension bars attached to the sides of the beam.

604. Design sag rods to be placed at the one-third points between roof trusses for a large industrial shed. Follow the details shown in *DS*17. Trusses are spaced at 20-ft. centers; roof slope, 30°; width of building, 65 ft.; eave overhang, 3 ft. Weight of roof covering, 6 psf; weight of purlins, 4 psf; snow load, 15 psf of roof surface. As a drafting room problem, sketch an elevation and plan of the roof showing details for placing the sag rods. Use *A*36 rods.

605. Design a sag rod for the side of an industrial building to support the girts at their midpoints. Column spacing, 16 ft.; height to eave, 30 ft.; weight of side-wall covering, including windows, 7 psf; weight of girts, 2 psf. Use *AASHO* Spec. 202 and illustrate all details clearly.

606. A balcony around a gymnasium floor is to be supported at its outer edge by tension rods or hangers connected to the roof trusses. If the balcony is 14 ft. wide, and the roof trusses are on 15-ft. centers, design the hangers for a dead load of 75 psf and a live load of 100 psf. Sketch a detail showing how to frame the floor system of the balcony to support it in this manner. *AISC* spec. for *A*7 steel.

Ans. 1 in. sq. or 1⅛ in. rd. upset rod.

Structural Shapes

122. Single Angle Tension Members Connected by One Leg. Whenever the force transmitted from a connection into a member is not in line with the center of gravity of the member, this eccentric force produces bending in the member. As far as possible, it is wise to design the connection to reduce this bending to a minimum. The use of members which are symmetrical about one or both axes is therefore desirable. Clearly, any single angle connected by one leg must resist such an eccentric force. Single angle tension members are widely used for light diagonal bracing.

The common specification is that the effective area of a single angle in tension shall be taken as *the net area of the connected leg plus one half the area of the unconnected leg.* The purpose of this specification is to allow empirically for the effect of the eccentric force. A lug angle connection, as shown in Fig. 112(a), is not to be considered as producing a connection to both legs, but it may be considered to transfer stress if it is welded to the main angle. It is far less effective for stress transfer if it is riveted to the main angle because of slip between the two. Nevertheless, a lug angle is always useful in resisting the moment acting on the rivets of the connection.

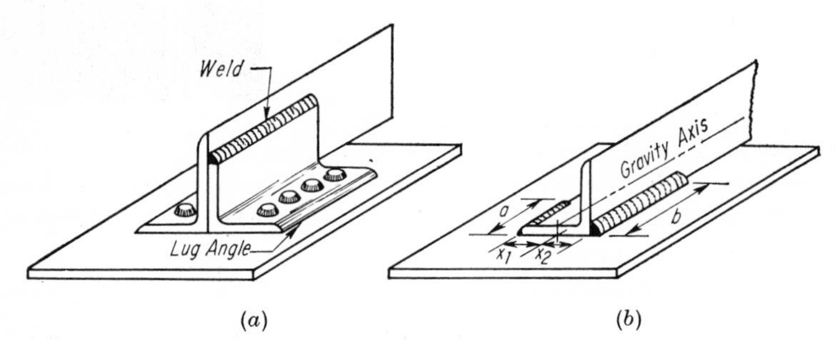

Fig. 112. Single Angle Connections.

Essentially the same specification applies to a single angle welded member as to a single angle riveted member. For the welded angle the gross area of the connected leg and one half of the gross area of the unconnected leg is effective. By use of a welded end connection, it is possible to make the connection resistance line up with the center of gravity of the angle in one plane (§113) although there will still be eccentricity of the load in the perpendicular plane. The proper detail is shown in Fig. 112(b). Of course, the combined length of the two welds a and b must be sufficient to develop the effective area of the member. Also, the moment of the force resisted by the weld a, about the gravity axis of the angle, must be the same as the moment of the force resisted by the weld b. It follows that the lengths of the welds a and b must be directly proportional to the distances x_2 and x_1 or $a \div b = x_2 \div x_1$. From this we obtain a convenient working formula, $\frac{a}{a+b} = \frac{x_2}{x_1 + x_2}$.

123. Examples of Angles Connected by One Leg, *DP*18 and *DP*19. The riveted single-angle tension member of the example *DP*18 is typical for a very light building truss. Trusses of standard weight usually have double angles of minimum section, even though they may not be needed for stress. Note that the end connection is designed to develop *the full value of the member* rather than its design stress. The resultant connection, 3 rivets, is the minimum connection usually accepted. A 2-rivet connection is regularly used for secondary members and by *AISC* specifications for light roof trusses. (Spec. 40.)

The welded tension diagonal of the example *DP*19 illustrates a typical arrangement of members for a fairly heavy welded roof truss. A split beam section makes an excellent chord member for such a truss in that the 9-in. web furnishes an adequate depth for attachment of the web members. The use of this section is limited to trusses for which the chord areas must be at least 4 sq. in. so that a 12-in. I-beam or WF beam may be split for the chords. The welded detail illustrates how the vertical and the diagonal may be welded to each other and to the chord by a single butt weld and by additional fillet welds.

Build-up Tension Members

124. Design of Riveted Tension Members other than Single Angles. The tension chords of riveted roof trusses and of highway bridge trusses often are formed of two or four angles, or, occasionally, of two channels. Roof trusses have single gusset plates, and the main tension members are usually two angles placed back to back on opposite sides of the gusset plate. Bridge trusses have double gussets. Light lower chord members may be double angles placed outside of the gusset plates. The diagonals for most highway bridge trusses are composed either of two angles with legs turned in, riveted inside of the gusset plates, or of a wide-flange beam section. The vertical members are small plate-girders or beam sections riveted between the gusset plates. The chord splice may be placed at a joint unless the number of rivets required to splice the angles of the chord is so great that excessively large gussets are required. This fact, however, has led specification writers to recommend that it is better to splice the chord between panel points. *Severe gusset-plate stresses* are also avoided thereby. Since both legs of the chord angles are fully connected to stiff plates which tend to prevent the angles from bending in either direction, even though the pull is slightly eccentric, the full net area of the chord angles may be taken as effective area. (Spec. 41.)

Stay or Tie Plates. All tension members composed of two or more separated pieces must have the parts connected by stay plates at intervals not exceeding 3 ft. clear. Stay plates serve to develop a reasonably uniform distribution of stress between separate parts of the member and to prevent

DP18. *Design a single angle web member of a light roof truss. Form a proper connection to a 5⁄16″ gusset with 3⁄4″ rivets. AISC spec. A36 steel, A141 rivets.*

Angle Size:

Design stress = 17,200# caused by DL + LL.

Net effective area = 17,200 ÷ 22,000 = 0.78 in.^{2}

Minimum angle. A 2½ × 2½ × 5⁄16″ angle is the minimum size.

Area furnished. Reduce area by 50 per cent of unconnected leg and deduct for one 7⁄8″ hole. (1⁄8″ larger than rivet diameter.)

$$A = (1.47 \times 0.75) - (0.875 \times 0.312) = 0.83 \text{ in.}^2$$

Rivets:

Rivet value in single shear = 0.44 × 15,000 = 6600#.
Rivet value in bearing = 0.312 × 0.75 × 48,500 = 11,400#.
Number of rivets = (22,000 × 0.83) ÷ 6600 = 2.8; use 3 rivets.

Remarks: *For light roof trusses this angle would ordinarily meet the strength requirement of most web members. Many designers would use the required net area of 0.78 in.*^{2} *to determine the number of rivets. Three rivets would still be needed. Note §125.*

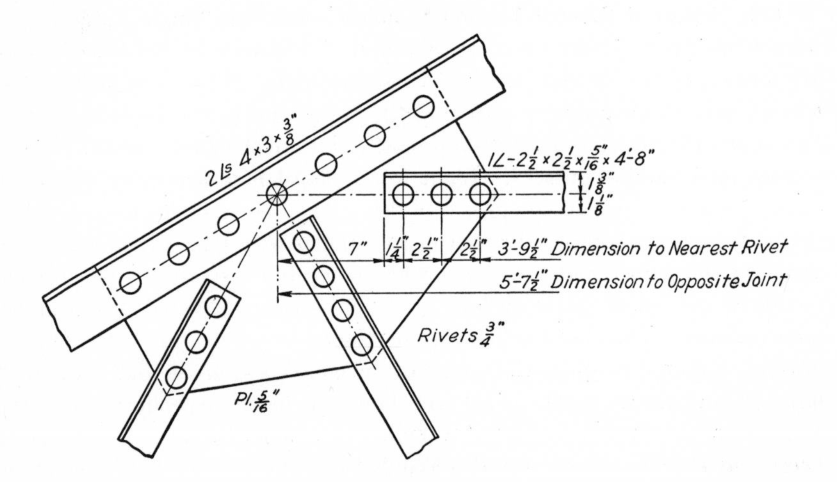

Detail: *The detail shown illustrates the proper way to dimension a member of a riveted joint. Information given on the angle controls its length and gage. Dimension lines show partial dimensions to locate the exact position of each rivet and the overall dimension for checking.*

bending or vibration of the individual parts. (Spec. 62.) A stay plate holding three rivets in each line is the minimum allowable size. End stay plates of main members are about twice this minimum length. The thickness of stay plates on main members must not be less than $\frac{1}{50}$ of the distance between the connecting lines of the rivets or welds. (Spec. 62.)

PROBLEMS

607. Redesign the tension member of *DP*18 for use in a welded structure. Design and detail the connection. Change the top chord to one half of a WF beam section equal to its present area. *AISC* spec.

608. Redesign the welded tension member of *DP*19 for use in a riveted structure. Change the lower chord to two angles of equivalent section and introduce a $\frac{5}{16}$-in. gusset plate between them.

609. A single angle member is to act as a hanger to support a balcony of a small theatre. The hangers are spaced 10 ft. apart to carry the outer ends of channel floor beams which frame into the walls at their other ends. The floor-beam channels are 15-in., 40-lb. sections. The width of the balcony is 18 ft. Design the hanger and a bolted connection to the channel web if the *DL* is 75 psf and the *LL* is 100 psf of floor area. Detail the connection to reduce eccentricity. Use *AISC* spec. Choose materials.

610. Redesign the hanger of Problem 609 if it is to have a welded connection. Design and sketch the connection detail.

611. Design the lower chord of a Fink roof truss for a stress of 62,000 lb. using *AISC* spec. This member is composed of two angles placed on opposite sides of a single $\frac{5}{16}$-in. gusset plate. Design the connection of the member to the end gusset plate to meet *AISC* Spec. 43. Detail the placing of rivets so that only a single rivet hole need be deducted from each angle.

125. Required Strength of Connections for Trusses. Specifications differ greatly on a most important subject, the required strength of connections in trusses. *AREA* has conservatively required that the connection develop the full strength of the member. In contrast, *AISC* requires that the connection be designed only to resist the maximum or actual stress, but not less than 50 per cent of the value of the member. Typically, *AASHO* takes a middle road by requiring that the connection develop the average of the actual load stress and the value of the member, but not less than 75 per cent of the value of the member. In main members for which excess area should be small, the author would recommend the design of connections that develop the members and thereby provide some excess strength at small cost. However, a secondary member may carry such a small stress that it would be ridiculous to develop the full value of the member. In such cases the reduced *AISC* connection of at least 50 per cent of the capacity of the member seems adequate.

DP19. *Design a welded double angle tension member for a diagonal of a light building truss (Pratt type) where the chords are split I-beams (18″-54.7#). AISC-A36.*

Size of Angles:

Maximum stress for the diagonal = 80,000#.

Gross area required = 80,000 ÷ 22,000 = 3.7 in.² or 1.85 in.² per ∠.

Angle size. A 3½ × 3 × 5⁄16″ angle has a gross area of 1.93 in.² The angles can be connected on the two sides of the I-beam web of the chord so that the entire gross area is considered effective.

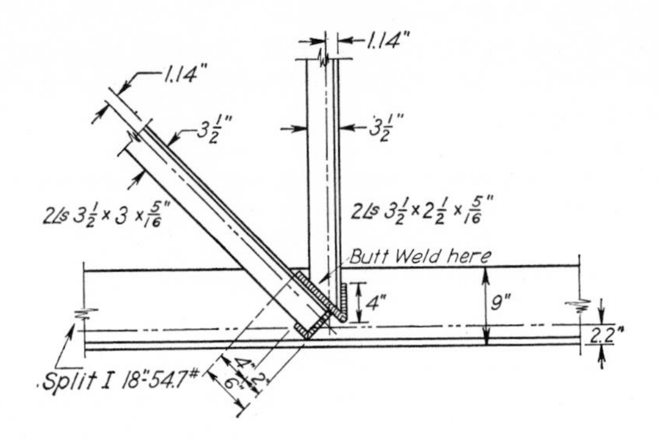

Connection:

Strength of the connection. Design for load of 40,000# per angle.

Value of weld. A 5⁄16″ fillet of a special E70 electrode weld will be used which has a safe load value of 1400# per ⅛″ of fillet leg.

Length of weld = 40,000 ÷ (1400 × 2.5) = 11.4″.

Division of weld. To shorten the side welds, a 3½″ weld can be placed across the end of the angle, leaving 7.9″ along the two sides. Then, by equations (4) and (5) from §113 where

L is the total length of the weld or 11.4″.

c is the width of the angle leg or 3.5″.

x is the distance of the gravity axis from the back of the ∠ or 1.06″.

$$a = \frac{Lx}{c} - \frac{c}{2} = \frac{11.4 \times 1.06}{3.5} - \frac{3.5}{2} = 1.7'', \text{ use } 2.0''.$$

$$b = 7.9 - 2.0 = 5.9''; \text{ use } 6'' \text{ as shown.}$$

Remarks: *The detail illustrates how the weld is to be placed on the diagonal. The use of a butt weld between the vertical and the diagonal can be avoided by shortening the vertical member sufficiently to allow space for two fillet welds.*

Compression Members

126. Design of Columns and Compression Members. The design of a compression member differs from the design of a tension member in two major characteristics: (1) the full gross area of a compression member is considered to be capable of taking stress (rivets are assumed to fill their holes completely); (2) the allowable stress on a compression member must be reduced below that of a tension member to allow a margin of safety against buckling. The need for this reduction of stress is clear if we realize that a long column centrally loaded will buckle and collapse under a load producing an *average* direct stress considerably below the elastic limit.

Column Formulas. Five types of column formulas have been widely recommended for practical use.

(1) The *Straight-Line* formula (*AREA* before 1935 and also used in building codes). Allowable $P/A = 15{,}000 - 50L/r$.

(2) The *Parabolic* formula (riveted end connections).

$$\text{Allowable } P/A = 15{,}000 - \frac{1}{4}\frac{L^2}{r^2} \quad (AREA \text{ and } AASHO). \text{ (Spec. 202.)}$$

(3) The *Rankine-Gordon* formula (*AISC* before 1962 for $L/r > 120$).

$$\text{Allowable } P/A = \frac{18{,}000}{1 + \dfrac{L^2}{18{,}000r^2}}.$$

(4) The *Secant* formula (*AREA* for $L/r > 140$ and riveted ends).

$$\text{Allowable } P/A = \frac{33{,}000/1.76}{1 + 0.25 \text{ sec.}\left(\dfrac{0.75L}{2r}\sqrt{\dfrac{1.76P/A}{E}}\right)} \quad \text{(factor of safety of 1.76).}$$

(5) The *Euler* formula (riveted ends and L/r above normal limits, i.e., > 200).

$$\text{Allowable } P/A = \frac{16E}{(L/r^2)} \div 2.2 \quad \text{(factor of safety of 2.2).}$$

AISC Column Formulas (Spec. 13). To cover all grades of structural steel the *AISC* column formulas are based upon the yield strength F_y.

$$(6)\ F_a = \text{Allowable } P/A = \left(\frac{1 - (L/r)^2/2C_c^2}{\text{Factor of Safety}}\right) F_y \text{ (used when } L/r < C_c).$$

$$(7)\ C_c = \sqrt{\frac{2\pi^2 E}{F_y}} \quad (C_c \text{ is the collapse value of } L/r \text{ when } F_a = 1/2F_y).$$

$$(8)\ FS = \text{Factor of Safety} = \frac{5}{3} + \frac{3(L/r)}{8C_c} - \frac{(L/r)^3}{8C_c^3} = 1.92 \text{ when } C_c = L/r.$$

(9) $F_a = \dfrac{149{,}000{,}000}{(L/r)^2}$ (Euler-type formula used when $L/r > C_c$).

The rather complex *AISC* procedure of column design as compared to the use of formulas (2) or (3) will be seen in the next sections to be an attempt to fit curves to test results for different elastic-limit steels and to recognize the validity of the Euler formula for slender columns. Table S-1 in the specifications provides a solution for formulas (6) to (9).

Column Action

127. Generalization about Test Results. It is possible to derive theoretical column formulas. Unhappily, test results do not usually agree with derived formulas, so that, finally, corrective constants have to be introduced. Therefore, we will approach this subject by reviewing tests first and then by considering a few useful theoretical expressions.

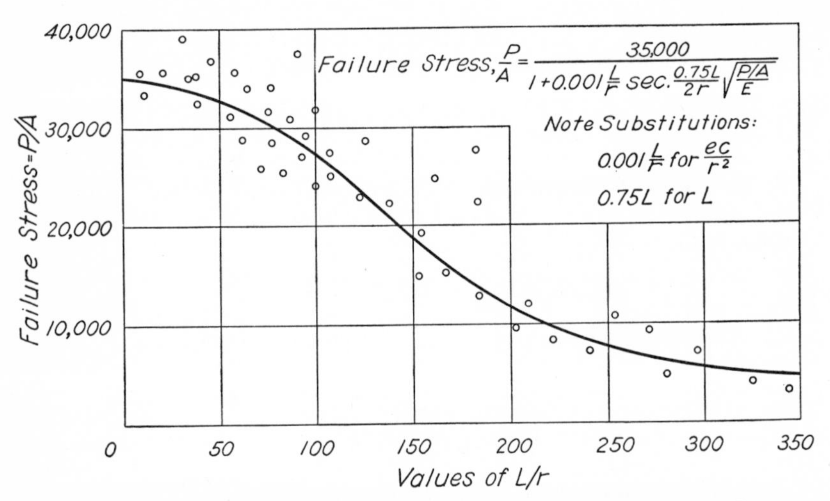

Fig. 113. Range of Test Results Compared with a Secant Curve for Built-up Steel Columns with Riveted Ends or Unlubricated Pins.

The plotting of column loads at failure in Fig. 113 indicates the general trend toward a reduction of strength with increase of slenderness, but, due to *non-homogeneity* or imperfections of materials, *inaccuracies* of manufacture, *differences of end restraint*, and *imperfect load application*, there is inevitably a considerable variation in test results obtained even in the same laboratory.[2] Columns in actual structures unquestionably vary to an even greater extent. Hence, for a limited range of L/r (say, from 40 to 140) either the straight line, the broken line, or the parabolic curve of Fig. 114

[2] Tests have also demonstrated that residual stresses influence the buckling resistance of columns in a rather complex manner.

might represent the test results of Fig. 113 with about the same effectiveness. Thus we are brought to the realization that the several column formulas of §126 may represent no greater differences of opinion as to column strengths than is inherent in the spread of test results. For the two decades before 1920, the straight-line formula was commonly recommended in standard specifications. Then the old Rankine-Gordon formula was resurrected and became popular. At the present time we have reverted to the parabolic formula, but the cycle will probably repeat itself in a generation or so. The fact is that no one of these formulas does a sufficiently good job of representing all test results to justify its use to the exclusion of all others.

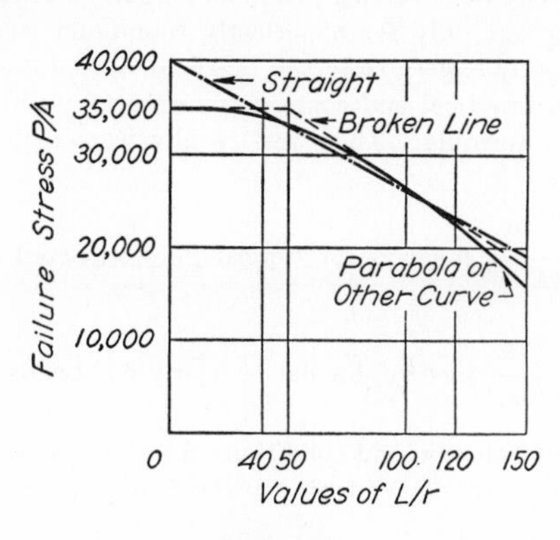

FIG. 114.
COMPARISON OF
COLUMN-LOAD CURVES.

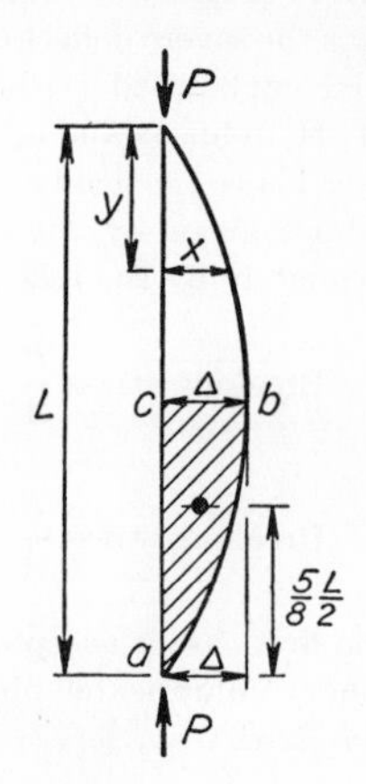

FIG. 115.
EULER DEFLECTION.

128. The Euler Formula for Slender Columns. The only inescapable theoretical conclusion in column studies is that *long slender columns* with perfectly round ends, when centrally loaded, buckle elastically and fail as described by the Euler formula. In Fig. 115 we have a deflected column with round ends supporting the load P. Evidently, the bending moment is Px, and the deflection curve has the same shape as the moment diagram. The stress just before buckling is almost entirely flexural stress if we restrict our study to long slender columns or splines. Hence, the deflection Δ can be computed as P/EI times the statical moment of the deflection area abc (cross-hatched)[3] about the point a. It is reasonably accurate to take the deflection curve and therefore the moment diagram as a parabola. Thus, we obtain

$$\Delta = \frac{P\Delta}{EI}\left(\frac{2}{3}\frac{L}{2}\right)\frac{5}{8}\frac{L}{2} = \frac{5}{48}\frac{PL^2}{EI}\Delta \tag{10}$$

[3] See *Theory of Modern Steel Structures*, Vol. 2. The deflection at A from a tangent drawn at B is equal to the statical moment of the M/EI area between A and B taken about the point A.

Since Δ occurs on both sides of the equation, it may be cancelled out. Hence, we obtain for the breaking load

$$P = \frac{9.6EI}{L^2}.$$

For the breaking stress, we write

$$\frac{P}{A} = \frac{9.6E}{(L/r)^2} = \frac{\pi^2 E}{(L/r)^2} \text{(nearly)}. \tag{11}$$

The final form of this expression is the theoretical Euler formula. The value of π^2 rather than 9.6 will appear if the elastic curve is used instead of a parabola.

Practical Revisions of Euler's Formula. First, the Euler equation should be divided by a factor of safety of about 2 because the load P is clearly the elastic buckling load that produces the severe deflection and heavy flexure occurring just before failure. Then, the deflected curve used is theoretically correct only for a perfectly round-end column. Both T. H. Johnson and J. B. Johnson, early experimenters in this field, agreed that the breaking loads for slender columns with practical end connections were very different from those given by the original Euler formula. Their test results were expressed approximately by the following formulas.

$$\text{Breaking stress } \frac{P}{A} = \frac{5}{3}\frac{\pi^2 E}{(L/r)^2} = \frac{16E}{(L/r)^2} \text{ (nearly) for typical pin connected ends,} \tag{12}$$

and

$$\text{Breaking stress } \frac{P}{A} = \frac{5}{2}\frac{\pi^2 E}{(L/r)^2} = \frac{25E}{(L/r)^2} \text{ (nearly) for flat or nearly fixed ends.} \tag{13}$$

The first case is accepted to represent common end conditions either due to the use of ordinary unlubricated pins or of riveted or welded ends that are slightly restrained but *far from fixed*.

129. Tangent Modulus Correction to the Euler Formula. In the derivation of the Euler equation, the M/EI area was used to compute the lateral deflection Δ. For structural steel it is natural to take E as constant and equal to 30,000,000. It is clear, however, that any reduction of E would be accompanied by an increase in Δ and in $M = P\Delta$, which would result in a reduction of the collapse load and in the calculated strength of the column. Aluminum alloys and many other alloys differ from carbon steel in that the stress-strain diagrams, beyond the straight line which terminates at the proportional limit, is a continuous gradually arched curve without a definite "yield point." For such materials the slope of the tangent to the stress-strain diagram is called the *tangent modulus of elasticity* whose value reduces gradually with each increment of stress beyond the proportional limit. See Fig. 116(*a*) for an example. The corresponding column formula is

$$P/A = \frac{\pi^2 E_t}{(L/r)^2}, \tag{14}$$

where E_t is the tangent modulus of elasticity corresponding on the stress-strain diagram to a compressive stress $F_a = P/A$.

In Fig. 116(*a*) use the top and left scales with the broken-line curve for tangent modulus.

For light-metal alloys the observed buckling loads have been found to agree quite closely with theoretical buckling loads computed from the Euler formula when adjusted (1) for appropriate end conditions and (2) for use of the tangent modulus of elasticity corresponding to the maximum sustained P/A stress. See Fig. 116(*b*) for an example.

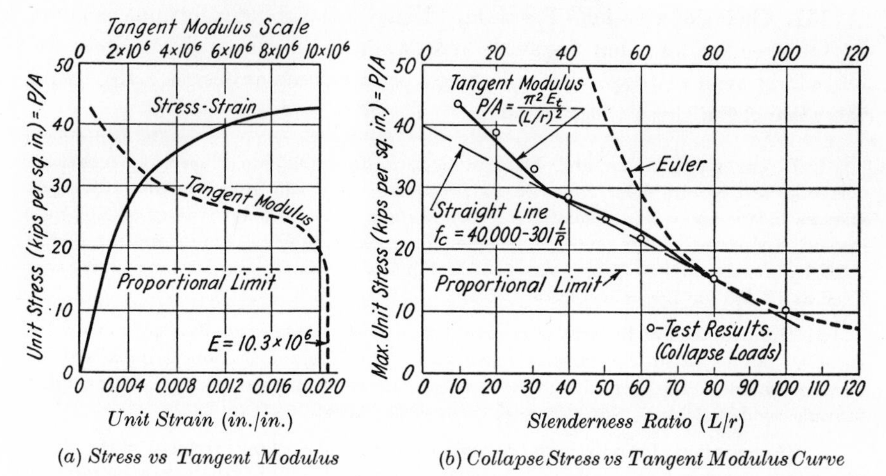

(*a*) *Stress vs Tangent Modulus* (*b*) *Collapse Stress vs Tangent Modulus Curve*

FIG. 116. COMPARISON OF TANGENT-MODULUS CURVE WITH TEST RESULTS FOR ROLLED ANGLE OF ALUMINIUM ALLOY AS GIVEN BY HILL AND CLARK.

130. The Secant Formula for All Column Lengths. For a column with an initial eccentricity of loading, e, which may be merely an initial crookedness, where c is the distance from the neutral axis of the section to the extreme compressive fiber, considerations inherent in an understanding of the Euler equation lead to the following formula:

$$\text{Breaking Stress } \frac{P}{A} = \frac{\text{Elastic Limit}}{1 + \frac{ec}{r^2} \sec \frac{L}{2r}\sqrt{\frac{P}{A}\frac{1}{E}}} \tag{15}$$

According to the *AREA* specifications this formula for working load becomes

$$\text{Allowable } \frac{P}{A} = \frac{33{,}000/1.76}{1 + 0.25 \sec \frac{0.75L}{2r}\sqrt{\frac{1.76}{E}\frac{P}{A}}} \tag{16}$$

This formula is intended to control columns with riveted ends above $L/r = 140$.

The secant formula can be made to fit test results for all values of L/r with good accuracy by proper choice of constants. (See Fig. 113, where a revised secant curve is used.) On the other hand, the fact that the working stress P/A, which we are trying to determine, also appears in the secant formula makes it so awkward to use that it will probably never be widely used. For a known load of eccentricity e, which produces both direct stress and flexure, it becomes the only column formula that logically attempts to express an allowable stress different from the one used for a centrally loaded column. The *AREA* specifications permit us to use equation (16) for all values of L/r when the eccentricity e is known; the crookedness factor 0.25 then is revised to become $(ec/r_2) + 0.25$.

131. Choice of a Column Formula. Usually the column formula is given by the specifications, but instances arise when the engineer must choose for himself, or even write specifications to govern a particular design. He should therefore check these observations:

1. If the straight-line and Rankine-Gordon formulas are chosen to represent correctly test results from $L/r = 50$ to $L/r = 120$, they will give excessive allowable stresses below $L/r = 50$. Usually, the formula is not used for low values of L/r, but, instead, a constant working stress is specified for stocky columns. For example, the 1920 *AREA* formula, 15,000-50L/r, was not used below $L/r = 50$; the working stress was fixed at 12,500 for L/r values from 0 to 50.

2. The straight-line formula may give values of allowable stress that are too low for slender columns where L/r exceeds about 120. The Rankine-Gordon formula may be used for values of L/r up to 200 or even more. However, for such slender columns this formula tends to give working stresses that are too high.

3. The parabolic formula may be made to represent working stresses for the range of L/r between 0 and 140 quite satisfactorily. Above this range, the parabolic formula is seriously in error on the conservative side.

4. The secant formula may be made to cover the entire range of L/r values with reasonable accuracy. It is cumbersome to use because the working stress to be computed also occurs in the formula, and it is extremely sensitive because of the great variation of the secant for angles near $\pi/2$. It is the only common formula, however, that offers a means of introducing a known eccentricity into the calculation of the allowable stress.

5. The Euler formula (11), which is the special case of the secant formula for zero eccentricity, should be used in studying very slender columns under centric loading (i.e. above $L/r = 200$). Remember that a factor of safety of about 2 should be introduced and remember to choose a proper coefficient to represent the best possible assumption about end conditions.

6. The tangent-modulus Euler formula ($P/A = \pi^2 E_t \div (L/r^2)$ is rational and is probably the best theoretical measure of collapse loading for aluminium and other light alloy columns. Its usefulness for structural steel columns is limited because the stress-strain diagram for mild steel does not change slope gradually. Hence E_t can not be determined with proper accuracy for all values of P/A, particularly between the proportional limit and the yield line.

7. The *AISC* parabolic formula (6), which is extended by formula (8) for L/r values above 120, offers the advantage of a variation of allowable stress with F_y in agreement with the observed variation of the strengths of stocky columns of different elastic-limit steels.

8. Plotted column formulas as shown by Fig. 117 should be compared with the range of test results, such as Fig. 113, to determine the range of slenderness ratio for which each column formula is applicable. Any formula becomes a good one that represents test results accurately for a given material and the range of L/r values under consideration.

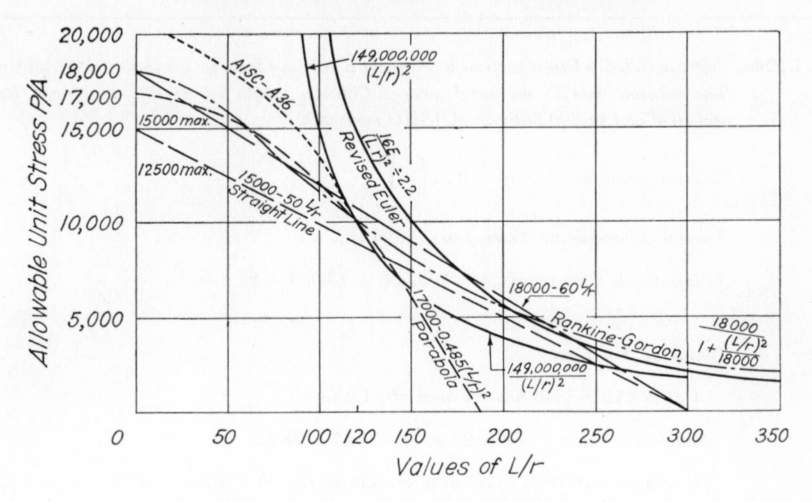

FIG. 117. COMPARISON OF COLUMN FORMULAS.

COLUMN DESIGN

132. Instructions to be Followed in Designing Compression Members.

1. Guess at the allowable unit stress, making it not more than the practical or stated upper limit for the column formula specified.

2. Divide the load by the assumed allowable stress to find the approximate gross area required.

3. Select a column cross section that will provide at least this required gross area, and compute the minimum radius of gyration for this section.

4. Calculate the maximum allowable unit stress for this section from the column formula using the least radius of gyration (minimum value of L/r) of the section selected.

5. If the calculated allowable stress does not exceed the actual average unit stress (total load divided by gross area of section selected) by more than 2 or 3 per cent, the section represents a good choice.

6. If the calculated allowable stress exceeds the actual unit stress by more than 5 per cent, the section is oversafe and uneconomical, and its area can usually, but not always, be reduced.

7. If the calculated allowable stress is smaller than the actual unit stress, the section is overstressed, and its area should be increased. It may be possible to make the column safe merely by spreading its parts further apart, so that its least radius of gyration will be increased. This change increases the allowable stress and therefore the allowable load without increasing the area of the section.

DP20a. *Select a rolled column section to support a balcony load in an industrial building. The column carries no wind stress. Column length is 20′-0″; total dead load and live load is 300,000#. AASHO spec. 202.*

Column formula. $15{,}000 - 0.25\left(\frac{L}{r}\right)^2$.

Assume allowable unit stress at 13,000 psi.

Approximate area required $= 300{,}000 \div 13{,}000 = 23.1$ *in.*^{2}

Tentative Section:

A 12WF79 section has an area of 23.2 in.^{2}

Slenderness ratio. $L/r = 20 \times 12 \div 3.05 = 78.8$.

Allowable unit stress by column formula $= 15{,}000 - 0.25 \times 78.8^2 = 13{,}450$ *psi.*

Revised Section:

The area can be reduced about 4 per cent if L/r is not changed appreciably. Try the 12WF72 section which has practically the same r-value as the 79# section.

Actual unit stress. $P/A = 300{,}000 \div 21.2 = 14{,}200$ *psi.*

Remarks: *The 12WF72 section is overstressed by 750 psi. Hence, we will choose the 12WF79 section since the overstress exceeded 1 per cent, a commonly accepted standard.*

DP20b. *Repeat DP20a by use of the AISC formulas, i.e., (6), (7), and (8) for A7 steel. Try the 12WF72 section checked above. Use* $L/r = 79.0$.

$$C_c = \sqrt{\frac{2\pi^2 E}{F_y}} = \pi\sqrt{\frac{2 \times 30{,}000{,}000}{33{,}000}} = 134.$$

$$\text{Factor of safety} = \frac{5}{3} + \frac{3}{8}\left(\frac{79}{134}\right) - \frac{1}{8}\left(\frac{79}{134}\right)^3 = 1.86.$$

$$F_a = \frac{1 - 1/2(79/134)^2 \times 33{,}000}{1.86} = 14{,}700 \text{ psi.}$$

For the 12WF72 section, P (allowable) $= 21.2 \times 14{,}700 = 310{,}000$#.

Remarks: *The section is understressed about 3 per cent, which is considered to be satisfactory design. A column base detail for this type of column is illustrated in Fig. 118. Calculations for the design of a column base plate for the 12WF72 section are given in §133.*

8. For columns below $L/r = 120$ the allowable stress by *AISC* and other specifications varies with the yield strength F_y. Economy may often be achieved by choice of a steel of high elastic limit even at an increased cost per pound.

The above instructions are applicable only to the design of a compression member for which the applied load is centric; that is, when there is no bending moment applied to the column.

133. Rolled Column Section. EXAMPLES *DP20a*, *DP20b*. Columns of rolled beam sections cost less per pound than built-up columns of angles and channels. They are therefore preferred unless a different shape of cross section is needed for convenient attachment of floor joists and girders. The illustrative problems *DP20a*, and *DP20b* show the selection of a typical building column for a story height of 20 ft. and for a column load of 300,000 lb. One section selected is a 12*WF*79 beam section for which the radii of gyration are 5.34 and 3.05. Since the least radius of gyration controls the allowable stress, a built-up section with equal radii about the two principal axes might weigh less. However, the fabrication cost would probably overbalance this possible saving.

Design of the Column Base. A column base will be designed to permit a bearing stress of 600 psi on the concrete footing.

Area of base plate required $= 300{,}000 \div 600 = 300$ sq. in. Try a standard base size 24×24 in. which produces a bearing pressure of 520 psi.

Bending moment in base plate. The base plate extends as a cantilever beam beyond the face of the column. The smaller dimension of the column is 12.08 in. It is common to reduce this dimension, which is the flange width b, to $0.8b$, as shown in Fig. 118, when computing the cantilever projection of the base plate. Therefore, the theoretical projection is $(24 - (0.8 \times 12.08)) \div 2 = 7.15$ in. The bending moment *per inch width* of plate is $\dfrac{520 \times 7.15^2}{2} = 13{,}300$ in-lb. For bearing plate flexure, $F_b = 25{,}000$ (*AISC*).

Section modulus required $= 13{,}300 \div 25{,}000 = 0.53$. Therefore, $d^2 = 6 \times 0.53$ or $d = 1.8$ in. Use a slab $24 \times 24 \times 1\frac{7}{8}$ in. of rolled *A*7 steel. If *A*242 or *A*440 steel is available, the allowable stress in flexure of a bearing plate is 34,500 psi for $F_y = 46{,}000$ psi, and the required thickness is found to be 1.5 in. which represents a significant economy.

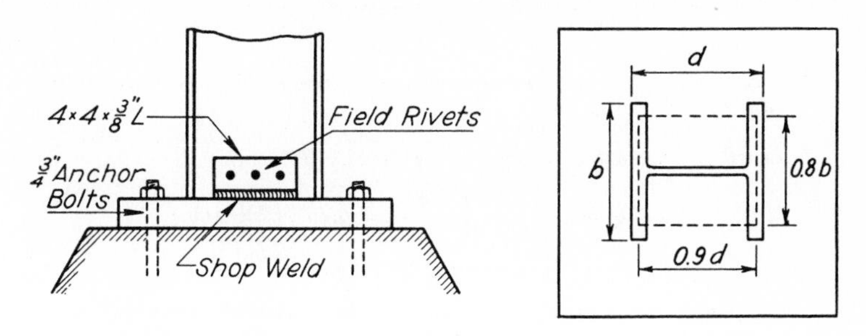

FIG. 118. COLUMN-BASE DETAIL.

Detail of base. The base usually is riveted to the column in the field by use of a pair of clip angles to the column web. The face of the column is planed flat to produce a perfect bearing on the rolled slab. The clip-angle connections may be welded to the base plate in the shop. Angles $4 \times 4 \times \frac{3}{8}$ in. are adequate since their only purpose is

DP21. *Design an eave strut for a large industrial building where the width of bay (strut length) is 20′-0″. The design stress is 5000# caused by wind. AISC spec. A36 steel.*

Section: *Two channels separated by the 12″ width of the vertical column and riveted to the faces of the column will be used. Channels will be laced top and bottom.*

Minimum radius of gyration.

Max. $L/r = 200$; *hence* $r_{min.} = 20 \times 12 \div 200 = 1.20''$.

Trial section. The lightest 4″ channel has a min. r of 0.45 and a max. r of 1.56.

Value of Section: *Area* = 3.12 *in.*². (4″[s @ 5.4#.)

$$\text{Allowable stress} = \frac{149{,}000{,}000}{(20 \times 12 \div 1.56)^2} = 6300 \text{ psi.}$$

Allowable load = 6300 × 3.12 = 19,600#.

The allowable wind load is 1.33 × 19,600 = 26,000#. (*Spec. 19.*)

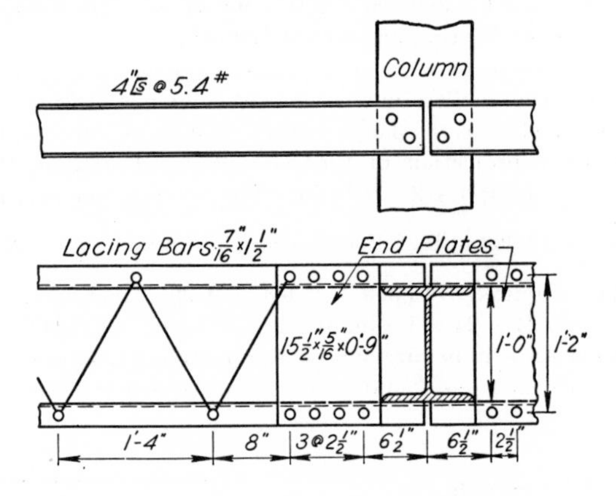

Lacing Bars: 60° *single lacing is adequate since L/r between rivets of channel* = 16/0.45 = 36. (*Spec. 60.*)

Length of bar between rivets = $\sqrt{14^2 + 8^2} = 16\tfrac{1}{8}''$.

$$\text{Min. thickness of bar} = \frac{1}{0.288}\left(\frac{16.12}{140}\right) = 0.40''. \text{ (Spec. 60.)}$$

Use a bar 1½″ × 7⁄16″ *punched for* ½″ *rivets.*

Tie plates. Select to fulfil Spec. 59 for intermediate tie plates.

End Connection: *Value of* ¾″ *rivets in bearing on channel web* = (0.75 × 0.18 × 48,500) 1.33 = 8700#. *Single shear value* = 6600#. (*A141 rivets.*)

Number of rivets to develop the 5000# stress would be only one. A minimum connection of two rivets through each channel web is provided.

to keep the column in its proper position. Four anchor bolts of ¾-in. diameter are used to locate the base plate accurately on the footing. (See Fig. 118.)

REMARKS. If any possibility exists that the column may be struck by a moving crane load or by a moving truck, it will be necessary to use heavier clip angles and to anchor the base plate to the footing with larger anchor bolts. Some designers prefer to use clip angles on both web and flange.

134. Struts and Light Compression Members. Stiff struts frequently are required in steel structures where the actual compressive load to be carried is relatively small. For instance, the eave strut in a mill building may have to carry a total load of only 2000 or 3000 lb. and still have to act as a horizontal column with an unsupported length of 16 to 24 ft. Any column which will meet the requirement that the maximum L/r must not exceed 200, will have several times the required strength. Where the span is relatively short, two angles placed back to back form a fair strut. A Tee formed of a channel and angle placed back to back or two channels provide a section that may be used for longer spans. However, the most satisfactory strut, for important uses, is formed by two channels with flanges turned out and laced on both sides. These sections are illustrated in Fig. 119.

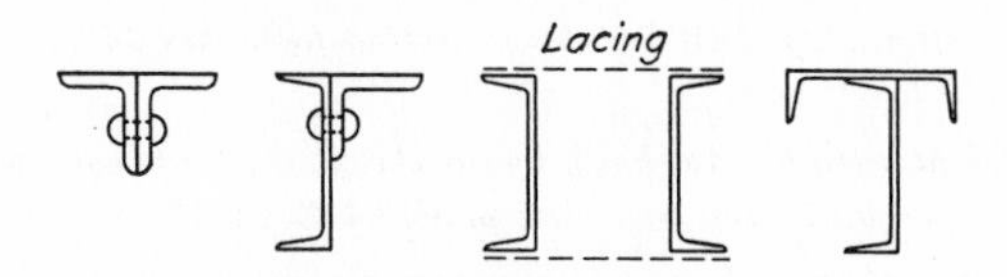

FIG. 119. SECTIONS FOR LIGHT STRUTS.

DESIGN OF A MILL BUILDING STRUT, *DP*21. Light eave struts and similar bracing members seldom carry enough stress to make an economical design possible. The strut of problem *DP*21 has a load of only 5000 lb., while the capacity of the minimum section is 26,000 lb. Since the member has to act as a beam of 20-ft. length to carry its own weight, which produces a fiber stress in flexure of about 2500 psi, the actual capacity of the member is considerably less than 26,000 lb. The design of a member to resist both direct stress and flexure will be discussed later, but it is evident that this member is amply strong and that a further anlaysis is unnecessary.

Lacing bars were selected to meet the requirement as to L/r value of 140 for single lacing (Spec. 60), but they were not checked to determine their capacity to resist a lateral shear. The requirement that they shall resist a lateral shear of 2 per cent of the direct stress would set up a compressive design stress of $(0.02 \times 5000) \div \sin 60° = 116$ lb. The unit stress in one bar would be $116 \div 2(0.44 \times 1.5) = 88$ psi. Evidently, this *specification stress* is insignificant for the lacing of light struts and will only influence the design of lacing bars for short columns that are heavily loaded.

It is also worth mentioning that the end tie plates selected do not meet the requirements for end tie plates from Spec. 59. They were chosen to meet the requirements for intermediate tie plates. The explanation is that this member is not in any sense a *main* compression member for which the end tie plates perform a very important function in distributing stresses uniformly. To meet the requirements for the end tie plate of a main compression member (Spec. 59) would overbalance the design.

DP22. *Design a split I-beam section to act as the compression chord of a quadrangular roof truss. There is lateral support provided at each panel point. A7 steel and AISC spec.*

Data:

Panel length is 12′-0″.

Design stress = 100,000# for DL + LL and 25,000# for wind.

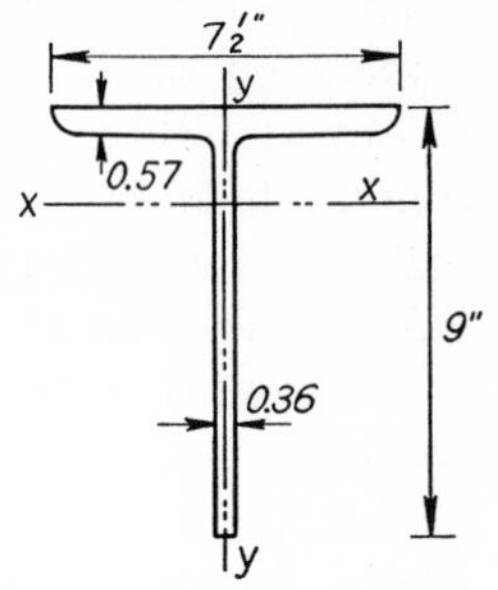

Working Stress:

$$\text{Allowable Compression} = \frac{1 - \frac{1}{2}\left(\frac{L/r}{C_c}\right)^2}{F.S} F_y.$$

$$C_c = \sqrt{\frac{2\pi^2 E}{F_y}} \text{ and } F.S. = \frac{5}{3} + \frac{3}{8}\left(\frac{L/r}{C_c}\right) - \frac{1}{8}\left(\frac{L/r}{C_c}\right)^3.$$

Allowable increase for wind = 33⅓ per cent.

Selection of Cross Section:

Assumed allowable stress = 14,000 psi.

Approx. area reqd. = 100,000 ÷ 14,000 = 7.15 in.²

Wind stress is neglected since it is less than ⅓ of DL + LL stress.

Trial section. An 18WF50 beam section furnishes 14.71 in.² or 7.35 in.² for each split tee.

Equivalent section. As shown by the sketch, the tee is equivalent to a horizontal plate 7.5″ × 0.57″ and a vertical plate 8.43″ × 0.36″.

Moment of inertia about axis of symmetry (minimum I).

$$\text{Horizontal plate.} \quad \frac{1}{12} \times 0.57 \times 7.5^3 = 20.07.$$

$$\text{Vertical plate.} \quad \frac{1}{12} \times 8.43 \times 0.36^3 = 0.03.$$

$$\text{Total } I = 20.10.$$

Radius of gyration.

$$r = \sqrt{\frac{I}{A}} = \sqrt{\frac{20.10}{7.35}} = 1.65''.$$

$$\text{Allowable stress.} \quad C_c = \pi\sqrt{2 \times 30{,}000{,}000 \div 33{,}000} = 133.$$

$$F.S. = 1.67 + \frac{3}{8}\left(\frac{87}{133}\right) - \frac{1}{8}\left(\frac{87}{133}\right)^3 = 1.87.$$

$$F_a = \frac{1 - 1/2(87/133)^2}{1.87} \times 33{,}000 = 13{,}900 \text{ psi.}$$

$$\text{Actual stress} = \frac{100{,}000}{7.35} = 13{,}600 \text{ psi.}$$

Remarks: *The 18WF50 section will be understressed by 2 per cent. It is therefore safe and reasonably economical The wind stress, being less than one third of the DL + LL stress does not influence the section.*

PROBLEMS

612. Select a rolled column section to carry a direct load of 500,000 lb. The length is 18 ft.-0 in. Use the appropriate *AISC* column formula. (Spec. 13.) Design a rolled base plate for this column, assuming an allowable bearing pressure of 600 psi. Check your design by *AISC* table of column base plates. Detail the base connection. *A*36 steel.

613. Same as 612, but change the column load to 750,000 lb. and the allowable bearing to 800 psi under the base plate.

614. Determine the allowable load on the following columns as controlled by the *AISC* specifications for *A*36 steel.

12-in. *WF*, 99 lb. per ft., length 35 ft.	*Ans.* 235 kips.
14-in. *WF*, 158 lb. per ft., length 14 ft.	*Ans.* 884 kips.
14-in. *WF*, 426 lb. per ft., length 26 ft.	*Ans.* 2033 kips.

615. Redesign the eave strut from *DS*21 by making use of a cross section composed of a channel and angle placed back to back. Design the connection of the strut to the column. Suggestion—try a 5-in. channel and a 4 × 3 × ¼-in. angle with the 4-in. leg outstanding.

616. Same as 615, but use two channels as a T-section. Use *A*7 steel.

617. Design by *AISC* specifications a two-angle strut with angles placed back to back to act as stiff bracing between the lower chords of steel building trusses. The length is 25 ft. The P/A stress to be carried may be considered negligible. Restrict the deflection to 0.5 in. caused by the dead weight of the member. Use *A*36 steel.

618. Design a vertical member of a highway bridge to carry a direct load of 120,000 lb. in compression. The length of the member is 22 ft.-6 in. Use two channels with flanges turned out, laced. Determine the required distance back to back of channels. Use the *AASHO* specifications for highway bridges.

Truss Members

135. Design of Compression Chords for Roof Trusses. The compression chord of a riveted or bolted roof truss is usually of two angles so that a single gusset plate can be placed between the angles for the joint connection. A welded roof truss, which needs no gussets, can be formed with a tee-shaped compression member obtained by splitting a wide flange beam section. The type of roof construction has much to do with the design of such a chord member. The free length for buckling is controlled by the connections for the diagonal roof bracing and is usually taken as the longest distance between such connections. Some *lateral stability* will be obtained from the purlins, but they are not ordinarily considered to be fully effective for this purpose.

Design of a Split-Beam Chord Member, *DP*22. This example illustrates the design of a split-beam compression section by use of the *AISC* parabolic type of column formula. The final allowable stress for the 18*WF*50 section is shown to be about 300 psi above the actual stress. For comparison the next lighter section is found to be about 500 psi overstressed.

DP23. *Design the center diagonal of a Warren bridge truss, which undergoes reversal. The member is 11′-3″ long. Use two angles with legs turned in. Use AASHO spec.*

Compression Member:

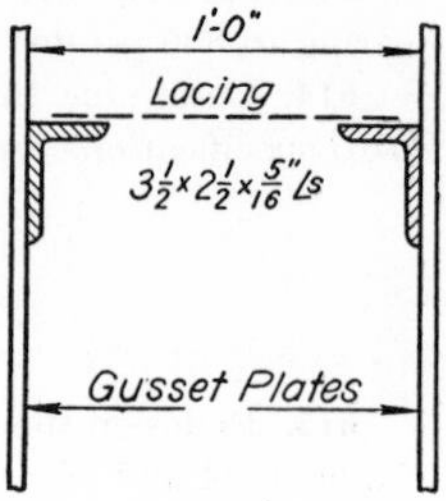

Maximum stresses are ±26,000#.

Design stresses = ±26,000 × 1.5 = ±39,000#.

AASHO spec. increases each by ½ of smaller.

A section will be selected for compression and checked for tension.

Column formula. $P/A = 15{,}000 - \frac{1}{4}\left(\frac{L}{r}\right)^2$.

Estimated allowable stress = 11,000 psi.

1′-0″
Lacing
$3\frac{1}{2} \times 2\frac{1}{2} \times \frac{5}{16}$″ ∠s
Gusset Plates

Approx. area reqd. = 39,000 ÷ 11,000 = 3.6 in.^{2}

Trial section. 2 angles 3½ × 2½ × 5⁄16″ furnish a gross area of 3.56 in.^{2}

The controlling value of r is 1.11.

Allowable unit stress $= 15{,}000 - \frac{1}{4}\left(\frac{135}{1.11}\right)^2 = 11{,}300$ *psi.*

The section is therefore satisfactory for compression.

Check on Tensile Stress:

Net area. Assume one ⅞″ hole to be deducted from each leg. The net area is 3.56 − 2 × 0.875 × 0.31 = 3.0 in.^{2}

Effective area. For this type of member with lacing and end tie plates the net area may be effective.

Tensile stress = 39,000 ÷ 3.0 = 13,000 psi. (Allowable $F_t = 18{,}000$.)

End Connection; Field Rivets:

Connection value = 2 × 26,000 = 52,000#. AASHO spec. requires use of max. + min. stress.

Rivet value in single shear = 0.44 × 13,500 = 5930#.

" " " *bearing = 0.312 × 0.75 × 27,000 = 6300#.*

Number of rivets = 52,000 ÷ 5930 = 8.8. Use 5 rivets in each ∠.

Controlling Specification: *If the alternate stresses occur in succession during one passage of the live load, each shall be increased by 50 per cent of the smaller. The connections of such members shall be proportioned for the sum of the net alternate stresses not so increased.*

PROBLEMS

619. Redesign the member from *DS*22 by making use of a section composed of two angles with legs turned in and tack welded together.

620. Design a member similar to the one designed on *DS*22 but where the total *DL* plus *LL* stress is 80,000 lb. and the wind stress is 30,000 lb. Use *AISC* specifications and working stresses for *A*36 steel.

621. Select the proper section for a top chord member of a welded roof truss where the design stress is 16,000 lb., of which 10,000 lb. is caused by wind. The panel length and the distance between purlins are both 5 ft. If a split I-beam or WF-beam is used as a T-section, remember that the depth must be great enough to hold the welded connections for the web members. This requires at least 5 in. Use *AISC* specifications. Length for buckling is 10 ft. between lateral diagonals. Choose material.

Special Problems in Column Design

136. Design of Members that Undergo Reversal. The diagonals of a Warren bridge truss and certain members of other trusses may reverse from tension to compression or *vice versa* during the passage of the live load. The usual bridge specification is that the maximum tensile and maximum compressive stresses shall be calculated and that each shall be increased by 50 per cent of the smaller stress; then the member shall be proportioned so that it will be able to resist each increased stress. Depending upon the ratio between these increased stresses, the member will be designed for tension and checked for compression or else the process will be reversed. In all cases the connections are designed to resist the sum of the original unincreased stresses.

Design of a Chord Member of a Warren Bridge Truss, *DP*23. In this member, which is at the center of the span, the maximum tension and the maximum compression are identically equal, the dead load stress being zero. The section is therefore selected as a compression member and checked for tension with one rivet hole removed from each angle leg. The connection must be able to resist the sum of the two maximum stresses since continued reversal of stress tends to loosen up the rivets of the end connections.

PROBLEMS

622. Design a member for reversal where the maximum and minimum stresses are each 34,000 lb. All other data are the same as those for the example worked out in *DP*23. Design the end connection, and select the end plate and size of lacing bar if the distance back to back of angles is 10 in.

623. Design a diagonal of a Warren truss for a maximum tensile stress of 40,000 lb. and a maximum compressive stress of 26,000 lb. The length of the member is 15 ft. Use two angles laced with flanges turned in. Follow *AASHO* specifications. Design the end connection and select the end tie plate and size of lacing bar if the distance back to back of angles is 12 in.

624. Design a diagonal of a deck Warren truss for a maximum stress of +60,000 lb. and for a minimum stress of −60,000 lb. The length of the member is 16 ft.-3 in. Follow *AASHO* specifications. Use two channels laced on both sides with flanges turned in. Select channels with web thickness at least 5/16 in. Redesign this member using two angles laced. Which is the better design?

137. The Importance of Careful Design of Compression Members. The design of each member in a structure is important, but there are reasons why the design of the compression members is critical. Distortion of a tension member starts taking place when the member passes the elastic limit, but a fracture will not occur until the tension stress reaches the ultimate strength which, for ductile structural steel, is nearly twice the elastic limit. In contrast, a compression member of ordinary proportions buckles and collapses at a load about equal to the elastic limit, while a slender strut may fail at one half of this unit stress. Evidently then, we do not really have as great an *ultimate factor of safety against complete collapse* in the compression members as in the tension members of our structures. Of course, this statement assumes that the quality of steel and the design are such as to provide ductility and thus avoid any possibility of brittle fracture of a tension number or a connection.

Another consideration should be the influence of eccentricity of load which may be caused either by load position, by initial crookedness, or from eccentric end connections. The deflection of an eccentrically loaded tension member decreases as the load is increased and is greatly reduced by the change in shape that takes place beyond the elastic limit. A column, on the other hand, changes shape in a direction that increases the initial eccentricity when the elastic limit is passed. Hence, the compression members are an unquestioned source of weakness for structures where the loads may become eccentric to the axes of the members. Even the possibility of a collision with resultant bending of a member is a much more serious consideration in the design of compression members than for tension members.

These thoughts simply clarify the need for careful analysis of all loads that may come onto the compression members of a structure and the importance of adequate design. Localized buckling needs study as much as buckling of the member as a whole. Designing such details as lacing bars and end tie plates in a conservative manner is a wise precautionary measure. The weakness of a lacing bar connection was believed to have caused one failure of the great Quebec cantilever bridge.

Combined Direct Stress and Flexure

138. Members that Resist Direct Stress and Flexure. All truss members which lie in a horizontal or inclined plane must resist a bending moment caused by their own weight. All such members, therefore, resist direct stress and flexure. Flexure is of less importance in the design of tension members than compression members, because the direct pull of a tension member tends to reduce lateral deflection while the thrust of a compression member tends to increase lateral deflection. The result for the compression member is that any applied centric force tends to become slightly eccentric. This is one of the reasons why specifications limit the slenderness ratio of compression members and struts below the limit for tension members. Whenever possible, a compression member that is not vertical should be designed sufficiently stiff so that the lateral deflection caused by its own weight will be negligible. Tension members should be designed with a large enough moment of inertia about the horizontal axis so that the flexural stress caused by dead load bending moment may be neglected. The specifications regarding slenderness ratio are usually such that the dead load flexure need not be considered.

Some members of trusses, particularly of roof trusses, must actually be designed to carry transverse loads. For instance, purlins are frequently placed away from the panel points of a roof truss, with the result that the top chord must act as a beam between panel points. Occasionally it is necessary to hang light fixtures or shafting from the lower chord of a roof truss away from a panel point. In such instances the member must be designed so that the fiber stress for combined direct stress and flexure will not exceed the proper allowable stress in tension or compression. The *AISC* Code limits the working stress to an intermediate value when the allowable stresses in direct stress and flexure are unequal. (Spec. 20.)

Columns may undergo flexure from the effect of an eccentric load or from the influence of wind shear. Building columns frequently support beams attached by clip angles to their flanges. The beam reaction has an eccentricity of at least one half of the width of the column. The portals of bridges and the transverse bents and portals of industrial buildings resist heavy bending moments caused by wind shear. These wind moments must be considered in the design of the columns.

139. Flexure of a Diagonal of a Bridge Truss Caused by Its Weight.

PROBLEM. Compute the bending stress in a diagonal member of a low truss Warren highway bridge caused by its own dead weight.

Data.

Panel length = 15 ft.-0 in.
Length of diagonal = 18 ft.-0 in.
Section. Two 6 × 4 × ⅜-in. angles with short legs turned in and laced together. (See Fig. 120.) This is a typical cross-section for a web member which is arranged to fit between a pair of chord channels

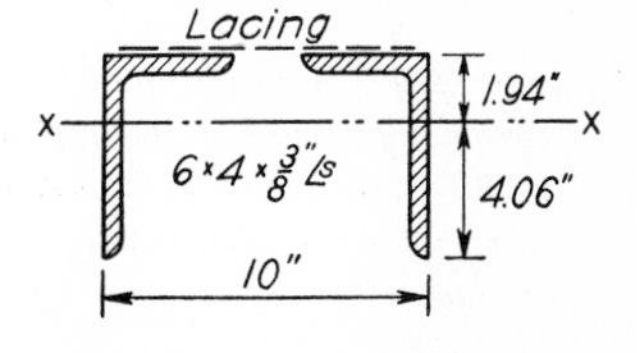

FIG. 120. CROSS-SECTION.

DP24. *The lower tension chord of a Fink roof truss carries a shaft load at its center in addition to its direct stress. Design the member for riveted construction. Let the legs of the chord angles be turned down.*

Data:

Direct stress = 11,000#.
Panel length = 18′-0″.
Transverse load = 300# at center of member.
Working stress = 22,500 psi in combined tension and flexure.

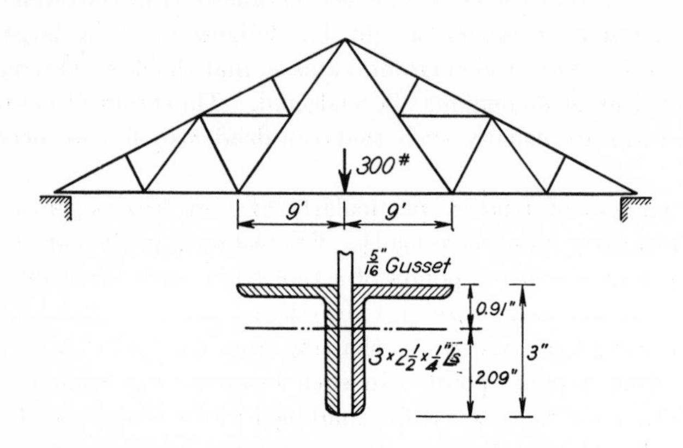

Minimum Section: *Try two 2½ × 2½ × ¼″ ∠s. (Note remarks.)*
Gross area = 2 × 1.19 = 2.38 in.²
Direct unit stress = 11,000 ÷ 2.38 = 4600 psi.
Gross section modulus = 2 × 0.39 = 0.78 (angle legs turned down).

$$\text{Bending moment} = \left(\frac{300 \times 18}{4} + \tfrac{1}{8} \times 8.2 \times 18^2\right)12 = 20{,}200''\#.$$

Flexural stress = 20,200 ÷ 0.78 = 25,900 psi.
Total stress = 4600 + 25,900 = 30,500 psi.

Revised Section: *Try two 3 × 2½ × ¼″ ∠s (3″ legs turned down).*
Gross area = 2 × 1.31 = 2.62.
Gross section modulus = 2 × 0.56 = 1.12.

$$\text{Bending moment} = \left(\frac{300 \times 18}{4} + \tfrac{1}{8} \times 9.0 \times 18^2\right)12 = 20{,}600''\#.$$

$$\text{Total stress} = \frac{11{,}000}{2.62} + \frac{20{,}600}{1.12} = 22{,}600 \text{ psi}.$$

Remarks: *The use of gross area and gross section modulus is correct, provided that holes are not punched in the angles near the midspan at the section of maximum moment. The shaft connection can be made by a clamp. The bending moment is greatly reduced at the end where net section would have to be considered. Bending moment due to the weight of the member is neglected in most designs.*

Weight of Member.

Weight of angles $= 2 \times 12.3 \times 18$ $= 442$ lb.
Weight of lacing bars and tie plates (assumed) $= 70$ lb.
Total $= 512$ lb.

Bending moment for span equal to a panel length $=$
$\frac{1}{8} WL = \frac{1}{8} \times 512 \times 15 \times 12 = 11{,}500$ in-lb.

Properties of the Section.

Moment of inertia $= 13.5 \times 2 = 27.0$ in.^{4}
Radius of gyration $= 1.93$ in. (about x–x axis).
Slenderness ratio $= (18 \times 12) \div 1.93 = 112$.

Flexural Stress.

$$S = \frac{Mc}{I} = \frac{11{,}500 \times 4.06}{27.0} = 1730 \text{ lb. per sq. in. (Tension)}$$

REMARKS. The bending moment computed above is high for two reasons. The gusset plate cuts down the length of the member for flexure, and it also partially fixes the end of the member so that the bending moment is reduced below $WL/8$. The stress of 1730 psi is not excessive and may be neglected unless the member also carries a high secondary flexural stress. A provision for a flexural stress of 30 per cent of the primary stress is made in setting the allowable stress.

THEORY OF COMBINED ACTION

140. Tension or Compression with Flexure. The simplest possible approach to this problem is to add the two fiber stresses as defined by the direct stress formula and the flexure formula. Thus we obtain

$$f = \frac{P}{A} + \frac{Mc}{I}. \tag{17}$$

This equation expresses the combined stress correctly, but there may be some question, especially for columns, as to what limitation should be placed upon the combined fiber stress. Some specifications (*AREA* for example) state quite plainly that the combined fiber stress shall not be greater than the allowable stress as controlled by the column formula. For use with such specifications, this formula may be rearranged as follows:

$$f = \frac{P}{A} + \frac{Mc}{Ar^2} \text{ (where } f \text{ is the actual unit stress),} \tag{18}$$

$$A = \frac{P}{f} + \frac{Mc}{fr^2}, \tag{19}$$

or, as a design formula

$$A = \frac{P + Mc/r^2}{F} \text{ (where } F \text{ is the allowable unit stress).} \tag{20}$$

Design problem $DP24$ is handled by use of equation (18).

The use of equation (20) is limited to the case where the same allowable stress is permitted for direct stress and for flexure. It also neglects the influence of lateral deflection upon flexure stresses. For determining the allowable load P of eccentricity e, we may solve equation (20) by substituting Pe for M. Thus we obtain

$$P = \frac{FA}{1 + ec/r^2}, \text{ and also } A = \frac{P}{F}\left(1 + \frac{ec}{r^2}\right). \tag{21}$$

141. Influence of Deflection. It will be possible to place limits upon the influence of deflection upon the design of members for the combination of direct stress and flexure. Of course, deflection may be neglected for tension members, since its small influence is toward the reduction of moment, but even for columns the actual influence of lateral deflection usually will be found to be small. Hence in practical design it is not common to introduce the influence of the deflection which changes the moment in equation (20) from M to M_t, where

$$M_t = M \pm P\Delta. \tag{22}$$

142. Different Working Stresses. The working stress for direct stress in a column F_a is controlled by a column formula, while the working stress for beam compression F_b is either a fixed value or it is controlled by a beam-flange compression formula to be discussed in §151. It is possible in most instances, therefore, to effect economy by the use of two separate working stresses in equations (19) or (20). The revised formula becomes

$$A = \frac{P}{F_a} + \frac{Mc/r^2}{F_b}. \tag{23}$$

Equation (23) cannot be derived from basic theory. It is an approximation drawn intuitively from equations (19) and (20). Another form of equation (23) is useful for checking a given section to determine the allowable value of a direct load P acting with a known eccentricity e. M then becomes Pe, and one may solve equation (23) for P.

$$P = \frac{AF_a}{1 + \frac{ec}{r^2}\left(\frac{F_a}{F_b}\right)} \tag{24}$$

The reader should note that L does not appear directly in equations (23) or (24), although it does influence F_a and F_b.

In equations (23) and (24) F_a is controlled by the column formula and F_b is controlled by the beam-compression formula. This procedure is not entirely logical, however. For example, the value of F_b may be controlled by a tendency to buckle in one direction, while F_a may have to be chosen for buckling about the other axis because of the direction of the lateral forces. Obviously, collapse must occur by buckling about one axis, or else torsional resistance should be considered. Also, most column failures start locally, while both F_a and F_b are based upon the action of the column as a whole. Nevertheless, equation (23) is usually considered to be a rational attempt at improved design.

INTERACTION FORMULAS. It has been noted that formulas (23) or (24) did not predict quite accurately the strength of columns undergoing beam action except when the bending moment was large and the direct load was relatively small. Hence the *AISC* specification introduces a factor (here termed k') into equation (23)

$$A = \frac{P}{F_a} + k' \frac{Mc/r^2}{F_b}, \tag{25}$$

where $k' = 1.0$ when $f_a/F_a < 0.15$, but otherwise

$$k' = \frac{0.85}{1 - f_a/F_e'}, \text{ where } F_e' = \frac{149{,}000{,}000}{(L/r)^2}. \tag{26}$$

If the area A furnished is equal to or greater than required by (25) we may write

$$\frac{P/A}{F_a} + k' \frac{Mc/I}{F_b} \leq 1.0 \quad \text{or} \quad \frac{f_a}{F_a} + k' \frac{f_b}{F_b} \leq 1.0, \tag{27}$$

which is merely a convenient form of equation (25) for use in testing a known section. It is believed that the use of the factor k' rather than unity as in equation (23) leads to improved design particularly when the major stress is P/A.

DESIGN PROBLEMS

143. Design of Truss Members for Direct Stress and Bending. EXAMPLES *DP*24, *DP*25. These problems illustrate the two techniques of design most commonly used. In *DP*24 there is a single working stress, because this is a tension member for which the allowable tensile stress is the same as the stress permitted for flexure. Accordingly, the procedure is to choose a section and then to compute the maximum combined fiber stress.

The design problem *DP*25 illustrates the design procedure when the allowable working stress for direct load is not the same as for flexure. One area is found for compression and a second area to resist flexure—the total area required being the sum of the two. It must be noted, however, that the calculated area for flexure is dependent upon the properties of the section (r and c), so that a change of section properties would vary the required area. Attention is also called to the fact that the smaller extreme fiber distance must be used, since this c-value controls the compression fiber stress. Evidently, the tension fiber stress due to flexure cannot be critical, because it is opposed to the average compressive stress produced by the direct load.

144. Design of a Steel Building Column. EXAMPLE *DP*26. The end conditions of the columns of an industrial building bent are seldom completely known. The assumption in *DP*26 is that the buckling tendency of the column acting in the plane of the bent will reach its maximum at the mid-height from the base to the connection of the lower chord of the roof truss. Thus, the moment of the horizontal reaction about this point is taken as the bending moment used to increase the area required to resist column buckling. Then, of course, the maximum moment at the connection with the lower chord of the truss must be used to check the stress existing there. However, the stress

DP25a. *Design a top chord member for a roof truss to carry a direct compressive stress and a vertical load at 2 ft. from a panel point. Use AISC specifications. A36 steel. Assume buckling must occur about x–x axis.*

Data:

Axial force in member = 75,000#.
Component of load perpendicular to member = 5000#.
Panel length = 5′-0″.

Trial Section: *Two angles 5 × 3½ × ⅜″ placed back to back on opposite sides of a 5⁄16″ gusset with 3½″ legs turned out.*
Gross area = 2 × 3.05 = 6.1 in.^{2}
$r_{y-y} = 1.44$; $r_{x-x} = 1.60$.
Section modulus about x–x axis = 4.6.
Simple beam moment reduced 20 per cent for continuity

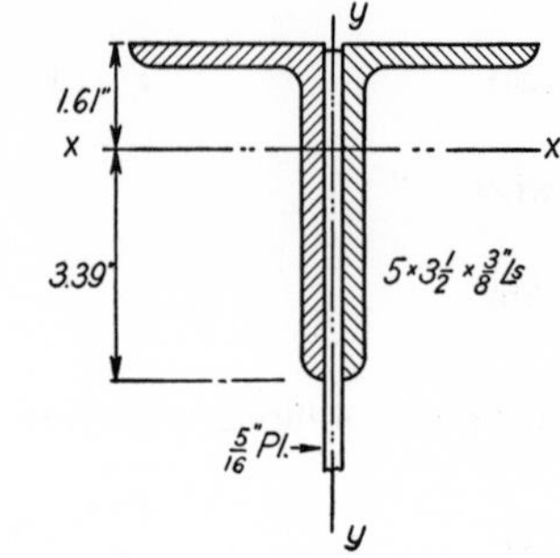

$$M = \left(\frac{5000 \times 3 \times 2 \times 12}{5}\right) 0.8 = 57{,}600''\#.$$

$$\text{Allowable column stress} = \left(\frac{1 - 0.04}{1.78}\right) 36{,}000 = 19{,}300 \text{ psi. (Spec. 13.)}$$

$$\text{Allowable beam stress} = 0.66F_y = 24{,}000 \text{ psi. (Spec. 14.)}$$

$$k' = \frac{0.85}{1 - (19{,}300/106{,}000)} = 1.04. \text{ [Equation (26).]}$$

$$\text{Required area} = \frac{75{,}000}{19{,}300} + 1.04\,\frac{57{,}600 \times 1.61}{24{,}000 \times 1.60^2} = 5.44 \text{ in.}^2 \text{ [Equation (25).]}$$

Area furnished = 6.1 in.^{2} *Use 2 ∠s 5 × 3½ × ⅜″.*

DP25b. *Repeat the design problem DP25a by use of AREA working stresses. The column formula is 15,000 – ¼ (L/r)*^{2}*, and the beam-flange formula is 18,000 – 5(L/b)*^{2} *for values of L/b not greater than 40. Assume 5 × 3½ × ⅜″ ∠s.*

$$\text{Allowable column stress} = 15{,}000 - 0.25\left(\frac{60}{1.60}\right)^2 = 14{,}650 \text{ psi.}$$

$$\text{Allowable beam stress} = 18{,}000 - 5\left(\frac{60}{7}\right)^2 = 17{,}600 \text{ psi.}$$

$$\text{Required area} = \frac{75{,}000}{14{,}650} + \frac{57{,}600 \times 1.61}{17{,}600 \times 1.60^2} = 7.18 \text{ in.}^2 \text{ [Equation (23).]}$$

Revised section. Area furnished by 5 × 3½ × ½″ ∠s is 8.0 in.^{2}

Remarks: *Notice that the r-value in the weak direction of the section is not used in the column formula, because buckling will not occur about the y–y axis due to lateral restraint at the load point.*

at that point may be compared with the allowable compressive stress for a *beam* since the buckling tendency as a *column* is small there.

The increase of working stresses for wind allowance is always stated in such a manner that the increased working stress is not permitted to reduce the area below that required for dead load and live load alone. Hence, we use the working stress for column compression without revision (because wind does not increase the direct stress by more than 33 per cent), but we increase the allowable beam stress 33 per cent, since the bending moment is caused entirely by wind.

PROBLEMS

625. Calculate the stress in an upper chord member of a bridge truss caused by its own weight. Panel length, 22 ft.-6 in. The section is composed of two 9-in., 13.4 lb. channels and a 16 × ⅜-in. cover plate. Channels are placed 10.75 in. back to back. Assume that the weight of lacing and tie plates adds 150 lb. to the total weight.

626. Calculate the stress in the bottom chord of a bridge truss caused by its own weight. Panel length, 18 ft. The section is composed of two 5 × 3½ × ⅝-in. angles with 5-in. legs turned down. Add 50 lb. for the weight of the tie plates.

627. Revise Problem *DP*24 for a maximum allowable stress of 20,000 psi.

628. Design a horizontal chord member of a roof truss to carry a direct tension of 30,000 lb. and a vertical concentrated load of 1500 lb. located 6 ft. from a panel point. The panel length is 15 ft. Two ⅝-in. holes must be drilled through the outstanding legs of the chord angles at the point of application of the concentrated load to provide a connection for a shaft bearing. The member is horizontal. *AISC* specifications. Use *A*36 steel.

629. Design a top chord member of a roof truss to carry a direct stress of 40,000 lb. and a normal purlin reaction of 3600 lb. located 2 ft.-2 in. from a panel point. Use the simple-span bending moment. The panel length is 6 ft.-8 in. Purlins are spaced 4 ft.-6 in. apart. Over 33⅓ per cent of the direct stress and of the purlin reaction are caused by wind. *AISC* specifications. *A*36 steel.

630. A horizontal top chord of a roof truss carries a direct stress of 65,000 lb. caused by dead load and snow load. A cinder concrete slab spans from roof truss to roof truss placing a uniform load of 1000 lb. per ft. on the top chord. The panel length is 6 ft.-0 in. The wind stresses are negligible. Design a top chord section using a mement of $wL^2 \div 10$. Choose material and specifications.

631. Redesign the column of *DP*26 if the total height is increased to 37 ft.-6 in. and the girt spacing is 7 ft.-6 in.

145. Practical Considerations. If we carry the matter of design for direct stress and flexure to its logical theoretical conclusion, we will find it necessary to design all tension and compression members for direct stress and flexure. Truss members all resist secondary flexural stresses. All except vertical truss members must resist bending from the influence of their own weights. Columns are never loaded axially, or at least *the occurrence of a column without bending is exceedingly rare*—so rare that it cannot even be produced in a laboratory without the greatest difficulty. But in most of the instances mentioned, the influence of flexure is not very serious, and it may be neglected without danger. The working stresses for truss design are expected to allow for flexural (secondary) stresses of about 30 per cent of

DP26. *Design an industrial building column to resist a vertical compression of 142,000 lb. caused by DL, LL, wind, and also for a wind shear of 5000 lb. The column is not fixed at its base, but is so restrained that its tendency toward buckling reaches a maximum halfway between the base and the lower chord connection. AISC working stresses. A36 steel. Girts attached to diagonal bracing provide lateral restraints.*

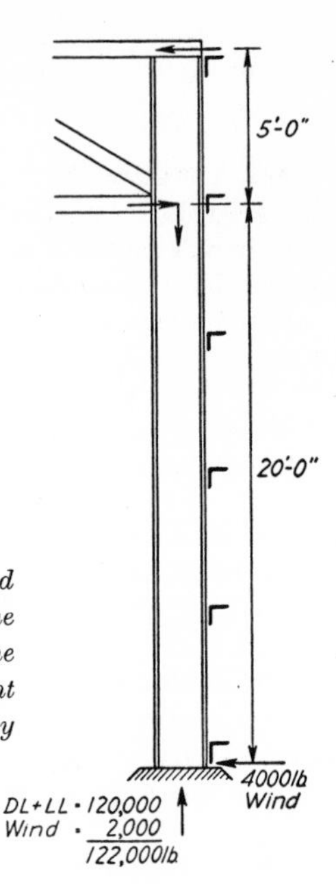

Column Moment:

Maximum wind moment at critical section
$= 5000 \times 10 \times 12 = 600{,}000''\#$.

Trial Section: *10WF45.*

$L/r = 20 \times 12 \div 4.33 = 55.5$.

L/r laterally between girts $= 5 \times 12 \div 2.0 = 30$.

Working stress for column buckling. (*Spec. 13.*)

$$F_a = \left(\frac{1 - 0.094}{1.82}\right) 36{,}000 = 17{,}900 \text{ psi.}$$

Working stress for beam action. (*Spec. 14.*)

$F_b = 0.66F_y = 0.66 \times 36{,}000 = 24{,}000$ *psi.*

Increment for Wind:

Since the vertical load is not appreciably increased by wind, the working stress F_a is 17,900 psi and the wind load is neglected. But for moment, the working stress F_b is to be increased by 33 per cent to 32,000 psi, since all moment is produced by wind.

Required Area:

$$A = \frac{P}{F_a} + k'\frac{Mc}{F_b r^2} \quad [\text{Equation (25).}]$$

(*r, c, and M are in the same plane*)

$$k' = \frac{0.85}{1 + (17{,}900/48{,}400)} = 0.62. \quad [\text{Equation (26).}]$$

$$A = \frac{142{,}000}{17{,}900} + 0.62\,\frac{600{,}000 \times 5.06}{32{,}000 \times 4.33^2} = 7.94 + 5.07 = 13.01 \text{ in.}^2$$

Area furnished $= 13.24$ *in.*^{2}

Maximum fiber stress just below chord connection

$$\frac{P}{A} + \frac{M}{I/c} = \frac{142{,}000}{13.24} + \frac{1{,}200{,}000}{49.1} = 10{,}700 + 24{,}400 = 35{,}100 \text{ psi.}$$

Since this is excessive, the 10WF54 section will be required.

Remark: *The combined stress at the truss connection for the 10WF54 section is 28,700 psi. Since this stress is due 70 per cent to wind flexure it need not be held far below the wind flexural stress of 32,000 psi.*

the primary stresses. There is no reason, therefore, why the specified working stresses for building columns should not be considered to cover an equal allowance for slight eccentricities that develop from unpredictable loadings. For the same reason, we seldom consider flexure caused by the dead weight of horizontal struts and of tension members that are not parts of a truss. Long horizontal tension members sometimes do need intermediate support.

The fact that deflection changes the eccentricity of the load for members resisting direct stress and flexure, may be given more consideration than it deserves. For typical instances the influence is found to be in the nature of a few per cent, and it may usually be neglected. Structural design in its very nature is subject to such approximations. However, the designer needs to understand this self-induced type of structual bending so that he may recognize the relatively few cases where it may become a significant or even critical factor in design. At one time the writer checked the design of a brace 120 ft. in length sloping upward at 45 degrees to the horizontal. In such a member the P/A stress may be almost negligible. The main stresses to be considered were the flexural stress due to the dead weight of the member and the flexural stress due to the eccentricity of the direct load since the member sagged about one foot at the center from its own weight.

CHAPTER 7

ROLLED BEAMS AND GIRDERS

146. Functions of Beams and Girders. The most important use for beams and girders is in supporting floors for buildings and bridges. The main carrying members are called *girders,* while the smaller members of shorter span are known as *beams.* The proper distinction is found in the manner of loading. A beam ordinarily receives its load directly from a floor slab resting upon its upper flange, while a girder receives a major part of its load from the *reactions* of smaller beams that it supports. An exception to this definition is the floor beam of a bridge which may receive a considerable part of its load from smaller beams, the stringers. The beams in building floors that serve the same purpose as the stringers of a bridge are known as *joists.*

Fundamental Theorems

147. Beam Formulas. Continued use will be made of the common beam-flexure formula and of the beam-shear formula. The beam-flexure formula is

$$f_b = \frac{My}{I}, \quad \text{or} \quad f_b\text{max.} = \frac{Mc}{I}, \tag{1}$$

where f_b is the fiber stress at the distance y from the neutral axis,
y is the distance from the neutral axis to any fiber,
c is the maximum value of y (at the extreme fiber),
I is the moment of inertia of the effective cross section about the neutral axis.

The beam-shear formula is

$$f_v = \frac{VQ}{It}, \tag{2}$$

where f_v is the unit shear in the beam web at a distance y from the neutral axis,
V is the total vertical shear at the cross section,
Q is the statical moment about the neutral axis of the cross-sectional area *outside* of the section on which shear is being calculated,
t is the thickness of metal at the section where the unit shear is desired,
I is the moment of inertia of the effective cross section (gross for shear).

The limitations upon the application of the beam theory are that sections which are plane before bending must remain plane after bending and that stress must be proportional to strain. This requirement limits all stresses to below the elastic limit. This is the basis of elastic theory as contrasted to plastic theory which will be discussed in Chapter 10.

148. The Section Modulus. The usual way to select a beam is by use of the section modulus. The beam-flexure formula may be rewritten as

$$\frac{M}{f_b} = \frac{I}{c} = S. \tag{3}$$

The factor S is the section modulus defined as the moment of inertia divided by the distance to the extreme fiber or by one half of the depth for an ordinary rolled beam section. The procedure for use of the section modulus in design is therefore as follows:

(*a*) Divide the controlling bending moment by the allowable fiber stress to obtain the required value of the section modulus.

(*b*) Select by use of the stuctural handbook a rolled beam section that will provide at least this required modulus. The criterion of economy is weight rather than modulus, and it is desirable therefore to select the beam of lightest weight that will provide the required section modulus.

Section Modulus Table. The *AISC* handbook provides a table of beam sections arranged in descending order of section modulus from the 36-in. *WF* beam sections to the 3-in. channels. This is sometimes called an economy table, because it makes possible the easy selection of the lightest beam to provide a required modulus.

Selection of Standard Sections

149. Economy in Rolled Beam Selection. Example *DP27a*. It is shown that the wide flange beam sections are the most economical for the case studied. This is usually true, and for this reason they have largely replaced the use of standard I-beams.

Section Selection with Flange Hole, *DP27b*. The procedure followed is to guess at a satisfactory section guided by the requirements for the beam without a flange hole (*DP27a*). Then, the section modulus for a hole in *each* flange is computed and deducted from the gross section modulus to arrive at the *effective section modulus*. The procedure of allowing for a hole in each flange may appear strange, since it is a compromise between theory and test results. Recent tests have not indicated any appreciable shift in the neutral axis due to a flange hole. Hence, there has been some thought that the influence of a hole might be neglected altogether. However, as long as holes in tension members are known to reduce the ultimate strengths of such members, there is reason to believe that beams will be similarly weakened by holes in the tension flange. A compromise is to retain the neutral axis at the mid-height by deducting equivalent areas from both flanges. This is undoubtedly conservative, but the alternative procedure of calculating a displacement of the neutral axis is probably no more representative of actual conditions. The example *DP27c* gives similar calculations for a beam with holes in the web.

150. Deflection Limitation upon Beam Design. There are two major reasons for limiting the deflections of beams. First, there is the problem of cracking plaster which can be avoided if the calculated deflection is less

DP27a. *Select a rolled beam section to support a load of 1100#/′ on a span of 30′. Allow a fiber stress of 22,000 psi and estimate the weight of beam to be 50#/′.*

Bending moment $= \frac{1}{8} \times 1150 \times 30^2 \times 12 = 1{,}560{,}000''\#$.

Required section modulus $= \dfrac{1{,}560{,}000}{22{,}000} = 71.0.$

First choice is a 16WF45 section which provides a modulus of 72.4.
Second choice is a 12WF53 section which provides a modulus of 70.7.
Other sections of sufficient modulus but greater weights are an 18–58.0 channel or an 18I54.7.

DP27b. *Redesign the rolled beam of DP27a on the supposition that it is necessary to punch a hole of 1″ diameter through the tension flange.*
ASSUMPTION. *Since tests do not show an influence upon the location of the neutral axis, the usual conservative design practice is to reduce the section modulus for a hole in each flange.*
Try a 16WF50 section.
Section modulus of rectangular holes $= 0.628 \times 1.0 \times 2 \times (8.12 - 0.314)^2 \div 8.12 = 9.4.$
Net modulus $= 80.7 - 9.4 = 71.3.$ *(71.0 reqd.)*

DP27c. *Redesign the beam of DP27a for a depth limitation of 12 in. to resist the moment of 1,420,000″# when a row of ¾″ holes is drilled in the web at 1″, 3″, 5″, and 7″ from the neutral axis. The required modulus is 71.0. Try a 12WF58 section, web thickness = 0.36″.*
Section modulus of rectangular holes =
$0.36'' \times 0.75 \times 2 \times (1^2 + 3^2 + 5^2 + 7^2) \div 6.08 = 7.5$
Net modulus $= 78.1 - 7.5 = 70.6$ *(acceptable).*

DP27d. *Limit the deflection of the beam of DP27a to 1/360 times the span.* (*Spec. 34.*)

Maximum $\Delta = \dfrac{1}{360} \times 30 \times 12 = 1.0''.$

Hence, $1.0 = \dfrac{5}{384}\dfrac{wL^4}{EI} = \dfrac{5}{384}\left(\dfrac{1150}{12}\right)\dfrac{360^4}{30{,}000{,}000 \times I}$, *or* $I = 700.$

Minimum weight section to provide this moment of inertia is 18WF50.

Remarks: *The limitation of 1/360 times the span was set originally as the practical maximum deflection that could be permitted for plaster on wood lath. Modern plaster ceilings are placed on metal lath, but tests of such construction have rejustified the limitation on deflection of 1/360 times the span.*

than $\frac{1}{360}$ times the span. Secondly, beams of different sizes often have to deflect alike; as, for example, when they are "bricked in" together. Such beams must have identical calculated deflections.

The deflection of a uniformly loaded beam with simple supports is

$$\Delta = \frac{5}{384}\frac{wL^4}{EI}. \tag{4}$$

In this formula w is the uniform load per unit length of span, and the other terms have their usual significance. This formula is used in *DP27d*. The *AISC* specifications limit the minimum depth of a beam to control deflection and vibration to $f_b/600{,}000$ times the unsupported length or free span. (Spec. 34.)

Buckling Resistance of Beams

151. Flange Buckling. The usual working stresses for beams are identical in tension and compression. Such working stresses presuppose restraint of the compression flange of the beam against *lateral buckling*, for, otherwise, failure would occur at or even below the elastic limit by lateral deflection of the compression flange. Evidently, the compression flange acts as a column, and its allowable stress should be controlled by a column formula. Some formulas in common use are:

$$F_b = 16{,}000 - 150\frac{L}{b} \quad \text{(straight-line type)}, \tag{5}$$

$$F_b = 18{,}000 - 5\frac{L^2}{b^2} \quad \text{(parabolic type; } AREA \text{ and } AASHO\text{)}, \tag{6}$$

$$F_b = 1 - \frac{1}{2}\left(\frac{L/r}{C_c}\right)^2 0.6F_y \quad \text{where } C_c = \sqrt{\frac{2\pi^2 E}{F_y}} \quad (AISC). \tag{7}$$

In formula (6) the maximum value of L/b, the ratio of unsupported length to width for the compression flange, is limited to 40 or less to maintain adequate lateral stiffness. In other words, a flange width of 6 in. requires a lateral support at least every 20 ft., even if the working stress is low. Formula (7) is identical with the *AISC* column formula except that the factor of safety does not vary with L/r but is fixed at 1.67. (Spec. 14.)

The Ld/A_f Formula. Another type of formula for controlling flange buckling has been adopted by *AISC* (Spec. 14). The criterion is Ld/A_f where L is the length of compression flange between lateral supports and A_f is the flange area while d is the depth of the beam. When this criterion exceeds 600 the formula

$$F_b = \frac{12{,}000{,}000}{Ld/A_f} \tag{8}$$

provides a reduction of compressive fiber stress below the maximum value for flexural compression. This formula may be derived semi-rationally from the Euler formula for a pin-end column as the writer has shown in *Design of Modern Steel Structures*. By *AISC* specifications the *larger value of* F_b from formulas (7) or (8) is the allowable compressive stress. (Spec. 14.)

152. Diagonal Web Buckling. The possibility of web buckling always exists, but it is not expected to be serious in rolled beams. Repeated tests have shown that web buckling, due to diagonal compression, will not occur where the value of h/t (distance between flanges divided by the web thickness) is less than 70. All rolled beam webs come within this range, and almost all are below 50 for h/t.

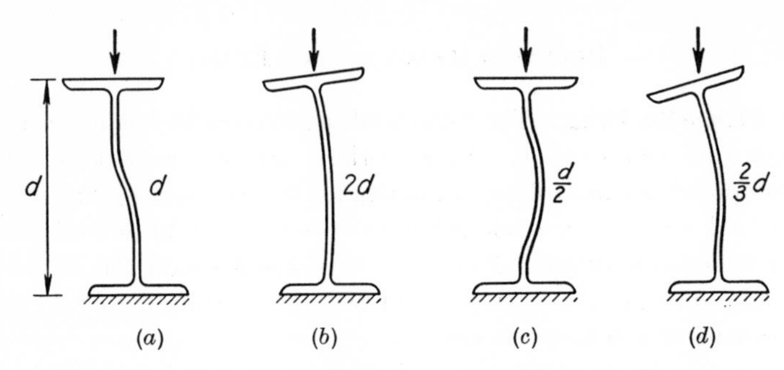

FIG. 121. FAILURE BY BUCKLING FROM VERTICAL LOADING.

153. Vertical Buckling and Crippling of Web. Much consideration has been given to the design of unstiffened webs as vertical compression members (at loads and reactions) with widely varying assumptions involved before application of the column formula. For instance, in Fig. 121 which type of buckling failure should we assume? The smallest resistance is provided by (*b*) and the greatest by (*c*); but is it logical to base a design upon the assumption that the upper flange is able to twist and also to move laterally as well? The range of buckling resistance for the cases illustrated by Fig. 121 is indicated by designation of the *free length for buckling* corresponding to each conformation. This length varies from $d/2$ to $2d$, a range of 400 per cent. Exceptional conditions of restraint or lack of restraint at ends and center of beams may make any form of buckling shown in Fig. 121 either possible or probable. Nevertheless, it has been common to base web or stiffener design under concentrated loads or reactions upon a free depth for buckling of $d/2$. If lateral restraint is not provided for the compression flange, a length of d is recommended.

The length of web along the beam that may resist a vertical load or an end reaction has been established as shown in Fig. 122 by drawing 45-degree lines from the ends of the bearing block. Thus the average width for *vertical buckling* of the web is $a + d/4$ at the end reaction and $b + d/2$ at the internal load point. An investigation of local buckling or *crippling*

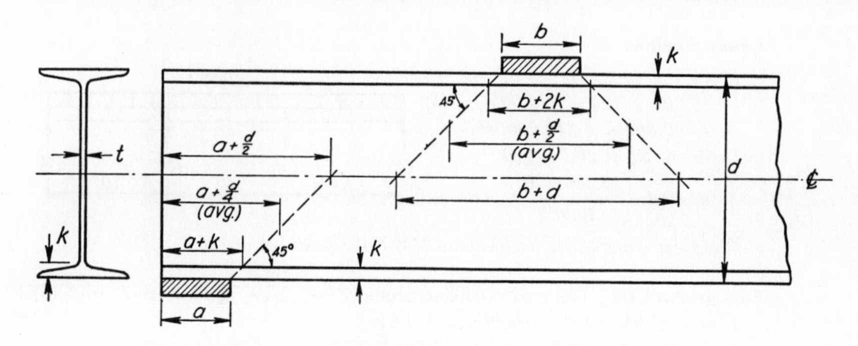

FIG. 122. BEARING AT LOAD AND REACTION.

at the juncture between the flange fillet and the web should be made for a bearing length of $(a + k)$ at the reaction, or $b + 2k$ under a load. Hence, by using the terminology of Fig. 122, we may write

(9) $$F_a = \frac{R}{(a + d/4)t} \quad \text{web } \textit{buckling} \text{ at reaction}$$

(10) $$F_a = \frac{P}{(b + d/2)t} \quad \text{web } \textit{buckling} \text{ at internal load,}$$

(11) $$F_p = \frac{R}{(a + k)t} \quad \text{web } \textit{crippling} \text{ at reaction,}$$

(12) $$F_p = \frac{P}{(b + 2k)t} \quad \text{web } \textit{crippling} \text{ at internal load.}$$

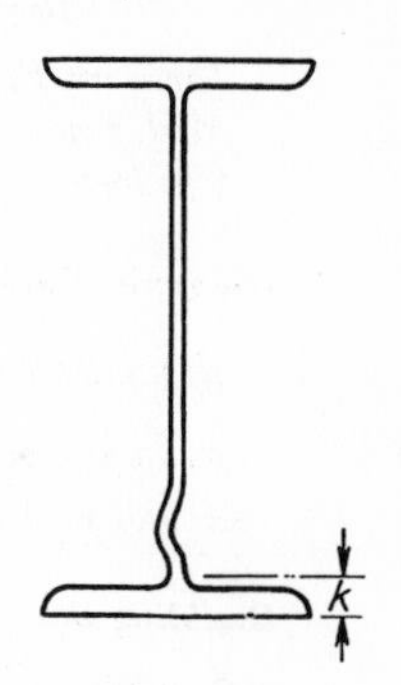

FIG. 123. FAILURE OF WEB BY LOCAL CRIPPLING.

The limitations upon F_a will be obtained from the applicable column formula by use of L as some function of the depth (usually $0.5d$ or $0.7d$) and of r as $0.29t$. The limitation upon F_p may be set in the specifications, or, if not, it can be taken at 0.75 F_y.

DESIGN FOR BUCKLING RESISTANCE, *DP*28. An ordinary floor girder is designed for flexure and is then checked for all possible conditions of buckling. Flange buckling is not significant here. The value of L/r for the flange between supports is only 50, and the value of Ld/A_f is only 500. The allowable compressive stress is $0.60F_y = 22{,}000$ psi. For this relatively long beam (30 ft.), the end shear is quite small, and the web is not stressed heavily in shear. Accordingly, the diagonal buckling stresses are insignificant. The possibility of vertical buckling over the reaction is found to be more serious. It was thought necessary to consider the clear depth of the web as the possible length for buckling, since the beam was merely to be seated on a column bracket without having adequate lateral resistance to displacement of the upper flange at the ends. See the controlling possibility of Fig. 121(*a*). Web crippling was not found to be serious.

DP28. *Design a girder of 30′-0″ span into which floor joists frame at the one-third points. The loading is as shown by the sketch. Distributed load including 70#/′ for girder = 400#/′. Use AISC spec. and A36 steel.*

Cross Section:

$M = \frac{1}{8} \times 400 \times 30^2 \times 12$
$+ 15{,}000 \times 120 = 540{,}000$
$+ 1{,}800{,}000 = 2{,}340{,}000''\#.$

Estimate F_b at 20,000 psi.

$$\text{Mod. reqd.} = \frac{2{,}340{,}000}{20{,}000} = 117.$$

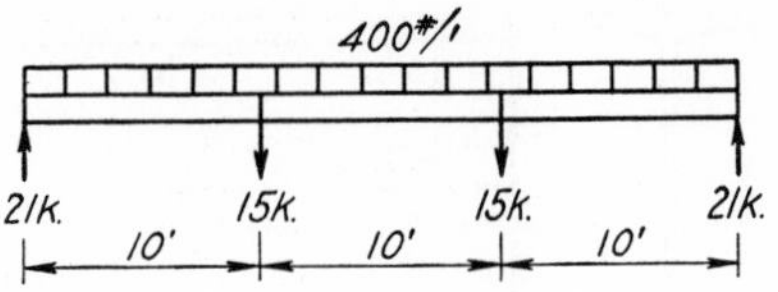

400#/′
21k. 15k. 15k. 21k.
10′ 10′ 10′

The most economical section is a 21WF62; modulus = 126.4.

Flange Buckling: *[Lateral restraint provided by joists, equations (7) and (8).]*

Flange width = 8.24″; thickness = 0.61″;

$L/r = 10 \times 12 \div 0.29 \times 8.24 = 50.0;\ C_c = 128$ *for A36.*

Equation (7)

$$F_b = \left[1 - \frac{1}{2}\left(\frac{50}{128}\right)^2\right] 0.6 \times 36{,}000 = 20{,}000 \text{ psi.}$$

Equation (8)

$$F_b = \frac{12{,}000{,}000}{10 \times 12 \times 21.0 \div 8.24 \times 0.61} = 24{,}000 \text{ psi.}$$

Limit on $F_b = 0.6F_y = 22{,}000$ psi for A36. (Spec. 14.)

Mod. reqd. = 2,340,000 ÷ 22,000 = 107.0.

The lowest-weight WF section providing this modulus is 21WF62.

Diagonal Buckling of Web: *(21WF62)*

$$\text{Web thickness} = 0.40'';\ h/t \text{ ratio} = \frac{20.99 - (2 \times 0.615)}{0.40} = 50.0.$$

For $h/t < 70$, $F_v = 13{,}000$ psi.

Actual unit shear = 21,000 ÷ (20.99 × 0.40) = 2500 psi.

Buckling over the Reaction:

Support pad is the width of the flange but only 5″ long.

Length of web resisting buckling = 5 + d/4 = 10¼″ approx.

$$\text{Unit vertical compressive stress} = \frac{21{,}000}{10.25 \times 0.40} = 5050 \text{ psi.}$$

L/r value for web = (20.99 − 2 × 0.615) ÷ (0.29 × 0.40) = 171.

$$\text{Allowable compression} = \frac{149{,}000{,}000}{171^2} = 5100 \text{ psi. (Spec. 13.)}$$

Note: L = d because of lack of lateral support of upper flange at end.

Crippling of Web over the Reaction:

Depth k from face of flange to toe of fillet = 1.25″.

$$\text{Bearing on web} = \frac{21{,}000}{(5.0 + 1.25)0.40} = 8400 \text{ psi. (27,000 allowed by Spec. 13.)}$$

154. Grillage under Column. A steel grillage is a common device for distributing a heavy column load over an area of concrete; for example, at the top of a caisson. The bearing on concrete commonly is limited to 600 psi. The proper arrangement is to let the column bear on a thick steel slab resting upon a tier of beams, as shown in Fig. 124.

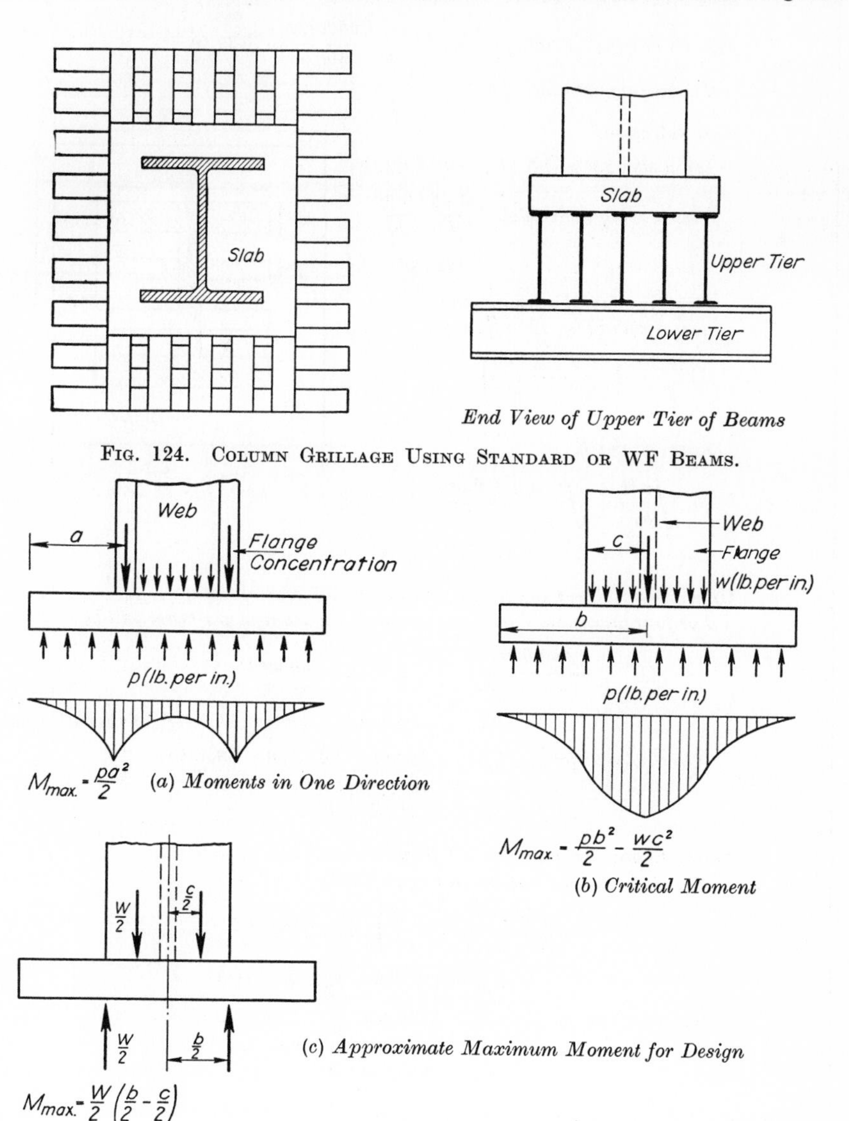

FIG. 124. COLUMN GRILLAGE USING STANDARD OR WF BEAMS.

FIG. 125. MOMENTS IN GRILLAGE SLAB.

These beams in turn bear upon a second tier at right angles to the first. Hence, the load is finally distributed more or less uniformly over the surface of the caisson or the foundation soil as the case may be. The bending moments produced in the grillage slab or column base are illustrated in Fig. 125.

DP29. *Design a steel grillage for the support of a building column which is a 14 × 16WF426 section stressed to 13,200 psi. Use AISC allowable stresses.*

Load on grillage $= 125.25 \times 13{,}200 = 1{,}660{,}000\#$.

Area for bearing on 2000 psi concrete $= \dfrac{1{,}660{,}000}{500} = 3320$ *in.*^{2}

Use bearing area 55″ × 60″.

Slab Selection:

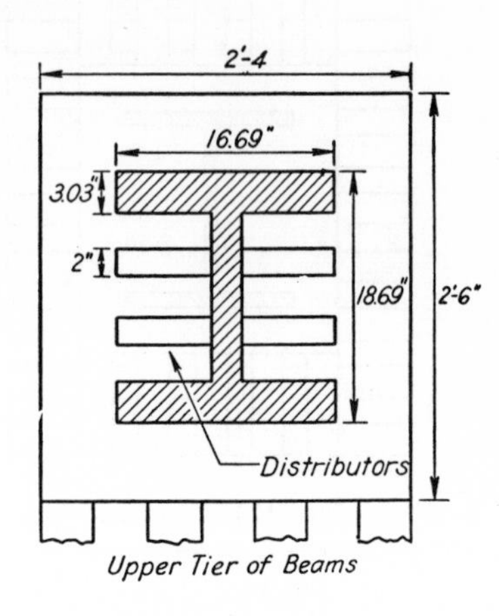

Try a slab 28″ × 30″ ($F_y = 42{,}000$).

Unit bearing under slab $= \dfrac{1{,}660{,}000}{28 \times 30}$

$= 2000$ *psi.*

Bending moment acting on long dimension of slab (Fig. 125(c)) =

$$\frac{1{,}660{,}000}{2}\left(\frac{28.0}{4} - \frac{16.69}{4}\right) = 2{,}350{,}000''\#.$$

Required depth

$$t = \sqrt{\frac{6M}{bF_b}} = \sqrt{\frac{6 \times 2{,}350{,}000}{30 \times 31{,}500}} = 3.85''; \text{ use } 4''.$$

Upper Beam Tier; *Length 60″ parallel to 30″ edge of slab:*

For four beams, as shown in the sketch, the moment per beam will be

$$\frac{1{,}660{,}000}{4 \times 2}\left(\frac{60}{4} - \frac{30}{4}\right) = 1{,}550{,}0000''\#.$$

$I/c = 1{,}550{,}000 \div 22{,}000 = 70.8$. *(A7 steel, Spec. 14.)*

Web thickness for bearing $= 1{,}660{,}000 \div 4 \times 30 \times 30{,}000^*$

$= 0.46''$; *use 18I54.7.*

$I/c = 88.4;\ t = 0.46$.

Lower Beam Tier: *Length 55″ parallel to 28″ edge of slab:*

For six beams the moment per beam will be

$$\frac{1{,}660{,}000}{6 \times 2}\left(\frac{55}{4} - \frac{28}{4}\right) = 930{,}000''\#.$$

$I/c = 930{,}000 \div 22{,}000 = 42.3$.

Web thickness for bearing $= 1{,}660{,}000 \div 6 \times 28 \times 30{,}000^*$

$= 0.33''$; *use 12I40.8.*

$I/c = 44.8;\ t = 0.46''$.

Web Buckling*: *These beam webs will buckle unless the grillage is poured solid with concrete as is usual. The web thickness would need to be increased to be self-supporting. See §153. The bearing stress of 30,000 psi is 0.90* F_y *by Spec. 15 rather than 0.75* F_y *by Spec. 13. This high bearing stress requires confined material.*

Design of a Grillage, *DP*29. The projection of the slab beyond the face of the column section acts as a *cantilever*, but the bending moment often is greater than this would indicate. Based upon the assumption that the pressure of the column section on the grillage slab is uniform, we find that the moment diagram of Fig. 125(*b*) is theoretically correct. In this figure, p represents the bearing pressure in pounds per lineal inch across the grillage slab, and w is the pressure per lineal inch produced by the two column flanges. The maximum moment clearly occurs along the center line directly under the web of the column, as shown in Fig. 125(*b*). This moment can be reduced by the use of welded stiffeners or distributors, as shown on *DS*29, since this increases the value of w and *decreases the web concentration to a negligible value.* The resultant moment is as indicated in Fig. 125(*c*) when distributors are used as in *DS*29.

PROBLEMS

701. Revise *DS*27. Assume availability of beams of *A*242 or *A*441 steel.
702. Revise *DS*28 for *A*7 steel of yield strength 33,000 psi.
703. Revise *DS*28 for beams of 50,000 psi yield strength steel.
704. Revise *DS*29 for plate and beam steel of *A*36; 36,000 psi yield strength.

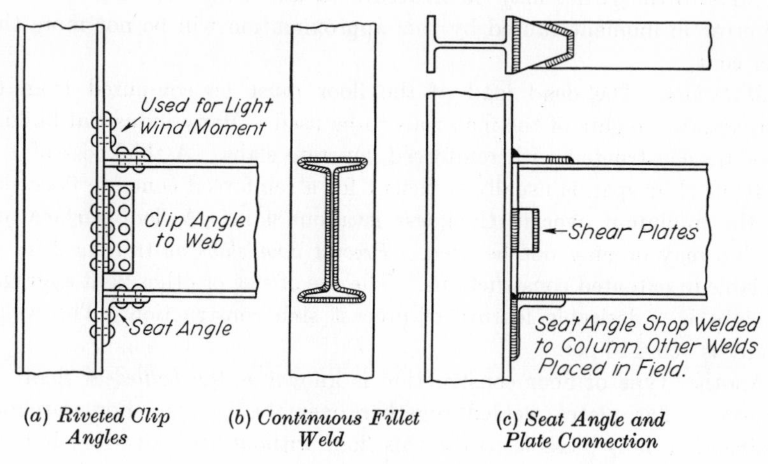

(*a*) *Riveted Clip Angles* (*b*) *Continuous Fillet Weld* (*c*) *Seat Angle and Plate Connection*

Fig. 126. Connections for Beams and Girders.

Floor Design

155. Building Floors. The framing of building floors is essentially the same whether the floor is for an office building, a warehouse, or an industrial plant. The usual method is to frame girders between the columns in one direction and then to connect floor joists perpendicularly between the girders. For low structures where the connections do not have to resist wind moments, they are usually formed of ordinary clip angles to the web. Light end moments may be resisted by top and seat angles, as shown in Fig. 126(*a*).

Welded connections may be made by direct welding, or *seat angles* and *plates* may be used (Fig. 126(*b*) and (*c*)). In order to provide field adjustment for plumbing the columns, a connection of the type (*c*) is necessary at one end of the girder when a direct weld as in (*b*) is used at the other end. The web welds in (*b*) are usually staggered.

Load Distribution. The load carried by a floor joist usually is taken to be uniform and is composed of (1) its own dead weight, (2) the dead load of the floor for a width equal to the distance between joists, (3) the live load from the same tributary area, and (4) an allowance for partitions. A girder must carry a uniform load caused by its own dead weight and the dead load and live load from the floor directly above its upper flange. It also must carry a set of load concentrations from the reactions of the floor joists. In practice, it is customary to consider all loads except the dead weight of the girder itself to be concentrated at the joist connections. If the joists are quite close together and the span of the girder is reasonably great, so that there are at least four interior joists per panel, the joist reactions to the girder may be treated as a uniformly distributed loading. The error in moment caused by this approximation will be not more than 4 per cent.

Materials. The dead load of the floor must be computed from the approximate weights of the materials to be used. Many industrial building floors are constructed with reinforced concrete slabs. A thickness of 1 in. per ft. of clear span is usually sufficient for a reinforced concrete floor slab, but the minimum over-all thickness is about 4 in. A floor surface over the slab may or may not be used. *Precast floor slabs* as thin as 2 in. are available in patented constructions. The use of slag or other light aggregate for slabs is a desirable feature of precast slab construction. The weight usually is 100–110 pcf.

Another type of floor construction is known as the *battledeck* floor. It consists of flat plates welded together over the beams. For warehouse construction, it is possible to use this floor without any covering, but it is desirable, in order to reduce noise, to cover the plates either with a mastic or a cork composition covering. The battledeck floor combines light weight with low cost but *it is not fireproof*, even though it is non-burning. Another steel floor deck that has some concrete protection for fire resistance is of pressed steel with deep corrugations that serve as joists.

Live Loadings. The live load varies considerably, but it is commonly taken at 100 psf or less where no heavy concentrations of machinery or other such loads exist. Storeroom floors are designed to carry loads from 100 to 400 psf or even more. The live load is also assumed to include any required allowance for impact. For this reason, the live load is taken as 100 psf wherever the gathering of a crowd of people seems probable, although a crowd of people will seldom produce a *static* load of over one half of this amount. Care must be used in load selection. The writer once was asked to explain floor cracks in a meat storage room. The stacked frozen meat was found to weigh 500 psf, which was five times the design load. At another time he observed bags of Portland cement stacked nine sacks deep on a light wood floor. It was more difficult to explain the lack of a complete collapse than the evident signs of distress. Although such excessive loads will occur occasionally, because of unsatisfactory control, the following loads are usually considered adequate for design purposes:

Minimum Design Loadings (including impact but not dead weight)

(a) Apartments, private rooms, classrooms	40 psf
(b) Public corridors, lobbies, dance halls, stairways	100 psf
(c) Theaters and public rooms with fixed seats	60 psf
(d) Office buildings, offices, court rooms	80 psf
(e) Stores, workshops, light manufacturing	125 psf

Load from Crowds. There has been considerable discussion in regard to the load produced by a crowd of people. Tests have shown that a static live load of over 150 psf can be produced by selecting individuals and packing them together in a small pen. However, such congestion could only occur in halls, ramps, and other such passages. Although the writer is not able to offer specific data, he does not believe that an unselected crowd of men and women would ever produce a load much in excess of 100 psf. Incidentally, it seems unlikely that such a dense crowd could produce an appreciable impact on the structure. A more serious live loading may conceivably develop from a less congested group where rhythmic movement is possible. For instance, a football crowd, swaying, cheering and rising in unison might produce reasonably heavy dynamic stresses in the structure. Where seats are provided for a crowd, the static loading will not exceed 50 psf, and a design load of 100 psf allows for impact of 100 per cent. Tests have not indicated dynamic effects of this magnitude.

156. Design of a Floor for an Industrial Building.

PROBLEM. Design the steel framing for supporting the second floor of an industrial building. The floor is supported by the exterior columns and by one line of columns down the center of the building.

Data.

Width of building = 60 ft. center to center of outside columns.

Width of bay or distance between columns = 15 ft. lengthwise of the building.

Live load. The live load may be taken at 80 psf since the floor is to be used for a combination drafting room and model shop.

Columns. All columns are of 12-in. width in a direction across the building.

Working Stresses.

Bending. 22,000 psi for fiber stress in beams laterally braced.

Other working stresses. *AISC* specifications for *A*7 structural steel.

Type of Floor. A battledeck floor will be used. This is a floor composed of steel plates welded together over the beams. Plate of about ⅜-in. thickness will be used and the joists will be placed 7 ft.-6 in. apart across the width of the building, as shown in

Fig. 127. A mastic surface and a cork composition floor covering will be selected weighing 15 psf. Girders frame laterally between columns at 15-ft. spacing and 29-ft. clear span to support joists at 7 ft.-6 in. centers. (See Fig. 127.)

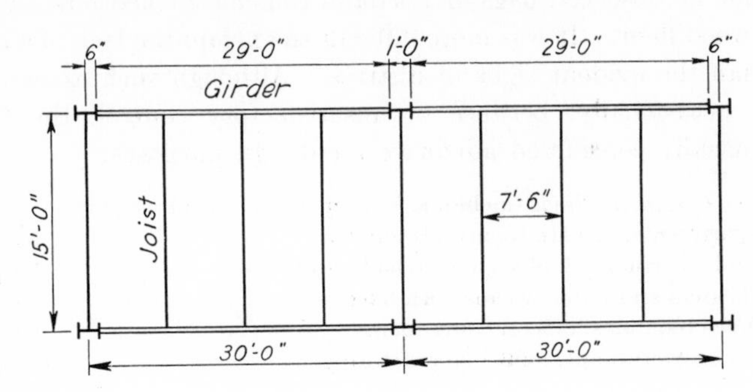

FIG. 127. FLOOR FRAMING.

Thickness of Floor Plate. For continuity, the plate may be welded to the beam flanges, reducing the moment in the plate 20 per cent and decreasing the free span between beam flanges from 7.5 ft. to about 7.1 ft. Estimate weight of floor at 35 psf.

$M = \frac{1}{12}(80 + 35) \times 7.1^2 \times 12 = 5800$ in-lb./ft.
$S = 5800 \div 22{,}000 = 0.26$ in.^{3} per ft. width of plate
$\therefore bd^2/6 = 0.26$, or $d = t = \sqrt{6 \times 0.26/12} = 0.36$ in. Use $\frac{3}{8}$-in. steel plate.

Design of a Floor Joist.

Dead Load. The $\frac{3}{8}$-in. plate weighs 15 psf which added to the weight of the floor covering makes the total weight of the floor 30 psf. The dead weight of a floor joist will be estimated at 20 lb. per lineal ft.

Uniform load per foot of joist.

Dead load $= (7.5 \times 30) + 20 = 245$ lb. per lineal ft.
Live load $= (7.5 \times 80) = 600$,, ,, ,, ,,
Total $= 845$,, ,, ,, ,,

Bending moment $= \frac{1}{8} \times 845 \times 15^2 \times 12 = 285{,}000$ in-lb.
Required section modulus $= 285{,}000 \div 22{,}000 = 13.0$.

Section Selected. The lightest standard beam that offers approximately this section modulus is the 8*WF*17 section. However, a depth of not less than $\frac{1}{20}$ of the span is commonly required for rolled beams to prevent excessive deflection. The allowable deflection is $\frac{1}{360} \times 15 \times 12 = 0.5$ in. (Also see Spec. 34.) The deflection of an 8*WF*17 section for a uniform load of 845 lb. per ft. is 0.57 in. Since this deflection of the 8*WF*17 section is excessive, we may use either an 8*WF*20 section for which the deflection is 0.46 in. or reduce the deflection of the 8*WF*17 section by welding its upper flange to the plate so that a T-section is provided of increased moment of inertia. Because the floor plate must be welded to the beam flange for other reasons, we can provide a T-section with a fully braced compressive flange at no extra cost. Accordingly, an 8*WF*17 beam section will be used.

Connection Between Joist and Girder.

Shear $= 845 \times 15 \div 2 = 6350$ lb.

Standard Connection. The standard connection for an 8*WF*17 beam, coped to place the beam and girder flanges on the same level, is shown in Fig. 128. The connection is amply strong with ¾-in. *A*141 rivets or *A*325 bolts, 26,500 lb.

Design of the Girder.

Loads. The girder carries three load concentrations of 12,700 lb. at 7 ft.-6 in. centers. (See Fig. 129.) It also supports its own dead weight which is estimated at 60 lb. per lineal ft.

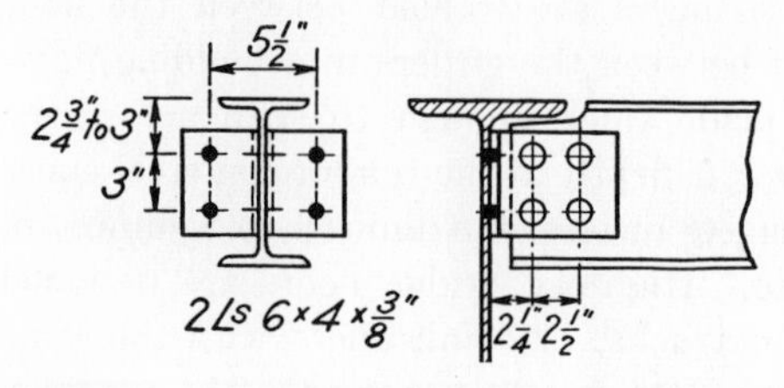

FIG. 128. JOIST CONNECTION TO GIRDER.

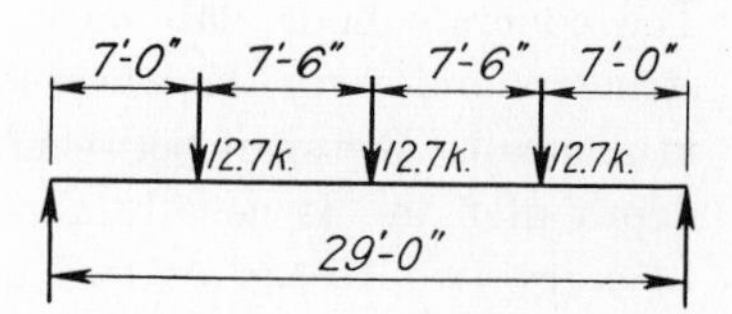

FIG. 129. GIRDER LOADING.

Bending Moment. The bending moment is found by taking moments about the center of the span; $M = 12{,}700 \times 1.5 \times 14.5 - 12{,}700 \times 7.5 + \frac{1}{8} \times 60 \times 29^2 = 187{,}000$ ft-lb. (See Fig. 129.)

Section modulus $= 187{,}000 \times 12 \div 22{,}000 = 102.0$.

Section Selected. An 18*WF*60 beam will furnish a modulus of 107.8, which is satisfactory. This beam also meets the requirements as to depth ratio, i.e., 1⁄20 of the span or 17.4″ is the minimum desirable depth. (Spec. 34.) It is the most economical section obtainable. The web shear is low.

Connection Between Girder and Column.

Shear $= 1.5 \times 12{,}700 + 14.5 \times 60 = 19{,}900$ lb.

Standard Connection. The standard connection for a 18*WF*60 beam is shown in Fig. 130. The critical condition is that of shear. This allowable value in shear is 53,000 lb. with ¾-in. rivets (eccentricity being neglected). The connection, therefore, is amply strong.

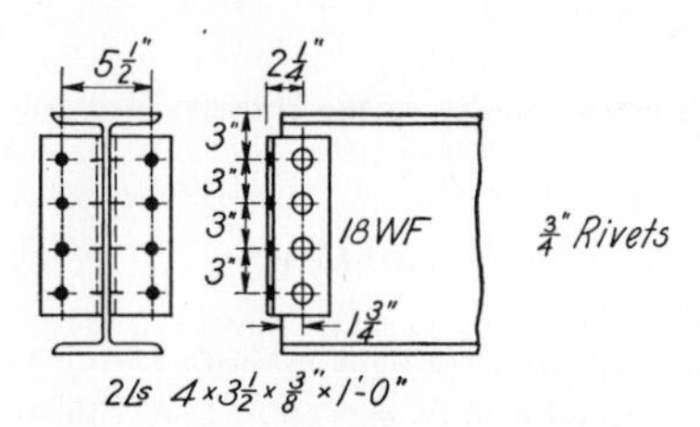

FIG. 130. STANDARD CONNECTION.

REMARKS. In the design of these beams, it was not necessary to reduce the working stress because of lack of lateral support for the top flange. The floor plates are welded together over the beams and are also welded to the beams. This *stiff plate prevents lateral buckling* of the top flange of the beam. If a concrete floor slab had been used, the top flange of the beams would have been allowed to project ½ in. into the concrete to obtain lateral support. These remarks also apply to the girders.

Spandrel beams and girders are those placed along the side of the building at the wall. A spandrel beam or girder receives but one half of the *dead and live* floor load that an interior beam or girder must carry. However, in most cases the masonry walls are merely enclosures supported by the structural frame of the building. In such construction the spandrel girder must carry a full story of the wall load. This type of construction is always used for tall buildings.

157. Bridge Floors. The floors of highway bridges are similar in their framing details to building floors. Usually, floor beams are supported by the trusses at panel points, and stringers are framed between the floor beams just as the joists are framed between the girders in a building floor. The concrete floor slab must be made thick enough to span across the stringers and carry the wheel loads. A depth to the reinforcing steel equal in inches to the span between stringers in feet, but limited to a minimum depth of 5 in., is usually adequate. Highway bridge floors are designed to carry two 15-ton or two 20-ton trucks, or semitrailers with the same maximum wheel loads, plus impact of about 30 per cent. The complex framing of a grade separation structure is well illustrated by Fig. 131.

Courtesy Eng. News-Record

FIG. 131. GRADE SEPARATION—HENRY HUDSON PARKWAY.

PROBLEMS

705. Redesign the floor of §156 for light manufacturing for which the live loading is 125 psf. Joists will be spaced at 5-ft. centers. Use *A*36 steel.

706. Redesign the floor system designed in §156 to carry a concrete floor slab of 4-in. total depth. Place the floor joists at 6 ft.-0 in. centers. Allow 12 psf for a wood floor.

707. Design a floor panel for a warehouse where the columns are at 20-ft. centers in both directions. Place the beams 6 ft-8 in. apart and use a concrete slab of 6.5-in. overall depth. The live load is 300 psf. Columns are 14*WF*87 sections. Use *AISC* specifications and *A*36 steel.

708. Design the floor framing for a 15-ft. balcony. The main girders are placed perpendicularly to the wall and are supported at one end by the wall and at the other end by hangers attached to the roof trusses. The roof trusses are spaced on 16-ft. centers. Floor joists may be spaced from 4 to 6 ft. apart. Take the live load at 100 psf and the dead load of the floor at 60 psf, not including the weight of the joists or girders. Use *AISC* specifications and *A*36 steel.

709. A one-story industrial building has plan dimensions of 40 ft. × 60 ft. The flat roof of the building supports a condenser box which carries a 10-ft. depth of water. The condenser box is made up of 5/16-in. plate supported by beams at 45-in. centers or less. The condensers themselves are carried directly to the columns by steel framing *inside* of the box. Design the roof framing of the building to support the load of water. Place columns as needed, but obtain as much clear space as is reasonably possible. Use working stresses as given in the *AREA* specifications.

158. Tables for Beam Design. Every structural handbook contains certain tables for aid in beam design. If used properly, such tables are valuable, but they are not helpful as devices to avoid the logical thinking that has been developed here. Standard tables that give *section properties* for designing and detailing are the basic ones. The data presented are: *weight* per foot, *area* of section, *depth* of section, *flange width* and *web thickness*, along with *moments of inertia*, *section moduli*, and *radii of gyration* about the principal axes. All of the *dimensions* that may be necessary for detailing are also given. The second table in point of usefulness is the economy table in which all available beam sections are arranged in the order of increasing weight for providing given section moduli. The use of this table aids us in the selection of the proper section for economy, or, if we choose a shallower section of heavier weight, the excess cost is readily evaluated. The third table considered is one that gives all data on standard beam connections. This table is useful, but the mistake must not be made of accepting the listed connection values unless the specifications to be used are exactly those for which the table was arranged.

Safe Load Tables. The final table that needs consideration is the table of allowable loads given in most steel handbooks. The tables in the handbook of *Steel Construction* (*AISC*) are typical. They give the *total allowable* load in kips (uniformly distributed) for different spans and for simple reactions. Additional data are deflection in inches, allowable total shear on the web, allowable end reaction, and length of bearing to develop the allowable web shear. Beam tables must be used with the following points in mind.

1. The allowable load is uniformly distributed. The beam is simply supported.
2. The allowable load is based upon a specified working stress in flexure.
3. The deflections listed are for uniform loads and simple supports.
4. The allowable web shear is based upon a fixed allowable unit shearing stress. Diagonal buckling is not considered, since $h/t < 70$ for rolled beams.
5. The allowable end reaction is obtained for a 3½-in. length of end bearing and for resistance to crippling based upon a specified bearing stress.
6. There is no consideration of possible lateral buckling of either the upper flange or the web.
7. The values of standard end connections neglect the moment of eccentricity, and are based upon one set of allowable stresses in shear and bearing.

Such tables must be corrected before they can be used with other specifications.

CHAPTER 8

PLATE GIRDER DESIGN

159. Types of Plate Girders and Their Uses. The plate girder is simply an oversize built-up beam; as such, it may be looked upon as intermediate in carrying capacity between the rolled beam and the truss. Steel bridges of under 100-ft. span are now usually of the beam type. Above a span of 100 ft. the plate girder may be found economical. The plate-girder bridge is used as a bridge structure for spans up to 150 ft. or even more, although it is not as economical of material as the truss for spans near this upper limit of length. *Fabrication and erection costs* are less for the plate girder than for the truss. This accounts for exceptional girder spans such as the 450-ft. main span of a 3-span continuous girder bridge at Niagara Falls.

Courtesy American Bridge Co.

FIG. 132. BUILDING GIRDER ONE STORY DEEP.

Notice the horizontal web splice. Plates 12 ft. deep are not obtainable. A butt welded horizontal splice might be preferred. Also notice the drift pins in use for making the initial connection of the girder to the left hand column.

Building Girders. The use of the plate girder is not confined to bridge structures. It is commonly used in all types of buildings to span between columns and to carry heavy concentrated loads. The analysis of a building girder such as Fig. 132 is relatively simple since there are no *moving* loads to be considered. An overhead crane is designed for a *moving* vertical load (as shown in Fig. 133) and also for a lateral traction force equal to 20 per cent of the lifting capacity of the crane. Many crane girders have parallel flanges.

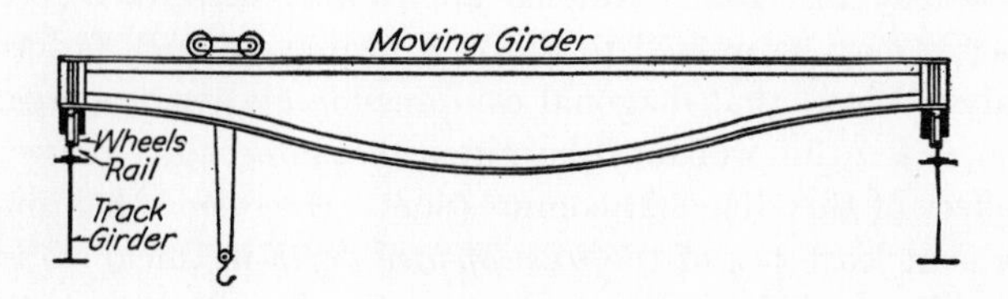

FIG. 133. OVERHEAD CRANE FOR A MILL BUILDING.

The Cross-Section. The typical cross-section of a riveted bridge girder is similar to Fig. 134(*a*). Heavier sections are obtained by the use of larger angles with double rows of rivets and the addition of extra cover plates. A typical section for a welded building girder is shown in (*b*). The cover plate may be avoided by changing the thickness of the main flange plate to fit the *M*-diagram. See Fig. 146. Flange plates of different thicknesses may be butt-welded together by use of a scarfed joint. Other sections are shown in (*c*) and (*d*). Figure 134(*e*) is a box-girder section that is used occasionally either in bridge construction or in building construction where great strength is required and the depth is limited. Type (*f*) makes use of split-beam sections in an economical manner. However, the preferred welded section uses a single flange plate, channel or Tee. See Spec. 27.

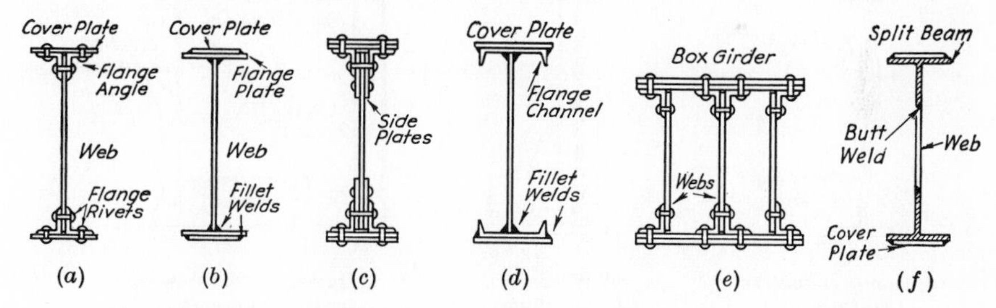

FIG. 134. TYPICAL RIVETED AND WELDED PLATE-GIRDER SECTIONS.

160. Stresses to be Considered in Girders. A plate-girder section is made up of a web and two flanges. The web and the flanges are connected by means of rivets or by arc welding. The main function of the web is to resist the *vertical shear.* The flanges, which are similar to the chords of a truss, produce the major resistance of the section to moment. The connection between the web and the flange must resist the *horizontal shear* existing along this line.

Web Stresses. The web of a girder, being relatively tall and thin, is a poor compression member. Wherever a load is concentrated upon the upper flange or a reaction acts upward upon the lower flange, the web must be stiffened to prevent it from *buckling* or *wrinkling*; these types of failure are illustrated by Fig. 135. Stiffener angles may be riveted to the web or stiffener plates may be welded to the web to prevent such failure.

An analysis shows that diagonal compression always accompanies shear. See Fig. 135(*c*). A thin web must be stiffened at intervals to prevent buckling from the effect of this diagonal compression. Experience has shown that a web which is at least $\frac{1}{70}$ of the *unsupported depth* in thickness is safe from buckling by diagonal compression, but a web that is thinner than $\frac{1}{70}$ of the unsupported depth must be stiffened at intervals not exceeding the *clear depth* of the web, unless diagonal wrinkles are to be permitted between stiffeners with diagonal tension only resisted by the web. Such tension-field girders are discussed below. *AISC* specifications permit h/t ratios up to 320 for *A*36 steel when the average unit web shear or diagonal tension does not exceed about 9000 psi, and the vertical stiffeners are spaced $0.8h$ apart. For $h/t = 180$ the average shear stress may be about 7000 psi, and the stiffeners may be twice the clear depth of the web apart. (See Spec. 29 and Table S-4.) The minimum web thicknesses commonly used are $\frac{1}{4}$ in. for building girders, $\frac{5}{16}$ in. for bridge girders, and from $\frac{1}{170}$ to $\frac{1}{345}$ of the unsupported depth or the clear depth between the flanges, depending upon the size, spacing, and arrangement of vertical and/or horizontal web stiffeners and upon the yield strength or stress level for the steel.

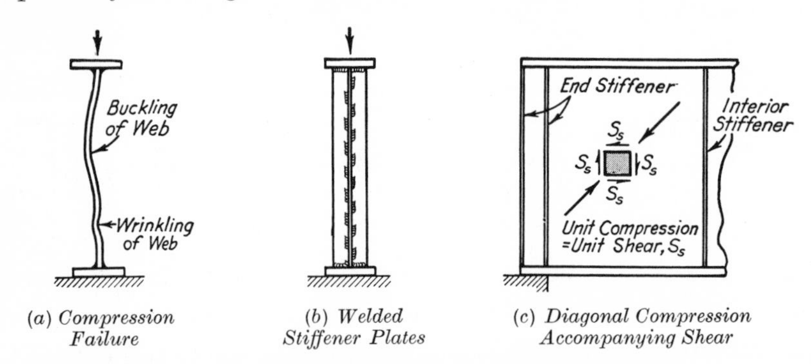

(*a*) *Compression Failure*

(*b*) *Welded Stiffener Plates*

(*c*) *Diagonal Compression Accompanying Shear*

FIG. 135. PURPOSE OF PLATE-GIRDER STIFFENERS.

The purpose of this chapter is to analyze the plate girder for all of the stresses mentioned above, and to determine in general how to apply these methods of analysis to the design of plate girders. It will not be possible to go into the subject of all standard specifications and their application to design.

Tension Field Girders. In airplane design it is necessary to reduce weight to the minimum. Hence webs may have to be much less than $\frac{1}{170}$ times the depth in thickness. Such thin webs will wrinkle at 90 degress to the direction of the diagonal compression shown in Fig. 135(*c*). Collapse would occur if the vertical stiffeners were to be omitted. However, with vertical stiffeners designed to resist compression, the thin web can reproduce the effect of the tension diagonals of a Pratt truss, and the resulting structure will be stable. The stress analysis of the chords and verticals would be identical with the analysis of a corresponding Pratt truss. The total stress calculated for a diagonal of the truss might be considered to be resisted by a diagonal strip of web equal to $\frac{1}{3}$ to $\frac{2}{3}$ of the depth. A width of web from $12t$ to $24t$ on each side of the stiffener adds to the stiffener area resisting compression. Such girders of steel have proved useful for deep building girders where a web thickness of $\frac{1}{170}$ times the depth would be highly uneconomical.

Approximate Analysis versus Beam Theory

161. Beam Formulas Applied to a Riveted Girder. The treatment of a plate girder as a solid beam for the calculation of stresses is the standard practice. This procedure needs no justification for a welded girder. However, an investigation of the preceding assumption becomes necessary for the riveted girder, since we know that there is slip of the rivets at a stress slightly above their normal working stress. The reader will notice that all flange rivets in the plate girder occur in long horizontal lines. See Fig. 141. Such a row of rivets will contain a hundred or more. We can normally expect better frictional resistance between the connected parts than would exist between the parts of a *small* riveted connection. Moreover, since the horizontal shear on all rivets of a row will not be a maximum at the same time, any tendency toward localized slip will be resisted by adjacent rivets. This argument seems to justify the assumptions that the riveted girder acts as a solid beam and that its fiber stress and its shearing stress at any point may be computed from the *beam formulas*:

$$f = \frac{Mc}{I}, \tag{1}$$

where [1]f = fiber stress (psi), M = bending moment at the section (in-lb.), I = moment of inertia of the cross-section about the neutral axis with an appropriate deduction for rivet holes (in.^{4}), c = extreme fiber distance measured from the neutral axis (in.); and

$$v = \frac{VQ}{I}, \tag{2}$$

where v = horizontal shear per lineal inch of girder (lb. per in.), V = vertical shear acting at the section (lb.), I = moment of inertia of the cross-section about the neutral

[1] In this chapter unit stress is designated as f. The symbol σ is also used for unit stress. Unit shear will be designated by f_v although τ may be used if desired.

axis, gross moment of inertia in this case (in.[4]), Q = statical moment about the neutral axis of that part of the cross-sectional area *outside* of the line on which shear is to be calculated (in.[3]).

162. Maximum Unit Shear in the Web of a Plate Girder. Since the horizontal and the vertical unit shears are equal at any point in the web of a girder, the unit vertical shear might be calculated by use of equation (2) above. The value of v in pounds per lineal inch of girder must be divided by the thickness of the web to obtain the unit shear f_v in pounds per square inch. The variation of shear will correspond closely to the variation for an I-beam, as shown in Fig. 136(a), where it is noticed that the average shear v_3 is but little smaller than the maximum shear v_1 at the neutral axis. For this reason, an exact computation of the maximum shear by means of the shear formula is seldom made. Instead, it is more common to assume that the vertical unit shear is *uniform over the entire depth of the web* and to select the web of such thickness that the average unit shear on its *gross area* will not exceed the allowable value of 11,000 to 20,000 psi according to the yield strength and the requirement of the specifications. It is assumed that the web carries the entire shear. The allowable unit shear is specified on the gross area of the web.

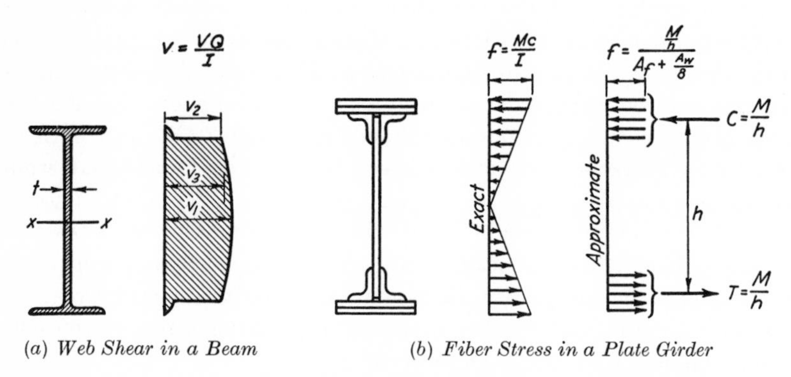

(a) *Web Shear in a Beam* (b) *Fiber Stress in a Plate Girder*

FIG. 136. STRESS VARIATION IN BEAMS AND GIRDERS.

163. Fiber Stresses by the Exact Method. *Welded Girder.* The flange stresses in a plate girder can be calculated exactly by use of the beam-flexure formula. [See equation (1).] When we use the term *exact calculation*, as above, it is naturally with the mental reservations that the assumptions involved in the flexure formula require. The use of the flexure formula for checking the fiber stress in a welded plate girder is extremely simple. The *gross* and *net* sections are identical; hence, the neutral axis must lie at the center of gravity of the cross-section or at the mid-height of a symmetrical section. The gross moment of inertia about the neutral axis is computed, and the fiber stresses are calculated, as for a rolled beam.

Riveted Girder. The calculation of the fiber stresses for a riveted plate girder is complicated by the fact that the *net* and *gross* sections have considerably different areas. There are three procedures in use for calculating the fiber stresses.

PROCEDURE 1. By *AISC* specifications for building girders we are permitted to use the *gross section* without deducting rivet holes except when the flange holes exceed 15 per cent of the flange area. The effect of this procedure is to increase the working stress in tension (not in compression) up to 15 per cent above the usual working stress for flexure. Tests seem to justify this increase in allowable stress.

PROCEDURE 2. For bridge girders the net area is considered effective on the tension side of the girder while the gross area is effective on the compression side. Since the neutral axis lies at the center of gravity of the effective section, it is *above* the mid-height of the normal symmetrical girder. When the neutral axis has been located, the moment of inertia of the effective section about this axis must be determined, and then the fiber stresses may be obtained by use of the flexure formula. This method is rather tedious and is not commonly used.

PROCEDURE 3. By this simplified method, the full gross area is considered effective for computing the fiber stress in the compression flange, but all rivet holes for the full depth of the girder are deducted to obtain the net section for calculating the stress in the tension flange. In both cases, the neutral axis lies at the mid-height if the girder is of the usual symmetrical type. Both net and gross moments of inertia are easily computed. This method of analysis gives nearly the same stresses as Procedure 2.

164. Approximate Method of Stress Calculation for Use in Design. In the design of a plate girder, one must obtain a reasonable cross-section before the moment of inertia can be calculated and the stresses checked. An approximate method is widely used for this purpose, and, in fact, frequently it is the only method used for the design of a deep girder. The stresses calculated by the approximate method for a shallow girder should be checked by one of the procedures just described.

The reader undoubtedly has observed that the flange material in a plate girder is grouped quite close together and that the moment of inertia of the section is furnished largely (about 85 per cent) by the flanges rather than by the web. Therefore the assumption that the flange stress is nearly constant over the entire area of the flange can not be seriously in error. See Fig. 136(*b*). If the distance between centers of gravity of the flanges could be known, we might divide the bending moment by this effective depth, shown as h in Fig. 136(*b*), and obtain the total flange stress C or T. Since the resistance of the web even then would have to be introduced by approximation, it is common practice to estimate the *effective depth* as the depth of the web or the distance back to back of flange angles for a deep girder with more than three cover plates, and from two to four inches less than the depth of the web for a girder of average proportions. Designers become expert in making such esimates.

Moment Resistance of the Web. Because present-day design allows for the moment resistance of the web, it is necessary to determine how much the net area of the tension flange may be assumed to be increased by the effect of the web. The moment of inertia of the gross web is $\frac{1}{12}th^3$ or $\frac{1}{12}A_wh^2$, where t is the web thickness, h is the web depth, and A_w is the gross web area. An area equal to $A_w/6$, if placed in each flange, would have an approximate moment of inertia of

$$2\left(\frac{A_w}{6} \times \frac{h^2}{4}\right) = \frac{1}{12}A_wh^2.$$

Therefore, we conclude that $\frac{1}{6}$ *of the gross area of the web* may be considered to form a part of the gross area of each flange for calculating the stress in a welded girder or of a riveted girder under *AISC* specifications.

Net Section of Bridge Girders. At the net section of a riveted girder, we allow for a vertical row of 1-in. holes in the web, spaced 4 in. apart. The cross-sectional area and the moment of inertia will be reduced 25 per cent when the holes are deducted. This reduces the factor $\frac{1}{6}$ down to $\frac{1}{8}$ and shows that but $\frac{1}{8}$ *of the gross area of the web* should be considered as net area of the tension flange under bridge specifications. Of course, by *AISC* specifications it is proper to use $\frac{1}{6}$ of the gross web area as effective tension flange area because rivet holes or bolt holes are not required to be deducted. (Spec. 25.)

Welded Web Splice. It is very easy to splice a welded girder because the full depth of the web is exposed. In fact, splice plates are usually dispensed with entirely. The abutting edges of the web may be Veed with a torch and butt-welded together to replace the full value of the web. A proper butt weld will reproduce the full strength of the web plate, for shear and moment.

PROBLEMS

801. A light plate-girder section is composed of 6 × 6 × ½-in. angles placed 40.5 in. back to back, a 14 × ½-in. cover plate for each flange, and a 40 × ⅜-in. web plate arranged as in Fig. 134(*a*). The total vertical shear is 150,000 lb. Compute the unit shear at the neutral axis and at the connection between web and flange by use of the shear formula. Compare the two computed values of the unit shear with the average unit shear in the web. *Ans.* Maximum unit shear = 10,900 psi.

802. Same as Problem 801 except the girder is of welded construction, having a web plate 42 × ⅜ in., a flange plate 12 × ⅝ in., and a cover plate 10 × ⅝ in. The section is made up as shown in Fig. 134(*b*). *Ans.* Maximum unit shear = 10,000 psi.

803. Locate the neutral axis and compute the fiber stresses caused by a moment of 1,000,000 ft-lb. in the girder of Problem 801. Deduct holes as follows from the tension side of the girder: two 1-in. holes from each tension angle, two 1-in. holes from the cover plate, a vertical row of 1-in. holes placed 4 in. apart from the tension side of the web. *Ans.* 16,000 and 18,600 psi.

804. Determine the fiber stresses for the girder of Problem 803 by using the full gross moment of inertia and the fully reduced net moment of inertia with the neutral axis at the mid-height. *Ans.* 15,700 and 18,900 psi.

805. Compute the fiber stresses for the girder of Problem 803 by use of the approximate method, using a lever arm first of the depth of the web and then of the distance back to back of angles. Compare these stresses with those of Problems 803 and 804. The discrepancy should be greater for this shallow girder than for a deeper one. Find the effective depth. *Ans.* 36.3 in.

806. A welded girder is composed of a 48 × ½-in. web, two 12-in. × 25-lb. flange channels, and two 14 × ½-in. covers as shown in Fig. 134(*d*). The bending moment is 1,600,000 ft-lb. Compare the fiber stress computed by the beam formula with the fiber stress determined from an estimated effective depth of 46 in.

165. Allowable Stress in the Compression Flange. The compression flange of a girder acts essentially as a *column.* Failure of this column may occur by local wrinkling of a plate or by sidewise buckling of the flange over a considerable length that is unsupported laterally. Specifications usually require that the outstanding or *unsupported projection* of a plate beyond a line of rivets which forms part of a compression member shall not exceed 12 times its thickness. *AISC* limits this ratio to $3000 \div \sqrt{F_y}$ or 16 for *A*36 steel. (Spec. 24.)

Column Action. The compression flange of a through railway girder can be supported laterally by brackets to the floor beams. The flange must act as an unsupported column between these brackets. If the length of span between lateral supports exceeds 15 times the flange width, there is danger that failure may occur from lateral buckling at a reduced stress. In order to compensate for this weakness, it is necessary to reduce the allowable flange stress in compression in the same manner that the allowable stress on a long column is reduced.

SPECIFICATIONS. All of the standard types of column formulas have been used to limit the allowable compressive stress in a girder flange which must be reduced with increase in the unsupported length L and with decrease in width b of the compressive flange. For example:

$$\frac{P}{A} = 18{,}000 - 5\frac{L^2}{b^2} \quad (\textit{AASHO} \text{ formula, Spec. 202}), \tag{3}$$

$$\frac{P}{A} = \frac{12{,}000{,}000}{Ld/A_f} \quad (\textit{AISC} \text{ formula, Spec. 14}), \tag{4}$$

where L is the unsupported length, d is the depth of the girder, b is the width, and A_f the area of its compression flange, all in inches.

166. Reduction of Flange Area. The maximum bending moment in a girder occurs near the center of the span. Irrespective of the type of loading, the variation in maximum moment for all points along the span is *nearly parabolic.* In other words, the maximum moment at the quarter point is approximately 75 per cent of the maximum moment at the center of the span, etc. Note that the reduction in maximum moment varies as the *square* of the distance out from the center. At one half of the distance from the center to the end, the reduction in moment will be one quarter, at three quarters of the distance from the center to the end the reduction will be nine sixteenths, etc.

Point of Cut-Off for the Cover Plate. Since an entire cover plate must be cut off at one point, this point of cut-off is determined by the resisting moment of the remainder of the section. Either by plotting a true curve of maximum moments, or by a simple computation based upon an assumed parabolic variation of maximum moment, the point is located at which the remainder of the cross-section without the cover plate is adequate to resist the bending moment. Then the cover plate is extended beyond this point a sufficient distance so that the extended portion may be attached to the girder with rivets or high strength bolts (friction joint) sufficient to develop the stress required in the cover plate to resist its share of the moment at the theoretical point of cut-off. Cover plates are usually of the same length for top and bottom flanges except that one cover plate on the top flange of a riveted bridge girder is extended the full length of the girder for weather protection. For a welded girder the flange plates may merely be changed in thickness, the plate ends being scarfed to match together and end butt-welded for full strength in tension or compression. This type of design is preferred to multiple welded cover plates of partial length because of better fatigue strength, as established by tests. (See Fig. 146 and Spec. 27.)

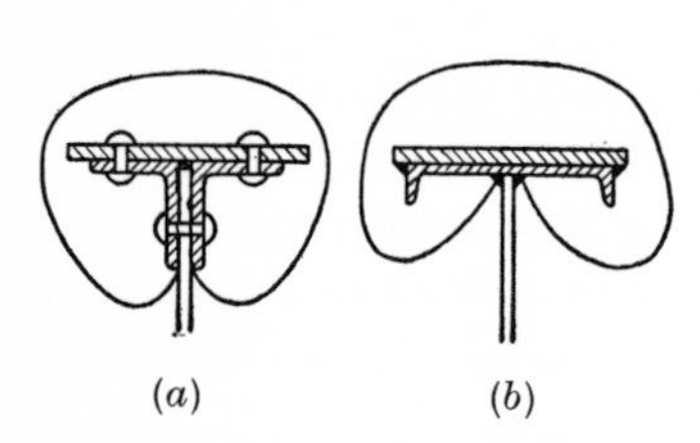

FIG. 137. CONNECTION BETWEEN WEB AND FLANGE.

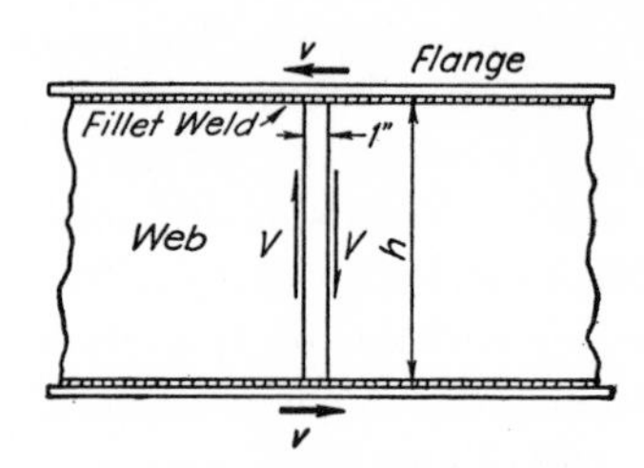

FIG. 138. SHEAR BETWEEN WEB AND FLANGE OF A GIRDER.

CONNECTIONS AND DETAILS

167. Shear Between Web and Flange—Exact Method. The connection between the web and the flange is made either by riveting, bolting, or welding the parts together. It will be observed that flange rivets, which pass through two angles and the web, are in double shear or in bearing on the web, while flange welds are simply stressed in longitudinal shear. It is sufficient that methods be developed for finding the longitudinal shear per lineal inch of girder. With this information, we can readily determine the shear per rivet or bolt and the required rivet spacing or the size of fillet for a longitudinal weld. The exact calculation of the horizontal shear per lineal inch between the web and the flange can be made by use of the *beam shear formula.*

$$v = \frac{VQ}{I}. \tag{5}$$

In this formula, Q is the statical moment about the *neutral axis* of the cross-sectional area of all metal *outside* of the section on which shear is to be calculated. In Fig. 137(a), this area includes two angles and a cover plate, while in (*b*) it includes the channel and the cover plate. If the shear acting between the angles and the cover plate of Fig. 137(*a*), or between the cover plate and the channel in (*b*), is desired, the value of Q is determined from the area of the cover plate only. In all cases I represents the moment of inertia of the *gross cross-section.*

168. Shear between Web and Flange—Approximate Method. The approximate method of determining shear between the web and the flange will be made dependent upon the assumption that the maximum web shear is the same as the average shear on the web. Clearly, the horizontal shear between the web and the flange per lineal inch of girder must be the same as the horizontal shear per lineal inch in the web itself near this connection line. Therefore, since the horizontal and vertical unit shears in the web are equal at any point, the horizontal shear per lineal inch between the web and the flange is equal approximately to the *average vertical shear*, or

$$v = \frac{V}{h}. \tag{6}$$

Equilibrium Derivation. The same relation may be derived from an ordinary equilibrium study of the section of web of unit length shown in Fig. 138. If all the horizontal stress is considered to be resisted by the flanges, the only forces acting on this piece of web are the total vertical shears V and the horizontal shears v between the web and the flange. Each of these pairs of forces forms a couple. For equilibrium these couples must have equal values and they must act in opposite directions. Therefore if h *is the vertical distance between the flange welds,* we may write

$$v \times h = V \times 1, \quad \text{or} \quad v = \frac{V}{h}. \tag{7}$$

Shear between Parts of the Flange. The determination of the shear between the angles and the cover plates by means of the approximate method is also quite simple. A study of the exact formula, $v = VQ/I$, shows that Q varies almost directly with the flange area *outside* of any given section, while V and I remain unchanged. Hence the shear per lineal inch between the cover plate and the angles of Fig. 137(*a*) can be found approximately by multiplying the shear per lineal inch between the web and flange by the ratio of the area of the cover plate to the total area of the flange.

Resultant Stress on Flange Rivets. In most building girders and in railway plate girders of deck construction, there is a vertical shear on the rivets connecting the flange to the web caused by the direct vertical load P on the top flange of the girder. The load P is assumed to be distributed over a length L. In addition, there is the horizontal shear discussed above. The maximum shear on a rivet is the *resultant* R of these horizontal and vertical shears times the rivet spacing. See Fig. 139.

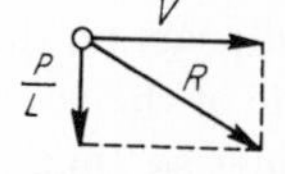

FIG. 139. RESULTANT RIVET SHEAR.

169. Web Stiffeners. The web of a plate girder is a relatively slender compression member. Either the compressive stress in the web must be kept low enough to prevent buckling[2] or else the web must be stiffened by the use of riveted *stiffener angles* or by welded *stiffening plates.* There are two kinds of stiffeners used on plate-girder webs which serve distinctly different purposes. End stiffeners, as shown in Fig. 135, are used to prevent the web from buckling or wrinkling under the effect of the concentrated end reaction. Similarly, stiffeners are used in building girders under any large concentrated load that is placed on the top flange. Interior stiffeners (Fig. 141) are used to prevent the formation of diagonal wrinkles in the web perpendicular to the direction of the diagonal compression. Such wrinkles must not develop except in the special case of tension-field girders discussed in §160, §171, and example *DP*30.

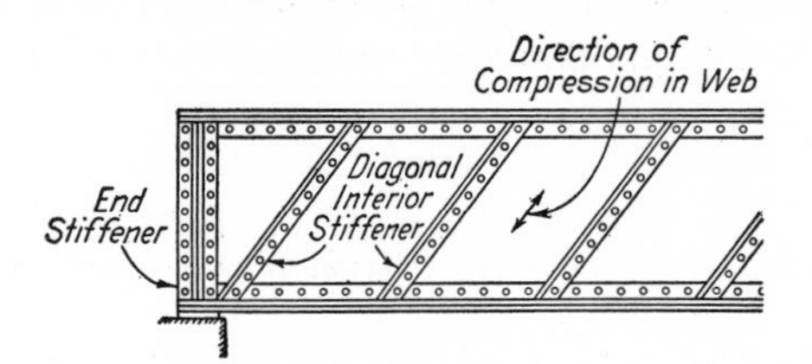

FIG. 140. DIAGONAL STIFFENERS ON A PLATE-GIRDER WEB.

Diagonal and Horizontal Stiffeners. It might seem that diagonal stiffeners (Fig. 140) rather than vertical stiffeners would be most effective in resisting the diagonal compression. This is probably true, but another point of view is of importance. The web itself will properly resist the diagonal compression if it is prevented from buckling by stiffeners. Vertical stiffeners as shown in Fig. 141 can prevent buckling as effectively as diagonal stiffeners, and they simplify the fabrication of the girder. *Horizontal stiffeners* have been used on very deep girders. To be effective they are placed well above the mid-height of the web in the compression zone. A single longitudinal stiffener running the full length of the girder above the mid-height may prove adequate as a replacement for closely spaced vertical stiffeners on the exposed side of the web. Vertical stiffeners on the opposite side of the web shorten the buckling length of the horizontal stiffener to one panel so that it need not be continuous. *AASHO* specifications cover the design of a horizontal stiffener.

170. Stresses in End Stiffeners. The load on the end stiffener is equal to the maximum end reaction of the girder. The usual assumption is that the *entire* load is carried by the stiffener without aid from the web. The outstanding legs of the stiffeners are milled to bear against the legs of the flange angles, or else the two are welded together. The area in bearing

[2] See *Theory of Plates and Shells,* S. Timoshenko, McGraw-Hill, 1940, pp. 311–328.

between the flange and the stiffener must be sufficient so that the allowable unit stress in bearing will not be exceeded. The contact area may be less than the stiffener cross-section. Compare F_a for stiffeners in Spec. 13 with F_p in Spec. 15.

Courtesy Illinois Central R.R.

FIG. 141. SWINGING A PLATE GIRDER INTO PLACE.

The crane is lowering the girder. The workmen at the left are guiding it downward while those at the right are waiting to seat it on the viaduct tower. Notice stiffeners.

Column Action. The end stiffener for a deep girder may be sufficiently tall to act as a slender column. More commonly, the slenderness ratio is small enough so that the allowable compressive stress is limited by the maximum value for compression members, 15,000 psi for railway girders and $0.60F_y$ for building girders (*AISC*). In calculating the value of L/r for an end stiffener, the value of L may be *one half* or more of the depth of the web ($0.75d$ by *AISC* spec.) to allow for the fact that the compressive stress is entirely transferred out of the stiffener within the depth of the web. The value of r to be calculated is a horizontal radius perpendicular to the plane of the girder web. Buckling of the end stiffener in the plane of the girder web is obviously impossible.

Connection to the Web. The end stiffeners should be riveted or welded to the web with a sufficient number of rivets, bolts, or length of weld to transfer the value of the end reaction from the stiffener into the web. In riveted construction, the rivets are either in double shear or in bearing on the web because web stiffeners are used in *pairs* on opposite sides of the web.

171. Need for Interior Stiffeners. Bridge girders must have interior stiffeners if the unsupported depth of the web exceeds 60 times the web thickness for carbon steel or $50t$ for low alloy steel. The unit shear as then allowed by bridge specifications is 11,000 psi on the gross area of the web for mild carbon steel. The specifications for building girders are more liberal. The *AISC* specifications give formulas that make the allowable shear stress in the web F_v depend upon the yield strength of the steel F_y, the h/t ratio (clear depth of web divided by web thickness), and the aspect ratio a/h (stiffener spacing divided by clear depth of web). See Spec. 29 and Table S-4. For $A7$ steel and $h/t = 70$ the allowable web shear is 13,000 psi for all values of a/h up to 3.0, and 12,600 psi for an unstiffened web (that is, $a/h = 3.0$). The h/t ratio of the web may be increased to 140 without reduction of the unit web shear below 13,000 psi if the distance between transverse stiffeners is reduced so that $a/h = 0.5$. In fact, the ratio h/t may be increased to 360 for an aspect ratio $a/h = 0.5$ if the allowable unit shear is no more than 9700 psi, but intermediate stiffeners must then represent 10 per cent of the cross-sectional area of the web. Somewhat larger shear values apply for $A36$ steel (Table S-4) and considerably higher unit shears are permitted for alloy steel of high yield strengths. The necessary *AISC* formulas are given in Specs. 25 to 33. Formulas are also given for the cross-sectional area of transverse stiffeners and the required shear value for rivets, bolts, or welds connecting the stiffener angles or plates to the web. For analytical methods and test results covering the strength of webs the reader is referred to the publications listed in the footnote.[3]

Diagonal Tension Field. It should be realized that the liberal specifications of *AISC* accept elastic web buckling as normal structural action and make the resistance of the web dependent upon diagonal tension fields between stiffeners wherever the *allowable* shear stress is less than $0.35\ F_y$. This occurs for h/t values between 80 and 120 for different values of F_y and a/h. In such cases the intermediate stiffeners function as vertical compressive members of a Pratt-type truss and must be designed for this function either by use of a column formula or by use of the *AISC* stiffener area formula (Spec. 31) with a required moment of inertia about the axis of possible buckling of $(h/50)^4$ for each stiffener. Also, at the end of the girder the stiffener spacing for one panel is limited to $11{,}000\ t/\sqrt{f_v}$ by *AISC* (Spec. 30), which is based upon compressive web resistance. This is a compromise with tension-field theory that may well disappear in future specifications. However, it reduces the most serious contribution to shear distortion.

[3] *Strength of Plate Girders in Shear, ASCE* Journal of the Structural Division, Oct. 1961. *Web Buckling Tests on Welded Plate Girders,* Welding Research Council Bulletin No. 64.

EXAMPLE *DP*30, TENSION-FIELD GIRDER. It is useful to check the permissible design of girder webs under *AISC* specifications by truss analysis whenever tension fields are required for shear resistance. The example of *DP*30 involves a slender web but not one of extreme proportions. The analysis shows that 45 per cent of the greatest diagonal width of web between stiffeners must act as a fully effective tension field. It also shows that a horizontal width of web equal to $61t$ must function effectively with the stiffener to form a vertical compressive member in order to hold the average unit compressive stress merely to $0.6F_y$, its maximum value for a very short column. These rather liberal values make it clear that such a girder has little unused capacity in the panel investigated. It could be strengthened by reducing the stiffener spacing near the ends (high shear area) and increasing it in the area of low shear. In fact, the length of the end panel would be limited to $11{,}000t/\sqrt{f_v} = 11{,}000 \times 0.5/\sqrt{10{,}000} = 55$ in. by *AISC* Spec. 30, but the next panel could remain at 80 in. even though its stresses are equally high.

PROBLEMS

807. The plate girder illustrated has two extra cover plates added. These plates are 14 × ½ in. If the length of the girder is 60 ft., find the theoretical point of cut-off for each of these plates. Assume that the section is fully stressed at the center of the span and that the curve of maximum moments is a parabola. Base your calculations on gross area.

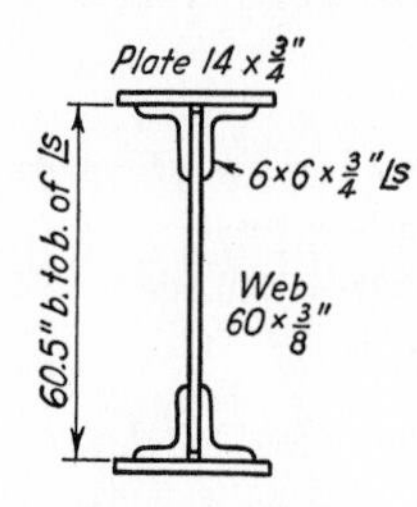

PROBLEM 807.

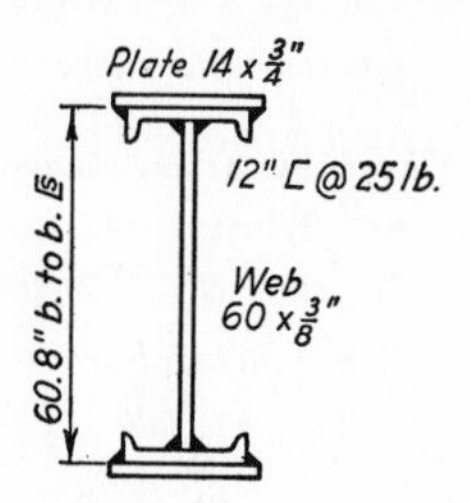

PROBLEM 812.

808. Same as Problem 807 except work on the assumption that the section is stressed to 95 per cent of its capacity at the center.

809. Compare the maximum shear at the neutral axis with the average shear in the web for the girder of Problem 807. The shear is 250 kips.

810. Determine the required spacing of ⅞-in. rivets connecting the web and flange of the girder of Problem 807, where the vertical shear is 170 kips. Allow 15,000 psi for single shear and 40,000 psi for bearing on the web. Use the exact method and check by the approximate method. *Ans.* Approximately 3½ in.

811. Compute the spacing of rivets between the cover plate and the flange angles for the girder of Problem 807. Again use the exact method and check by the approximate method.

812. If the welded girder shown in the sketch is subjected to a vertical shear of 150 kips, compute the horizontal shear per lineal inch between the cover plate and the channel and between the channel and the web. Check by the approximate method.

813. Determine the reduction in the required spacing of rivets in Problem 810 if there is a vertical wheel load of 36,000 lb. distributed over 36 in. to be considered as well as the shear of 170 kips. Increase the wheel load for 100 per cent impact. *Ans.* Reduced approximately ⅛ in.

DP30. *For A36 steel AISC specifications permit a web shear $F_v = 10{,}000$ psi when $h/t = 160$ and $a/h = 1.0$. The corresponding stiffeners for web depth h must equal 8 per cent of the web cross-section. The girder illustrated meets these requirements. Its design will be checked by truss analysis for panel BC.*

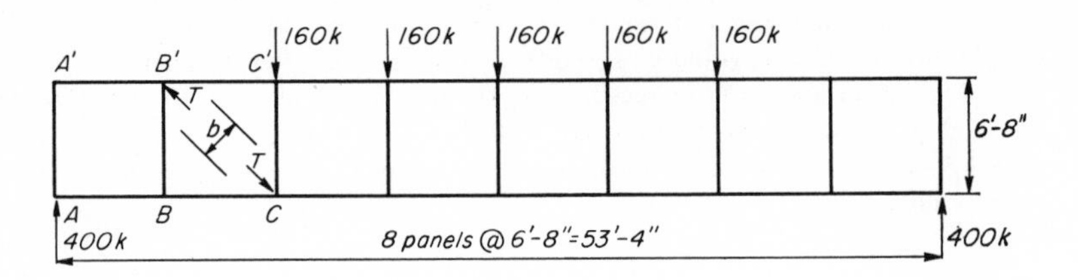

Design by Specifications: *The web shear for panels AB and BC is 400k.*

At 10,000 psi, $A_w = 400{,}000 \div 10{,}000 = 40$ in.^{2} requiring an $80 \times \frac{1}{2}''$ plate.

Note $h/t = 80 \div 0.5 = 160$; $a = h = 80''$; and $a/h = 1.0$.

Stiffener area $= 0.08 \times 80 \times 0.5 = 3.2$ in.^{2} A pair of $3 \times 2\frac{1}{2} \times \frac{5}{16}''$ ∠s, or two $3\frac{1}{4} \times \frac{1}{2}''$ welded plates, will furnish this area and fulfill Spec. 31 for moment of inertia.

Check by Truss Analysis: *The h/t ratio of 160 requires acceptance of minor web buckling and tension-field resistance to vertical shear.*

In panel BC, $V = 400$k., and $T = 1.414 \times 400$k. $= 565{,}000\#$.

Width of web b required to resist T for A36 steel.

$A_t = 565{,}000 \div 22{,}000 = 25.7$ *in.*^{2}; $b = 25.7 \div 0.5 = 51.4''$.

Vertical truss members are formed by stiffeners plus an effective width of web.

Consider web as stem of double compressive Tee for which

Width-to-thickness ratio $= 4000/\sqrt{F_y} = 4000/190 = 21(t)$. (Spec. 24.)

Effective web width $= 2(21 \times 0.5) = 21''$; $A_W = 21 \times 0.5 = 10.5$ in.^{2}

Area of vertical truss member $= 10.5 + 3.2 = 13.7$ in.^{2}

Unit compressive stress $= 400{,}000 \div 13.7 = 29{,}200$ psi.

Maximum allowable compressive stress for stiffener $= 0.6F_y = 21{,}600$ psi.

At this unit stress, active compressive width required of web $= (18.5 - 3.2) \div 0.5 = 30.6''$.

Summary: *The AISC specifications in this example require that the width of active tension-field plate be $51.4'' = 0.65h = 0.45(BC') = 103t$. To hold the stress in the vertical truss member to $0.6\ F_y$ requires an effective width of compressive plate of $30.6'' = 61t$. These are liberal values. A higher factor of safety may be desired.*

814. Revise $DP30$ for $F_y = 50$ ksi steel. Draw conclusions.

815. For $A7$ steel (*AISC* specifications) permit $F_v = 8400$ psi for $h/t = 212$ and $a/h = 1.0$. (See Table S-4.) The stiffener cross-section must increase the web area by 10.5 per cent. In $DP30$ reduce the individual loads from $160k$ to $100k$ and check by truss analysis the widths of web that must carry tensile and compressive stresses in panel BC. The web is 3/8 in. *Ans.* $67t$ for C and $125t$ for T.

172. Design of a Welded Building Girder.

PROBLEM. A welded girder is to be designed to carry a concentrated load plus a uniform load. These are static loads obtained from heavy equipment placed in an industrial building. The ends of the girder are supported on concrete pilasters. The compression flange is supported laterally against buckling by the floor slab.

Data.

Span = 50 ft.-0 in.

Depth. Not limited.

Concentrated center load = 67,000 lb.

Uniform load = 2750 lb. per ft. not including the weight of the girder.

Impact. No allowance for impact.

Allowable Stresses Controlled by Local Building Code. (A-7 steel.)

Flexure. 20,000 psi where flanges are supported laterally.

Fillet welds. 13,600 psi shear on throat.

Specifications.

AISC specifications for Buildings, §308, except for allowable stresses.

172a. Design of the Web and Stiffeners.

Depth of Girder. Taken at 1/10 of the span or 5 ft.-0 in.

Web depth = 58 in. (Economical depths range from 1/8 to 1/12 of the span.)

The weight of the girder is estimated at 200 lb. per lineal ft.

End shear $= (67{,}000 \div 2) + (25 \times 2950) = 107{,}300$ lb.

Estimated web thickness $= 107{,}300 \div (13{,}000 \times 58) = 0.143$ in.

Minimum web thickness = 0.25 in. $h/t = 58 \div 0.25 = 232$ which meets Spec. 26.

Maximum unit web shear $f_v = 107{,}300 \div (58 \times 0.25) = 7400$ psi.

Need for Stiffeners. If h/t is equal to or greater than 150, intermediate stiffeners are required wherever the actual unit web shear exceeds 3700 psi. (See Table S-4.)

Allowable V without stiffeners $= 3700 \times 58.0 \times 0.25 = 54{,}000$ lb.

$V = 54{,}000$ lb. at $(54{,}000 - 0.5 \times 67{,}000) \div 2950 = 7.0$ ft. from center line of span.

$$\text{End stiffener spacing (Spec. 30)} = d = \frac{11{,}000t}{\sqrt{f_v}} = \frac{11{,}000 \times 0.25}{\sqrt{7400}} = 32.0 \text{ in.}$$

The first interior stiffener will be placed at 32-in. spacing. Stiffeners will be used throughout the length of the span for tension-field resistance.

At 3 ft. from the end of the span the shear $V = 107{,}300 - 3 \times 2950 = 98{,}400$ lb. $f_v = 98{,}400 \div 58 \times 0.25 = 6800$ psi. For $h/t = 232$ and $f_v \leq 6800$. Max. $a/h = (260/232)^2 = 1.25$ (Spec. 30). Max. stiffener spacing $= 1.25 \times 58 = 72.5$ in. Use spacings shown in Fig. 142.

Stiffener plates for girders of ordinary depth should preferably have a width equal to 2 in. $+ d/30$. Accordingly, 4-in. stiffener plates will be used. The thickness will be made 1/16 of the width to meet Spec. 24, or, $t = 4/16 = 0.25$ in. Use $4 \times 1/4$-in. plates placed in pairs on opposite sides of the web. See Fig. 142 for details.

Comment on Stiffeners. By *AISC* specifications 4-in. × ¼-in. stiffeners alternated on opposite sides of the web would meet the minimum requirement for area and moment of inertia. (Spec. 31.) However, double stiffeners spaced throughout the span is inexpensive insurance against web damage in handling or change in type of loading.

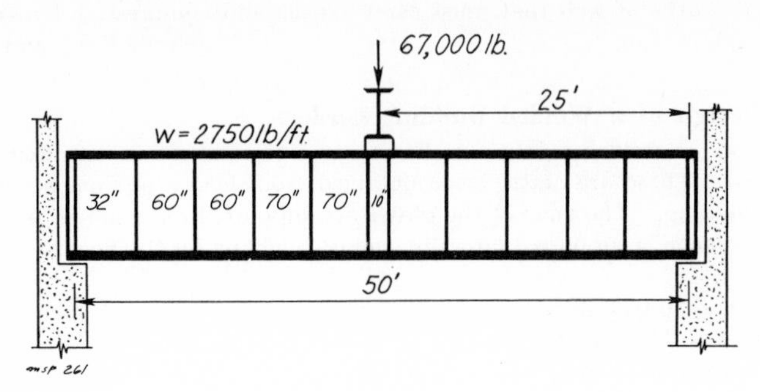

FIG. 142. GIRDER DIMENSIONS AND LOADS.

Strength of Stiffener Welds. At 13,600 psi on the throat, the value of a fillet weld in shear or tension is 1200 lb. per lineal in. per ⅛ in. of fillet leg. This means that a 5/16-in. weld has a value of 3000 lb. per lineal in., a ¼-in. weld has a value of 2400 lb., etc. Intermittent welds are used where the full length of fillet is not required. The minimum intermittent length of weld is 1½ in. (Spec. 56.)

Welding stiffeners to web. The connecting welds between a single stiffener or a pair of stiffeners and the web (Spec. 32) is

$$f_{vs} = h\sqrt{(F_y \div 3400)^3}$$

$$= 58\sqrt{(33{,}000/3400)^3}$$

$$= 1760 \text{ lb. per lineal in.}$$

Minimum length ¼-in. fillet welds have a value of 2400 × 1.5 in. = 3600 lb. Pairs of intermittent fillet welds ¼ in. × 1½ in. may be spaced 6 in. on centers as in Fig. 143 or alternated at 4-in. spacing. The 6-in. spacing might be increased to 8 in. for stress, but a spacing of $24t$ between welds is a desirable maximum for an outstanding compressive plate.

End Stiffeners. The reaction to be transferred into the web is 107,300 lb. The stiffeners act as a column whose height is usually taken at ¾ of the depth of the web. (Spec. 28.) This is a stiff short column for which the allowable stress is nearly the maximum of $0.6F_y = 20{,}000$ psi; 107,300 ÷ 20,000 = 5.37 sq. in. of area. By Spec. 28 we may use $(12t + 6\text{in.})t = 2.25$ in.^{2} as effective area from the web. We will furnish about ⅔ of the remainder, or 0.67 (5.37 − 2.25) = 2.08 sq. in. in one pair of end stiffeners, because it is probable that one pair will receive more than one half of the total reaction since they are spaced 6 in. apart. (An even distribution of end reaction could only be obtained by use of a pin-connected end bearing.) Use two pairs of 4 × ¼-in. plates as end stiffeners as in Fig. 143. The area furnished by each pair is 2.0 sq. in. Neither web crippling nor bearing on the ends of the stiffener plates need be investigated, since the compressive stress is restricted to 20,000 psi. The end stiffeners will be butt welded to the flanges with full penetration welds. (See Fig. 143.)

Welding end stiffeners to web. A reaction equal to 20,000 × 2.0 = 40,000 lb. might be transferred into the web by one pair of stiffeners. The length of ¼-in. weld required is 40,000 ÷ 2400 = 16.7 in. The length furnished by four intermittent welds of minimum size (¼–1½–6) in the 58-in. depth of the web is 58 in. Accordingly, the intermittent weld used on the intermediate stiffener is also ample for the end stiffeners. The concentrated center load is smaller than the end reaction. Hence two intermediate stiffeners may be used at the mid-span as shown by Fig. 144.

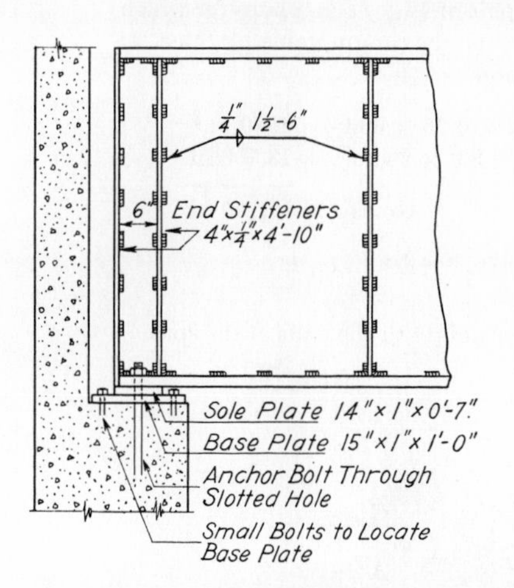

FIG. 143. END STIFFENER AND SEAT.

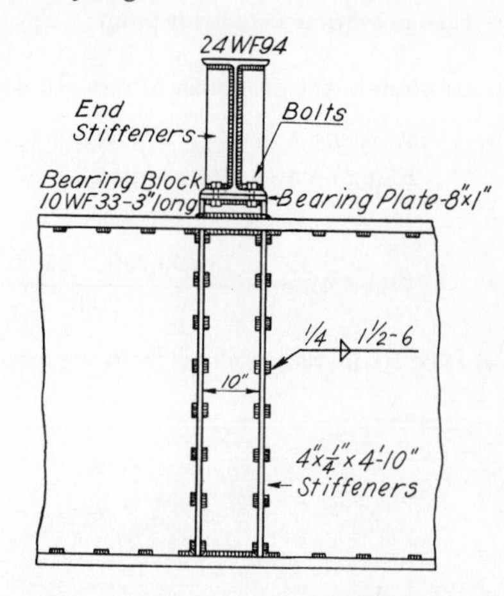

Note How Bearing Block Bears on Stiffeners and Web.

FIG. 144. LOAD SEAT.

172b. Design of the Flange (*assuming lateral support adequate for* $F_b = 0.60\ F_y$).

$$\text{Maximum moment} = \left(\frac{67{,}000 \times 50}{4} + \frac{2950 \times 50^2}{8}\right) = 21{,}100{,}000 \text{ in-lb.}$$

Approximate effective depth. Assumed as depth of web + 1 in. = 59 in.
Flange area required = 21,100,000 ÷ (59 × 20,000) = 17.9 sq. in.
Effective area of web = ⅙ × ¼ × 58 = 2.4 sq. in.
Area in flange plate at mid-span = 17.9 − 2.4 = 15.5 sq. in.

Flange Section at Mid-Span. Try 16 × 15/16-in. flange plate which will furnish a gross area of 15.0 sq. in.

Gross moment of inertia

Web (58 × ¼ in.)	$= \frac{1}{12} \times 0.25 \times 58.0^3 =$	4050 in.^{4}
Flange plates (16 × 15/16 in.)	$= 2 \times 15.0 \times 29.47^2 =$	26,000 in.^{4}
	Gross $I =$	30,050 in.^{4}

$$\text{Fiber stress} = \frac{21{,}100{,}000 \times 29.94}{30{,}050} = 20{,}500 \text{ psi.}$$

The 16 × 1-in. flange plates will be used at the mid-span, which also allows for a small compressive stress reduction required by Spec. 33.

Change of Flange Section at the Quarter Point of the Span.

$$\text{Moment} = \left[0.5\left(\frac{67{,}000 \times 50.0}{4}\right) + 0.75\left(\frac{2950 \times 50.0^2}{8}\right)\right]12 = 13{,}400{,}000 \text{ in-lb.}$$

Approximate effective depth. Assumed as depth of web = 58.0 in.
Flange area required = 13,400,000 ÷ (58.0 × 20,000) = 11.6 sq. in.
Area needed in one flange plate = 11.6 − 2.4 (from web) = 9.2 sq. in.
Flange section at quarter point. Try a pair of 16 × ½-in. plates for which $b/t = 8.0 \div 0.5 = 16.0$, which approaches the maximum value by Spec. 24.
Gross moment of inertia of reduced section

Web (58 × ¼ in.)	= $\frac{1}{12} \times 0.25 \times 58.0^3$	= 4050 in.^{4}
Flange plates (16 × ½ in.)	= $2 \times 8.0 \times 29.25^2$	= 13,700 in.^{4}
	Gross I	= 17,750 in.^{4}

$$\text{Fiber stress} = \frac{13{,}400{,}000 \times 29.50}{17{,}750} = 22{,}300 \text{ psi.}$$

Use 16 × 9/16-in. flange plates from the quarter points to the ends of the span.

Courtesy Eng. News-Record.

FIG. 145. WELDED GIRDER 165-FT. LONG, WEIGHING 65 TONS, IS TRUCKED TO SITE.

Flange Welds. The purpose of the flange welds is to resist the horizontal shear between web and flange or between component parts of the flange. The shear per lineal inch between web and flange may be found by the exact formula, VQ/I, or by the approximate formula, V/h, where

V = total shear at the section,
I = gross moment of inertia of the cross section,
Q = statical moment about the neutral axis of the area of flange outside of the section on which shear is being calculated,
h = depth between top and bottom welds.

Weld between web and 16-in. flange plate at reaction.

$$\text{Shear} = \frac{VQ}{I} = \frac{107{,}300}{19{,}500}(9.00 \times 29.28) = 1440 \text{ lb. per lineal in.}$$

A ¼-in. intermittent weld 1½ in. long, spaced 3½ in. in the clear on each side of the web produces a shear value of 1440 lb. per lineal in. This is adequate resistance.

Butt Weld between Flange Plates. The detail Fig. 146 shows the butt weld and chamfer used to provide full value at the flange splice and gradual stress transition between the 9⁄16-in. and 1-in. plates.

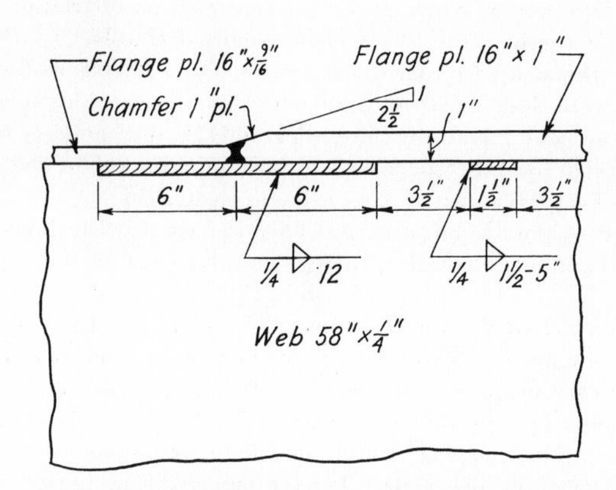

FIG. 146. DETAIL AT FLANGE-PLATE SPLICE.

172c. Bearing for Concentrated Load. A short length of 10*WF*33 beam section makes an excellent bearing block for the concentrated load. This section is welded to the top flange, and its web bears directly over the web of the girder while its flanges bear directly over the stiffeners. The detail is shown in Fig. 144.

Bearing for End Reaction. A sole plate 14 in. wide and 7 in. long will localize the bearing pressure and transmit it properly into the end stiffeners. Since the girder rests upon the edge of the concrete, a bearing plate 15 in. × 12 in. is required to keep the bearing pressure below 600 psi. Plates 1 in. thick are ample because the cantilever extension of the base plate beyond the sole plate is only 2½ in. The detail is shown in Fig. 143.

Weight Estimate of Welded Girder.

Web. 58 × ¼ in., one piece, 51 ft.-0 in. long	=	2500 lb.
Flange plates. 16 × 1 in., 2 pieces, each 25 ft.-0 in. long	=	2730
Flange plates. 16 × 9⁄16 in., 4 pieces, each 13 ft.-0 in. long	=	1590
Stiffener plates 4 × ¼ in., 28 pieces each 4 ft.-10 in. long	=	460
Total	=	7280 lb.

Unit weight = 142 lb. per ft.

Comparison of Weights. The welded girder weighs 20 per cent less than a comparable riveted girder if rivet holes are deducted, and about 10 per cent less under *AISC* specifications. (Spec. 25.) Its cost, however, would not necessarily be as much as 20 per cent less than the cost of the riveted girder. Costs depend upon many factors other than the weight of steel. Costs are completely determinable only when comparative bids are available.

PROBLEMS

816. Redesign the welded girder of §172 using *AISC* specifications for riveted construction. Compare the weight with the value from §172.

817. Redesign the welded girder designed in §172, but change the span to 54 ft.-6 in. Compute the weight. Use *A*7 steel and *AISC* specifications.

818. Same as Problem 817 but use bolted construction of friction type with *A*325 bolts. Exclude bolt threads from shear planes where desirable.

819. Redesign the welded girder of §172 using $F_y = 50{,}000$ psi for the flanges and 33,000 psi for the web. Use *AISC* allowable stresses and specifications.

820. Double the center load on the girder of §172 and increase the uniform load 25 per cent. Redesign by *AISC* specifications for minimum weight choosing material for flange and web to best advantage. Use welded construction.

821. Same as Problem 820 but use *A*325 bolts in friction with threads excluded from shear planes for all connections unless there is no advantage in such exclusion. Check Spec. 16.

822. Design the web at the section of maximum shear and the flanges at the section of maximum moment for a railway plate girder of riveted construction where the span is 80 ft.-0 in. The structure is of the deck type. Assume the dead loading including the weight of two girders to be 1600 lb. per lineal ft. of bridge. The equivalent uniform live load for maximum moment is 7500 lb. and for maximum shear is 9300 lb. per ft. of track. Use the *AREA* specifications. Let the flanges be supported laterally at panel points 16 ft. apart. This is a single track structure with stringers and floor-beams.

823. Redesign the girder of Problem 822 for welded fabrication. Use *AASHO* and *AWS* specifications.

173. Plate-Girder Design. The plate girder is one of the most common fabricated steel structures. Its design should therefore be simplified as much as possible so that designers will continue to take advantage of its wide usefulness. There has been a tendency to complicate specifications in recent years in a search for greater economy. The welded girder is designed rapidly because its gross section is effective. Also, its simple cross-section makes it possible for the designer to guess at the effective depth without the possiblity of serious error. Some specifications permit the gross cross-section of the riveted girder to be considered effective. The corresponding neglect of rivet holes in the tension flange is difficult to justify theoretically.

For many years the plate girder was considered to be uneconomical for spans above 150 ft. However, attitudes and costs have changed. The Quinnipiac River Bridge at New Haven carrying six lanes of turnpike traffic has a center span of 387 ft. flanked by side spans of 258 ft. Even though a plate-girder bridge proves to be heavier than a truss bridge of equal strength, it may be chosen because of several advantages: its fabrication and erection costs are less per pound of weight, it can be erected more rapidly than a truss, and its appearance is in harmony with modern architectural design. A few riveted aluminum girders have been used, and a welded aluminum alloy highway bridge has two 69-ft. and two 41-ft. spans.

CHAPTER 9

ROOFS FOR INDUSTRIAL BUILDINGS

174. Design of Roofs for Industrial Buildings. The roof covering for an industrial building such as a shop, foundry, garage, warehouse, or for a gymnasium having a sloping roof is usually of light-weight self-supporting material such as corrugated steel or corrugated asbestos. These materials will span from 2 to 5 ft. between purlins. The purlins support the roof loads between trusses which in turn are supported upon columns or masonry walls. Typical roof structures are shown in Fig. 147 and Fig. 148.

Courtesy Ingalls Iron Works Co.

FIG. 147. ERECTION OF AN INDUSTRIAL BUILDING WITH FLAT ROOF.

175. Roof Loads. Industrial building roofs must be designed to carry their own dead loads plus the snow load and wind load. The selection of loadings is usually covered by the applicable building code or specification. However, the designer has considerable opportunity to influence the over-all mass of the structure. For example, he may choose a high-strength or a low-strength steel, a light or heavy roof covering, and side walls of masonry or of light prefabricated panels. A light structure may rest on much smaller footings than a massive structure, thus influencing over-all costs of both superstructure and substructure. Cost competition has led to reduction of weight of modern structures by choice of light-weight materials. Extra weight placed high in a building must be carried horizontally to a column, then vertically to the foundation, and then horizontally again to spread the column load over the ground. Hence structural costs are related to the average length of the load path to the ground.

Weights of Building Materials. Weights of plaster, floors, partitions, and walls are covered adequately in the *AISC* Manual of Steel Construction. Data on roofing materials and wind and snow loads are given in Chapter 3.

Courtesy Ingalls Iron Works Co.

FIG. 148. ERECTION OF A STEEL-FRAME BUILDING WITH SLOPING ROOF.

RIVETED ROOF TRUSS DESIGN

176. Design of a Roof for a Gymnasium. The procedure developed for the design of this roof will apply to the design of any roof supported by simple trusses. A short span truss is chosen for simplicity. Economical roof trusses are usually of much longer spans.

PROBLEM. Design a Fink type roof truss with purlins and bracing to serve as a roof for a small air-conditioned gymnasium. The truss is to be supported upon brick bearing walls. Make a detail drawing of the structure. The design is controlled by a *City Building Code* which specifies that connections develop essentially the values of the members, and requires three rivets as a minimum connection. The *City Building Code* also specifies allowable stresses, but otherwise accepts the *AISC* specifications.

Data.

Dimensions of building to outside of walls. 37×50 ft.

Clear height desired = 20 ft.

Wind pressure = 20 psf on a vertical surface.

Snow load = 30 psf on a horizontal surface.

Type of construction. Riveted structure of $A7$ steel.

Allowable Stresses.

Tension = 20,000 psi. Compression for $L/r < 120 = 17{,}000 - 0.485\ L^2/r^2$.

Compression for $L/r > 120 = \dfrac{18{,}000}{1 + \dfrac{L^2}{18{,}000r^2}}$.

Rivet shear ($A141$) = 15,000 psi. Bolt shear ($A307$) = 10,000 psi.

Rivet bearing ($A141$) = 40,000 psi. Bolt bearing ($A307$) = 25,000 psi.

The low value of 25,000 psi for bolt bearing is specified for rough bolts in punched holes.

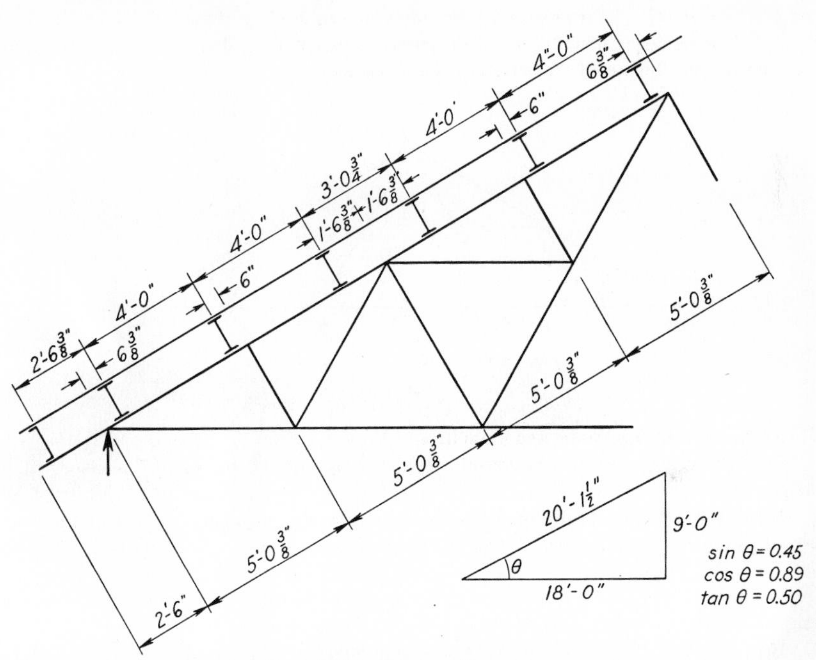

Fig. 149. Purlin Spacing.

Note that the purlins are not placed at the panel points, which results in bending of the upper chord.

176a. General Design.

Thickness of walls. 12-in. bearing walls are required by nearly all building codes and will be used here. With air conditioning, walls are not pierced by large openings.

Span of roof truss = 37 ft.-0 in. less 1 ft.-0 in. = 36 ft.-0 in.

Spacing of roof trusses. The economic spacing of short span roof trusses usually is between 15 and 20 ft. Two end trusses and two interior trusses will be used. The spacing will be 16 ft-3 in.

Roof covering. ¼-in. corrugated asbestos roofing will be used to cover the roof and the gable ends of the building. This material is capable of spanning 4 ft.-0 in. between purlins and as much as 6 ft.-0 in. between girts.

Pitch of roof. The height of the roof will be made ¼ of the span or 9 ft.-0 in. This is a ¼ pitch.

Bracing. Diagonal bracing will be used in the plane of the upper chords. Two longitudinal struts will be used as near as possible to the one-third points of the span in the plane of the lower chords.

Type of roof truss. A Fink roof truss will be used with the upper chord divided into four equal panels. The panel length is 5 ft.-⅜ in. An eave overhang of 2 ft.-6 in. is allowed. (See Fig. 149.)

Arrangement for Transportation. In order to ship the trusses to the site by truck, it is necessary to fabricate them in three parts and then to connect the parts in the field. The truss is divided up as shown in Fig. 150, which makes necessary the arrangement of field connections at L_2, L_3 and U_4.

Flexure of Upper Chord. A simpler design would be obtained by placing the purlins only at panel points. Generally speaking, it is undesirable to introduce flexure into a compression chord. However, when economy or availability of material or architectural reasons dictate closer spacing of purlins than of truss panels, flexure must be taken into consideration. This roof truss is one such instance.

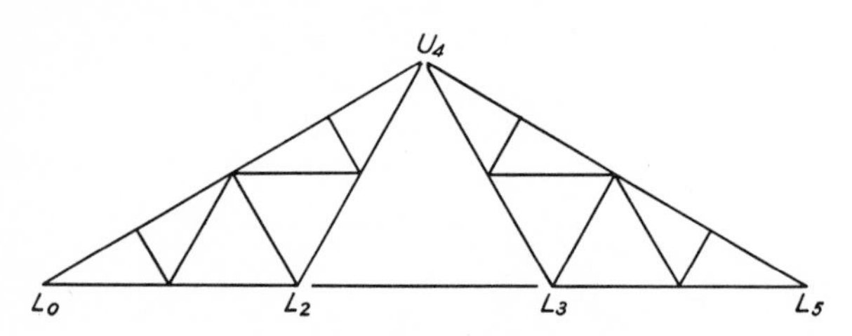

Fig. 150. Field Connections.

176b. Weight Estimate and Loadings. *Dead Load.*

Roof covering. ¼-in. corrugated asbestos weighing 3.0 psf of roof surface will be satisfactory.

Insulation board. ½-in. insulation board weighing 1½ psf is attached to the under side of the purlins. Purpose, to improve the inside appearance of the roof and to reduce heat loss.

Purlins. Steel purlins at 4-ft. centers to carry medium loads for a medium span length of 16 ft. are estimated to weigh 3.0 psf of roof surface.

Roof trusses. Estimated at 2.0 psf of roof surface.

Struts and bracing. Adequate bracing will weigh about 1½ psf of roof surface.

Total dead weight $= 3 + 1\frac{1}{2} + 3 + 2 + 1\frac{1}{2} = 11.0$ psf.

Dead weight per panel $= 11.0 \times 5.03 \times 16.25 = 900$ lb. This load is to be considered as acting at the upper chord panel points.

Snow Load.

Location. The building is assumed to be in the central part of the United States.

Snow load on a horizontal surface = 30 psf.

Snow load on a roof of ¼ pitch = 20 psf of roof surface.

Panel concentration $= 20 \times 16.25 \times 5.03 = 1640$ lb.

Wind Load.

Location. Unexposed location protected by surrounding buildings.

Pressure on a vertical surface = 20 psf.

Pressure on a roof of ¼ pitch. ¼ pitch makes an angle of 26°-40′ with the horizontal plane.

$$P_n = \frac{P\theta}{45} = \frac{20 \times 26.6}{45} = 11.8 \text{ psf. of roof surface.}$$

Panel concentration $= 11.8 \times 16.25 \times 5.03 = 960$ lb.

176c. Design of Purlins. Purlins on a sloping roof must resist bending in two planes, perpendicular and parallel to the plane of the roof. Reference has been made elsewhere to the bending of unsymmetrical sections, but space does not permit offering a study of other than the simplest purlin section here. Accordingly, the purlins will be selected from among the smaller beam sections, which are the only rolled sections that are symmetrical about both major axes. For this section (and for channels) the true fiber stress can be found merely by computing the fiber stresses caused by bending in the two principal planes, and by adding these stresses algebraically. Loads are assumed to act through the center of gravity of the section in order to avoid reference to torsion. See Fig. 151.

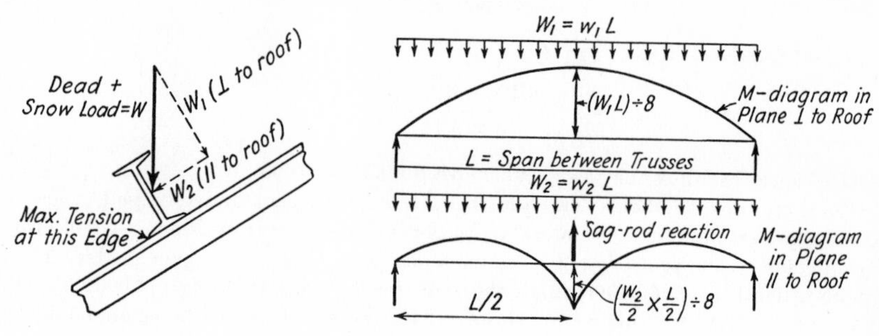

FIG. 151. PURLIN DESIGN LOAD AND ITS MOMENT DIAGRAMS.

Loadings to be Considered. Two combinations of load must be considered: (1) dead load plus full snow load, and (2) dead load plus one half snow load and full wind load. The purlin spacing for computing these loads will be taken as 4.0 ft.

Dead load on a purlin $= 7.5 \times 4.0 \times 16.25 = 490$ lb. (7.5 psf is the weight of purlins, roofing, and insulation board.)

Snow load on a purlin $= 20.0 \times 4.0 \times 16.25 = 1300$ lb.
Wind load on a purlin $= 11.8 \times 4.0 \times 16.25 = 770$ lb.

Components of Dead Load and Snow Load. (Purlin loads for 16.25-ft. span)

Dead load perpendicular to roof	$= 490 \times 0.89 = 440$ lb.	1600 lb. per panel
Snow load perpendicular to roof	$= 1300 \times 0.89 = 1160$ lb.	
Dead load parallel to roof	$= 490 \times 0.45 = 220$ lb.	800 lb. per panel
Snow load parallel to roof	$= 1300 \times 0.45 = 580$ lb.	

Maximum Loading. The total dead load plus snow load per purlin for a span of 16.25 ft. taken perpendicular to the roof is 1600 lb. while the component of load taken parallel to the roof is but 800 lb. This latter load which bends the purlin in its weaker direction is so great that one sag rod must be used per bay. The loading to be used will consist of *dead load plus full snow load,* because, when wind is considered, the snow load is reduced 50 per cent and all working stresses are increased 33⅓ per cent at the same time. Hence the wind load is not large enough to influence the section of the purlin. The point of maximum stress in the purlin will occur at the center of the span due to flexure in both planes. Sag rods provide reactions parallel to the roof midway between trusses.

Bending Moments—Following Fig. 151.

Moment about major axis at center of purlin $= \dfrac{1600 \times 16.25 \times 12}{8} = 39{,}000$ in-lb.

Moment at sag-rod support about minor axis of purlin $= \dfrac{400 \times 8.12 \times 12}{8}$

$= 4870$ in-lb.

Trial Section. Try a 5-in., 10-lb. standard I-beam for which the values of the section moduli are 4.84 and 0.82, respectively.

Maximum Stress at Mid-Span.

$$f_b = 39{,}000 \div 4.84 + 4870 \div 0.82 = 14{,}000 \text{ psi. (tension or compression).}$$

Deflection Perpendicular to Roof.

$$\frac{5}{384} \times \frac{1600 \times 16.25^3 \times 1728}{30{,}000{,}000 \times 12.1} = 0.43 \text{ in.}$$

Lateral Stability. (Spec. 14.)

$$\frac{Ld}{A_f} = \frac{8.125 \times 12 \times 5}{3 \times 5/16} = 520.$$

By *AISC* spec. 14, allowable $F_b = 20{,}000$ psi for $Ld/A_f < 600$.

Choice of Purlin Section. The 5-in. I-beam is 30 per cent understressed, since its upper flange is secured against lateral deflection by the sag-rod reaction. A deflection perpendicular to the roof of 0.43 in. is moderate being 1/450 of the span. Also, *AISC* suggests a depth of $f_b/600{,}000$ times the span for purlins, which is (14,000/600,000) $16.25 \times 12 = 4.6$ in. for this roof. However, if a depth of 1/30 of the span should be thought desirable to avoid all possibility of slight vibration during a high gusty wind, it will be found that the 7-in. channel at 9.8 lb. per ft. or the 8 × 4-in. joist section at 10 lb. per ft. are safe and economical. See *AISC Manual* for properties.

Check on Assumed Weight.

7 purlins at 10 lb. per ft. each = 70 lb. per lineal ft. of roof.

Weight per sq. ft. $= 70 \div 22.6 = 3.1$ psf.

The estimated weight was 3.0 psf.

Connection to Roof Truss. Purlins may be bolted to the roof trusses with at least two ½-in. bolts at each connection.

176d. Design of Sag Rods.

Tension in sag rod. The combined purlin reaction on one side parallel to the roof for a length of 8.12 ft. produces the design stress in the sag rod. $(7.5 + 20)0.45 \times 8.12 \times 22.6 = 2270$ lb. (7.5 psf is the weight per sq. ft. of purlins, roofing, and insulation; 20 psf is the snow load.)

Net area required $= 2270 \div 20{,}000 = 0.114$ sq. in.

Size used. The diameter required to furnish this area is ⅜ in. A ⅝-in. non-upset rod furnishes a diameter of 0.507 in. at the roof of the thread. This is the smallest sag rod commonly used since workmen frequently damage the threads by overtightening smaller rods. A detail of the sag rod connection at the ridge is shown in Fig. 152.

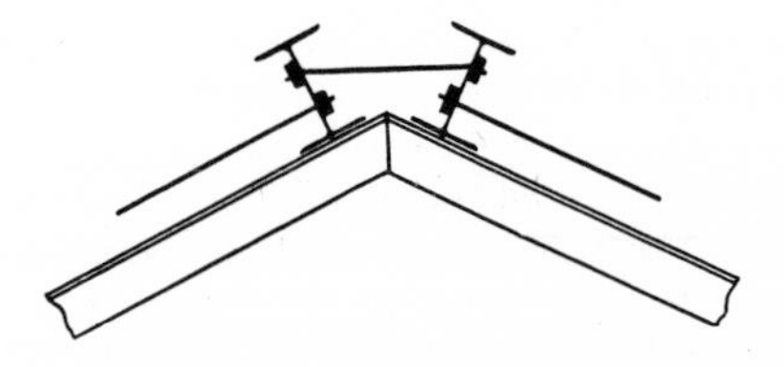

Fig. 152. Sag-Rod Connection.

176e. Analysis of Stresses. The stress analysis for a Fink truss is often performed graphically because of the numerous sloping members. Stress diagrams for dead load and for wind load are shown in Fig. 153. The stresses for snow load are obtained by multiplying the dead load stresses by the ratio 1640/900. In the analysis of wind stresses, the right-hand reaction is assumed to resist all of the horizontal component of the wind. Accordingly, two wind-stress diagrams were drawn: (1) for wind from left, and (2) for wind from right. It happens in this structure that the maximum stresses for the left half and right half of the truss are identical.

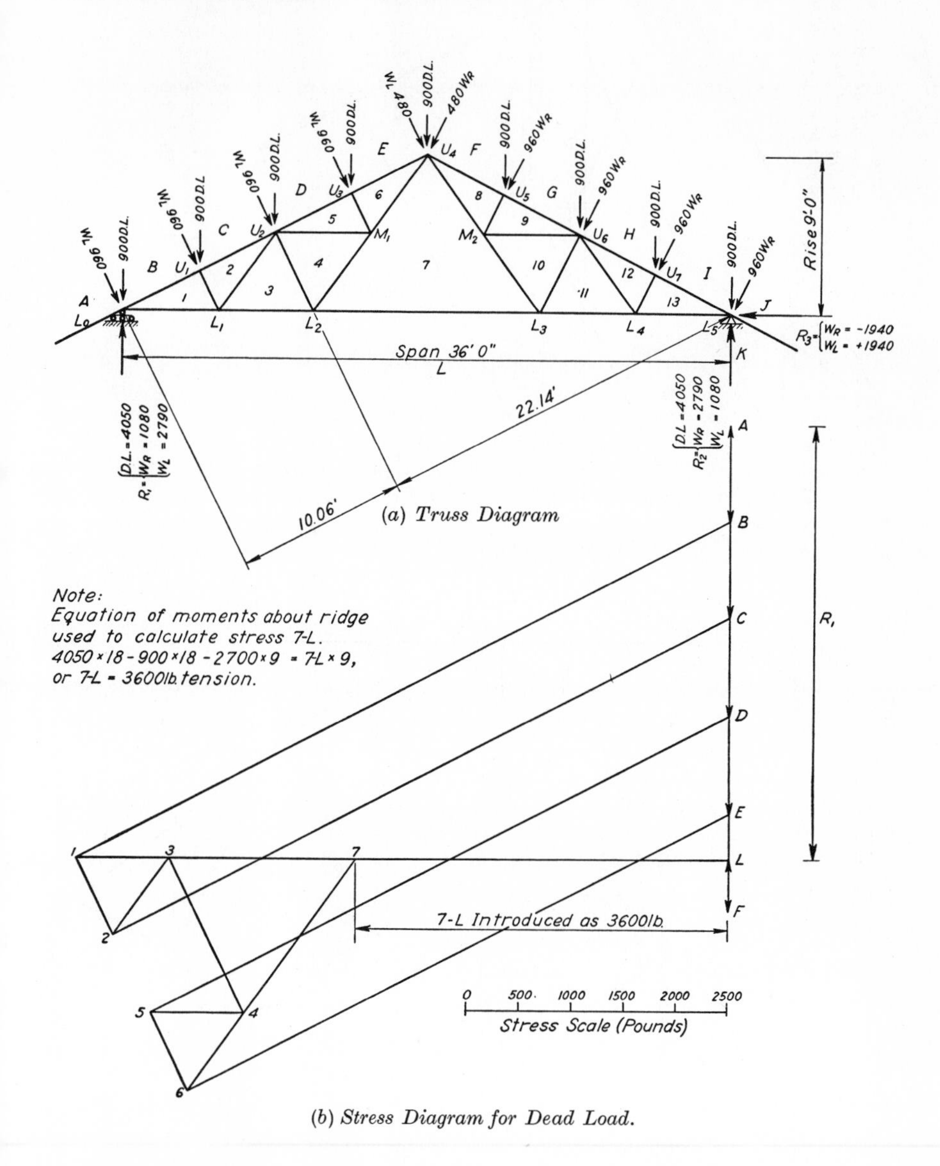

(b) *Stress Diagram for Dead Load.*

FIG. 153. STRESS DIAGRAMS FOR A FINK ROOF TRUSS.

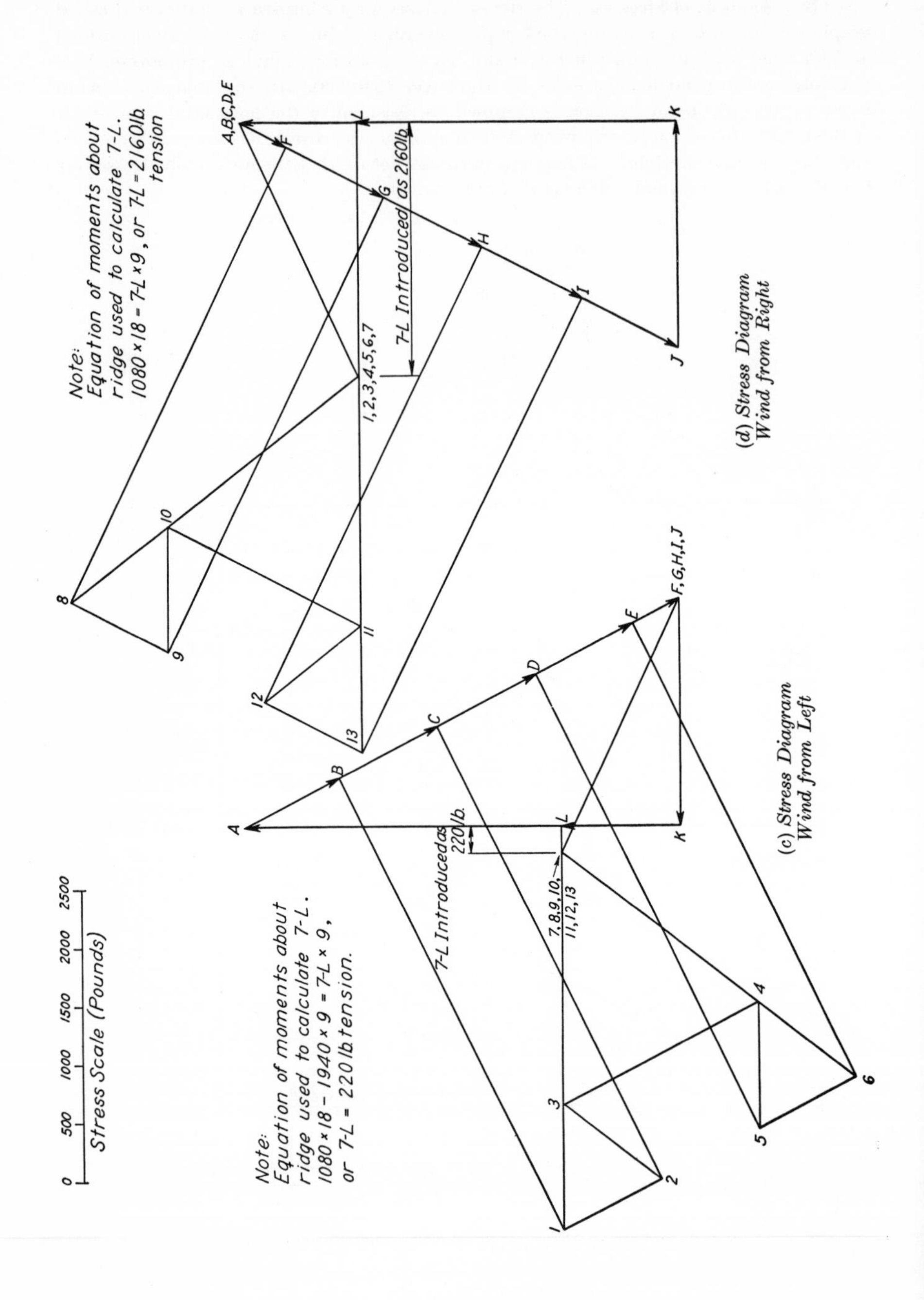

Fig. 153. Stress Diagrams for a Fink Roof Truss (*concluded*).

176f. Maximum Stresses. The dead-load, snow-load, and wind-load stresses are combined for the maximum stresses in Table 6. Three combinations are to be considered: (1) dead load plus full snowload, (2) dead load plus full wind load plus one half snow load, and (3) wind load minus dead load for a member that reverses. No member in this truss has a reversal stress. The final column of Table 6 gives an alternate design stress caused by a uniform vertical load of 31 psf of roof surface (dead load plus snow load). The stresses as given by this alternate loading are sufficiently close to the maximum stresses to be satisfactory for design purposes for many roof trusses. For the particular truss which is being designed here, these alternate stresses actually control the design, for in no case is the exact maximum stress 33⅓ per cent larger than the alternate stress (stress caused by dead load plus snow load), and by Spec. 5 and Spec. 19, one is allowed to increase the working stress 33⅓ per cent when wind is considered in the analysis. Accordingly, the alternate stresses caused by dead load plus full snow load (31 psf of roof surface) will be used with normal working stresses for the design of members and connections.

176g. Design of Truss Members. Design details for members and connections are summarized in Table 7. Most members are composed of one or two minimum angles, $2 \times 2 \times \frac{1}{4}$ in. The minimum thickness of ¼ in. is controlled by corrosion; the 2-in. leg being required to hold a ⅝-in. rivet. All rivets and bolts will be made ⅝ in., the minimum for most structural work. Gusset plates ¼-in. thick should prove adequate for this light truss. Double angle members of symmetrical section will be used in all except the lightest stressed members. Single angle members are objectionable, for they tend to twist the truss by producing an eccentric force at the joint. All end connections will be designed wherever reasonable to develop the full strengths of the members, although judgment will be exercised in this regard. This procedure is not required by *AISC* specifications. Hence, many designers use only enough rivets to develop the calculated stresses for light trusses. The saving averages about one rivet in each connection. Table 7 gives minimum *AISC* connections as well as full-value connections.

176h. Design of Lower Chord Members. The lower chord will be field spliced at L_2 and L_3 and, accordingly, L_0L_1 and L_1L_2 may be made of one section and L_2L_3 of another. Member L_0L_1 has rivet holes deducted from the vertical legs only. Members L_1L_2 and L_2L_3 have rivet holes deducted from both legs to allow for the splice connection. Members L_0L_1 and L_1L_2 are 5 ft.-7½ in. long (67½ in.) while member L_2L_3 is 13 ft.-6 in. (162 in.) long.

Member L_0L_1.

Maximum stress = 17,760 lb. tension.

Minimum section. Two angles $2 \times 2 \times \frac{1}{4}$ in. placed back to back on opposite sides of a single ¼-in. gusset.

Net effective section. Two holes must be deducted since connections are only to the vertical legs. The full net area is considered effective for angles placed in this manner.

Net area $= 2 \times 0.94 - 2 \times 0.19 = 1.50$ sq. in.

Value of member $= 1.50 \times 20{,}000 = 30{,}000$ lb.

Radius of gyration about the horizontal axis = 0.61.

Slenderness ratio $= 67.5 \div 0.61 = 110$. (Note Spec. 23.)

End connection. Rivets are in bearing on the ¼-in. gusset. Rivet value = 6250 lb. $30{,}000 \div 6250 = 5$ rivets.

Member L_1L_2.

Maximum stress = 15,240 lb. tension.

Minimum section. Two $2 \times 2 \times \frac{1}{4}$-in. angles.

Net effective section. Four holes must be deducted from the gross area because of the splice connection. The full net area is considered effective as for the member L_0L_1.

TABLE 6—STRESSES IN POUNDS FOR MEMBERS OF THE FINK ROOF TRUSS OF FIG. 153

Stress		Dead Load (1)	Full Snow (2)	One Half Snow (3)	Wind from Left (4)	Wind from Right (5)	Columns to be Combined for Max. (6)	Maximum Stress (7)	Stress Caused by an Alternate Vertical Load of 31 psf (8)	Member
Upper Chord	1B	−7050	−12,840	−6420	−4320	−2440	1 & 2	−19,890	−19,890	U_1L_0
	2C	−6650	−12,100	−6050	−4320	−2440	1 & 2	−18,750	−18,750	U_1U_2
	5D	−6250	−11,400	−5700	−4320	−2440	1 & 2	−17,650	−17,650	U_2U_3
	6E	−5850	−10,640	−5320	−4320	−2440	1 & 2	−16,490	−16,490	U_3U_4
	13I	−7050	−12,840	−6420	−2440	−4320	1 & 2	−19,890	−19,890	U_7L_5
	12H	−6650	−12,100	−6050	−2440	−4320	1 & 2	−18,750	−18,750	U_7U_6
	9G	−6250	−11,400	−5700	−2440	−4320	1 & 2	−17,650	−17,650	U_6U_5
	8F	−5850	−10,640	−5320	−2440	−4320	1 & 2	−16,490	−16,490	U_5U_4
Lower Chord	1L	+6300	+11,460	+5730	+3430	+2160	1 & 2	+17,760	+17,760	L_0L_1
	3L	+5400	+ 9,840	+4920	+2380	+2160	1 & 2	+15,240	+15,240	L_1L_2
	7L	+3600	+ 6,560	+3280	+ 220	+2160	1 & 2	+10,160	+10,160	L_2L_3
	11L	+5400	+ 9,840	+4920	+ 220	+4300	1 & 2	+15,240	+15,240	L_3L_4
	13L	+6300	+11,460	+5730	+ 220	+5400	1 & 2	+17,760	+17,760	L_3L_5
Left Web	1–2	− 810	− 1,470	− 740	− 960	0	1,3,4	− 2,510	− 2,280	U_1L_1
	2–3	+ 900	+ 1,640	+ 820	+1070	0	1,3,4	+ 2,790	+ 2,540	U_2L_1
	3–4	−1620	− 2,950	−1480	−1920	0	1,3,4	− 5,020	− 4,570	U_2L_2
	4–5	+ 900	+ 1,640	+ 820	+1070	0	1,3,4	+ 2,790	+ 2,540	U_2M_1
	5–6	− 810	− 1,470	− 740	− 960	0	1,3,4	− 2,510	− 2,280	U_3M_1
	6–7	+2700	+ 4,920	+2460	+3200	0	1,3,4	+ 8,360	+ 7,620	U_4M_1
	4–7	+1800	+ 3,280	+1640	+2130	0	1,3,4	+ 5,570	+ 5,080	M_1L_2
Right Web	13–12	− 810	− 1,470	− 740	0	− 960	1,3,5	− 2,510	− 2,280	U_7L_4
	12–11	+ 900	+ 1,640	+ 820	0	+1070	1,3,5	+ 2,790	+ 2,540	U_6L_4
	11–10	−1620	− 2,950	−1480	0	−1920	1,3,5	− 5,020	− 4,570	U_6L_3
	10–9	+ 900	+ 1,640	+ 820	0	+1070	1,3,5	+ 2,790	+ 2,540	U_6M_2
	9–8	− 810	− 1,470	− 740	0	− 960	1,3,5	− 2,510	− 2,280	U_5M_2
	8–7	+2700	+ 4,920	+2460	0	+3200	1,3,5	+ 8,360	+ 7,620	U_4M_2
	10–7	+1800	+ 3,280	+1640	0	+2130	1,3,5	+ 5,570	+ 5,080	M_2L_3

Member		Design Stress, lb.	Section Selected	How Placed	Holes Out	Area, sq. in.		Slenderness Ratio, L/r		Value of Member, lb.	Full Connection		Minimum Connection	
						Gross Area	Net Effective Area	Actual	Allowed		⅝″ Rivets	⅝″ Field Bolts	⅝″ Rivets	/8″ Bolts A307
Upper Chord	U_1L_0	−19,890	2 ∠s 3½ × 2½ × ¼ in.	Long leg down	0	2.88	2.88	54	200	Designed for flexure	6		5	
	U_1U_2	−18,750	2 ∠s 3½ + 2½ × ¼ in.	”	0	2.88	2.88	54	200	”				
	U_2U_3	−17,650	2 ∠s 3½ × 2½ × ¼ in.	”	0	2.88	2.88	54	200	”				
	U_3U_4	−16,490	2 ∠s 3½ × 2½ × ¼ in.	”	0	2.88	2.88	54	200	”		7		5
Lower Chord	L_0L_1	+17,760	2 ∠s 2 × 2 × ¼ in.	long leg up	2	1.88	1.50	110	240	+30,000	5		3	
	L_1L_2	+15,240	2 ∠s 2 × 2 × ¼ in.	”	4	1.88	1.12	110	240	+22,400	2	4	2	4
	L_2L_3	+10,160	2 ∠s 2½ × 2 × ¼ in.	”	4	2.12	1.36	207	240	+27,200	4	3	4	2
Web	U_1L_1	− 2,280	1 ∠ 2 × 2 × ¼ in.		0	0.94	0.705	77	200	− 7,300	3		2	
	U_2L_1	+ 2,540	1 ∠ 2 × 2 × ¼ in.		1	0.94	0.52	173	240	+10,400	3		2	
	U_2L_2	− 4,570	2 ∠s 2 × 2 × ¼ in.		0	1.88	1.88	99	200	−23,200	4		3	
	U_2M_1	+ 2,540	1 ∠ 2 × 2 × ¼ in.		1	0.94	0.52	173	240	+10,400	3		2	
	U_3M_1	− 2,280	1 ∠ 2 × 2 × ¼ in.		0	0.94	0.705	77	200	− 7,300	3		2	
	U_4M_1	+ 7,620	2 ∠s 2 × 2 × ¼ in.		2	1.88	1.50	144	240	+26,200		7		4
	M_1L_2	+ 5,080	2 ∠s 2 × 2 × ¼ in.		2	1.88	1.50	144	240	+26,200	5		3	
Special Members	Purlin		5-in., 10-lb. I-beam*									2		2
	Sag-rod	+ 2,270	⅝-in. non-upset rod			0.307	0.156			+ 3,100				
	Diagonal Bracing	+ 940	1 ∠ 2 × 2 × ¼ in.		1	0.94	0.52	278	300	+10,400		3		2
	Strut	Negligibly small	1 ∠ 3 × 2½ × ¼ in. riveted to a 4-in., 5.4-lb. channel	Short leg down		2.87		200	200	−16,100		3		3

* Or 8 × 4-in., 10-lb. rolled joist section for greater stiffness.

Net area = 2 × 0.94 − 4 × 0.19 = 1.12 sq. in.

Value of member = 1.12 × 20,000 = 22,400 lb.

Slenderness ratio. Same as L_0L_1.

End connection. The end connection for this member will be worked out when the joint L_2 is designed.

REMARKS. Since two 2 × 2 × ¼-in. angles are satisfactory for both L_0L_1 and L_1L_2, this section will be used for the double length member.

TABLE 8

VALUES OF ⅝-IN. RIVETS AND BOLTS

TYPE	WORKING STRESS (psi)		RIVET AND BOLT VALUES (lb).		
	Shear	Bearing	Single Shear	Double Shear	Bearing ¼-in. Metal
Power driven rivets (*A*141)	15,000	40,000	4600	9200	6250
Unfinished bolts (*A*307)	10,000	25,000	3070	6140	3910

Member L_2L_3.

Maximum stress = 10,160 lb. tension.

Unsupported length = 162 in. This member usually is controlled by the requirement that its L/r value about the horizontal axis shall not exceed 240. A member of this stiffness will not sag or vibrate. (Spec. 23.)

Minimum radius of gyration about a horizontal axis = 162 ÷ 240 = 0.68.

Required minimum section. Two 2½ × 2 × ¼-in. angles placed with the 2-in. legs outstanding furnish a radius of gyration of 0.78 about the horizontal axis and 0.89 about the vertical axis.

Net area = 2 × 1.06 − 4 × 0.19 = 1.36 sq. in.

Value of member = 1.36 × 20,000 = 27,200 lb.

End connection. The end connection for this member will be worked out when the joint L_2 is designed.

176 i. Design of the Upper Chord. The entire upper chord will be made of one section. Any saving that might be made possible by changing the sizes of the members would be overbalanced by the cost of a splice and by a loss in the lateral stiffness of the structure.

Length for Buckling. In a vertical plane the length for possible buckling is a panel distance of 5.03 ft. The top chord is supported laterally in the plane of the roof by the purlins. Accordingly, the unsupported length in this plane is the purlin spacing or a maximum of 4.0 ft.

Trial Section. Try two 3½ × 2½ × ¼-in. angles with the 3½-in. legs turned downward. Gross area is 2.88 sq. in. Gross moment of inertia about the horizontal axis is 3.6 and r is 1.12. Extreme fiber distances are 1.11 and 2.39 in.

Allowable Stresses. At the joint U_2 where the fiber stress may become a maximum, the member can buckle laterally over an unsupported length of 36.75 in. The radius of gyration for the angles placed ¼ in. back to back is 1.04 in. $L/r = 35.2$.

$$F_a = 17{,}000 - 0.485 \times 35.2^2 = 16{,}400 \text{ psi.}$$

Midway between panel points the allowable stress is determined from an unsupported length of 60.37 in. between joints and a value of r of 1.12 in. $L/r = 53.9$.

$$F_a = 17{,}000 - 0.485 \times 53.9^2 = 15{,}600 \text{ psi.}$$

Location of Maximum Stress. From the purlin loads and the purlin spacing as shown in Fig. 154, it is evident that the theoretical maximum moment occurs at L_0. The maximum direct stress occurs in U_1L_0 but the stress in U_1U_2 is nearly as great and, hence, the combined stress in U_1U_2 will also be studied. It is important to note that negative moment over a support produces a larger compressive fiber stress than an equal positive moment at the center of the span because the extreme fiber distance to the compression edge is much greater for negative moment.

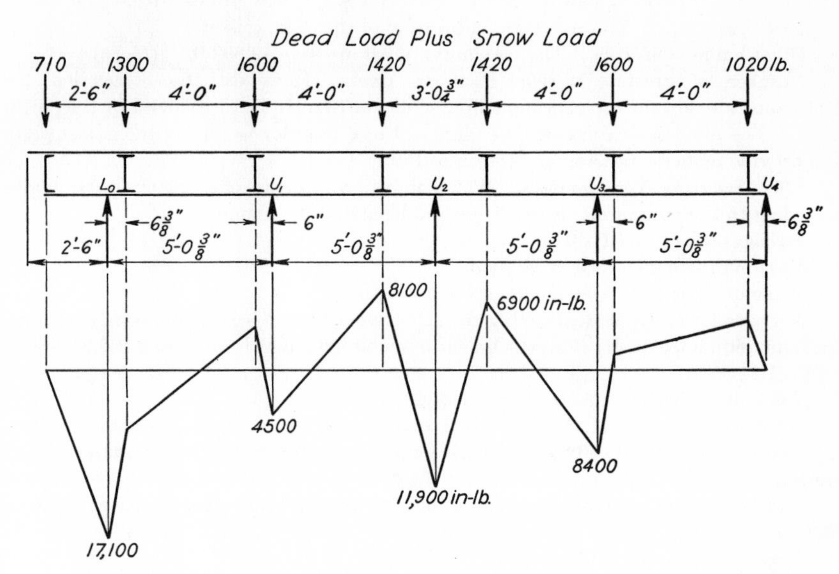

FIG. 154. UPPER CHORD MOMENTS FOR DEAD AND SNOW LOADINGS.

Bending Moments. In continuous beams the bending moments may be computed by moment distribution as described in Vol. 2, *Theory of Modern Steel Structures.* The moment curve of Fig. 154 is an approximate one obtained by distributing moments with two-place numerals. It is satisfactory for use in design except that the moments at the joints may be reduced to the moments near the ends of the gusset plates. The moments are for $DL + SL$ which control the design.

Negative moment at $L_0 = 17{,}100$ in-lb (unreduced).
Negative moment at $U_2 = 11{,}900$ in-lb (unreduced).
Maximum moment under any load $= 8100$ in-lb.

1.11"
2.39"
Upper Chord Section

Combined Stresses, $P/A + Mc/I$. (Use the larger value of c with negative M.)

$$\text{At } L_0 \text{ the combined stress} = \frac{19{,}890}{2.88} + \frac{17{,}100 \times 2.39}{3.6} = 18{,}300 \text{ psi. C.}$$

However, this is a theoretical stress that is reduced to a safe value by the influence of the gusset plate, since the moment of 17,100 in-lb. decreases 50 per cent within 6 in. to the right of L_0.

$$\text{At } U_2 \text{ the combined stress} = \frac{18{,}750}{2.88} + \frac{11{,}900 \times 2.39}{3.6} = 14{,}400 \text{ psi. C.}$$

Again, the influence of the gusset will greatly reduce the stress.

Under the purlin in the panel U_1U_2 the combined stress is

$$\frac{18{,}750}{2.88} + \frac{8100 \times 1.11}{3.6} = 9000 \text{ psi. C.}$$

Note the use of the smaller extreme fiber distance to the most heavily stressed fiber directly under the purlin. This stress may be increased if the purlin connection is made by loose bolts that do not fill the holes. Nevertheless, it will still be within safe limits.

End Connection. The rivets are in bearing on the ¼-in. gusset.

Rivet value = 6250 lb. The maximum direct stress is 19,890 lb. (U_1L_0).

Number of rivets = 19,890 ÷ 6250 = 4 rivets. However, the connection for U_1L_0 must also aid the top chord to a limited degree to resist flexure caused by the purlin loads. The number of rivets will be increased to 6 in order to fill out the gusset plate and provide moment resistance. (See Fig. 162.)

176 j. Selecting Web Members. Web members will consist of single or double angles according to the magnitude of the stress and length of the member.

Members M_1L_2 and U_4M_1.

Maximum stress = 7620 lb. tension.

Minimum section. Two angles 2 × 2 × ¼ in.

Net area for one hole deducted from each attached angle leg and an extra hole from one outstanding leg at M_2 (for attachment of an electric light fixture) = 2 × 0.94 – 3 × 0.19 = 1.31 sq. in.

Value of member = 1.31 × 20,000 = 26,200 lb.

Slenderness ratio = 11.25 × 12 ÷ 0.96 = 141 (take r about axis of symmetry since L is the double length). This slenderness ratio indicates acceptable resistance to vibration.

End connection. Rivets at L_2 are in bearing on the ¼-in. gusset. Rivet value = 6250 lb. 26,200 ÷ 6250 = 5 rivets required.

Members U_2L_1 and U_2M_1.

Maximum stress = 2540 lb. tension.

Minimum section. One angle 2 × 2 × ¼ in. (Actually, double angles are used for symmetry (Fig. 164), but the calculations show that a single angle would be acceptable.)

Effective area = (0.94/2 – 0.19) + 0.94/4 = 0.52 sq. in. Effective area is net area of connected leg plus one half of gross area of unconnected leg.

Value of member = 0.52 × 20,000 = 10,400 lb.

Slenderness ratio = 67.5 ÷ 0.39 = 173 (take r about the diagonal axis).

End connection. Rivets are in single shear or bearing on the ¼-in. leg. Rivet value = 4600 lb. 10,400 ÷ 4600 = 3 rivets required.

Members U_1L_1 and U_3M_1.

Maximum stress = 2280 lb. compression.

Minimum section. One angle 2 × 2 × ¼ in.

Gross area of section = 0.94 sq. in.

Slenderness ratio = 30.2 ÷ 0.39 = 77.4 (using minimum r).

Allowable column stress = 1700 – 0.485 × 77.4^2 = 14,100 psi.

Eccentricity of load = 0.59 + 0.25/2 = 0.72 in. (i.e., from c.g. of angle to mid-thickness of gusset plate).

Allowable eccentric load. See equation (24), p. 184 where c and r are taken in the direction of e. Hence $r = 0.61$ in. and $c = y = 0.59$ in. for maximum compression.

$$P_e = \frac{F_aA}{1 + \frac{ec}{r^2}\left(\frac{F_a}{F_b}\right)} = \frac{14{,}100 \times 0.94}{1 + \frac{0.72 \times 0.59}{0.61^2}\left(\frac{14{,}100}{20{,}000}\right)} = 7300 \text{ lb.}$$

End connection. Rivets are in single shear or bearing on the ¼-in. leg. Rivet value = 4600 lb. 7300 ÷ 4600 = 2 rivets required; 3 rivets are used as the minimum connection.

Member U_2L_2.

Maximum stress = 4570 lb. compression.

Minimum section. Slenderness ratio requires two minimum angles, 2 × 2 × ¼ in.

Gross area = 2 × 0.94 = 1.88 sq. in.

Slenderness ratio = 60.2 ÷ 0.61 = 98.7.

Allowable column stress = $17{,}000 - 0.485 \times 98.7^2 = 12{,}300$ psi.

Value of member = 1.88 × 12,300 = 23,200 lb.

End connection. Rivets are in double shear or bearing on the ¼-in. gusset. Rivet value = 6250 lb. 23,200 ÷ 6250 = 4 rivets required.

REMARKS. Single angle members were used for U_1L_1, U_3M_1, U_2L_1 and U_2M_1. It is common practice to design the sub-struts U_1L_1 and U_3M_1 as single angles, but the tension members U_2L_1 and U_2M_1 are usually made of double angles. This is the arrangement shown on the truss drawing, Fig. 164. For a truss of much longer span or for one designed for heavy loads, all members should be of symmetrical sections. A heavier truss and joint are illustrated by Fig. 155.

FIG. 155. INTERIOR JOINT OF BUILDING TRUSS WITH LATERAL TRUSS CONNECTION.

176k. Design of Joints. The number of rivets in the end of each member has been determined on the assumption that all rivets are power driven rivets. Since this building will need but few field connections, and field rivets require power equipment, it may be desirable to use unfinished bolts *A*307 for field connections. (Spec. 9.) A shear of 10,000 psi and bearing values of 25,000 psi are allowed for rough bolts. *A*325 bolts replace *A*141 rivets on a one-for-one basis for bearing-type connections. In order to haul the trusses to the site by truck, it is necessary to divide the truss into three parts: left half, right half, and the member L_2L_3. Field connections are required at U_4, L_2, and L_3. The *minimum number of rivets* in any connection will be set at three although *AISC* specifications permit the use of two rivets in light structures. (Spec. 40.)

Joints U_1 *and* U_3. This joint is shown in Fig. 156. Clearly, the 3 rivets in the member U_3M_1 must be balanced by at least 3 rivets through the top chord and gusset plate. These rivets are spaced 3 in. apart in order to obtain a reasonable moment resistance. Purlins placed between joints produce moments at the joints.

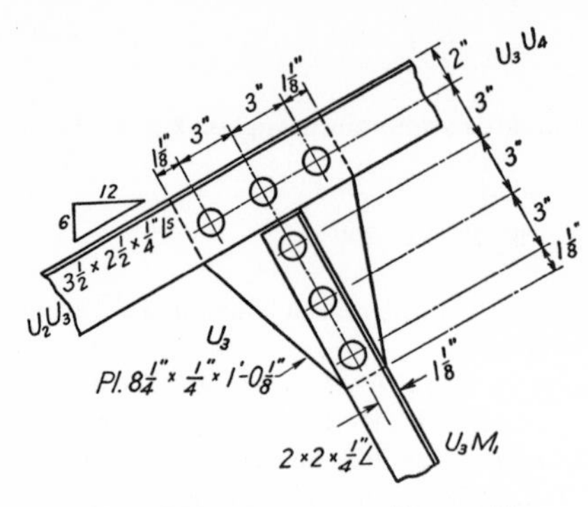

Fig. 156. Detail at U_1 or U_3.

Joint L_1. The gusset plate must be riveted to the bottom chord with sufficient rivets to resist the maximum possible combined horizontal thrust of the members U_1L_1 and U_2L_1. (See Fig. 157.) Of course, $\Sigma F_y = 0$.

Value of $U_1L_1 = 5100$ lb.
Horizontal component of
$U_1L_1 = 5100 \times 0.45 = 2300$ lb.
Value of $U_2L_1 = 9350$ lb.
Horizontal component of $U_2L_1 =$
$10{,}400 \times 0.60 = 6250$ lb.
Total horizontal thrust
$= 2300 + 6250 = 8550$ lb.

Connection. Rivets are in bearing on the ¼-in. gusset. Rivet value $= 6250$ lb. $8550 \div 6250 = 2$ rivets required. The minimum number of 3 rivets will be used.

Joint M_1. The gusset plate must be riveted to the member U_4L_2 for exactly the same resistance that was found necessary at the joint L_1. Compare Fig. 158 with Fig. 157.

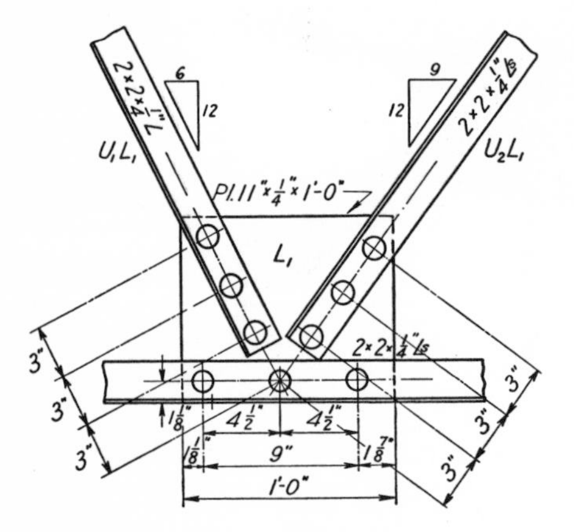

Fig. 157. Detail at L_1.

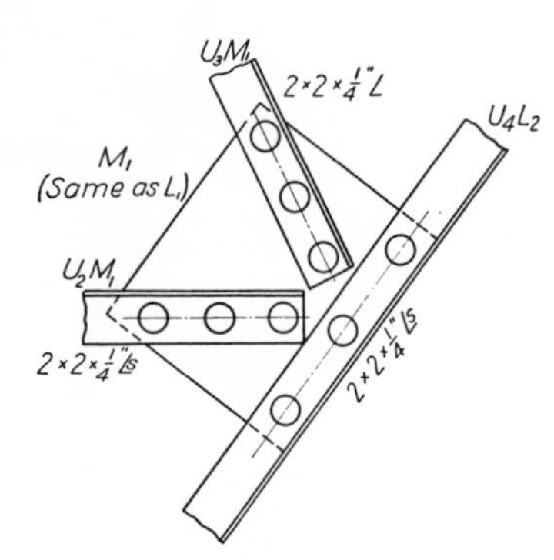

Fig. 158. Detail at M_1.

Joint U_2. The summation of stresses in the members U_2L_1, U_2L_2, and U_2M_1, taken parallel to the upper chord is zero. (See Fig. 159.) The summation of stress for these members taken perpendicular to the upper chord shows a resultant normal thrust of 2280 lb. which is balanced by the downward thrust of the loads at this joint. One rivet would carry this load, but the detail shown in Fig. 159 is arranged to meet the common requirement that the rivet spacing in a gusset shall not exceed 6 in.

Joint L_2. Specifications have often recommended that chord members be spliced at some distance away from the joints of a truss. The reason is that a splice at a joint makes use of the gusset plate as a splice plate. This use is objectionable if the gusset plate itself is not carefully analyzed and designed to function as a splice plate. Of course, the joint splice does save rivets and extra shop work and is therefore economical.

Accordingly, we will give due care to the analysis of stresses in the gusset plate and make use of it as a splice plate. Its analysis will be considered under the heading *Checking the Gussets* on page 244.

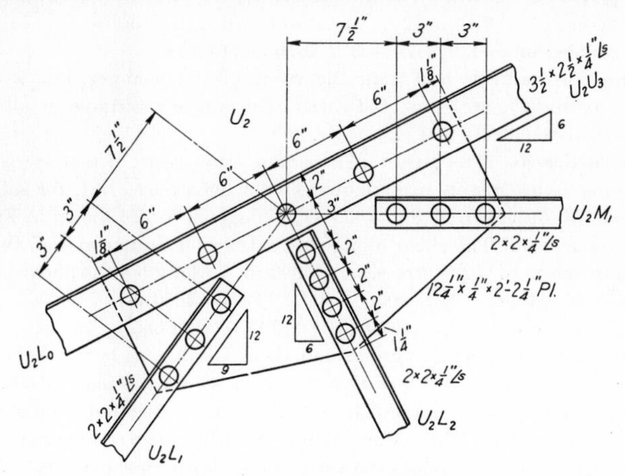

FIG. 159. DETAIL AT U_2.

The design of joint L_2 involves the design of a simple splice in a tension member. The lower chord is broken here and is spliced by means of the gusset plate and a horizontal splice plate. (See Fig. 160.) This splice plate will also be used as the connection plate for a longitudinal strut.

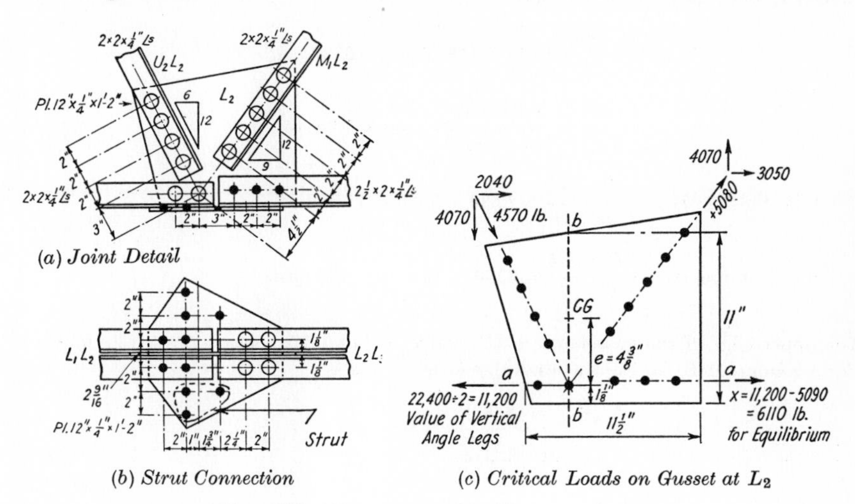

(b) *Strut Connection* (c) *Critical Loads on Gusset at* L_2

FIG. 160. DETAIL AT L_2—TENSION SPLICE.

Value of the lower chord member $L_1L_2 = 22{,}400$; $L_2L_3 = 27{,}200$ lb.

Placing rivets. The greatest value that can be obtained from the lower splice plate is the value of the outstanding horizontal legs of the lighter member, or 11,200 lb.

Member L_1L_2. Place 2 shop rivets through the vertical legs and 4 field bolts through the horizontal legs. Rivets are in bearing at 40,000 psi and bolts in single shear at 10,000 psi.

Value of connection $= 2 \times 6250 + 4 \times 3070 = 24{,}800$ lb.

Member L_2L_3. Place 4 shop rivets through the horizontal legs and 3 field bolts through the vertical legs. Value of member $= 27{,}200$ lb.

The 4 shop rivets are credited with the bearing value of field bolts because the other end of the plate is connected with only an equal number of field bolts.

Value of connection $= 4 \times 3070 + 3 \times 3910 = 24{,}000$ lb.

The connection value is less than the value of the member, but it is considered satisfactory since the 2½-in. leg of L_2L_3 was used only for stiffness, its stress actually being smaller than the stress in L_1L_2.

Checking the Gussets. The gusset plates of a truss resist direct stress, shear, and flexure. Usually ¼-in. gussets are adequate for a light truss, but, for safety, we will check the gusset at L_2 shown in Fig. 160. The diagonal forces shown in Fig. 160(*c*) are maximum web stresses. The shear along the section *a-a* cannot exceed the sum of the horizontal components of these stresses, or 5090 lb. Along *b-b* the shear is 4070 lb.

Unit shear on *a-a* $= \frac{3}{2} \times 5090 \div (\frac{1}{4} \times 11\frac{1}{2}) = 2650$ psi.

Unit shear on *b-b* $= \frac{3}{2} \times 4070 \div (\frac{1}{4} \times 11) = 2220$ psi.

(For a rectangular section the maximum unit shear is taken as $\frac{3}{2}$ times the average.)

Direct Stress and Flexure. Since this gusset forms only a part of the lower chord splice, an assumption must be made if its analysis is to be isolated from the analysis of the horizontal splice plate. This assumption is that the splice plate joins the horizontal angle legs and that the gusset splices the vertical legs of the chord angles. Therefore, we show a force of 11,200 lb. acting to the left as the maximum force that can be delivered to the gusset by L_1L_2. Since four maximum stresses would not be in equilibrium, the stress in L_2L_3 is computed by statics to be $11{,}200 - 5090 = 6110$ lb. Hence, on the section *b-b* we have a force of $6110 + 3050 = 9160$ lb. applied at an eccentricity *e* of 4⅜ in. from the mid-height of the section. (The fact that the chord stresses are not exactly in line will be neglected here.)

$$\frac{P}{A} = 9160 \div (11 \times \tfrac{1}{4}) = 3330 \text{ psi.}$$

$$\frac{Mc}{I} = \frac{9160 \times 4\frac{3}{8} \times 5\frac{1}{2}}{\frac{1}{12} \times \frac{1}{4} \times 11^3} = 7930 \text{ psi.}$$

$$\text{Max. tensile stress} = \frac{P}{A} + \frac{Mc}{I} = 3330 + 7930 = 11{,}260 \text{ psi.}$$

$$\text{Max. compression} = \frac{P}{A} - \frac{Mc}{I} = 3330 - 7930 = -4600 \text{ psi.}$$

The upper edge of the gusset has an L/t value of $11.0/0.25 = 44$ or $L/r = 150$ approx. For a column of $L/r = 150$ the allowable stress would be

$$\frac{18{,}000}{1 + \dfrac{150^2}{18{,}000}} = 8000 \text{ psi.}$$

The estimated stress in tension would be increased slightly by a consideration of the fact that there is a rivet hole on the section *b-b*, but it is evident that the gusset is under-stressed in tension, compression, and shear. If the stresses had appeared serious, we might have decided that it would also be necessary to analyze the entire splice (gusset plus horizontal splice plate) as a T-section. See *DS*5. Of course, such stress calculations are merely reasonable estimates, because the beam formula does not apply accurately to deep sections.

Joint U_4. This joint will be designed for field bolts, since it is desirable to make it symmetrical. (See Fig. 161.)

Value of member $U_4M_1 = 26{,}200$ lb. (Calculated on p. 240.)

Value of unfinished ($A307$) bolts in bearing on the ¼-in. plate at 25,000 psi = 3910 lb.

Number of bolts required = 26,000 ÷ 3910 = 7 bolts. In order to reduce the size of the gusset in Fig. 161, 5 finished bolts ($A325$) may be substituted in U_4M_1.

Value of member U_3U_4. This member was designed for compression plus bending. Direct compression = 16,490 lb.

Number of unfinished ($A307$) bolts required = 16,490 ÷ 3910 = 5 bolts. This number will be increased to 7 to provide excess resistance to the end moment produced in the upper chord by the purlins. These bolts would not develop the value of the member in direct compression, but this is not necessary because the member will always have to resist flexure. If desired, the 7 $A307$ bolts at 2-in. spacing in U_3U_4 (Fig. 161) could be replaced with 5 $A325$ bolts at 2½-in. spacing. The number and spacing of rivets in U_4U_5 would correspond for symmetry.

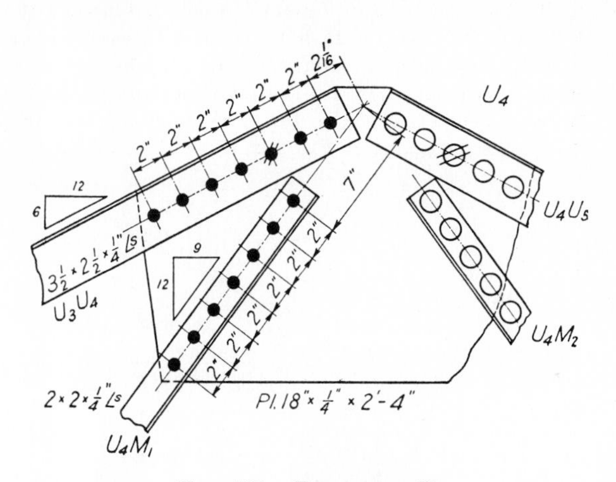

FIG. 161. DETAIL AT U_4.

Joint L_0. The number of rivets required in the lower chord member L_0L_1 has already been determined to be 5, and the number through the upper chord member U_1L_0 has been set at 6. (See Fig. 162.)

End reaction caused by dead load = 4050 lb.

,, ,, ,, by snow load = 7400 lb.

,, ,, ,, by wind load = 2790 lb.

Maximum end reaction for shoe design = 4050 + 7400 = 11,450 lb.

Rivets through shoe angles = 11,450 ÷ 6250 = 2 rivets. Use 3 rivets as shown in the detail, Fig. 162. Use two 3 × 3 × ⅜-in. shoe angles, 8 in. long.

Bearing on masonry = 11,450 ÷ (8 × 6.37) = 225 psi. (The bearing plate is 8 in. long by 6⅜ in. wide.) This is sufficiently low for bearing on a brick wall. (Spec. 18.)

Bearing plate. The thickness is determined by flexure as a cantilever. Let $L = 3$ in.

The thickness of angles should not be considered as a part of the depth of the bearing plate because the rivets joining the two together will not be designed for horizontal shear.

$$\text{Moment} = \frac{225 \times 3^2}{2} = 1020 \text{ in-lb. per in. width.}$$

$$\text{Section modulus} = \frac{1020}{20{,}000} = 0.051 = d^2/6.$$

$$\text{Depth} = d = \sqrt{6 \times 0.051} = 0.55 \text{ in.}$$

Use a ⅝-in. bearing plate riveted with 4 countersunk rivets to the ⅜-in. angle legs.

Allowance for expansion. (100 degrees F. is ample.) $36 \times 12 \times 100 \times 0.0000065 = 0.28$ in.

Slotted holes. Use a slot of length equal to the diameter of the anchor bolt plus about twice the expected expansion to allow for inexact setting of the bolt in the masonry. A slot ⅞ × 1¼ in. or 1½ in. will be used to accommodate a ¾-in. anchor bolt.

Location of shoe. Place the shoe with its center directly under the intersection of the lower and upper chords so that there will be no moment of eccentricity introduced by the vertical reaction. The horizontal wind reaction of 1940 lb. acting at 5½ + 1¾ + ⅝ = 7.87 in. below L_0 or L_5 produces a moment of $1940 \times 7.87 = 15{,}300$ in-lb. The wind reaction actually is divided between L_5 and L_0 where it is resisted by friction of the bearing plate. Hence, the moment of 15,300 is divided between the members U_1L_0, L_0L_1, L_4L_5 and U_7L_5. Also, since the snow load is reduced 50 per cent with wind, and since the allowable stress is increased by one third, the moment of the wind reaction will not overstress the truss members at L_0 or L_5. This analysis shows that the vertical distance of 5½ in., however, as shown in Fig. 162, should be reduced if feasible.

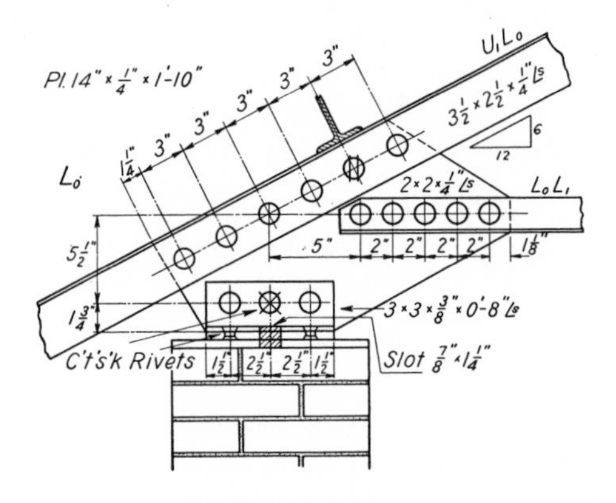

FIG. 162. DETAIL L_0.

Bed plate on masonry. A bed plate, 10 in. × 12 in., is bolted to the masonry to provide a surface upon which the shoe can slide. The thickness of this plate is also made ⅝ in.

Minimum Connections. The final column in Table 7 gives the *AISC* minimum connections to develop either the total calculated stress in each member or 50 per cent of the calculated value of the member, whichever is greater. These minimum connections are more commonly used than the full-value connections. However, this truss was to be designed with full-value connections which are shown on Fig. 156 to Fig. 162 and also on the detail drawing, Fig. 164. For comparison the drawing of Fig. 164(*a*) shows minimum connections.

176l. Design of Diagonal Bracing. Diagonal bracing will be used in the plane of the upper chords. The purlins will perform the function of struts. Two pairs of crossing diagonals will be used in each outside bay on each side of the roof. These diagonals brace the trusses together in pairs, and the action of the purlins as continuous struts completes the necessary upper chord bracing. The purpose of this bracing is to stiffen the structure, since the diagonals have no calculated stresses. There will be no diagonal bracing used in the plane of the lower chords for this small structure. If vibration due to heavy machinery had been anticipated, such extra bracing could readily have been added. Diagonal bracing in a vertical plane along the centerline or along the sloping plane from U_4 to L_2 would be useful during erection, and such bracing also resists wind pressure on the end of the building. It is a very important structural element in a building with light end walls of nonmasonry materials.

Bracing in Plane of Roof. Minimum angles 2 × 2 × ¼ in. will be used.

Slenderness ratio. The angles will be clamped to each purlin at their crossing points. (Clamps require no holes and do not weaken the purlins.) Accordingly, their unsupported length is

$$\tfrac{1}{2}\sqrt{8^2 + 16.25^2} = 9.0 \text{ ft.} \quad L/r = \frac{9.0 \times 12}{0.39} = 278 < 300. \quad (\textit{AISC} \text{ Spec. 23}).$$

Use of flats. Angles will project downward and interfere with the insulation board that is to be placed against the bottom flanges of the purlins. Laterals composed of 2½ × ¼-in. flats would overcome this difficulty. Such laterals should be clamped or wired to each purlin to prevent sagging and erected with initial tension of about 5000 psi by use of drift pins. *However, the use of angle diagonals is more common.* (Fig. 163.)

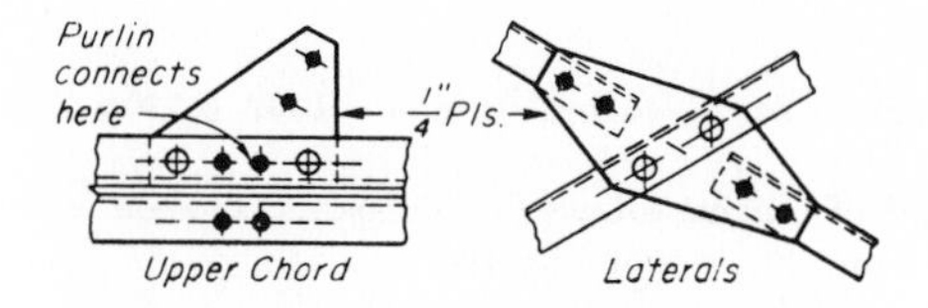

Open holes are 11/16" for ⅝" unfinished bolts.

FIG. 163. DETAILS FOR 2-BOLT LATERAL CONNECTION.

End Connections. The diagonals should be connected to the undersides of ¼-in. lateral plates riveted to the undersides of the top chords of the roof trusses. Three ⅝-in. bolts are shown for each diagonal in Fig. 164 although a 2-bolt connection, as in Fig. 163, would be more typical. Even where the building code specifies a minimum 3-rivet or 3-bolt connection, bracing members are often excluded when their calculated wind stresses are below 6000 lb. (Spec. 40.) Where the angle diagonals cross each other, one must be cut and spliced with a ¼-in. plate which is also riveted to the continuous diagonal.

Vertical Bracing. It is desirable to introduce diagonal bracing at least in the end bays between pairs of trusses for squaring the structure during erection. Pairs of crossing diagonals (2 × 2 × ¼-in. angles) should be used in a vertical or sloping plane near the mid-span of the trusses. Possibilities are in the plane from U_2 to L_2, from U_3 to L_2, or from U_4 to L_2. Diagonal bracing in a single vertical plane through U_4 would be preferred, but this would require adding a vertical member from U_4 to the lower chord not shown in Fig. 164. The calculated stresses in the diagonals caused by wind on the end of the building will be small. Two ⅝-in. bolts are ample for the end connections of the diagonals. Adjustable tension rods (⅝-in. d) might be preferred. Note the diagonal rod connection in Fig. 164(a).

176m. Design of Struts. Two continuous struts will brace the lower chords of the roof trusses together at the joints L_2 and L_3. No diagonal bracing is needed in the plane of the lower chords for a small roof truss.

Stiffness. The maximum value of L/r permitted for secondary compression members is 200. (Spec. 23.) Therefore, minimum $r = \dfrac{16.25 \times 12}{200} = 0.98.$

Section Used. A 3 × 2½ × ¼-in. angle riveted to a 4-in., 5.4-lb. channel makes a strut having a minimum radius of gyration of 0.99. The weight is 9.9 lb. per lineal ft. The gross area is 2.87 sq. in. The allowable stress is 5600 psi.

Value of member = 2.87 × 5600 = 16,100 lb.

End connection. The strut is shown bolted to the connection plate at each truss joint with three ⅝-in. field bolts.

176n. Final Computation of Dead Weight. The dead weight will be computed per bay and will then be divided by 730, the number of square feet of roof surface per bay.

Purlins. 14 purlins 16.25 ft. long at 10 lb. per ft. = 2270 lb. This is equivalent to a weight of 3.1 psf of roof surface.

Bracing.

Diagonals. 8 pieces 19.1 ft. long at 3.2 lb. per ft.	=	490 lb.
Struts. 2 pieces 16.25 ft. long at 9.9 lb. per ft.	=	322 lb.
Diagonals in planes U_4L_2 and U_4L_3 4 pieces 19.5 ft. long at 3.2 lb. per ft.	=	250 lb.
Total	=	1062 lb.

Weight of bracing per sq. ft. of roof surface = 1062 ÷ 730 = 1.4 psf.

This estimated weight of bracing allows for diagonals between each pair of roof trusses rather than the minimum bracing of Fig. 164.

Weight of Truss.

Top chord.	Two 3½ × 2½ × ¼-in. angles; 45.0 ft. at 9.8 lb. per ft.	=	441 lb.
Bottom chord.	Two 2 × 2 × ¼-in. angles; 22.1 ft. at 6.4 lb. per ft.	=	141 lb.
,, ,,	Two 2½ × 2 × ¼-in. angles; 13.5 ft. at 7.2 lb. per ft.	=	98 lb.
Web[1]	Two 2 × 2 × ¼-in. angles; 30.2 ft. at 6.4 lb. per ft.	=	193 lb.
,,	One 2 × 2 × ¼-in. angle; 28.6 ft. at 3.2 lb. per ft.	=	92 lb.
	Truss members	=	965 lb.
Gussets.	About 25 sq. ft. of ¼-in. plate at 12.5 psf; 25 × 12.5	=	250 lb.
Rivet heads, lateral plates, ring fills, etc. (Details add about 10 per cent to weight of members)		=	95 lb.
	Total weight of one truss	=	1310 lb.

Weight of trusses per sq. ft. of roof surface $= \dfrac{1310}{730} = 1.8$ psf.

Roof Covering and Insulation. 4.5 psf of roof surface.

Total Dead Weight. 3.1 + 1.4 + 1.8 + 4.5 = 10.8 psf of roof surface.

Estimated Dead Weight. 11.0 psf of roof surface.

[1] In this weight estimate members U_2L_1 and U_2M_1 are taken as single angles, which were found to be adequate in strength, although double angles as shown in Fig. 164 are commonly used.

REMARKS. The weight estimate used in computing dead load stresses was close enough to the computed weight so that a revision in dead load stresses is unnecessary. The drawing of this roof truss, Fig. 164, gives the design details. This is a student drawing, but, a similar commercial drawing, Fig. 164*a*, is presented for comparison. It would be possible to fabricate the truss from such a sheet, but it is more common to produce one or more sheets of shop details. The shop details show each member and each plate separately with all shop dimensions given. When shop details are to be made up, it is not necessary to show all dimensions on the general drawing of the truss.

WELDED TRUSS DESIGN

177. Design of a Welded Roof Truss for a Gymnasium.

PROBLEM. Redesign the roof truss from §176 for fabrication and erection by arc welding.

Working Stresses. Use the same working stresses for main members that were used in the riveted design, §176. Shear on the roots of fillet welds will be limited to 13,600 psi.

Comments. The stress analysis does not need to be performed again and many of the members will be used unchanged from the riveted design. Because of the small space available for welding, it is found to be impossible to develop the full strengths of the web members at the welded joints. The lengths of weld shown on the detail drawing (Fig. 165) are in each case capable of developing more than twice the actual stress in the web member, and this is thought to be sufficient. The chords are welded to produce a resistance equal to the value of the member.

Type of Welded Design. The top chord and bottom chord angles will be turned with legs in the form of a *U-section* or channel section. The web members will be of smaller angles, also with legs turned in, and they will fit into the U-sections of the chords. The upper chord will have 2½-in. in-turned angle legs stitch welded together to form a 5-in. channel. With ¼-in. angles, the inside width will be 4½ in. The bottom chord must also have 2½-in. in-turned angle legs. The web members will all have 2-in. in-turned angle legs stitch or strap welded ⅜ in. apart. These angles will then be 4⅜ in. back to back, which allows ⅛ in. of clearance when they are inserted into the chords.

Other Arrangement of Members. The U-section chords were chosen here for close comparison with the riveted design. Actually, split-beam sections make good chord members of T-shape. Also, small beam sections may be turned with flanges vertically so that the web members may be welded to the chord flanges. Other arrangements may be found described in the literature on welded structures.

Minimum Angles. For welded design there seems to be no need to limit the minimum angle leg to 2 in. This limitation is necessary in riveted work because a 2-in. leg is required to hold a ⅝-in. rivet which is the smallest structural rivet in common use. Accordingly, 1½-in. angle legs will be allowed in the welded design where they are adequate to meet the required slenderness ratio. A minimum thickness of ¼-in. should be maintained in both riveted and welded work of first quality.

177a. Design of Members.

Top Chord. The upper chord will have exactly the same section as the riveted structure, that is, two angles 3½ × 2½ × ¼ in. However, the short legs will be turned in and tack welded together while in contact.

Bottom Chord. The entire lower chord will be made of 2½ × 1½ × ¼-in. angles. The long legs will be turned in and tack welded together while in contact. In order to use this section, the center member L_2L_3 will have to be supported at the center by a hanger, as shown in Fig. 165.

Gross area of angles = 2 × 0.94 = 1.88 sq. in.
Maximum stress (L_0L_1) = 17,760 lb. tension.
Value of member = 1.88 × 20,000 = 37,600 lb.
Slenderness ratio (L_2L_3) = 81 ÷ 0.41 = 198.

Field Splice.

Legs Spliced	Area In.²	Value lb.	Splice Plates	Fillet Welds	Weld Value lb.
2—2½ × ¼	1.25	25,000	1—4 × 5⁄16 × 0′-4½ in	1(5⁄16—8½)	8.5 × 3000 = 25,500
2—1¼ × ¼	0.63	12,600	2—1 × 5⁄16 × 0′-4 in	2(3⁄16—5)	2 × 5 × 1800 = 18,000

Tension Web Members. The highest stressed web member is U_4M_1. A similar member (U_2M_1) has the greatest horizontal length, 5 ft.-7½ in. Two 2 × 1½ × ¼-in. angles will be used if satisfactory. Long legs are turned in and stitch welded together or strap welded at a clear distance of ⅜ in. apart and a spacing of not more than 2 ft. (Spec. 61.)

Gross area of angles = 2 × 0.81 = 1.62 sq. in.
Maximum stress (U_4M_1) = 7620 lb. tension.
Value of member = 1.62 × 20,000 = 32,400 lb.
Slenderness ratio (U_2M_1) = 67.5 ÷ 0.43 = 157.
Value of welded connection = 9 × 2400 = 21,600 lb. (9 in. of ¼-in. fillet.)

Sub-Struts, U_1L_1 and U_3M_1. These members will be made of two 2 × 1½ × ¼-in. angles connected together only at their ends.

Gross area of angles = 2 × 0.81 = 1.62 sq. in.
Maximum stress = 2280 lb. compression.
Slenderness ratio for min. r = 30.2 ÷ 0.32 = 94.
Allowable column stress = 17,000 − 0.485 × 94² = 12,700 psi.
Value of member = 1.62 × 12,700 = 20,600 lb. (Small eccentricity of connection neglected.)
Value of welded connection = 8 × 2400 = 19,200 lb. (8 in. of ¼-in. fillet.)

Web Compression Member, U_2L_2. The L/r requirement controls the design of this member. Two 2 × 2 × ¼-in. angles are required as in the riveted structure. They are connected together by stitch or strap welds at 2-ft. spacing.

Gross area of angles = 2 × 0.94 = 1.88 sq. in.
Maximum stress = 4570 lb.
Slenderness ratio = 60.4 ÷ 0.61 = 99.
Allowable column stress = 17,000 − 0.485 × 99² = 12,200 psi.
Value of member = 1.88 × 12,200 = 23,000 lb.
Value of welded connection = 9 × 2400 = 21,600 lb. (9 in. of ¼-in. fillet or equivalent in butt welds.)

177b. Design of Joints. The design of joints is made clear by a study of the sheet of welded details, Fig. 165. This sheet should be studied in connection with the standard welding symbols for draftsmen adopted by the American Welding Society and given in Fig. 104. The system used here is to weld one web member to the chord, and then *to weld the second web member to the first and possibly also to the chord.* This detail has the advantage of permitting a considerable amount of weld to be placed in a small space. It also seems reasonable that the transfer of stress is better effected by this arrangement than by one where both diagonals are welded only to the chord. The reason is that a part of the stress passes from one web member into the other without going through the chord. Of course, we must consider the matter of stress transfer in order to proportion the lengths of weld properly. There must be sufficient length of weld connecting the two web members to the chord to take care of the change in chord stress and to transfer any load acting normal to the chord into the web members. The weld between the web members must be satisfactory to care for the direct transfer of stress, or else the excess stress must be considered to be transferred from one web member to the other through the chord.

Joints U_1 and U_3. Sub-struts are welded to the upper chord with 8 in. of ¼-in. fillet.

Joints L_1 and L_2. The tension diagonals U_2L_1 and M_1L_2 are welded to the chord with 9 in. of ¼-in. fillet, and the members U_1L_1 and U_2L_2 are welded to the tension diagonals and to the chord with 9 in. of ¼-in. fillet.

Joint M_1. The diagonal U_2M_1 is welded to the back of member $U_4M_1L_2$ with 4 in. of ¼-in. fillet. The sub-strut U_3M_1 is welded to the back of $U_4M_1L_2$ with 5 in. of ¼-in. fillet, and U_2M_1 is welded to U_3M_1 and to $U_4M_1L_2$ with 5 in. of ¼-in. fillet.

Joint U_2. The tension diagonals U_2M_1 and U_2L_1 are each welded to the upper chord with 9 in. of ¼-in. fillet. Then the compression member U_2L_2 is butt welded to the diagonals (diagonals and struts are separated ⅛ to ¼ in.) and the same weld connects the strut U_2L_2 to the chord. The combined length of these butts weld is 6 in. There are two extra 1½-in. fillet welds connecting U_2L_2 to the chord.

Joint C. The hanger U_4C is welded on the outside of the bottom chord, and also of the top chord, with 5 in. of ¼-in. fillet.

Joint U_4. The diagonal U_4M_1 is welded to the upper chord with 9 in. of ¼-in. fillet. The two sections of the upper chord are butt welded together all around the inside with a ¼-in. flush butt weld for a length of 12 in. The members should be separated about ⅛ in. before welding. This joint is capable of developing the strengths of the members in compression.

Joint L_0. The upper and lower chords are butt welded together at L_0 with two 5-in. lengths of butt welds. The members should be separated at least ⅛ in. before welding to obtain a good butt weld through the entire thickness of the metal. This joint will be strong enough to develop the full resistances of the members in compression and shear. The separated welds of the eave extension angle provide necessary moment resistance.

177c. End Bearing and Bracing. The *end bearing* for this truss is extremely simple. A sole plate, $6 \times ⅝ \times 9$ in. is welded to the bottom of the lower chord. The cantilever projection is but 2 in. and the ⅝-in. plate was found satisfactory for a 3-in. projection in the riveted design. The bearing pressure is $11{,}450 \div (6 \times 9) = 212$ psi, slightly less than in the riveted design. The base plate is made $9 \times ⅝ \times 12$ in. Details of slotted holes, etc., are similar to those used in the riveted design.

Diagonal Bracing and Struts. The lateral bracing and struts may be the same sections that were used in the riveted structure. An angle + channel strut may be given partial continuity quite economically without additional welding by cutting the angle and channel about two feet apart near its connection to an interior truss. The struts will be welded to the lower chords with 6 in. of ¼-in. fillet at each connection. The diagonal bracing will be welded to the bottom flanges of alternate purlins, or the end connections may be made directly to the truss chords if practicable. At least a 4-in. length of ¼-in. fillet should be used at each lateral connection. A detail is shown on the drawing, Fig. 165. Welded diagonals will need to be 3 in. longer than the riveted laterals of Fig. 164. A welded plate connection similar to the riveted detail of Fig. 163 will be used where the laterals intersect. Diagonal bracing and struts may have bolted connections for convenience in erection.

Purlins. The purlins are unchanged from the riveted design. They will be welded directly to the upper chords with 5 in. of ¼-in. fillet for each end or intermediate connection. A special arrangement must be made for purlins that act as members of the upper chord system of bracing. These purlins must be bolted to each truss during erection in order to square the building. If convenient, bolt holes may be punched through the purlin flange; but, to save the cost of carrying the purlins to a punch, it is preferable to weld on small plates previously punched to match with similar plates welded to the upper chord of the truss. The detail for this truss, using plates and clip angles, is shown in Fig. 166.

Minimum AISC Connections. Following the *AISC Building Code* both the welded and riveted connections of Figs. 164 and 165 could be reduced. By Spec. 40 the minimum connection may be designed for 6000 lb. which requires only 2.5 in. of ¼-in. weld. The minimum weld, which is 3⁄16-in. by Spec. 53, would need to be only 3.5 in. long. To resist at least 50 per cent of the effective strengths of the truss members, as required by Spec. 43, the fillet welds on Fig. 165 could be reduced from ¼-in. to 3⁄16-in. Fillet welds of 3⁄16-in. leg would also be adequate for the connections of bracing members and purlins. The saving would be significant.

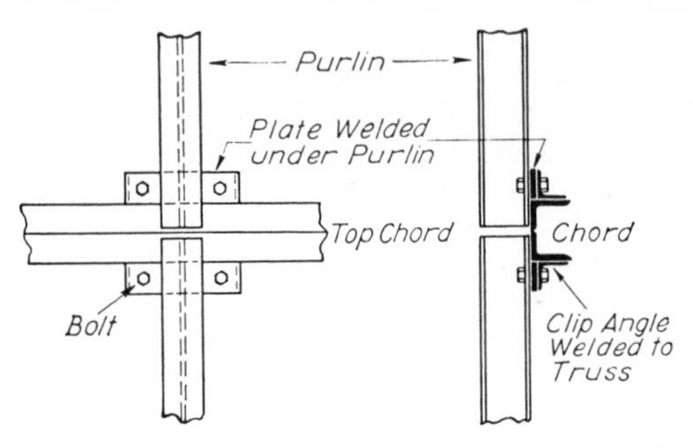

FIG. 166. PURLIN CONNECTION FOR THE TRUSS OF FIG. 165.

177d. Weight of the Welded Roof Truss.

Top chord.	Two 3½ × 2½ × ¼-in. angles; 40.2. ft. at 9.8 lb. per ft.	=	394 lb.
Bottom chord.	Two 2½ × 1½ × ¼-in. angles; 37.4 ft. at 6.4 lb. per ft.	=	240 lb.
Web.	Two 2 × 1½ × ¼-in. angles; 54.9 ft. at 5.6 lb. per ft.	=	308 lb.
	Two 2 × 2 × ¼-in. angles; 10.0 ft. at 6.4 lb. per ft.	=	64 lb.
Hanger.	Two 1½ × 1½ × ¼-in. angles; 9.0 ft. at 4.7 lb. per ft.	=	43 lb.
Eave extension.	Two 2 × 2 × ¼-in. angles; 4.7 ft. at 6.4 lb. per ft.	=	30 lb.
Lateral plates.	4 × ¼ × 6 in.; 6 plates at 2 lb. each	=	12 lb.
	Total weight of one truss	=	1091 lb.

REMARKS. Although the weight of weld metal has not been included here, it is evident that the weight of the welded truss would be less than the weight of the riveted truss designed in §176. The weight of the riveted truss was 1215 lb., not including the weight of rivet heads. The saving in weight is of small importance and might readily be overbalanced by a slightly greater cost of welding over riveting. No attempt should be made to form an opinion as to the relative costs of welded and riveted structures from the information obtained from these designs. The comparison would not be valuable since these trusses contain too many members of minimum section where stress did not control the design. The welded structure would show to greater advantage if the full gross sections of its tension members could be utilized. Present practice indicates that the saving in weight obtained by welding about compensates for the greater cost of welding over riveting and places the two structures on a competitive basis. A great deal depends upon the designer. A clever designer can arrange for many parts of a welded structure (purlins for instance) to be shipped directly from the mill or warehouse to the job, thus saving the shop cost. Where such methods are employed, the welded job may show considerable economy.

PROBLEMS

901. Redesign the roof of §176 to carry a wind pressure of 30 psf on the vertical surface and a snow load of 40 psf on the horizontal surface or 30 psf of roof surface for a roof of ¼ pitch. Use riveted construction and *AISC* working stresses and specifications including minimum connections. Place purlins at the panel points and eaves. Use *A*36 steel.

902. Redesign the welded roof truss of §177 using split beam sections for the chord members. Change to *AISC* allowable stresses. Double the wind-load for hurricane exposure. Use *A*36 steel. Provide minimum welded connections by *AISC* specifications.

903. Redesign the roof truss of Problem 901 using welded construction, U-section chords, and *A*36 steel. Follow *AISC* working stresses.

904. Redesign the roof truss of Problem 901 using welded construction and split beams for chord sections. Use *AISC* specifications and working stresses for *A*36 steel.

905. Design a bolted roof truss for a gymnasium similar to the type designed in §176, but for these changed conditions: Outside dimensions of the building = 70 × 140 ft. Wind load = 30 psf of vertical surface. Snow load = 15 psf of roof surface. Use ⅜-in. corrugated asbestos roofing which permits a purlin spacing of 6 ft. Keep the distance between roof trusses under 20 ft. Allow for diagonal bracing in the planes of both the upper and lower chords. Use a Fink truss of ⅓ pitch designed for *AISC* working stresses. Use *A*325 bolts and *A*36 steel.

906. Redesign the roof truss of Problem 905 for welded construction. Use your own judgment in the selection of type of section for the chords.

907. Design a flat roof to span 60 ft. and to carry a total vertical load of 75 psf of horizontal projection. This load includes the weight of snow, of concrete slab, and of waterproof covering. Use the Warren type of roof truss of riveted construction as shown in the illustration. Place purlins only at the panel points. Space trusses 20 ft. apart. A field splice is required in order to reduce the length to 40 ft. for shipping. Assume that the roof is protected from the wind by a breast wall and that wind pressure may be neglected. Use *AISC* specifications and allowable stresses for *A*36 steel.

908. Redesign the roof truss of Problem 907 for welded fabrication.

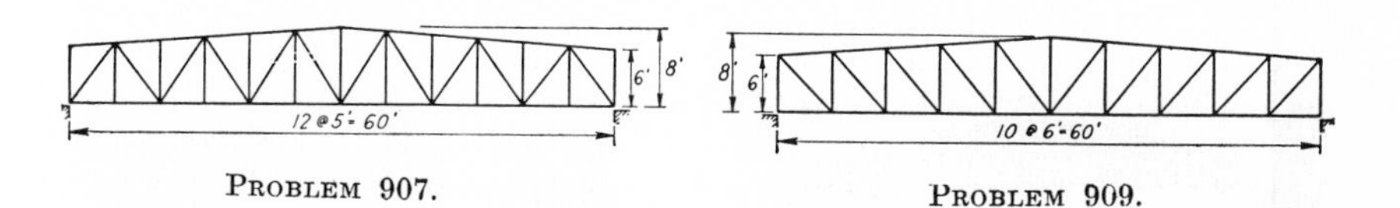

PROBLEM 907. PROBLEM 909.

909. Design a welded roof of Pratt type to replace the riveted Warren truss of Problem 907. The type of truss is illustrated. The purlin spacing is limited to 5 ft.-0 in. in order to use a 2-in. precast roof slab.

910. Design a roof truss of 80-ft. span and 9-ft. constant depth from center to center of chords. Choose and follow a city building code or other specifications. Choose the yield point of the steel and welded, bolted, or riveted construction. The fixed loading to be carried is 1600 lb. per foot of truss plus the dead load of steel. It is suggested that a Pratt truss be used with 8-ft. panels to support a precast roof slab. Stringers are placed only at the panel points of the trusses.

178. Other Roof Structures. Roofs for industrial buildings take on new and different forms with each advance in the construction art. Welding has made possible the use of rectangular or polygonal roof arches at low cost. Wide flange beam sections may be split, bent, and rewelded to form structures of almost any shape. For example, note the tapered steel girders of Fig. 167(*a*). The clean-cut modern appearance of indeterminate frames, as contrasted to the rather cluttered appearance presented by a roof truss, has encouraged architects to make use of such continuous structures. The roof truss, however, is still the most economical structure for medium spans and ordinary roof loading.

(*a*) 60-*ft. Tapered Girders*

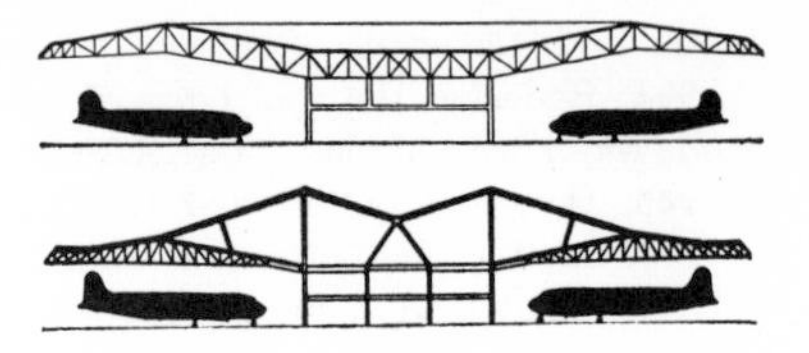

(*b*) 133-*ft Tied Cantilevers*

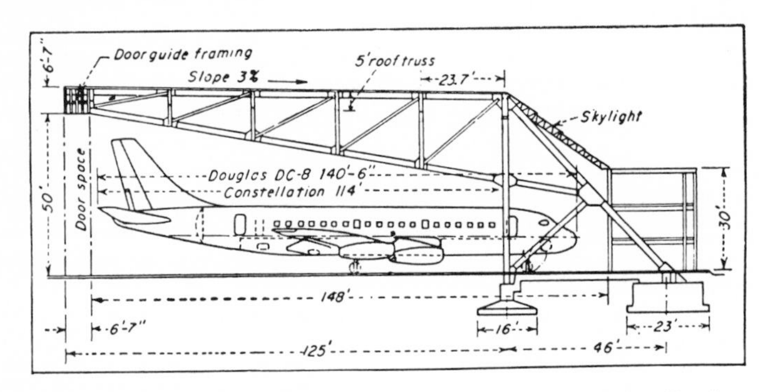

(*c*) *French Hangar Has 20* × *30-in. Steel Legs and 20-in. Chords*

(*d*) *332-ft. Tension Ring of Dome*

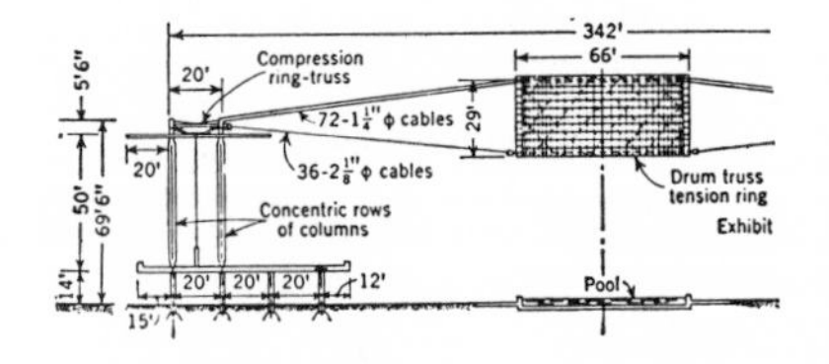

(*e*) *342-ft. Compression Ring Truss*

FIG. 167. MODERN DESIGN COMBINES TRUSSES, ARCHES, CABLES, AND CANTILEVERS.

CHAPTER 10

PLASTIC DESIGN FOR ULTIMATE LOADING

179. Working Stress and Factor of Safety. When structural materials were limited to wood, stone, and cast iron, the factor of safety was defined as the breaking stress divided by the working stress. With the adoption of structural steel and later of reinforced concrete as the primary structural materials, the numerical value of ultimate strength gradually lost its importance. Steel, either in the form of structural shapes or as reinforcing

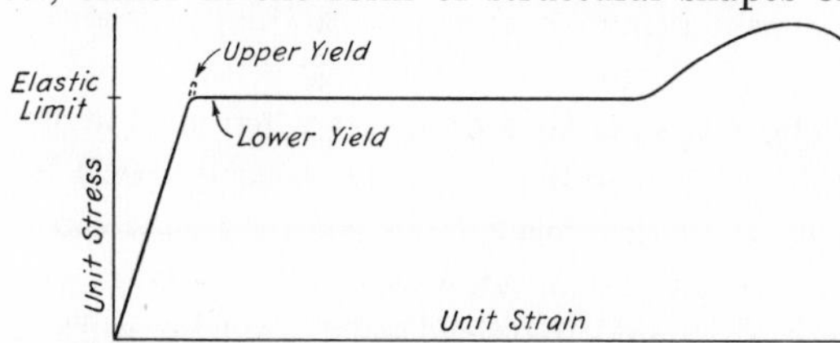

(*a*) *Stress-Strain Diagram for Structural Steel Loaded in Uniaxial Tension.*

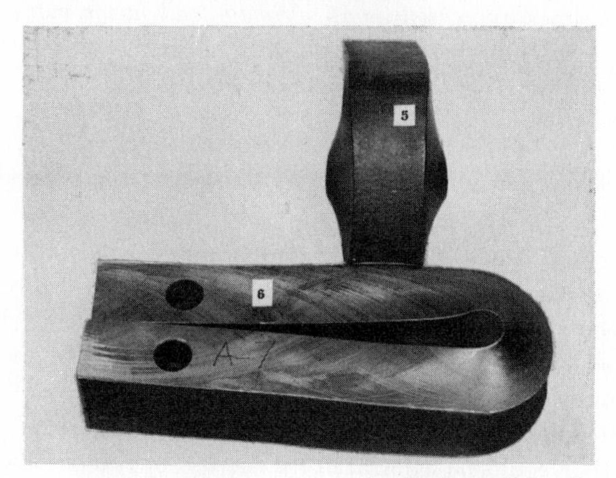

Courtesy Brown University

(*b*) *Ductility of A7 Steel Shown by Bend Test*

FIG. 168. DUCTILITY OF STRUCTURAL STEEL JUSTIFIES PLASTIC DESIGN.

rods, shows a well-defined elastic limit in tension or flexure sufficiently high to have been accepted as a reasonable upper limit upon capacity to resist stress or load. As shown in Fig. 168, there is a proportionality of stress to strain up to the first break in the curve commonly termed the yield point. The *upper yield point* is variable, since it is dependent upon the method and speed of load application. Hence we will discuss only the *lower yield point* which is readily determined. For the purpose of plastic design of steel structures, the lower yield point and the elastic limit may be assumed to be numerically identical. Based upon the concept that the only useful part of the stress-strain curve is that below initial yield, the factor of safety has been defined, since the beginning of this century, as the yield stress divided by the working stress. For example, for steel specified by *AISC* to have a lower tensile yield of 36,000 psi a working stress in tension of 22,000 psi corresponds to a factor of safety of $36{,}000/22{,}000 = 1.64$.

180. Ultimate Load Factor. Engineers have always recognized that a major part of the stress-strain curve for structural steel occurs in the region beyond initial yielding or beyond the elastic limit. However, usage and custom during the early part of the present century had almost produced a taboo against consideration of this part of the stress-strain diagram as a dependable factor for resisting load. As may be seen in the photographs of Fig. 169, large deflections can and do occur when steel structures are overloaded, but such large deflections do not necessarily result in rupture of the material. Experience with overloaded structures that did not rupture or collapse increased the interest of engineers in the possible economy of using the resistance of steel beyond its initial yield—not for working loads, but as a factor of safety based upon collapse loading. This concept of factor of safety is sometimes expressed as an *ultimate load factor*, which is the ratio of the collapse load to the actual applied load or working load. The load factor is covered by *AISC* specifications in §197.

Justification of Plastic or Ultimate-Load Design

181. Structural Analysis Simplified for Ultimate Loads. Stress analysis by statics is quite simple for the structures classed as statically determinate that have been studied in previous chapters. It has been noted, however, that all portal frames or bents are statically indeterminate structures. Accordingly, simplifying assumptions were necessarily introduced in Chapter 3 to reduce the number of unknown reactions for portal-type structures to the number that could be calculated by the use of the equations of statics. It will be clear that any analysis by statics which involves an assumption, for example, equal shear distribution between the columns of either a single or multiple-bay bent, is an approximation. Depending upon the validity of the assumption, the stresses computed may closely approach those for elastic loading or they may represent a rather poor approximation. At this point it is important to recall that *the stress or load distribution in any statically indeterminate structure changes with changes in the cross-sections of the members.*

This significant factor is lost entirely when we accept a simplifying assumption to control the division of shear, moment or direct stress in the several parts of a statically indeterminate structure.

(*a*) *Test of Structural Frame at Lehigh University Demonstrates Large Deflection Without Fracture.*

(*b*) *Test Under Author's Direction Demonstrates Formation of a Plastic Hinge with Angle Change at Corner.*

FIG. 169. PRACTICALITY OF ULTIMATE LOAD DESIGN BASED UPON PLASTIC ACTION IS DEMONSTRATED BY LARGE-SCALE TESTS.

It has been recognized as early as 1917 by N. C. Kist, a professor at the University of Delft in Holland, that ductility or the initial plastic action of steel as it reached its yield stress provided a mechanism for *stress redistribution in a statically indeterminate structure* that could be predicted by simple calculations. However, the acceptance of plastic theory and ultimate-load design was delayed by lack of understanding of the physical property of *ductility* of steel and the contrasting phenomenon, *brittle fracture*. Evidently, if brittle fracture is a strong possibility, an analysis or design based upon the theory of plasticity or ductility would be unacceptable.

The author undertook the test[1] of a large scale structural frame to demonstrate that ductility could be a reliable characteristic of well-designed welded structures. (See Fig. 169.) Others made tests that step by step have placed limits upon the conditions under which structural steel may act as a brittle material. The result has been that plastic theory is now accepted as a logical tool for use in several areas of structural design. Nevertheless, before considering certain useful tools of plastic or ultimate load analysis it will be desirable for the reader to understand the reasons why structural materials such as mild steel may behave in a very ductile manner in a simple tension test but may rupture without visible deformation in a large plate-type structure.

Brittle Fracture. In this entire discussion we are necessarily ruling out the possibility of "brittle fracture" without visible deformation which occurs most frequently in flat plate structures such as welded ships, tanks, or built-up girders. *Cleavage or brittle fracture is due to a combination of factors that reduce the residual ductility of the material.* Such factors are shock loadings, temperatures below the "transition temperature," which for some steels is above the ambient winter temperature, triaxial tensions such as occur near a notch or a welded corner, compressive prestraining due to straightening, punching holes, or forcing misfit members into place, and the use of steels that are known to be subject to rupture with low deformation. Much has been learned about brittle fracture, which is a type of rupture that occurs with little plastic deformation, but much remains to be learned. It need only be said that the types of construction and of materials for which brittle fracture is more than a rare occurrence are now well known. The use of ultimate load design will be restricted here to beam and frame structures acting under static loads for which brittle fracture is so uncommon that it may be eliminated as a factor of present concern.

182. Basic Concepts of Plastic Action. Mild steel has a stress-strain diagram in tension as illustrated by Fig. 170(*a*), which may be idealized as shown in (*b*). This leads to an elementary theory of plasticity of great usefulness. Physically the material is considered to be perfectly elastic from zero stress up to its yield stress f_{yield} at which the strain is ε_1. Then without increase of load or stress the strain may increase rather rapidly up to ten or twenty times the initial yield strain ε_1. This unit strain represented by ε_2 is so large, Fig. 170(*a*), that it is given no value in (*b*) but is considered to be as

[1] L. E. Grinter, Charles Peller, and John Butkus, *Stress distribution in plastic range in a rigid frame*, The Welding Journal Research Supplement, March, 1951.

large as is needed for the application of plastic theory. Also, the upper yield is shown in (*a*) but is omitted in (*b*) since its magnitude varies with the manner of loading. Therefore, it is not a dependable resistance for use in practical design.

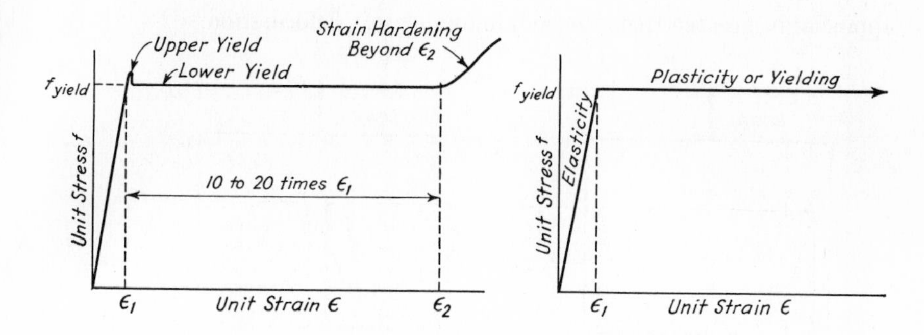

(*a*) *Stress-Strain Diagram for Mild Steel* (*b*) *Idealized Stress-Strain Diagram*

FIG. 170. COMPARISON OF ACTUAL AND IDEALIZED STRESS DIAGRAMS FOR MILD STEEL IN TENSION.

A basic concept of the theory of plasticity as applied to entire structures, structural members, and details is that the elastic stress distribution will undergo a major readjustment when the maximum stresses reach the yield stress. Up to this stage the stress-strain relations are elastic and are all controlled by the initial sloping line of Fig. 170(*a*) or (*b*). For greater loads those members or areas of members that have already developed a stress f_{yield} will not experience an increase of stress but will adjust to whatever additional strain is necessary to permit load or stress to be transferred to other members or to adjacent material that is still within the elastic range and consequently able to resist an increased stress. Thus plasticity is a stress equalizing factor as will be demonstrated in the next section.

183. Stress Concentrations Reduced by Plasticity. The action of ductility in reducing a stress concentration may be illustrated by considering its action upon the stresses around a circular notch or hole in a simple tension member as illustrated in Fig. 171. For stresses that are below the elastic limit at every point in the tension bar of Fig. 171(*b*) the theoretical stress concentrations at the ends of the horizontal diameter of the hole are $3\ P/A$. As the load P is increased in magnitude to P_1 we will assume that the stress concentration will reach the yield stress. Further increase in the load can no longer increase the maximum stress. Instead, to maintain equilibrium the average stress will increase as indicated by successive broken lines in Fig. 171. Note, however, that a part of the cross-section is stressed below the yield stress even when the average stress approaches f_{yield} for the load P_5. We conclude then that the elongation of the bar is limited to the maximum elastic elongation until the final uniform stress distribution is reached with all fibers stressed theoretically to the yield stress. Therefore, internal stress concentrations at sections that become wholly plastic will be wiped out before overall deformations of the structure or its members become appreciably greater than the maximum elastic deformation.

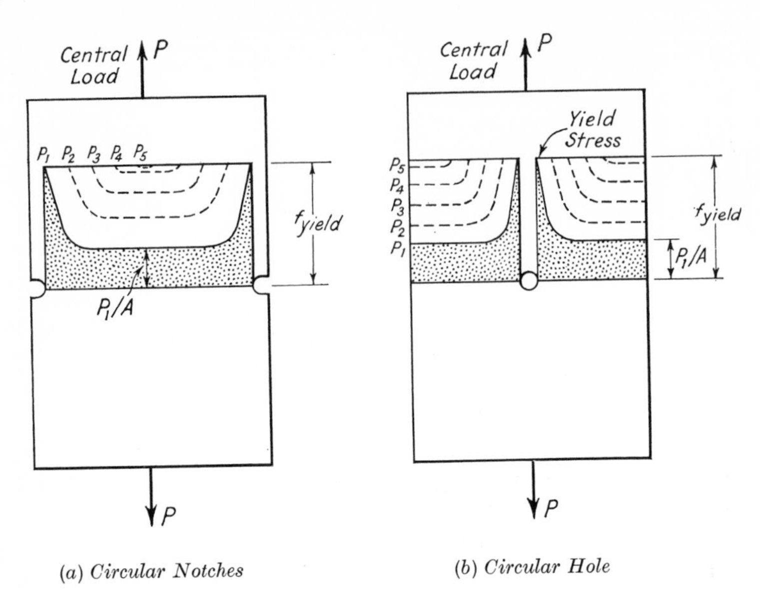

(a) *Circular Notches* (b) *Circular Hole*

FIG. 171. ELASTIC AND PLASTIC STRESS DISTRIBUTIONS NEAR CIRCULAR NOTCH OR HOLE AS LOAD IS INCREASED FROM P_1 TO P_5.

Another way to express this important observation is to say that upon removal of the loading (when $P/A < f_{\text{yield}}$) the members and the structure as a whole will return approximately to their original shapes and dimensions. Nevertheless, all internal stresses will not return to zero or to their original values because there will be residual stresses due to localized plastic deformations around holes, flaws, notches, or other areas of potential stress concentrations. It is correct to say that an extremely small inelastic change in length of a simple tension member under central loading will eliminate stress concentrations and produce a uniform stress P/A over the cross-section equal to the yield stress. One may think of this condition as *a state of unstable plastic deformation* corresponding to the beginning of the horizontal part of the stress-strain diagram of Fig. 170. Any disturbance such as vibration or a small increase of load will cause the tension member to stretch one or two per cent of its length and thus distort the structure permanently. However, the intermediate state of unstable but limited plastic deformation is the essential theoretical basis for plastic or ultimate-load analysis and design.

184. Extent of Plastic Deformation Required to Eliminate Brittle Fracture. As has been shown for the tension bar with a circular hole or notch, the amount of plasticity needed to redistribute stresses is quite limited. Any material providing a small but highly dependable plastic deformation, even though the total elongation before fracture might be only a fraction of that indicated in Fig. 170(*a*), would be usable in a structure designed by plastic theory. The only danger of limited plasticity is that other influences which suppress ductility may be present and may reduce plastic deformation to such a low value that a brittle fracture may result. Specifications for structural steels such as *A*7 and *A*36 are intended to assure adequate ductility to justify dependence upon plastic action for continuous beams and structural frames.

Ultimate-Load Analysis and Design of Beams

185. Plastic Stress Distribution on Beam Sections. Structures consisting of beams and frames may collapse by flexural distortion. The sections where concentration of rotation takes place are visible before final collapse. These sections, or localized areas of plastic distortion, are called *plastic hinges.* They are visible in the photograph of Fig. 169(*a*). It is possible by simple theory to predict with reasonable accuracy the bending moment that will produce a plastic hinge in a beam of either a rectangular section or one of *I* or *H* section. The illustration, Fig. 172, shows how an elastic stress distribution (*b*) for the cross-section of a typical beam section changes in (*c*) or (*d*) to an elasto-plastic distribution and in (*e*) to a fully plastic stress distribution.

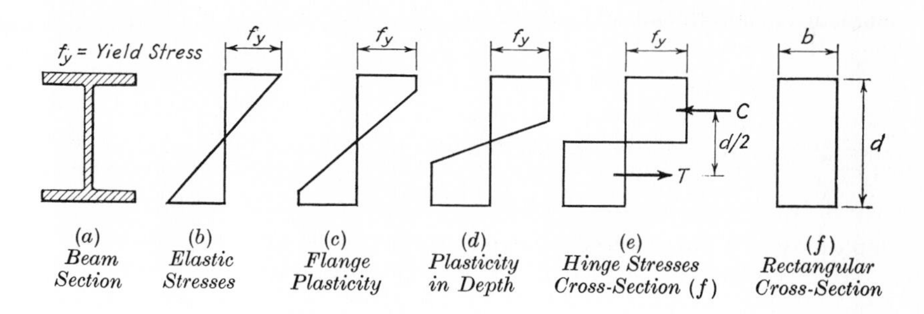

Fig. 172. Growth of Plasticity for Beam Sections.

After the fully plastic stress distribution is reached there can be no increase of the load or the bending moment because the stress cannot exceed yield (usually designated f_{yield} or f_y) at any point until strain hardening takes place. Observe the stress-strain curve of Fig. 170(*a*). Strain hardening does not occur until the unit deformation reaches ε_2 in Fig. 170(*a*), which is at least ten times ε_1, the unit strain at the beginning of yield. Strain hardening is not considered to be a useful factor in plastic design for ultimate load for which the maximum strains need not exceed ε_1 appreciably.

The Plastic Hinge. The growth of the plastic hinge is illustrated by Fig. 173. The yield stress is reached first at the extreme fibers under the load. As the load is increased the upper and lower areas of plasticity are extended both in length and in depth. With sufficient increase in load the upper and lower plastic areas will join together at the stage illustrated by Fig. 173 with the formation of a plastic hinge. Thereafter, any attempt to increase the load will produce a severe localized rotation resulting in a permanent angle change at the central hinge.

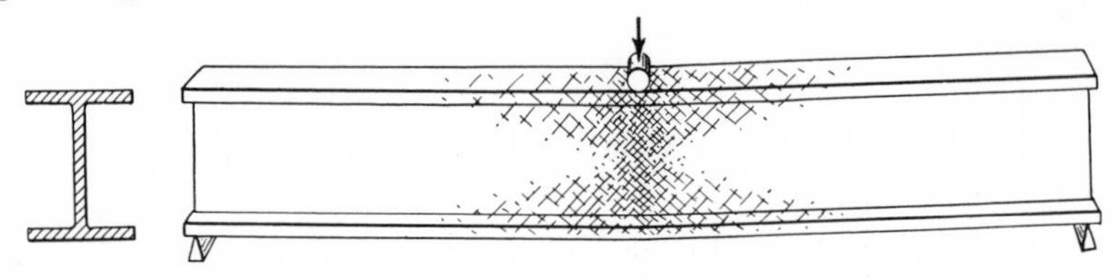

FIG. 173. AREA OF PLASTICITY AT HINGE INDICATED BY SLIP LINES.

186. The Shape Factor for Rectangular and I Cross-Sections. The yield moment of a beam cross-section is defined as the moment that will produce a yield stress at the extreme fiber as in Fig. 172(*b*). The plastic moment is that moment which will develop full plasticity of the cross-section according to the stress distribution of Fig. 172(*e*) with a resulting plastic hinge. The ratio of the plastic moment to the yield moment or M_p/M_y is the *shape factor*. This factor will range from 1.5 for a rectangular cross-section down to 1.15 or 1.12 for a rolled beam section. The shape factor defines the extra moment beyond the initial yield moment that is required to produce a plastic hinge.

By considering the rectangular cross-section of Fig. 172(*f*) we may compute the shape factor easily. For an elastic stress distribution and a rectangular cross-section, the flexure formula

$$f = Mc/I = M/S \tag{1}$$

applies up to a fiber stress f_y. Hence we may write

$$M_y = Sf_y = f_y(bd^2/6). \tag{2}$$

For the fully plastic stress distribution of Fig. 172(*e*) applied to the rectangular cross-section (*f*) we may write the expression for the plastic moment.

$$M_p = f_y(bd/2)\,d/2 = f_y(bd^2/4). \tag{3}$$

Hence *the shape factor for a rectangular section* is

$$\frac{M_p}{M_y} = \frac{f_y \times \text{plastic modulus}}{f_y \times \text{elastic modulus}} = \frac{(bd^2/4)}{(bd^2/6)} = \frac{3}{2}. \tag{4}$$

Since rolled beam sections vary greatly in their proportions it is not possible to compute a single shape factor for I-sections or H-sections. However, the normal range of *the shape factor for rolled beams* is from 1.12 to 1.15, and the maximum range is from about 1.1 to 1.2. Of course, the shape factor may be computed readily for any particular section. The shape factor is the plastic modulus divided by the elastic modulus. *The plastic modulus for a symmetrical beam section is twice the statical moment of either half of the cross-section about the centroidal axis.* Tables are available that give the elastic modulus, the plastic modulus, and the shape factor for the common beam sections. See the current *AISC Manual.*

187. Load Factor is the Product of Factor of Safety and Shape Factor. The factor of safety that should properly be used in the design of a given structure would depend upon a number of uncontrollable variables that are seldom given sufficient consideration. These include (1) the specified or obtainable quality of workmanship, (2) the variation below the minimum specification that is statistically probable for the elastic limit of the material, (3) the possibility of residual stresses particularly at notches that may change the ductile character of fracture, (4) the degree of uncertainty that must be attached to the type of design calculations used, and (5) the question of a future change in the character or magnitude of the loading. Until studies, largely of a statistical nature, are performed to establish the *range of variation* of each of the above-mentioned factors we must depend upon experience to establish a logical factor of safety to be used over a broad range of structures. If one accepts the ratio of working stress in flexure to specified minimum yield strength for *A*36 or *A*7 steel under *AISC* specifications as typical of the factor of safety provided for building frames, it is 1.65.

The load factor is related to the factor of safety for a beam-type structure in the following manner:

$$\text{Load Factor} = \text{Factor of Safety} \times \text{Shape Factor}. \tag{5}$$

This follows since the factor of safety is the ratio of the yield moment to the allowable moment and the shape factor is the ratio of the plastic moment to the yield moment. Hence we may write

$$\text{Load Factor} = \frac{M_{\text{plastic}}}{M_{\text{allowable}}} = \frac{M_{\text{yield}} \times \text{Shape Factor}}{M_{\text{allowable}}} = (FS) \times (SF) \tag{6}$$

where FS is the factor of safety and SF is the shape factor.

188. Range of the Load Factor. Having reached the conclusion previously that the most probable range of shape factor is 1.12 to 1.15, and accepting a factor of safety of 1.65, we reach the conclusion that a realistic load factor would be from 1.85 to 1.90. The author doubts the wisdom of establishing a single load factor for all structures. In fact, there would be great value in encouraging the use of *a load-factor range from 1.70 to 2.0* with the responsibility of choice of load factor placed upon the designer.

Whenever loads are known with certainty, quality workmanship is specified, and other conditions are favorable, a load factor of 1.70 would seem adequate. Where such characteristics are not adequately controlled, a load factor of 2.0 would be chosen to provide an extra margin for safety. *AISC* specifications (see §197) recommend 1.70 for beams and 1.85 for frames.

Load Factor with Wind. The maximum increment of allowable stress when wind forces are included is 33 per cent. Since allowable stress or moment occurs in the denominator of the expression for the load factor, an allowable stress increased by the ratio $4/3$ corresponds to a reduction of the load factor by the ratio $3/4$. Hence, with wind and other lateral forces included, the load factor range is from $0.75 \times 2.0 = 1.50$ to $0.75 \times 1.70 = 1.28$. For a mean load factor of 1.87 the comparable value with wind included would be $0.75 \times 1.87 = 1.40$. This corresponds to the *AISC* recommendation in §197.

Load Factor for Flange Buckling. In applying the load factors developed above to beams or frames it is assumed that the compression flange will withstand the yield stress of 33,000 psi for *A*7 steel or 36,000 psi for *A*36 steel without buckling or wrinkling. If this is not true, the compression flange should be adequately braced or poured in concrete to prevent premature collapse. Otherwise, the load factor will be reduced to account for collapse due to flange buckling at a reduced ultimate load. Experimental and theoretical data on flange buckling are given in a *Guide to Design Criteria for Metal Compression Members* of the Column Research Council. The *AISC* specifications (§197) limit beam shear and specify stiffeners to provide web resistance to ultimate loads.

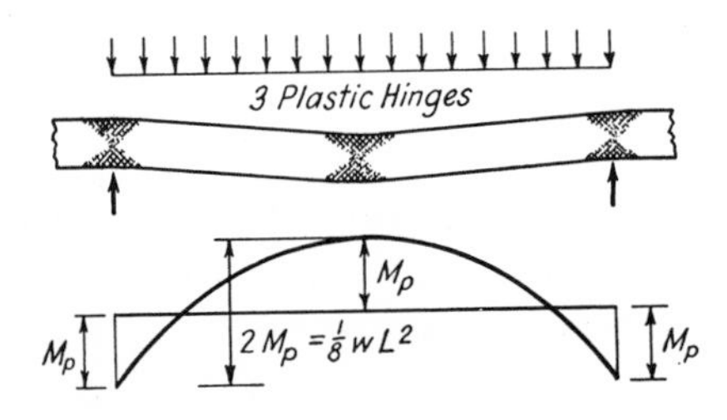

FIG. 174. LOCAL COLLAPSE OF A CONTINUOUS BEAM.

189. Collapse Load of Beam with Restrained Ends. In continuous beams, bents, and more complex structural frames any loaded span may collapse locally, as shown in Fig. 174, by the development of three plastic hinges. These three plastic hinges permit the span to deflect as a jointed mechanism. Since the plastic moments are determinable at the three hinges (from the yield stress and the beam cross-section), it is a simple matter to draw the collapse moment diagram and from it to determine the collapse loading. In

Fig. 174 a typical collapse moment diagram for uniform loading with equal positive and negative maximum values (marked M_p) is illustrated. Since the height of the moment diagram is $\frac{1}{8}wL^2$ which just equals $2M_p$ at collapse, we obtain for the ultimate load,

$$w_{\text{collapse}} = 16M_p/L^2. \tag{7}$$

Continuous Beams

190. Ultimate Load Design of a Continuous Beam of Constant Section. We will design the continuous uniform beam of Fig. 175(a) for a yield stress of 40,000 psi and a factor of safety of 2.0 based upon collapse. Therefore, the fixed working load of 5,000 lb. per lineal ft. would correspond to a collapse loading of 10,000 lb. per lineal ft. The simple-span bending moments produced by the collapse loading of 10,000 lb. per lineal ft. are shown in Fig. 175(b).

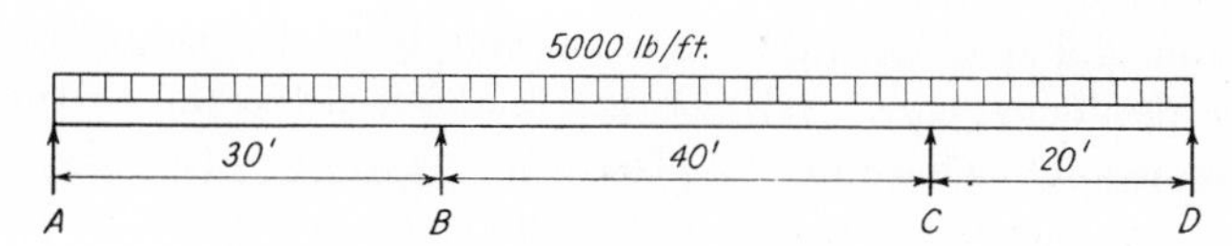

(a) *Three-Span Continuous Beam and Loading*

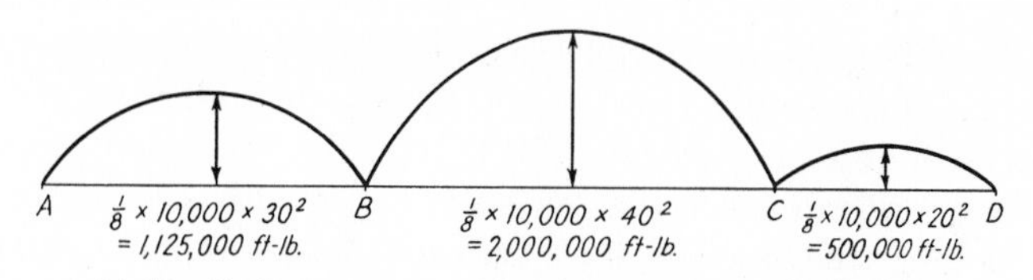

(b) *Simple-Span Moment Diagrams for Collapse Loading*

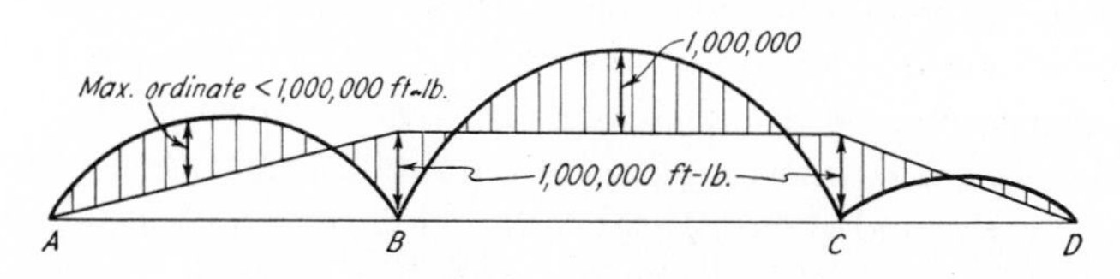

(c) *Moment Diagram after Development of Plastic Hinges*

Fig. 175. Ultimate-Load Design of a Continuous Beam of Constant Section.

Example of Determination of Controlling Moment. In span BC of Fig. 175(c) the plastic hinge moment (equal maximum positive and negative moments, with symmetry, produced by plastic collapse) would be 50 per cent of the simple-span moment, or 1,000,000 ft-lb. In the end span AB, where $M_A = 0$, the plastic hinge moment for equal maximum positive and negative moments is found by geometry to be 69 per cent[2] of the

[2] The decimal fraction 0.69 is derived in *Theory of Modern Steel Structures*, Vol. 1, Third Edition, p. 278, from an unsymmetrical parabolic moment diagram.

simple-span moment or $0.69 \times 1{,}125{,}000 = 776{,}000$ ft-lb. Evidently, the maximum moment available for producing possible plastic collapse of span CD is even lower than for AB. Therefore, the value of $M_p = 1{,}000{,}000$ ft-lb. for BC controls the selection of the uniform beam $ABCD$.

(8) $$\text{Moment at first yield} = M_p \div \text{shape factor} = \frac{1{,}000{,}000}{1.15} = 870{,}000 \text{ ft-lb.}$$

$$\text{Elastic section modulus required} = \frac{870{,}000 \times 12}{40{,}000} = 261 \text{ in}^3. = \frac{I}{c}.$$

In the section modulus table of the steel handbook we find that the lowest weight steel beam furnishing this modulus to be 27*WF*102, which will therefore be selected. The economy of this design, however, is not highly satisfactory, since the spans AB and CD are greatly understressed. The ultimate loading of 10 kips per foot would produce only a local collapse in the span BC. A computation shows that the shape factor of the beam used is 1.14 rather than 1.15 as assumed. The modulus provided is still adequate, however.

General Procedure for Design of Uniform Continuous Beams. Determine the moment for plastic collapse of the more critical end span by using a base line that makes the maximum positive and negative moments equal. Select the interior span having the greatest simple-span moment, and draw in a base line producing equal end moments that are also equal to the greatest positive moment. This interior plastic moment may then be compared with the plastic moment for the critical end span and the larger one used to select a uniform section to be used for all spans. Any type of fixed loading may be used. If spans may be loaded or unloaded, the controlling plastic moment may be determined for each possible combination of loadings. Then the final design of the cross-section is made dependent upon the largest plastic moment and the greatest shear that occurs under any probable load combination. All computations are made by equations of *statics*.

191. Varying the Section for Improved Economy. To improve the economy of the continuous beam of Fig. 175, it would be desirable to select a different cross-section for each span. However, it is evident from inspection of the ultimate moment diagram of Fig. 176 that two plastic moments control collapse; i.e., M_{p1} and M_{p2}. The logical approach to economical design, therefore, is to select a basic section for M_{p1} and then to strengthen this section with welded flange plates over that length of beam, marked x_2 in Fig. 176, for which the plastic moment M_{p2} controls the cross-section. The length x_2 must be such that an extra plastic hinge will not develop at either of its ends, which means that the bending moment there on the ultimate-load moment diagram must be less than M_{p1}. As indicated previously, M_{p1} is 69 per cent of the simple span moment for the span AB. We may find M_{p2} by the geometry of the parabola in span BD, knowing that M_B is M_{p1}, that M_C and M_D must be equal plastic hinge moments, and that the total height of the parabola at its center (near but not at C) is $\frac{1}{8}w_cL^2$, where w_c is the collapse loading being used in the design. The same principles can be applied to more than three spans.

General Procedure for Design of Continuous Beams of Varying Section. Determine the plastic collapse moment for either an end or interior span (called span A) for which the bending moments are relatively light, and use this moment to select a section for span A. The plastic moment resistance of the section selected then becomes one end moment (or both end moments if the span is interior) of span A. Using this fixed point on the ultimate moment diagram for an adjacent span B, draw in a base line for span B that makes its opposite-end moment and its maximum positive moment equal. These two equal moments are the plastic moment for the second span B, and this plastic moment may be used to determine the necessary reinforcement for a part of the length of span B of the section initially selected for span A. *In sequence one can then design span after span, always having an end plastic moment known from the plastic moment resistance of the section used for the preceding span.* Several changes in cross-section may be involved in a multiple-span beam without complicating the design procedure.

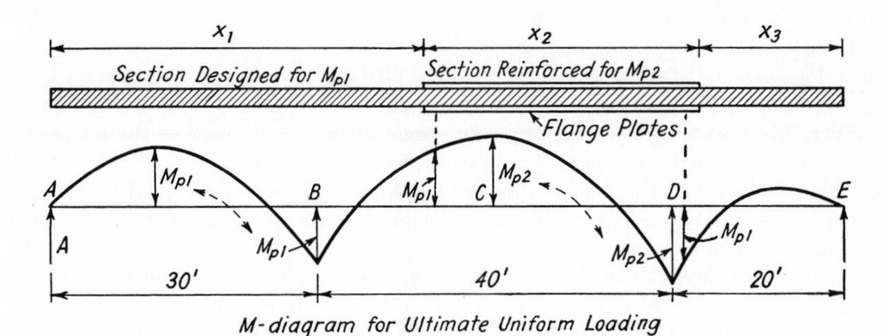

FIG. 176. VARIATION OF CROSS-SECTION FOR ECONOMY.

The only difficulty experienced is for a span loaded so lightly that even the lightest practical section will not develop plastic hinges. The moment diagram for such a span cannot easily be determined. When such a span is reached one passes it and initiates a new design, starting possibly with an end span and working back toward the troublesome span. The section for each half of this span is then made identical with the section of the corresponding adjacent span, in order that it may match in resistance the plastic moments at its supports. More careful study may indicate that more than one half of the length of the span may be provided of the lighter section.

PROBLEMS

Compute the yield moment, the shape factor, and the plastic moment for the sections of Problems 1001–1007 for $f_y = 36{,}000$ psi.

1001. American standard I-beam, 12 in.—31.8 lb. *Ans.* Shape factor = 1.15.

1002. Wide-flange beam section, 16 in.—40 lb. *Ans.* $M_p = 217{,}000$ ft-lb.

1003. Wide flange beam section, 36 in.—300 lb.

1004. Box section 8 in. wide by 12 in. deep outside and ¾ in. thick.
Ans. $M_p = 328{,}000$ ft-lb.

1005. Two channels 15 in.—33.9 lb. placed back to back.

1006. The plate girder section of Problem 807 using gross section.
Ans. $M_p = 5{,}800{,}000$ ft-lb.

1007. The plate girder section of Problem 812.

1008. Determine M_p for the moment diagram of Fig. 175(*c*) in span *AB* for an ultimate loading w_u per foot of span. *Ans.* $M_p = 0.69\ M_{\text{static}}$.

1009. A three-span continuous beam has spans of 36, 45, and 36 ft. There is a uniform load of 100 lb. per ft. over all spans and a 8000-lb. load at the one-third points of each span. If the moment is zero at each exterior support determine the controlling plastic moment. *Ans.* 82,700 ft-lb.

1010. Same as Problem 1009 except that the spans are 30, 50, and 40 ft., respectively.

1011. Design a two-span continuous beam of uniform section with simple end reactions. Spans are 25 ft.-0 in. The uniform working load including the weight of the beam is 4600 lb. per lineal ft. Allow for a yield stress of 33,000 psi and an "ultimate load factor" of 1.75. The shape factor of the section is 1.14.
Ans. Mod. reqd. = 138.0; Use 21*WF*68.

1012. Repeat Problem 1011 for 20-ft. spans and an ultimate load factor of 2.0 with a yield stress of 38,000 psi and a shape factor of 1.14. *Ans.* Use 18*WF*50.

1013. Determine the required section for a three-span continuous beam using the data of Problem 1011 for the end spans. How long may the center span be made without reducing the collapse loading of 4600 lb. per lineal ft.? *Ans.* 29.3 ft.

1014. Use a strengthened section with flange plates over a part of the length of a three-span continuous beam for the data of Problem 1011. Each span is 25 ft. Determine the basic section, the flange area, and the length of plates. *Ans.* 18*WF*60.

1015. Select a single section for a four-span continuous beam carrying fixed concentrated loads of 20 kips at 10-ft. intervals. Spans are 30—40—50—30 ft. The extreme ends of the beam are simply supported. Allow for a yield stress of 33,000 and load factor of 1.89. Select an approximate section of 18-in. depth for resisting the concentrated loads, and then include the weight of the beam itself for determining M_p and revising the section. *Ans.* 18*WF*105.

1016. Improve the design in Problem 1015 by selecting a section for M_p in the end spans. Determine the required flange plates and their exact length to resist the controlling value of M_p for the interior spans. Make a preliminary design based upon concentrated loads alone, and then allow for the effect of the weight of the beam itself. Use the *AISC* load factor of 1.70 for continuous beams.

Ultimate-Load Analysis and Design of Bents

192. Ultimate-Load Action of Bents with Pin-End Columns. Bents carry both vertical and horizontal loads. Such loads may be concentrated or distributed without influencing the basic concept or technique of application of plastic or ultimate-load analysis. This concept is that *the ultimate load will produce a sufficient number of plastic hinges in the bent to turn it into a simple mechanism that will collapse with any further increase in the loading.* See Fig. 169(*a*). For pin-end columns a single-bay bent has one redundant reaction. Hence the development of one plastic hinge will make the bent statically determinate while a second plastic hinge will turn it into a mechanism undergoing the initial stage of collapse. In Fig. 177 the positions at which plastic hinges may be expected to develop under vertical and horizontal loads are indicated along with the corresponding moment diagrams. It is assumed here that the column action of the vertical legs of the bent is either restrained by side walls, or girts and bracing, or that the P/A stress is so small that collapse will be caused by flexure rather th buckling.

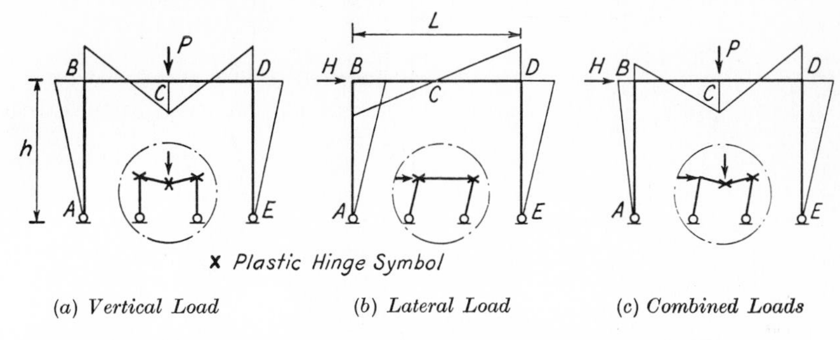

(*a*) *Vertical Load* (*b*) *Lateral Load* (*c*) *Combined Loads*

FIG. 177. PLASTIC HINGE LOCATIONS FOR A SIMPLE BENT.

193. Ultimate Load Design of Bents. A simple bent or portal may carry either vertical or horizontal loads or both. For convenience of explanation we will use one horizontal and one vertical concentrated load. Multiple loads, including distributed loadings, do not change the basic approach in ultimate-load design. The typical plastic hinge moment diagrams for three load conditions and pin-end columns are shown in Fig. 177. The small diagrams with x-marks indicate the positions of the plastic hinges. Evidently, the development of a plastic hinge under the vertical load at C requires a bending moment there equal to the plastic moment resistance of the horizontal beam, but the corner hinges at B and D can develop when the moment resistance of either the beam or column, whichever is smaller, is overcome.

For a bent of uniform section loaded as shown in Fig. 177(a) we may write

$$M_p = M_B = M_C = M_D = \frac{0.5\,PL}{4} = \frac{PL}{8}. \tag{9}$$

For a bent of identical columns loaded as shown in Fig. 177(b) we may write

$$M_p = M_B = M_D = 0.5\,Hh = \frac{Hh}{2} \tag{10}$$

For a bent of uniform section loaded as shown in Fig. 177(c) we may write

$$M_p = M_C = M_D = \frac{PL}{8} + \frac{Hh}{4}. \tag{11}$$

Equation (11), which is of considerable importance, is derived from Fig. 178 as follows From $\Sigma H = 0$,

$$H + \frac{M_B}{h} - \frac{M_p}{h} = 0. \tag{12}$$

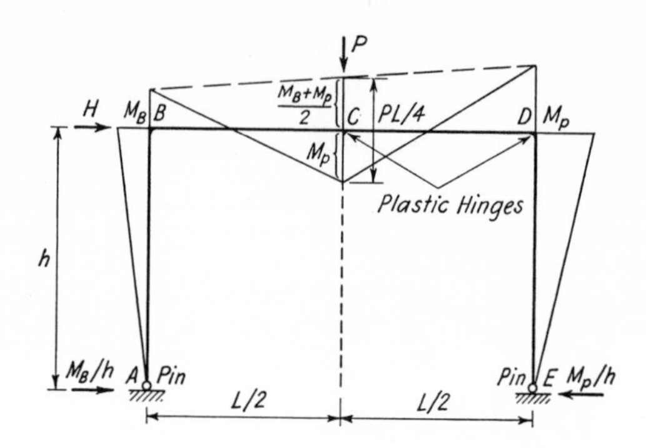

FIG. 178. COLLAPSE MOMENTS FOR BENT.

From the geometry of the triangle for span BD (Fig. 178),

$$\frac{PL}{4} = M_p + \frac{M_B + M_p}{2}. \tag{13}$$

By eliminating the unknown elastic moment M_B from equations (12) and (13), we obtain

$$M_p = \frac{PL}{8} + \frac{Hh}{4}. \tag{14}$$

Moreover, if H is large relative to P the sign of M_B is reversed in both equations, (12) and (13), so that equation (14) remains unchanged. It is well to notice that the required plastic moment for vertical and horizontal loads [equation (14)] is not the sum of the plastic moments required to support the same loads applied separately [equation (9) plus equation (10)]. This observation is expressed by the statement that the *laws of superposition* do not hold for loads producing plastic structural action.

Example of Bent Design. Determine the required wide-flange beam section for a uniform bent loaded as shown in Fig. 179. The yield stress is 36,000 psi and the ultimate load factor is to be 1.40.

From $\Sigma H = 0$, assuming the loads of Fig. 179 to produce yield,

$$3{,}000 = \frac{M_p}{20} + \frac{M_B}{20}, \quad \text{or} \quad M_B = 60{,}000 - M_p. \tag{15}$$

From the triangles of length BD in Fig. 179(b),

$$M_p = M_{\text{static}} + \frac{1}{3}M_B - \frac{2}{3}M_p, \tag{16}$$

where M_{static} is the simple-span moment under the load.

Substituting $60{,}000 - M_p$ for M_B from equation (15), we have

$$M_p = 46{,}600 + (20{,}000 - \frac{1}{3} M_p) - \frac{2}{3} M_p, \tag{17}$$

$$M_p = 66{,}600 - M_p, \tag{18}$$

$$M_p = 66{,}600 \div 2 = 33{,}300 \text{ ft-lb.} \tag{19}$$

By statics or the geometry of Fig. 179(*b*), we may now show that M_B is 26,700 ft-lb. This is less than M_p, which confirms the fact that the plastic hinges will develop at *C* and *D* as assumed.

The value of M_p of 33,300 ft-lb. from equation (19) would be correct for a factor of safety against collapse or load factor of 1.0 because working loads were given in Fig. 179(*a*). For a load factor of 1.40, $M_p = 33{,}300 \times 1.40 = 46{,}700$ ft-lb. Initial yielding of the extreme fiber occurs before M_p is reached as controlled by the shape factor, which is about 1.12 for a *WF* cross-section of shallow depth.

$$M_{\text{yield}} = 46{,}700 \div 1.12 = 41{,}700 \text{ ft-lb.}$$

Elastic section modulus $= (41{,}700 \times 12) \div 36{,}000 = 13.9$. Use an 8*WF*17 section for which $S = 14.1$.

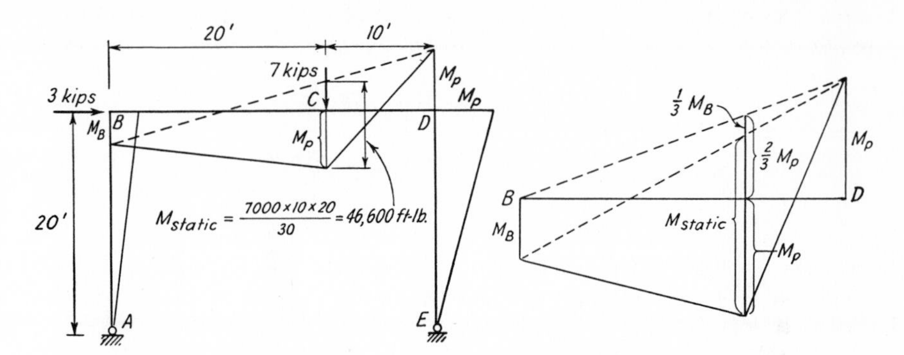

(*a*) *Working Loads and M-Diagram* (*b*) *Development of Plastic M-Diagram*

Fig. 179. Development of *M*-Diagram for Pinned-Base Bent.

194. Check on Bent Design by Virtual Work. The theory of virtual (imaginary) work is often useful either in making an original design or in checking a design for ultimate loading. Since collapse involves the formation of an unstable mechanism through the development of plastic hinges, we have indicated in Fig. 180 the deflections at the load points and the corresponding angular changes at these hinges when the structure is permitted to move laterally a virtual unit distance or one foot. From the geometry of Fig. 180, $\theta_{BC} = \theta_{AB} = \theta = 1/20$. Hence, since the lengths *AB* and *BC* are equal, the vertical deflection at *C* is the same as the horizontal movement at *B*, or 1.0 ft. Also, since *BC* is twice the length of *CD*, it is clear that $\theta_{CD} = 2\theta$. The angle change at the hinge C equals $\theta_{BC} + \theta_{CD} = \theta + 2\theta = 3\theta = 3/20$. Similarly, the angle change at the hinge D is $\theta_{CD} + \theta_{DE} = 2\theta + \theta = 3\theta = 3/20$. In Fig. 180 the internal work due to the indicated movements of the loads would be

$$W_{\text{int}} = M_p\left(\frac{3}{20}\right) + M_p\left(\frac{3}{20}\right) = M_p\left(\frac{3}{10}\right). \tag{20}$$

Equating the internal and external virtual works gives

$$M_p\left(\frac{3}{10}\right) = (7 \times 1.0) + (3 \times 1.0) = 10 \text{ ft-kips, or } M_p = \frac{10}{3} \times 10 = 33.3 \text{ ft-kips,}$$

which agrees with the calculation by statics from Fig. 179 and equation (19). For many structures the calculation of M_p by virtual work is actually simpler than its calculation by statics. The two methods may be used alternately as preferred. Note that equation (20) will contain two unknown values of M_p if the girder BD and the column DE have different plastic resisting moments. In order to solve equation (20) we must then know the ratio of one plastic resisting moment to the other. For a broader understanding of virtual work read Chapter 14 in the author's *Engineering Mechanics* or the *Theory of Modern Steel Structures*, Vol. II, revised edition, p. 85.

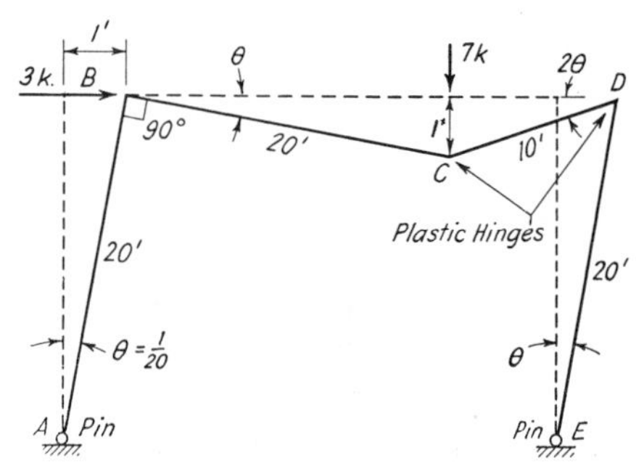

FIG. 180. VIRTUAL MOVEMENT OF COLLAPSE MECHANISM.

Use of Virtual Work for Design. When the analysis by virtual work is made for the true collapse mechanism, as above, it gives us the correct value of M_p, the plastic moment. If any other collapse mechanism is assumed, the plastic moment calculated will be less than the correct value of M_p. Hence, virtual work may be used for calculating the plastic moment for each of several possible collapse mechanisms. Then the largest value of M_p will be the correct one to use in design.

Column Bases Fixed. If Fig. 181(a) represents the collapse mechanism for a bent with fixed bases, the pins shown at A and E will also become plastic hinges at which there will be moments M_p producing rotations θ. See Fig. 181(b). The internal plastic work equation (20) then becomes

$$W_{\text{int}} = M_p\left(\frac{1}{20}\right) + M_p\left(\frac{3}{20}\right) + M_p\left(\frac{3}{20}\right) + M_p\left(\frac{1}{20}\right) = M_p\left(\frac{4}{10}\right). \tag{21}$$

Equating the internal and external virtual works gives

$$M_p\left(\frac{4}{10}\right) = (7 \times 1.0) + (3 \times 1.0) = 10 \text{ ft-kips, or } M_p = \frac{10}{4} \times 10 = 25.0 \text{ ft-kips}$$

Hence the use of fixed bases reduces M_p from 33.3 to 25.0 ft-kips for Fig. 180.

It is noted that there is little complication added to the plastic analysis by fixed bases despite the fact that the number of redundant reactions increases from one to three when pin bases are fixed.

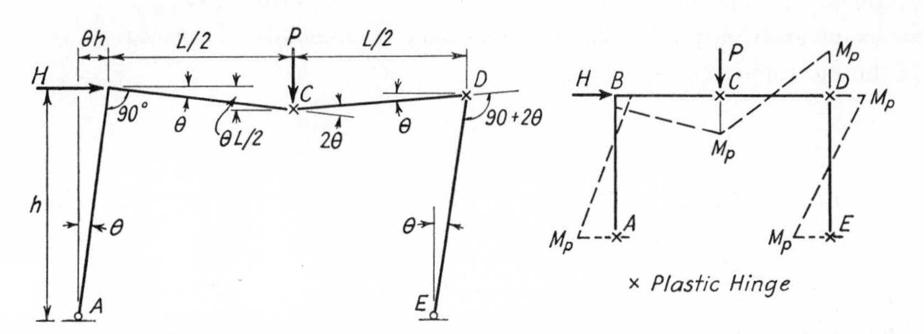

(*a*) *Lateral Movement or Side Lurch* (*b*) *M-Diagram with Fixed-End Columns*

FIG. 181. ANGLE CHANGES AT PLASTIC HINGES FOR FIG. 177(*c*); ALSO FOR FIXED BASES.

195. Distributed Loading on Bents. Since dead load and wind loads are either uniform or distributed loadings it is necessary to take into account the movement of each part of the distributed loading in setting up the expression for internal virtual work. Consider a light uniform load of w lb. per ft. to represent dead load for the bent of Fig. 181(*a*). If the load P is considerably larger than wL, the plastic hinge will remain at C. For a triangular deflection of BCD the average vertical displacement of w will be one half of the vertical displacement of the point C. All members may be taken as straight lines for plastic analysis, and both internal and external *elastic work* may then be omitted from the work equation. Hence, we may write an equation of virtual work including the work of a dead load of w lb. per lineal ft. in Fig. 181(*a*):

$$H(\theta h) + P(\theta L/2) + wL(\theta L/2)/2 = M_C(2\theta) + M_D(2\theta). \tag{22}$$

By substituting M_p for M_C and M_D for members of the same section,

$$M_p = \frac{Hh}{4} + \frac{PL}{8} + \frac{wL^2}{16}. \tag{23}$$

[Applicable for plastic hinge at C of Fig. 181(*a*)].

If the wind force H should be distributed uniformly from A to B the first term in equation (22) would be reduced to $H(\theta h)/2$, as may be seen from Fig. 181(*a*), and the first right-hand term in equation (23) would become $Hh/8$.

Approximating Hinge Location for Distributed Load. When a distributed load acts with concentrated loads the plastic hinge is usually, but not always, under a concentrated load. When a distributed load acts alone there is an infinity of possible locations for the positive-moment hinge. However, after two or three trial mechanisms have been checked by a virtual work computation of M_p, and moment diagrams have been drawn, it will be possible to locate the critical hinge within a foot or two of its true location with a resulting negligible influence on M_p. Some aid may be obtained from graphical measurements from a scale diagram for bending moment. Of course, an exact location of the plastic hinge may be calculated from the geometry of the parabolic moment diagram.

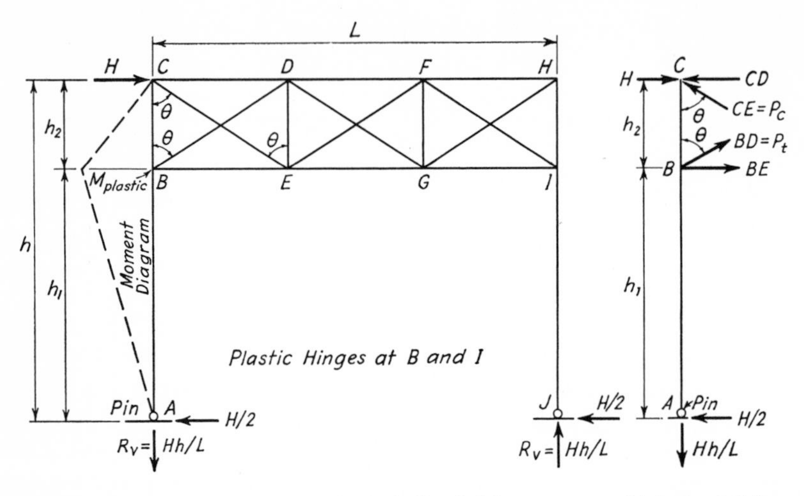

(*a*) *Forces and M-Diagram for Left-Hand Column* (*b*) *Isolated Column*

Fig. 182. Plastic Analysis of Trussed Bent with Pinned Columns.

Trussed Portal

196. Plastic Analysis of Trussed Portal with Pin-End Columns. If headroom is not critical, a trussed bent or portal will probably be more economical than a simple girder bent for which the bending moments are quite severe. The portal of Fig. 182 is typical of trussed bents. It has double diagonals which give it internal redundancy, and pin-end columns which provide one redundant reaction. Such a bent is readily handled by plastic or ultimate-load analysis, but we must know or assume the ultimate compressive strength of the compression diagonals which will be termed P_c.

By writing a simple equation of statics for $\Sigma M = 0$ about either base pin we obtain

$$Hh - R_v L = 0, \quad \text{or} \quad R_v = \frac{Hh}{L}. \tag{24}$$

For identical columns with plastic moments at B and I it is self-evident that each horizontal reaction must be equal to $M_p \div h_1$, which for overall equilibrium must equal $H/2$. Note that R_v also represents the vertical shear across each panel or pair of crossing diagonals of the horizontal truss. By designating the ultimate load or buckling resistance of each diagonal by P_c, since reversal of the load H can stress any diagonal in compression, we obtain the plastic resistance in tension of each diagonal as P_t:

$$P_t = \left(\frac{Hh}{L} - P_c \cos\theta\right) \sec\theta = \frac{Hh}{L} \sec\theta - P_c. \tag{25}$$ [3]

Even with the stresses in all diagonals known, it is necessary to isolate the left hand column as in Fig. 182(*b*) to determine the chord stresses BE and CD. Because C is a point of zero column moment, an equilibrium equation about C will be convenient for the computation of the stress in BE. Compare with §61 and Fig. 49. From $\Sigma M_C = 0$ we write

$$\frac{Hh}{2} - (BD) \sin\theta\, h_2 - (BE)h_2 = 0. \tag{26}$$

From this equation we obtain the stress in BE since the stress in BD is P_t. Then, from $\Sigma F_x = 0$, we write

$$H - \frac{H}{2} + (BE) + (BD) \sin\theta - (CE) \sin\theta - (CD) = 0. \tag{27}$$

At this stage all stresses are known in equation (27) except for CD, which may therefore be determined. All other stresses in the truss may be obtained by the algebraic method of joints since the stress in each diagonal is known to be either P_c or P_t. Of course, each column must be able to resist its plastic moment which is $(H/2)h_1$, as well as vertical axial load Hh/L. Commonly, in bents the relative influence of a column load is sufficiently small so that it can be carried by all or a part of the web of a rolled column section, which leaves the flanges free for providing the resistance required by the plastic moment $Hh_1/2$. This technique of subdividing the column section into two parts for resisting direct stress and flexure has been clarified by a discussion concerning resistance of a cross-section to eccentric loading in §258 of the book referred to in the footnote below.

Influence of Fixed-End Columns. The effect in Fig. 182 of fixing the lower ends of the columns is to produce two plastic hinges in each column, i.e., at A and B and at I and J. Therefore, at the exact mid-point between A and B there will be a point of zero moment. We may therefore reduce the length of h_1 in Fig. 182 to $h_1/2$ and treat the mid-point of each column as a pinned base. Of course, the plastic moment for the design of the columns will be halved and the stresses in the truss members will be reduced considerably. The procedures of analysis are the same as were explained for the bent with pin-end columns.

[3] For a detailed explanation of equation (25) see the writer's *Theory of Modern Steel Structures*, Vol. 1, 3rd ed., p. 262.

197. Specifications for Plastic Design, *AISC*. The load factor is controlled by *AISC* specifications at not less than 1.70 times the applied dead and live load for beams and 1.85 for continuous frames. The load factor is reduced to 1.40 when 1.40 times the specified wind load is added to 1.40 times the dead load and live load. Of course, this reduction of the load factor with wind included must not reduce sections required for $DL + LL$ alone. Steels with adequate ductility for use in plastic design are $A7$ for riveting and $A373$ for welding (yield stress 33,000 psi) and $A36$ for either riveting or welding (yield stress 36,000 psi). See the current *AISC* Manual for an elaboration of the following specifications and for changes that will occur as test results are reported.

Columns. The design of compression members is the most critical factor in plastic or ultimate-load designs. The *AISC* specifications preferably limit such columns to $L/r = 120$ at which P_u, the full ultimate-load capacity of the column, is restricted to $0.6P_y$, where P_y is the product of the yield point stress and the cross-sectional area. When slender compression members (above 120 L/r) are used, the ultimate load P_u is restricted by the ratio $P_u/P_y = 8700/(L/r)^2$. Specifications are also given by *AISC* to control the size of columns in continuous frames where capacity to resist an ultimate loading depends both upon axial load and upon end moments.

Stiffness. The webs of columns, beams, and girders are to be stiffened when the unit shear in the web exceeds 0.55 times the yield stress. Web crippling at points of load concentration is controlled by specified use of stiffeners. Beam and girder webs are restricted to a maximum h/t value of 70.

Connections. Rivets, $A307$ bolts, and welds may be used in ultimate-load design of connections at 1.67 times allowable elastic stresses. Groove welds are considered preferable to fillet welds. Bolts may not be permitted at higher ultimate loads than rivets of the same diameter.

Bracing. It is important to provide lateral resistance to motion at or near points where plastic hinges are to develop at ultimate loading to prevent plastic buckling. The greatest distance from the plastic hinge to the nearest connection of lateral bracing or other lateral support may range from $35r_y$ to $60r_y$, where r_y is the radius of gyration of the member about its weak axis. This variation is dependent upon the shape of the moment diagram for the member at ultimate loading, but the limit of $35r_y$ may be used without such consideration.

Workmanship. Sheared edges, if used near a plastic hinge location, must be ground or planed smooth. Rivet holes in the tension area near a plastic hinge must be drilled or subpunched and reamed to eliminate possible micro-cracks.

PROBLEMS

1017. A girder bent with uniform members and pin-end columns is 15 ft. high and 24 ft. wide. It carries 6000-lb. loads at the one-third points of the girder. There is also a uniform vertical loading of 100 lb. per lineal ft. Find M_p by adjusting the moment diagram. *Ans.* $M_p = 331{,}000$ in-lb.

1018. If the girder bent of Problem 1017 must resist a lateral force of 2000 lb. applied at the level of the girder in addition to the vertical loads, find M_p by virtual work. Try two positions of the positive-moment hinge and select the largest M_p.
Ans. $M_p = 446{,}000$ in-lb.

1019. Repeat Problem 1018 by use of the moment diagram without use of virtual work. Note that the difference of the column shears must equal 2000 lb. which produces one equation. Then the two plastic moments may be equated so that the end moments for the girder may be computed.

1020. Compute M_p for Problem 1018 for the case of fixed-end columns.

Ans. $M_p = 268{,}000$ in-lb.

1021. A girder bent is 25 ft. high and 40 ft. wide center to center of pin-end columns. It carries a concentrated load of 10 tons at 15 ft. from the left end of the girder. Allow for a uniform load of 200 lb. per lineal ft. on the girder and find M_p of the girder if the plastic section modulus of the girder is twice that of the column.

Ans. $M_p = 1{,}800{,}000$ in-lb.

1022. Compute M_p for Problem 1021 for the case of fixed-end columns of the same cross-section as the girder. Determine whether hinges develop at the column bases.

Ans. $M_p = 1{,}350{,}000$ in-lb.

1023. Revise Problem 1021 to allow for a distributed lateral force of 400 lb. per lineal foot acting on the left-hand column. *Ans.* $M_p = 2{,}425{,}000$ in-lb.

1024. Same forces as for Problem 1023 but compute M_p for fixed-end columns.

Ans. $M_p = 1{,}710{,}000$ in-lb.

1025. Revise Problem 1021 to allow for a concentrated lateral force of 7000 lb. acting to the left at the top of the right-hand column for a bent with columns and girders of the same modulus. *Ans.* $M_p = 1{,}740{,}000$ in-lb.

1026. Same as Problem 1025 but use fixed-end columns.

Ans. $M_p = 1{,}270{,}000$ in-lb.

1027. A girder bent of the same section for columns and girder has a height of 20 ft. and a girder span of 30 ft. The only loading is a vertical uniform load of 600 lb. per lineal ft. acting on the right half or right 15 ft. of the girder. Find M_p by trial, assuming one plastic hinge to occur at the top of the right-hand column and a second hinge to develop successively at 13 ft., 12 ft., 11 ft., and 10 ft. from the right-hand end of the girder with necessary side lurch to the right. The largest computed value of M_p should approximate the true value. *Ans.* Max. $M_p = 18{,}900$ ft-lb.

1028. The trussed portal of Problem 319 has diagonals for which the compressive buckling load is 6400 lb. Determine the plastic moment and direct compressive stress for a column, and compute all truss stresses. Replace the 4000-lb. working load with an ultimate or collapse load of 18,000 lb.

1029. Design a building bent 25 ft. high and 48 ft. wide to carry vertical concentrations of 20 kips at 8-ft. intervals and a lateral wind force at the top of 40 kips. Use pin-end bases, *A*36 steel, and a load factor of 1.40. Allow for a vertical uniform load of 400 lb. per lineal ft. First, assume girder and columns to have the same plastic moments. Then adjust sections as needed. Choose column web to carry axial load and flanges for M_p. Assume that the column is "built-in" to a masonry wall and cannot buckle. Check design by omitting lateral wind force and increasing load factor to 1.85.

1030. Design a building bent 32 ft. high and 42 ft. wide to carry vertical concentrations of 10 kips at 7-ft. intervals and a lateral force at the top of 25 kips. Use fixed-end bases, *A*441 steel ($f_y = 50{,}000$ psi) and a load factor of 1.50. Allow for a vertical uniform load of 300 lb. per lineal ft. The last five sentences of Problem 1029 also apply.

198. Conclusion. Structural design based upon plastic resistance was introduced initially under the concept that it would save steel or concrete by distributing and thus reducing the bending moments used in design. This factor of moment reduction is fortunate, but it may well be of less significance than the effect of the simple ultimate-load concept of design upon the safety and economic serviceability of complex structures. The convenience with which ultimate load design may be carried out for statically indeterminate frames avoids crude analytical approximations, guessing at cross-sections, and acceptance of uneconomic or unbalanced design merely because a reanalysis and redesign would require more time than may be available. Since ultimate load analysis gives the designer an improved understanding of the conditions leading to final structural collapse, he is better prepared to provide for safety as a normal step in design. At the same time, his design procedure produces balanced sections leading to important economies over handbook design. The one factor not directly considered in the ultimate load technique is that of deflection preceding collapse. Because serviceability of a structure may involve a limit upon deflection or vibratory motion, this factor may require separate study.

CHAPTER 11

TIMBER CONSTRUCTION

199. Wood Structures. Timber is used for temporary structures because of its low cost. When maintained either continuously dry or continuously wet, timber structures have a life that may exceed twenty or even thirty years. Submerged piles of Roman origin have been found in good condition. Timber will have a short life if it is alternately wet and dry. It is also attacked by certain insects and worms such as the termite and the teredo, or marine borer.

Courtesy Florida Architect

FIG. 183. MODERN METHODS OF LAMINATION HAVE REVIVED INTEREST IN TIMBER AS AN ARCHITECTURAL MATERIAL.

Defects in Timber. Natural defects in wood, as shown in Fig. 184, influence its strength. A knot on the top or bottom of a structural piece reduces the flexural strength in proportion to the relative width covered by the knot. "Shakes" are separations between fibers of the wood along the grain. "Checks" and "splits" are similar defects that cross the annual rings. Such defects reduce the shearing strength parallel to the grain. A "wane," which is merely bark along one corner of the timber, is not very serious in its effect on strength, since only a small wane is permitted in structural timber. Slope of the grain is objectionable in that it reduces the strength of both beams and columns. The strength is reduced for slopes greater than 1 in 20; the necessary reduction is about 50 per cent for a slope of 1 in 6 either in beams or columns.

Structural Timber Classifications and Dimensions. Structural timbers are classified under three groups: (1) *joists* and *planks* of nominal thicknesses 2 in., 3 in., and 4 in. and nominal widths up to 16 in. by even inches, loaded on any face; (2) *beams* and *stringers* of nominal widths and depths

TABLE 9

FROM NATIONAL DESIGN SPECIFICATION FOR STRESS-GRADE LUMBER

Species and Commercial Grade[1]		Allowable Unit Stress, (psi)				Modulus of elasticity $E \div 1000$
		Flexure f and tension parallel to [3]grain t	Horizontal shear H	Compression perpendicular to grain $c \perp$	Compression parallel to grain c	
Douglas Fir, Coast						
Dense Select Struct.[2]	J.&P.	2,050	[5-6-8]120	455	1,650	1,760
Select Struct.	J.&P.	1,900	[5-6-8]120	415	1,500	1,760
Dense Construction[2]	J.&P.	1,750	[5-7-8]120	455	1,400	1,760
Construction	J.&P.	1,500	[5-7-8]120	390	1,200	1,760
Standard	J.&P.	1,200	[5-7-8] 95	390	1,000	1,760
Dense Select Struct.[2]	B.&S.	2,050	[9]120	455	1,500	1,760
Select Struct.	B.&S.	1,900	[9]120	415	1,400	1,760
Dense Construction[2]	B.&S.	1,750	[9]120	455	1,200	1,760
Construction	B.&S.	1,500	[9]120	390	1,000	1,760
Dense Select Struct.[2]	P.&T.	1,900	[9]120	455	1,650	1,760
Select Struct.	P.&T.	1,750	[9]120	415	1,500	1,760
Dense Construction[2]	P.&T.	1,500	[9]120	455	1,400	1,760
Construction	P.&T.	1,200	[9]120	390	1,200	1,760
Douglas Fir						
Dense Select Struct.[2]	J.&P.[12]	2,050	[5-6-8]120	455	1,650	1,760
Dense Select Struct.[2] MC15[11]	J.&P.[12]	2,300	[5-6-8]125	455	1,850	1,760
Select Struct.	J.&P.[12]	1,900	[5-6-8]120	415	1,500	1,760
Select Struct. MC15[11]	J.&P.[12]	2,100	[5-6-8]125	415	1,650	1,760
Dense Construction[2]	J.&P.[12]	1,750	[5-7-8]120	455	1,400	1,760
Dense Construction[2] MC15[11]	J.&P.[12]	2,050	[5-7-8]120	455	1,600	1,760
Construction	J.&P.[12]	1,500	[5-7-8]120	390	1,200	1,760
Standard	J.&P.[12]	1,200	[5-7-8] 95	390	1,000	1,760
Dense Select. Struct.[2]	B.&S.	2,050	[9]120	455	1,500	1,760
Select Struct.	B.&S.	1,900	[9]120	415	1,400	1,760
Dense Construction[2]	B.&S.	1,750	[9]120	455	1,200	1,760
Construction	B.&S.	1,500	[9]120	390	1,000	1,760
Dense Select Struct.[2]	P.&T.	1,900	[9]120	455	1,650	1,760
Select Struct.	P.&T.	1,750	[9]120	415	1,500	1,760
Dense Construction[2]	P.&T.	1,500	[9]120	455	1,400	1,760
Construction	P.&T.	1,200	[9]120	390	1,200	1,760

[1] Abbreviations: (For description of classification of materials, see Spec. 102) J&P = Joists and Planks; B&S = Beams and Stringers; P&T = Posts and Timbers; LF = Light Framing; KD = Kiln Dried; SR = Stress Rated.

[2] These grades meet the requirements for density.

[3] In tension members the slope of grain limitations applicable to the middle portion of the length of the Joist and Plank and Beam and Stringer grades used shall apply throughout the length of the piece. For Southern Pine read footnote 4.

of 5 in., 6 in., and up to 20 in. by even inches, loaded on a narrow face; and (3) *posts,* or square timbers carrying longitudinal loads, in nominal sizes of 5 in., 6 in., and of larger dimensions in even inches. Dressed joists and planks are reduced 3/8 in. in thickness and also in width up to 6 in. Commercial beams, stringers, posts, and also joists or planks of widths greater than 6 in. are reduced 1/2 in. by planing. Timber sawed green shrinks and reduces somewhat in its dimensions. Several attempts have been made to adopt slightly reduced dimensions for finished lumber so that green-dressed and kiln-dried lumber will have the same final dimensions.

Strength Determined by Stress Grading. Timber classification is based upon strength either in flexure for joists and beams or in compression for posts. Such classifications are given in Table 9 for commercial timbers.

TABLE 9 (*Continued*)

Species and Commercial Grade[1]		Allowable Unit Stress (PSI)				Modulus of elasticity $E \div 1000$
		Flexure f and tension parallel to [3]grain t	Horizontal shear H	Compression perpendicular to grain $c \perp$	Compression parallel to grain c	
Pine, Southern[10]						
Dense Struct. 86[2]	2″ thick only	2,900	150	455	2,200	1,760
Dense Struct. 72[2]	,,	2,350	135	455	1,800	1,760
Dense Struct. 65[2]	,,	2,050	120	455	1,600	1,760
Dense Struct. 58[2]	,,	1,750	105	455	1,450	1,760
No. 1 Dense[2]	,,	1,750	120	455	1,550	1,760
No. 1	,,	1,500	120	390	1,350	1,760
No. 1 Dense KD[2]	,,	2,050	135	455	1,750	1,760
No. 1 KD	,,	1,750	135	390	1,500	1,760
Dense Struct. 86[2]	3″ & 4″ thick	2,900	150	455	2,200	1,760
Dense Struct. 72[2]	,,	2,350	135	455	1,800	1,760
Dense Struct. 65[2]	,,	2,050	120	455	1,600	1,760
Dense Struct. 58[2]	,,	1,750	105	455	1,450	1,760
No. 2 Dense SR[2]	5″ thick & up	[13]1,400	105	455	1,050	1,760
No. 2 SR	,,	[13]1,200	105	390	900	1,760
Dense Struct. 86[2]	,,	[13]2,400	150	455	1,800	1,760
Dense Struct. 72[2]	,,	[13]2,000	135	455	1,550	1,760
Dense Struct. 65[2]	,,	[13]1,800	120	455	1,400	1,760
Dense Struct. 58[2]	,,	[13]1,600	105	455	1,300	1,760
No. 1 Dense SR[2]	,,	[13]1,600	120	455	1,500	1,760
No. 1 SR	,,	[13]1,400	120	390	1,300	1,760

[4] Southern pine grading rules are uniform for all sizes and lengths of lumber.
[5] Value applies to pieces used as planks.
[6] Value applies to 2 in. thick pieces of Select Structural grade used as joists.
[7] For 2 in. thick pieces of Construction, Standard and standard Structural grades used as joists:
H = 120 when length of split is approximately equal to 1/2 the width of piece
H = 100 when length of split is approximately equal to the width of piece
H = 70 when length of split is approximately equal to 1 1/2 times width of piece
[8] For 3 in. thick pieces of Select Structural, Construction, Standard and standard Structural grades used as joists:
H = 120 when length of split is approximately 2 1/4 in.
H = 80 when length of split is approximately 4 1/2 in. and
For 4 in. thick pieces of Select Structural, Construction and Standard grades used as joists:
H = 120 when length of split is approximately 3 in.
H = 80 when length of split is approximately 6 in.
[9] For Beams and Stringers and for Posts and Timbers:
H = 120 when length of split is equal to 1/2 the nominal narrow face dimension
H = 100 when length of split is equal to the nominal narrow face dimension
H = 80 when length of split is equal to 1 1/2 times the nominal narrow face dimension
Note. Values for lengths of split other than those given in Notes 7, 8 and 9 are proportionate.
[10] Longleaf may be substituted for *Dense* at the same allowable stresses.
[11] These grades apply to 2 in. thickness only.
[12] The allowable unit stresses listed apply to lumber 2 in. to 4 in. thick and 6 in., wide or wider.
[13] These stresses apply for loading either on narrow face or wide face.

In order to maintain the strength requirements of commercial timber, rigorous specifications have been accepted by the lumber industry. Such specifications control the allowable sizes and locations of knots, shakes, checks, splits, and wanes. Also, the maximum slope of the grain is specified. The qualifying adjectives "dense" and "close grained" are defined with respect to the *number of annual rings per inch* for each species of wood. One can now feel that the specification "2050*f* dense structural southern pine" or "1400*c* select structural Douglas fir (coast)" will produce timber adequate to resist the unit stress designated by the classification. By this method of designation 2050*f* is timber selected to resist flexure at an extreme fiber stress of 2050 psi. Correspondingly, 1400*c* designates a timber selected not for flexure but for direct column stress of 1400 psi parallel to the grain for a short column or post.

NOTATION. For a definition of each letter and symbol used in this chapter see the list of symbols in the front matter. A special list applicable to timber design is included.

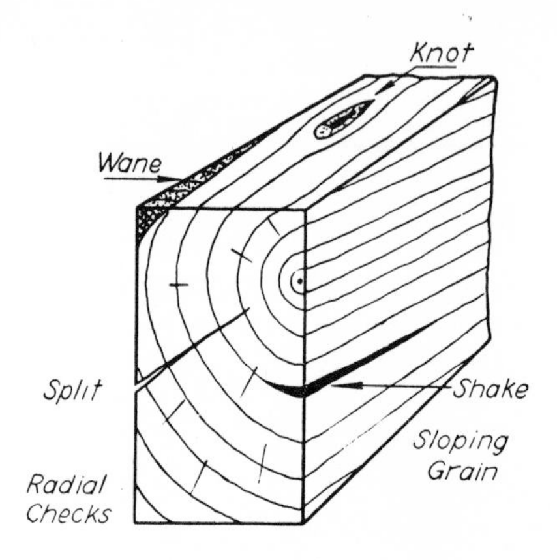

FIG. 184. FAULTS IN TIMBER.

ALLOWABLE STRESSES

200. Allowable Unit Stresses. Comparisons may be made from Table 9 of the relative unit stresses permitted in timber for different load conditions. The allowable compression parallel to the grain is roughly 75 per cent of the value in flexure, while allowable compression perpendicular to the grain is only about 20 per cent of the flexure value. Horizontal beam shear is limited to less than 10 per cent of the allowable stress in flexure, although most specifications allow a 50 per cent increase for unit horizontal shear in timber details. These percentages vary greatly for different species of timber and should not be used in computations. Instead, in Table 9 are given allowable unit stresses for commercial timber designated (1) Joists and Planks, (2) Beams and Stringers, and (3) Posts and Timbers.

There are many other grades of Douglas Fir and Southern Pine besides those listed in Table 9. Also, other species of wood are classified as to allowable stresses in the *National Design Specification for Stress-Grade Lumber* of the National Lumber Manufacturers Association. The modulus of elasticity given in Table 9 is for stress parallel to the grain.

Bearing Oblique to the Grain.[1] An expression has become commonly accepted for the calculation of the allowable unit compression or bearing at any angle to the grain. It is known as Hankinson's formula.

$$u = \frac{pq}{p \sin^2\theta + q \cos^2\theta}. \tag{1}$$

In this relation u is the unit allowable compression or bearing at the slope θ with the grain (Fig. 185), p the allowable unit compression parallel to the grain, and q the allowable unit compression perpendicular to the grain. The angle θ is shown in Fig. 185.

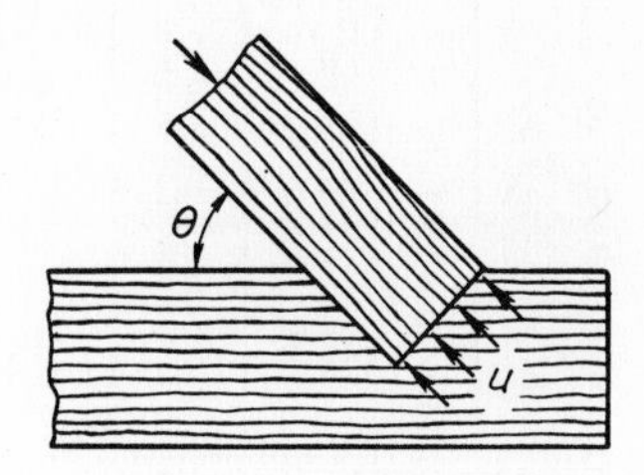

FIG. 185. BEARING AT AN ANGLE TO THE GRAIN.

TABLE 10

STRENGTH CORRECTION FACTORS FOR UNUSUAL CONDITIONS OF SERVICE OR LOADING

SERVICE OR LOADING		FLEXURE	SHEAR ‖ GRAIN	COMPRESSION ⊥ GRAIN	COMPRESSION ‖ GRAIN	MOD. OF ELASTICITY
Continuously Saturated		−10%	0%	−33%	−33%	−9%
Short-Term or Impact Load (Time Listed)	60 days	+15%	+15%	+15%	+15%	
	7 days	+25%	+25%	+25%	+25%	
	1 day	+33%	+33%	+33%	+33%	
	Impact	+100%	+100%	+100%	+100%	
Long-Term or Dead Load		−10%	−10%	−10%	−10%	−10%*
Shear in Joint Details			+50%			
Bearing on Metal Plates					+20%†	
Inadequate Seasoning						−9%

* Reduce E only for use in column formula to determine allowable stress.

† The figure of 20 per cent is an average value. Recommendations for various species are covered in *National Design Specification for Stress-Grade Lumber*.

[1] The formula given is from the *Wood Handbook* of the Forest Products Laboratory. Much of the data to be given on resistance of nails, screws, bolts, and connectors is taken from the publications of the Forest Products Laboratory, to which the reader is referred for important information on special cases not covered here.

TABLE 11

Allowable Unit Stresses for Structural Glued-Laminated Softwood Timber

(The allowable unit stresses below are for normal loading conditions and dry conditions of use. $E = 1{,}800{,}000$)

No.	Species and Combinations of Lumber Grades			Allowable Unit Stresses in PSI							
	Outer Laminations		Inner Laminations	Extreme Fiber in Bending "f"		Tension Parallel to Grain "t"		Compression Parallel to Grain "c"		Horizontal Shear "H"	Compression Perpendicular to Grain "$c\perp$"
	Grade	Number, Each Side	Grade	From 4 to 14 Laminations	15 or More Laminations	From 4 to 14 Laminations	15 or More Laminations	From 4 to 14 Laminations	15 or More Laminations		
DOUGLAS FIR, COAST REGION*											
5	Select Structural	All	Select Structural	2,600	2,600	2,600	2,600	2,200	2,200	165	415
6	Select Structural	Two	Construction	2,600	2,600	2,600	2,600	2,000	2,000	165	415
7	Clear (Close Grain)	One	Construction	2,600	2,600	2,200	2,400	1,900	2,000	165	385
8	Dense Construction	All	Dense Construction	2,400	2,600	2,600	2,600	2,200	2,300	165	450
9	Dense Construction	1/14 of total	Construction	2,400	2,600	2,400	2,400	1,900	2,000	165	450
10	Select Structural	One	Construction	2,400	2,600	2,200	2,400	1,900	2,000	165	415
11	Select Structural	Two	Standard	2,600	2,600	2,400	2,400	2,000	2,000	165	415
12	Clear (Medium Grain)	One	Standard	2,200	2,200	2,000	2,400	1,800	1,900	165	385
13	Select Structural	One	Standard	2,200	2,200	2,000	2,400	1,800	1,900	165	415
14	Construction	All	Construction	2,000	2,200	2,200	2,400	1,900	2,000	165	385
15	Construction	One	Standard	2,000	2,200	2,000	2,400	1,800	1,900	165	385
16	Standard	All	Standard	1,600	2,000	2,000	2,400	1,800	1,900	165	385
PINE, SOUTHERN†											
1–1	No. 1 Dense	All	No. 1 Dense	3,000	3,000	3,000	3,000	2,400	2,500	200	450
1–2	B & B Dense	One	No. 1	3,000	3,000	2,600	2,600	2,100	2,100	200	450
1–3	No. 1 Dense	1/14 of total	No. 1	3,000	3,000	2,600	2,600	2,100	2,100	200	450
1–4	B & B Dense	One	No. 2 Dense	2,800	2,800	3,000	3,000	2,400	2,400	200	450
1–5	No. 1 Dense	1/5 of total	No. 2 Dense	2,800	3,000	2,800	3,000	2,300	2,400	200	450
1–6	No. 1	All	No. 1	2,600	2,600	2,600	2,600	2,100	2,100	200	385
1–7	B & B Dense	1/14 of total	No. 2	2,400	2,800	2,600	2,600	2,000	2,000	200	450
1–8	B & B	One	No. 2	2,400	2,400	2,600	2,600	2,000	2,000	200	385
1–9	No. 1	1/5 of total	No. 2	2,400	2,600	2,400	2,600	2,000	2,000	200	385
1–10	No. 2 Dense	All	No. 2 Dense	2,000	2,600	2,600	3,000	2,200	2,300	200	450
1–11	No. 2 Dense	1/14 of total	No. 2	2,000	2,600	2,200	2,600	1,900	2,000	200	450
1–12	No. 2	All	No. 2	1,800	2,200	2,200	2,600	1,900	2,000	200	385

* *Standard Specifications for Design and Fabrication of Structural Glued Laminated Lumber*, West Coast Lumberman's Association.
† *Standard Specification for Structural Glued Laminated Southern Pine*, Southern Pine Inspection Bureau.
Note: Allowable stresses in bending apply with horizontal laminations, assuming vertical loads. For wet conditions of use reduce the modulus of elasticity to 1,600,000 and reduce allowable stresses 10–33 per cent as given by The *National Design Specification for Stress-Grade Lumber*. (See Spec. 107.)

Strength Correction Factors. Table 10 gives approved percentages by which the working stresses of Table 9 should be changed to care for special conditions of loading or service. Timber that is continuously wet is weakened particularly in compression. Frequent variation of moisture results in decay and should be considered by a reduction of working stress up to 25 per cent. If the decay hazard is sufficiently serious to require a greater stress reduction, it is desirable to use *treated timber*. Creosote and other timber preservatives requiring the use of heat, vacuum, and pressure weaken the timber up to as much as 25 per cent, but the gain in decay resistance is usually considered to justify the use of unreduced working stresses.

Continuous Loading, Impact, and Fatigue. Timber is able to withstand greatly increased loads momentarily. Hence, impact is seldom considered in the design of a wood structure, unless, as indicated in Table 10, the impact exceeds 100 per cent of the live load. Other loadings of a temporary nature of less than 60 days duration also justify increased working stresses. The allowable stresses for dead loading and for other loads continuously applied should be decreased 10 per cent. The fatigue limit for rectangular beams is about one third of the modulus of rupture. Since the allowable working stress is only about one sixth of the modulus of rupture, the danger of fatigue failure is negligible. Wood stressed slightly below the fatigue limit may be expected to withstand at least *15,000,000* repetitions of stress. For a stress slightly above the fatigue limit, this factor will drop to *2,000,000* repetitions of stress.

201. Laminated Glued Timbers. The shortage of material from which first-quality beams and posts can be cut and the availability of greatly improved glues has led to the gradual increase in use of laminated timbers. Such timbers can also be assembled with bolts and fasteners. By selecting the planks and placing them so that knots and defects will not weaken the beam, a superior timber to resist flexure can be manufactured. Table 11 lists standard allowable stresses for laminated glued timbers of Douglas fir or Southern Pine. They are also available in hardwoods. It is recommended for economy that intermediate combinations rather than those

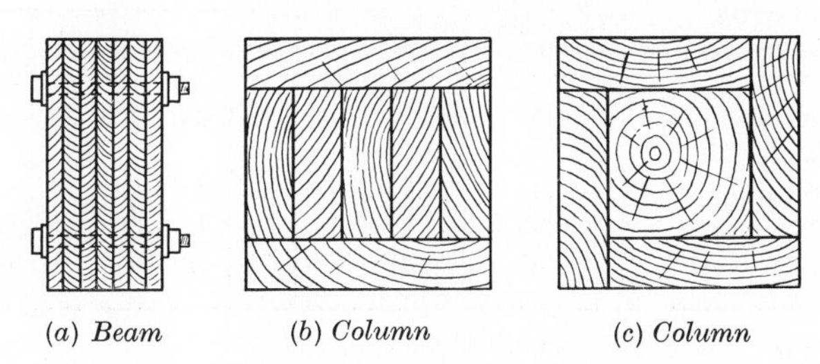

(*a*) *Beam* (*b*) *Column* (*c*) *Column*

Fig. 186. Heavy Laminated Timber.

of highest allowable stress be selected. In very large sizes those combinations with the lower stresses may be the only ones readily available. It is worth noting that timbers below 6 in. wide are actually $\frac{3}{4}$ in. narrower than the nominal width, and from 6 to 12 in. the actual finished dimension is 1 in. less than the nominal width. Depths required should be specified accurately. Glued laminated beams usually have horizontal laminations. Other combinations are shown in Fig. 186.

Holding Power of Nails and Screws

202. Holding Power of Wire Nails and Spikes. There is considerable variation of test results on the holding power of nails because of the number of variables involved. These may be listed as (1) quality and species of wood, (2) edge distance, (3) nearness of a knot or fault, (4) method of driving, and (5) moisture content when driven and when pulled. Since these factors are not all under control, particularly the human element in driving, it has seemed best to reduce ultimate holding power by a factor of 6 for working loads. Thus we obtain the following approximate relationship:

$$p = 1350G^{5/2}d. \tag{2}$$

In this formula, p is the safe load in tension per lineal inch of penetration, G is the specific gravity of the wood (oven dry), and d is the diameter of the nail or spike in inches.

The only important case in which this formula needs correction is for application to southern yellow pine. Then, a factor of 80 per cent should be introduced up to the twelvepenny size, and a factor of 70 per cent is used above the twentypenny size. Thus, we get the values offered in Table 12.

TABLE 12

Safe Holding Power of Wire Nails and Spikes*

(values are in pounds per lineal inch of penetration)

Timber Species	Specific Gravity (Oven dry) G	Size of Nail (penny designation and diameter)								
		$G^{2.5}$	8 0.13	12 0.15	16 0.16	20 0.19	30 0.21	40 0.22	50 0.24	60 0.26
Redwood, ponderosa pine, low s.g. woods	0.42	0.11	21	23	25	30	33	35	38	41
Douglas fir, coast	0.51	0.19	34	38	42	49	53	58	62	66
Southern yellow pine	0.59	0.27	38	42	45	49	53	57	62	67
Beech, birch, hardwoods	0.67	0.37	66	75	82	97	105	114	124	133

* Reduce 33 per cent if driven parallel to the grain.

Sizes of Wire Nails and Lag Screws. The common designation of wire nails and small spikes is by *weight per thousand.* Thus a thousand sixpenny nails weigh six pounds, etc. The diameter of the nail or screw is needed in the determination of holding power and is given in Table 13.

Spikes are larger in diameter than nails for equal lengths. They are available in lengths from 3 in. to 12 in. Boat spikes are square and have a chisel point. They are obtainable in sizes varying by sixteenths of an inch from ¼ in. to ⅝ in. and in lengths up to 14 in.

TABLE 13

SIZES OF ORDINARY WIRE NAILS AND LAG SCREWS IN INCHES

Size of Nail		Diameter, d	$d^{3/2}$	Length	Diameter of Lag Screw	Length
Eightpenny	8d	0.13	0.047	$2\frac{1}{2}$	$\frac{5}{16}$	$1\frac{1}{2}$–6
Twelvepenny	12d	0.15	0.058	$3\frac{1}{4}$	$\frac{3}{8}$	$1\frac{1}{2}$–6
Sixteenpenny	16d	0.16	0.065	$3\frac{1}{2}$	$\frac{7}{16}$	$1\frac{1}{2}$–8
Twentypenny	20d	0.19	0.083	4	$\frac{1}{2}$	$1\frac{1}{2}$–10
Thirtypenny	30d	0.21	0.096	$4\frac{1}{2}$	$\frac{9}{16}$	2–12
Fortypenny	40d	0.22	0.105	5	$\frac{5}{8}$	2–12
Fiftypenny	50d	0.24	0.120	$5\frac{1}{2}$	$\frac{3}{4}$	$2\frac{1}{2}$–12
Sixtypenny	60d	0.26	0.135	6	$\frac{7}{8}$	3–12

Variations of Holding Power. Nails are available in special shapes. A long sharp point increases the holding power but also increases the splitting tendency. The reverse is true of blunt points. The Forest Products Laboratory has developed a chemically etched nail with holding power increased at least 90 per cent under all conditions. This nail has become commercially available. Green wood shrinks, causing nails to lose a considerable part of their holding power. In order to avoid much of this loss of strength, the designer may specify either barbed or spirally grooved nails for use in green wood. Prebored holes of smaller size than the diameter of the nail and slant driving increase the holding power. However, it is not usual to increase the values given by equation (2). Nails driven parallel to the grain should be reduced 33 per cent in holding power.

203. Holding Power of Drift Bolts. A drift bolt is a pin driven into a hole about $\frac{1}{8}$ in. smaller in diameter than the bolt. Although test results vary considerably, the following formula seems to be reasonably satisfactory for the holding power of drift bolts in dry wood, since it is based upon a factor of safety of 5 for different species.

$$p = 1200G^2d. \tag{3}$$

In this equation, p represents the permissible tension in pounds per lineal inch of penetration, G is the specific gravity of the wood (oven dry), and d is the bolt diameter in inches.

204. Holding Power of Screws. The equations recommended by the *National Design Specification for Stress-Grade Lumber and Its Fastenings* are

$$p = 2850G^2d \text{ (wood screws),} \tag{4}$$

$$p = 1800G^{3/2}d^{3/4} \text{ (lag screws).} \tag{4a}$$

Again, p is the tension resistance in pounds per lineal inch of penetration (penetration is $\frac{2}{3}$ of length for wood screws and usually the threaded length for lag screws), G is the specific gravity of the wood (oven dry), and d is the diameter of the shank in inches. Screws in ordinary timber are

DP31 *Find the number and size of nails, drift bolts, and lag screws to resist a pull of 5000# between a 2″ and a 6″ thickness of Douglas fir of specific gravity 0.51 when oven dry. The nails passing through the 2″ plank penetrate the 6″ timber. The force is in the direction of the nails.*

Nails: *In order for the penetration to be ⅔ of the length of the nail, the nail must be 6″ long. This is a 60d nail. The holding power from equation (2) and Table 12 is* $p = 1350G^{5/2}d$
$= 1350\sqrt{0.51^5} \times 0.26 = 65\#/''$.

For a penetration of 4⅜″ use

$$\frac{5000}{65 \times 4.37} = 18 \text{ nails.}$$

The contact area 9½″ × 9½″ would be barely adequate for driving 18 nails.

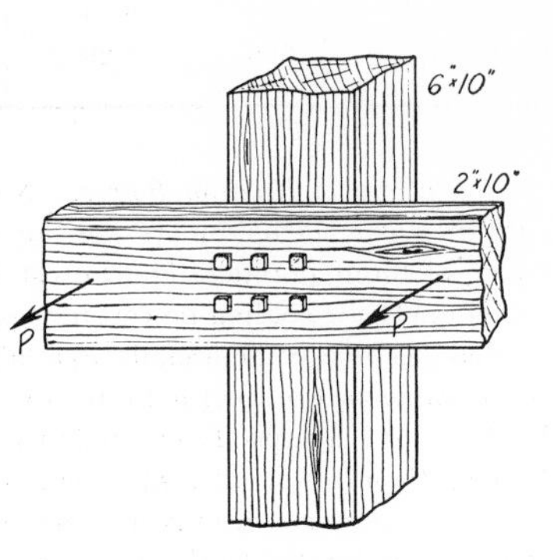

Drift Bolts:

Try ¼″ bolts 7″ long, penetration 5⅜″.

$p = 1200G^2d = 1200(0.51^2)0.25$
$= 78\#/''$. [*Equation (3).*]

Pull per bolt $= 78 \times 5.37 = 420\#$.

Use $\frac{5000}{420} = 12$ *drift bolts (¼″ × 7″).*

The contact area 9½″ × 9½″ could be arranged to hold 12 drift bolts. However, it is usually more economical to use fewer fasteners of greater individual resistance.

Lag Screws:

Try 5⁄16″ lag screws 6″ long, penetration = 3¼″. (Length of thread less tip.)

$p = 1800G^{3/2}d^{3/4} = 1800(\sqrt{0.51^3})\sqrt[4]{0.31^3}$

$= 273\#/''$. [*Equation (4a).*]

Pull per screw $= 273 \times 3.25 = 890\#$.

Use $\frac{5000}{890} = 5.6$ *or 6 lag screws (5⁄16″ × 6″).*

Remarks: *The illustration shows the design for lag screws. This problem indicates how the use of lag screws may be made to simplify timber joints. It would be difficult to find space either for 18 nails or 12 drifts bolts.*

inserted into holes about 70 per cent of the root diameter of the screw. The holding power is reduced 25 per cent for lag screws inserted parallel to the grain. Usually a penetration of 10 diameters will develop the tensile strength of the screw in axial withdrawal.

205. Lateral Shear Resistance of Nails and Screws. The values in pounds per nail or screw to be specified for shear resistance of bolts and wood screws are intended to give a factor of safety of about 6.0 against ultimate failure or 1.6 against elastic failure. There is usually an initial inelastic slip of about 0.01 in. Penetration is assumed to be $2/3$ of the length and at least 7 diameters for wood screws. Values of shear resistance as computed from Table 14 should be reduced 25 per cent where unseasoned wood is used. They should be reduced 33 per cent if the screw is inserted parallel to the grain of the wood. The lateral shear resistance of the nail or screw may be increased 25 per cent for a metal-to-timber connection. The values in Table 14 for nails, spikes, and wood screws are for load at any angle to the grain.

Lag screws are inserted in larger holes than wood screws and have a shorter thread. Their resistance to lateral force for the same diameter is less than that of wood screws. Table 14 gives lateral resistance for side-

TABLE 14

FORMULAS FOR SAFE LATERAL RESISTANCE OF NAILS AND SCREWS IN POUNDS*

TIMBER SPECIES	NAILS OR SPIKES (Inserted into side grain)	WOOD SCREWS (Inserted into side grain)	LAG SCREWS (Load ‖ to grain)
Fir or pine, white	$P = 1080d^{3/2}$	$P = 2520d^2$	$P = 1800d^2$
Redwood or cypress	$P = 1350d^{3/2}$	$P = 3240d^2$	$P = 2040d^2$
Elm, gum, soft maple	$P = 1500d^{3/2}$	$P = 3480d^2$	$P = 2280d^2$
Douglas fir, coast or inland	$P = 1650d^{3/2}$	$P = 3960d^2$	$P = 2280d^2$
Southern yellow pine	$P = 1650d^{3/2}$	$P = 3960d^2$	$P = 2280d^2$
Oak, hardwoods	$P = 2040d^{3/2}$	$P = 4800d^2$	$P = 2640d^2$

* P is the total safe lateral load per nail or per screw; d is the shank diameter in inches. For resistances due to increased penetration refer to *National Design Specification for Stress-Grade Lumber and Its Fastenings.*

grain insertion of lag screws when the load is parallel to the grain. For side-grain insertion and load perpendicular to the grain, reduce lag screw values 50 per cent for 1-in. diameter, 33 per cent for $1/2$-in. diameter, and 15 per cent for $5/16$-in. diameter. For loads other than 0 to 90 degrees to the grain use Hankinson's formula, equation (5), which applies to both screws and bolts.

DP32. *Find the number and size of nails, lag screws, and bolts to resist a lateral force of 5000# between a 2″ and a 6″ thickness of southern pine (1400f). Consider possible loads parallel and perpendicular to direction of grain.*

Nails:

For a penetration of ⅔ of the length of the nail into the 6″ timber, the nail should be 6″ long. This requires a 60d nail, Table 13. The lateral resistance of a nail in southern yellow pine (Table 14) is given as

$$P = 1650d^{3/2} = 1650(0.26)^{3/2} = 218\#.$$

Use $\frac{5000}{218} = 23$ *nails (60d).*

This number of nails seems impractical.

Wood or Lag Screws:

From Table 14 we may compute the resistance to shear of a No. 20 wood screw embedded at least 7 diameters in southern pine (d = 0.32″) to be

$$P = 3960d^2 = 3960 \times 0.32^2 = 406\#.$$

Use $\frac{5000}{406} = 13$ *No. 20 wood screws 4½″ long.*

Even 13 screws would be too many for convenient construction.

Bolts:

The allowable shearing force for bolted joints parallel and perpendicular to the grain for southern pine are as given in Table 15. Try ⅝″ bolts.

By Table 15 for a thickness of 2 × 1⅝ = 3″ approx. we obtain bolt values of 1980# and 1000# for bearing parallel and perpendicular to the grain. These values are halved for load applied to one end only of the bolt. Values in Table 15 are for symmetrical loading.

$$P = 0.5 \times 1980 = 990\#.$$

$$Q = 0.5 \times 1000 = 500\#.$$

Use $\frac{5000}{990} = 5$ *bolts for load parallel to the grain, or,*

$\frac{5000}{500} = 10$ *bolts for load perpendicular to the grain.*

Remarks: *Nails would be used only for a temporary structure. Note that nails and screws are not given different values for loads parallel and perpendicular to the grain.*

Bolted Joints in Timber

206. Bearing Pressure Under Bolts. The actual bearing pressure under a bolt is never uniform and becomes extremely variable, as indicated by Fig. 187, for long slender bolts. The action of a bolted timber joint under load is not elastic in the usual sense. There is, instead, a slip which is proportional to the load. *The limit beyond which the slip increases more rapidly than the load is treated as a proportional limit.* Working stresses for shear on bolted joints as given in Table 15 are based upon this limit.

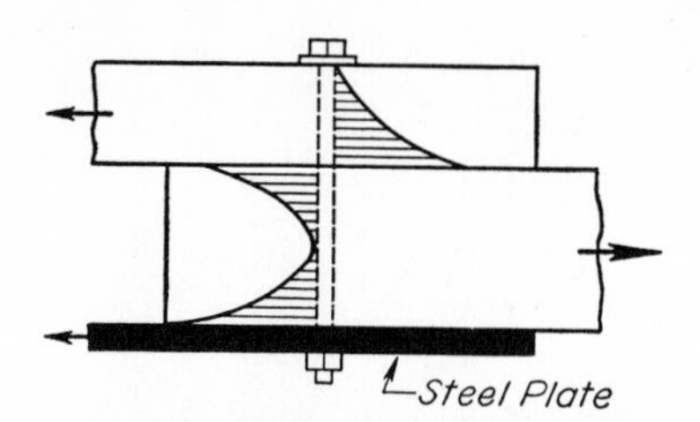

Fig. 187. Variation of Bearing Pressure Under a Bolt.

207. Corrections for Determining Bolt Resistance. The lateral resistance per bolt in Table 15 represents double shear developed by a joint, such as sketch A, where b is the controlling thickness. For single shear, as in sketch B, one must reduce the values from Table 15 by 50 per cent, but the controlling thickness may be taken as $2c$ rather than b. For triple shear the values of Table 15 may be increased 50 per cent.

Unseasoned or Damp Wood. Timber that changes occasionally in moisture content should be discounted 25 per cent with reference to bolt resistance. Continuously wet timber should be discounted 33 per cent. For unseasoned timber, discount bolt values 60 per cent when there are multiple rows of bolts and wood side members.

Metal Side Plates. The safe bolt resistances given in Table 15 can be increased 25 per cent for load parallel to the grain when metal side plates are used. It is not recommended that the values for bearing perpendicular to the grain be increased. Washers are omitted if metal side plates are used. Otherwise, washers are required.

Loads Applied Obliquely to the Grain. The common formula for determining allowable pressure on a bolt or lag screw at an angle to the grain is

$$N = \frac{PQ}{P \sin^2 \theta + Q \cos^2 \theta}. \tag{5}$$

Here, N is the allowable bolt load at the angle θ to the grain, P is the allowable bolt load *parallel* to the grain, and Q is the allowable bolt load *perpendicular* to the grain. The allowable values of P and Q for bolts can be obtained from Table 15, and the value of N follows from equation (5). The example $DP33$ illustrates the use of this formula in a practical design.

DP33. *A tension diagonal is joined to a vertical compression member at an angle of 60 degrees as shown. Design a proper bolted connection with the use of ¼″ gusset plates to develop the net tension value of the diagonal member at 1050 psi stress.*

Materials:

Steel plate, AISC spec. Compression member: 1200c Douglas fir (coast).

Tension member: 1500f Douglas fir (coast). Actual thickness = 3.62″.

Vertical post: 1500f Douglas fir (coast), Same thickness.

Horizontal strut: 1500f Douglas fir (coast). Same thickness.

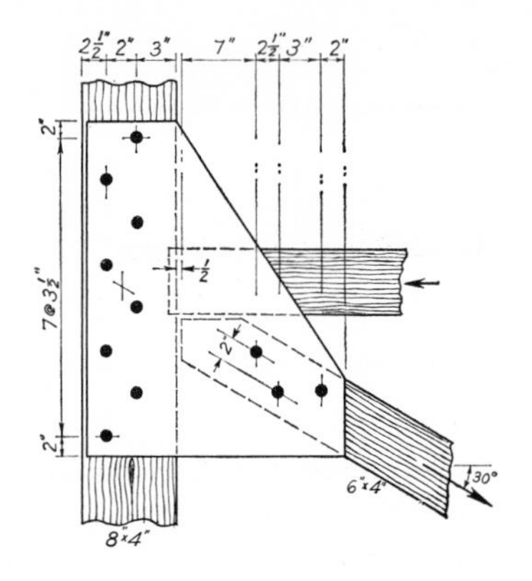

Net Section:

Allow for two 15⁄16″ holes for ⅞″ bolts. (Required because spacing < 8d.)

$A_{net} = (5\frac{1}{2} - 2 \times \frac{15}{16})3\frac{5}{8} = 13.1$ *in.*^{2}

Tension value $= 13.1 \times 1050 = 13{,}700\#$.

Bolt Value ⅞″: *Interpolate between 3″ and 4″ thickness in Table 15.*

Bearing parallel to grain = 3610, or 4510 with metal plates (+25 per cent).

Bearing perpendicular to grain = 1480, not to be increased for metal plates.

$$\text{Bearing at 60 degrees to grain} = \frac{4510 \times 1480}{4510 \times 0.866^2 + 1480 \times 0.5^2} = 1780\#.$$

[N in equation (5).]

Number of bolts required = 13,700 ÷ 1780 = 7.65. Use 8 bolts through post.

Number of bolts in tension member where bearing is parallel to grain = 13,700 ÷ 4510 = 3.03. (Use 3 bolts).

Details: *The details of bolt spacing and margins are arranged to agree with specifications from §208 for bolts of ⅞″ diameter. No connection is shown for the horizontal strut which bears directly against the post.*

TABLE 15

ALLOWABLE LOADS IN POUNDS PER BOLT FOR BOLTED TIMBER JOINTS IN DOUBLE SHEAR

(For all Grades of Douglas Fir, Coast or Inland, and Southern Pine*)

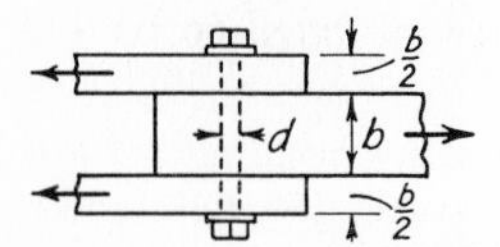

Case A, use $L = b$
Load in lb. $= P$ *or* Q

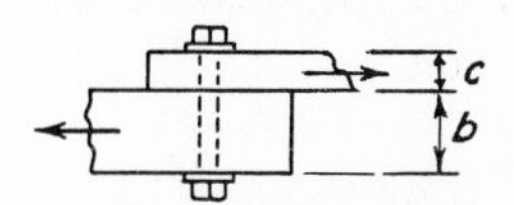

Case B, Use $L = 2c$
Load in lb. $= P/2$ *or* $Q/2$

LENGTH OF BOLT THROUGH MAIN MEMBER, L	DIAM. OF BOLT d	P PARALLEL TO GRAIN LB.	Q PERPENDICULAR TO GRAIN LB.	LENGTH OF BOLT BOLT THROUGH MAIN MEMBER, L	DIAM. OF BOLT d	P PARALLEL TO GRAIN LB.	Q PERPENDICULAR TO GRAIN LB.
1⅝	½	1010	480	6	⅝	2010	1420
	⅝	1290	540		¾	2890	1970
	¾	1550	600		⅞	3940	2410
	⅞	1810	670		1	5140	2680
	1	2070	730		1⅛	6500	2920
2	½	1180	590	8	¾	2890	1840
	⅝	1560	670		⅞	3940	2470
	¾	1910	740		1	5140	3150
	⅞	2230	820		1⅛	6500	3750
	1	2550	890		1¼	8040	4170
3	½	1290	890	10	⅞	3940	2290
	⅝	1980	1000		1	5140	3000
	¾	2660	1120		1⅛	6500	3790
	⅞	3250	1230		1¼	8040	4610
	1	3790	1340				
				11½	1	5140	2850
4	½	1290	1040		1⅛	6500	3660
	⅝	2010	1330		1¼	8040	4490
	¾	2890	1490				
	⅞	3830	1640	12	1	5140	2790
	1	4720	1790		1⅛	6500	3600
					1¼	8040	4450

* For other species of timber consult National *Design Specification of National Lumber Manufacturer's Association.* Values do not change with change in grades.

208. Bolt Spacing and Edge Requirements. Bolts should be spaced at least 4 diameters apart center to center. Net section requirements in tension members may require even a greater lateral spacing. The end margins for a compression member may be 4 diameters from the center of the bolt, but a margin of 7 diameters is recommended for structural tension members to avoid splitting at the end. The edge distance where the load is parallel to the edge need be no more than 1½ diameters, but an allowance of 4 diameters is required if the bolts bear against the wood forming the edge margin. These factors were considered in arranging the detail for the example *DP*33. Bolt holes are assumed to be ¹⁄₁₆ in. larger than the bolt.

Timber Ring Connectors

209. Purpose and Usefulness. The idea of using either metal or wood shear developers between the interior surfaces of timber joints is nearly as old as the use of bolts. Two such devices are shown in Fig. 188. The

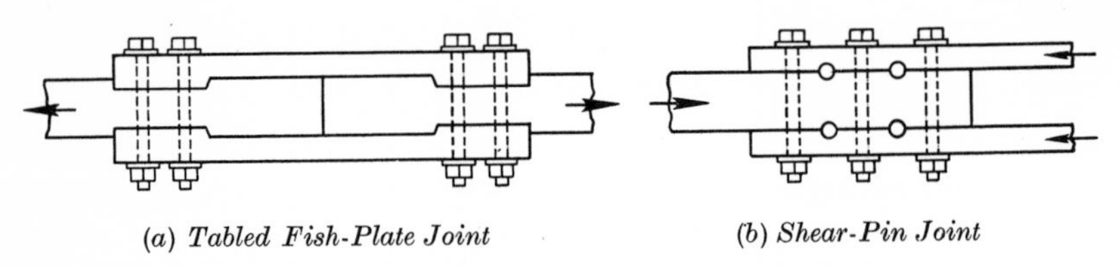

(*a*) *Tabled Fish-Plate Joint* (*b*) *Shear-Pin Joint*

Fig. 188. Obsolete Splices in Timber Members.

tabled fish-plate joint (*a*) is an obsolete form that was replaced at the beginning of this century by the use of shear pins (iron pipes), as illustrated in (*b*).

The modern device to take the place of fish plates and shear pins is the *smooth ring* or *toothed ring connector*. Since 1933 their use has developed extensively in the United States, although they have long been used in Europe and have been available in a few forms for more than half a century. In all of its forms, the modern connector is simply a *shear developer* which takes the place of nails or bolts for shear resistance. Bolts must still be used to hold the joint together, but the bolts are often placed in oversized holes and consequently they can resist little shear, except in one form, known as the "shear-plate" type.

210. Split-Ring Connectors. A split ring of either type shown in Fig. 189(*a*) is introduced between two pieces of timber as shown in (*b*). The grooves for the ring are cut by a special tool. They are slightly larger than the ring, so that the ring must be spread before it is inserted. Thus the ring is tight in its groove and initial slip is reduced to a small factor. These rings are readily available in diameters of 2½ and 4 inches.

Load capacities of split-ring connectors may be corrected for special conditions from the values given in Table 16. An illustration of the use of these values is given in the design examples *DP*34*a* and *DP*35*a*.

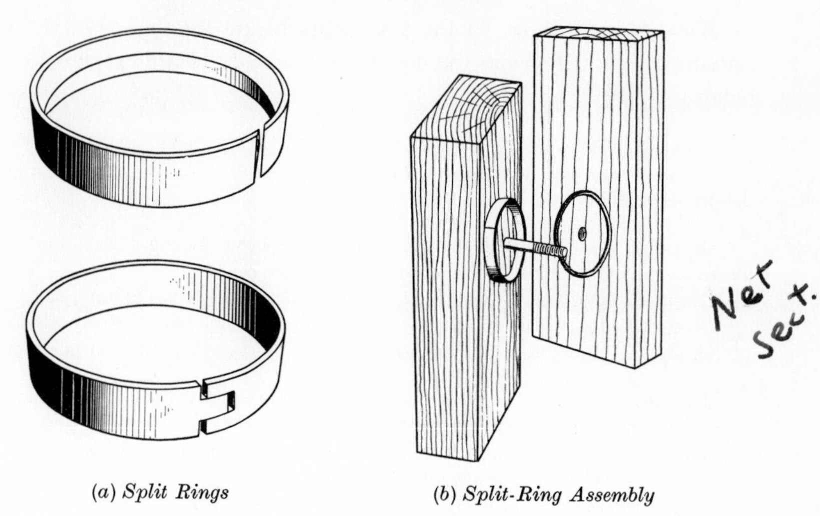

(*a*) *Split Rings* (*b*) *Split-Ring Assembly*

FIG. 189. SPLIT-RING CONNECTORS.

TABLE 16

ALLOWABLE LOAD IN POUNDS FOR ONE SPLIT-RING CONNECTOR AND BOLT IN DOUGLAS FIR OR SOUTHERN PINE (Group B)

Split Ring Diam.	Ring Depth	Bolt Diam.	Edge Dist. from Ring Center		Depth Timber	Allowable Loads			
						Parallel to Grain		Perpendicular to Grain	
			Load ∥	Load ⊥		Rings on One Face of Piece	Rings on Two Faces	Rings on One Face of Piece	Rings on Two Faces
In.	In.	In.	In.	In.	In.	Lb.	Lb.	Lb.	Lb.
					1	2270		1620	
2½	¾	½	1¾	2¾	1⅝	2730	2270	1940	1620
					2+		2730		1940
					1	3510		2440	
4	1	¾	2¾	3¾	1⅝	5260	3690	3660	2570
					2		4250		2960
					2⅝		5160		3600
					3+		5260		3660

* Safe loads on all types of connectors are set to maintain a factor of safety of 4.0 with respect to ultimate or failure loads. The factor of safety is about 1.6 with respect to the elastic limit. Data for safe loads for all connectors have been drawn from tests made at the United States Forest Products Laboratory and at George Washington University.

† Correct for (1) *wood classification*, (2) *moisture content*, (3) *direction of load*, (4) *margins and spacing* as indicated after *Wood Classification* on p. 296.

Wood Classification. Values in Table 16 are for timber of the Group B classification. They may be corrected for other classifications as indicated below.

Group A. 116%; Group B 100%; Group C 83%; Group D 72%.

The standard classifications of the common species of timber grouped for connector design are as follows:

Group A. Hardwoods including oak, maple, pecan, hickory, birch, and beech, plus all dense classifications of Douglas fir and southern pine.

Group B. Douglas fir coast and inland, southern pine, larch, and gum.

Group C. Redwood, cypress, eastern or Sitka spruce, and Norway pine.

Group D. Western red cedar, white and ponderosa pine, fir, and hemlock.

Moisture Content. Test results are obtained on seasoned wood specimens of 15 per cent moisture content. Green wood has about 28 per cent moisture and is often discounted one third for connector design, the same percentage as wood continuously saturated. Between the limits of 15 and 28 per cent moisture content, the discount factor may be approximated by direct proportion based upon a linear variation. This correction is not as essential in the design of split ring connectors as it is for connectors of fixed diameter. In fact, it is not common to introduce a moisture correction for the split-ring type of connector unless the moisture change is very severe.

Duration of Loading. Allowable loads for split-ring connectors may be adjusted for time of loading by use of the factors from Table 10.

Direction of Load. The resistance of a split-ring connector for load perpendicular to the grain is less than the resistance for load parallel to the grain, as is shown by Table 16. The allowable load at an angle θ to the grain may be found from the allowable loads parallel and perpendicular to the grain, P and Q, by Hankinson's formula (5).

Edge Distance. The minimum width of lumber for the 2½-in. and 4-in. connectors is respectively the nominal 4-in. and the nominal 6-in. size. The corresponding minimum edge distances from the outside surface to the cut groove are about ½ in. The unloaded edge distance *from the center of a ring* is 1¾ in. for a 2½-in. ring and 2¾ in. for a 4-in. split ring as given in Table 16. If the load acts at 30 degrees or more to the direction of the grain, the specified load from Table 16 should be reduced to 83 per cent for these minimum margins. No reduction is necessary for a clear margin of 1½ in., while between ½ in. and 1½ in. the reduction of load may be approximated by proportion.

Ring Spacing. Split rings in a single line for load parallel to the line of connectors should be spaced at 6¾ in. center to center for 2½-in. rings and 9 in. center to center for 4-in. rings. If the load is normal to the line of connectors, they may be spaced closer together. The minimum spacing is the diameter of the ring plus 1.0 in., with loads, when acting parallel to the grain, reduced to 75 per cent of those given in Table 16, but a greater spacing is preferred in order that the wood between rings may not be damaged.

End Margin. For 100 per cent value of the connector with tensile loading, the end margins from the center of the split ring should be 5½ in. for 2½-in. rings and 7 in. for 4-in. rings. The minimum clear end distance measured along the grain for a compression member is 1½ in. The safe load should be reduced to 62.5 per cent of Table 16 if the minimum end margin is used.

Minimum Lumber Sizes. The information needed for providing precut grooves for the installation of split ring connectors is collected in Table 17. The minimum sizes given should be increased wherever possible in order to increase connector resistance and to reduce the possibility of splitting the wood.

TABLE 17

LUMBER SIZES FOR SPLIT-RING CONNECTOR DESIGN*

Diameter of Groove			Width of Timber		Edge Margin In.	Groove Depth In.	Ring Depth In.	Thickness of Timber	
Nominal	Inside	Outside	Nominal	Actual				Single Groove	Double Groove
2½ in.	2.56	2.92	(4) in.	3⅝	0.35	0.37	0.75	1⁵⁄₁₆ (1½)	2⅝ (3)
4	4.08	4.50	(6)	5½	0.50	0.50	1.00	1⅝ (2)	2⅝ (3)

* Nominal or commercial sizes of timber are placed in parentheses.

211. Toothed-Ring Connectors. The alligator or toothed ring functions in much the same manner as the split ring, but it is designed for installation without the need for a cut groove. As shown in Fig. 190, the sharp teeth of the alligator connector will cut into the timber if sufficient pressure is applied. The necessary pressure is produced by tightening down on an *alloy steel bolt* of high tensile strength that passes through the center of each ring. The hole for the bolt is drilled $\frac{1}{16}$ in. oversize so that the bolt of alloy steel can easily be removed and replaced by an ordinary steel bolt after the connector has been embedded in the wood. Allowable loads for toothed-ring connectors may be obtained by correcting the values of Table 19 for wood classification, moisture content, direction of load, edge distance, etc. Illustrations are offered in the design problems *DP*34*b* and *DP*35*b*.

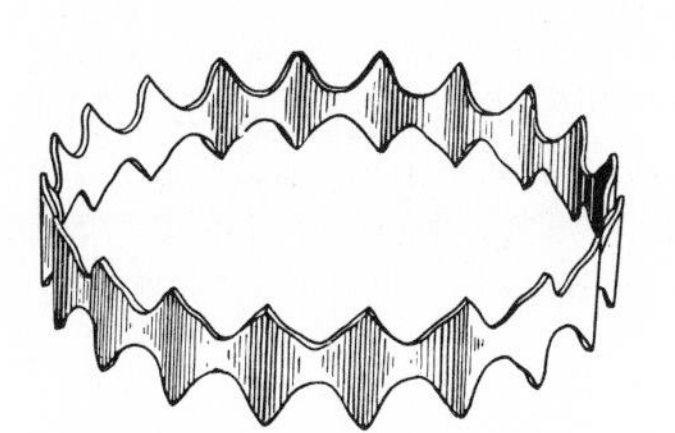

FIG. 190. TOOTHED RING.

TABLE 18

DIMENSIONS OF CIRCULAR DAP FOR INSTALLATION OF RING CONNECTORS

Type	Nominal Diameter	Diameter of Ring O.D.	Groove O.D.	Groove I.D.	Groove Depth
Split Ring	2½ in.	2.82 in.	2.92 in.	2.56 in.	0.375 in.
Split Ring	4	4.39	4.50	4.08	0.50
Shear Plate	2⅝	2.62	2.63	2.25	0.45
Shear Plate	4	4.02	4.03	3.49	0.64

DP34a. *A tension diagonal joins a vertical compression member at an angle of 60 degrees as shown. Design a proper split-ring connection with plywood gussets to develop the net section of the diagonal at 400 psi tensile stress. Seasoned timber and gusset material are of Group A classification.*

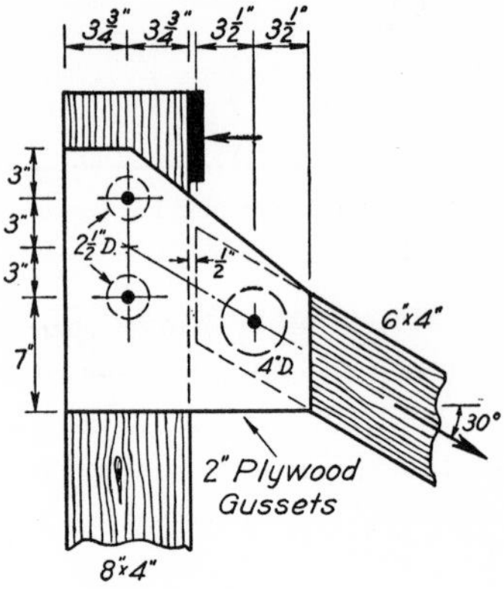

Net Section:

The cross-sectional area removed by the ring groove amounts to only ¼ in.² which is neglected. Deduct hole for the ¾″-bolt. Net width = 5½″ − 13⁄16″.

Diagonal Load:

(5½ − 13⁄16) × 3⅝ × 400 = 6800#.

Ring Values:

Value of 4″ split rings used in pairs. End margin for diagonal is min. std.; use 62.5 per cent of connector value parallel to grain from Table 16 for 3⅝″ timber.

2(0.625 × 1.16 × 5260) = 7700#.

(The factor 1.16 is for wood of Group A classification.)

Load averages 45 degrees to grain for plywood gusset; Ring value in gusset = 2 × 1.16 × 4300 = 10,000#. From equation (5) and Table 16.

$$N = \frac{5260 \times 3660}{5260 \times 0.707^2 + 3660 \times 0.707^2} = 4300\#.$$

Use a pair of 4″ split ring connectors.

Values of 2½″ split rings = 2730# and 1940#, respectively (parallel and perpendicular to grain). Load at 60 degrees to grain controls their design.

$$\text{At 60 degrees to grain, } N = \frac{2730 \times 1940}{2730 \times 0.5^2 + 1940 \times 0.866^2} = 2500\#.$$

Value of two pairs of 2½″ split rings = 4 × 1.16 × 2500 = 11,600#. Increased 16 per cent for Group A timber. Margins and spacing shown are substandard in gusset but acceptable for low loading.

DP34b. *Repeat problem DP34a for toothed-ring connectors with bolts placed through loose holes in Group A timber. Develop the allowable load of 6800#.*

Diagonal Load = 6800# to be resisted in shear by toothed rings.

Load at 45–60 degrees to grain on gussets and post limits connector value.

Try two pairs of connectors on post and on diagonal.

Required resistance per connector = 6800 ÷ 4 = 1700#.

Since this value is for Group A timber, the value in Group B timber would be 1700 ÷ 1.10 = 1550#.

From Table 19 for loads ⊥ to grain the values per connector are 1570# for 2⅝″, and 2320# for 3⅝″. Use two pairs of 2⅝″ rings.

Remarks: *The use of one pair of 4″ ring connectors as shown in the illustration would produce a pin-connected joint that should permit a slight rotation under load.*

TABLE 19

ALLOWABLE LOADS IN POUNDS FOR ONE TOOTHED-RING CONNECTOR AND BOLT IN DOUGLAS FIR OR SOUTHERN PINE (Group B)

Tooth Ring Diam.	Ring Depth	Bolt Diam.	Edge Dist.		Depth Timber	Allowable Loads*			
						Parallel to Grain		Perpendicular to Grain	
			Load ‖	Load ⊥		Ring on One face	Rings on Two Faces	Ring on One Face	Rings on Two Faces
In.	In.	In.	In.	In.	In.	Lb.	Lb.	Lb.	Lb.
					1	1100		840	
2	0.94	½	1¼	2	1⅝	1210	1100	930	840
					2+		1210		930
					1	1650		1260	
2⅝	0.94	⅝	1¾	2½	1⅝	2030	1650	1570	1260
					2		1830		1400
					2⅝+		2030		1570
					1	2150		1720	
					1⅝	2890	2150	2320	1720
3⅜	0.94	¾	2¼	3¼	2		2350		1880
					2⅝		2690		2150
					3+		2890		2320
					1	2590		2060	
					1⅝	3360	2590	2690	2050
4	0.94	¾	2¾	3¾	2		2790		2240
					2⅝		3150		2520
					3+		3360		2690

* Correct for (1) *wood classification,* (2) *moisture content,* (3) *direction of load,* (4) *margins and spacing.*

Wood Classification. Adjust values in Table 19 by using the following factors for correction where the timber classification is other than Group B. (See §210 for the classification of various species of timber.)

Group A 110%; Group B 100%; Group C 90%; Group D 78%.

Moisture Content. Use the same specification as for split-ring connectors, §210. This specification should be applied rigorously to toothed-ring connectors and to other rings of fixed diameter.

Direction of Load. The safe load values of Table 19 for loads applied perpendicularly to the grain may be used for loads at any angle of more than 45 degrees to the direction of the grain. At less than 45 degrees, the safe load value may be obtained by use of Hankinson's formula when the angle of the load to the direction of the grain is doubled.

Margins and Spacing. Minimum margin requirements are about the same as for split-ring connectors, although greater edge distances are desirable because of the splitting action when the connector is installed. Connectors in line with the load should be spaced two diameters apart. If rings must be spaced with ½ in. clearance along the grain, use only 75 per cent of load values from Table 19 for load parallel to the grain but 100 per cent for load perpendicular to the grain.

212. Shear-Plate Connectors. In many cases timbers are connected between steel plates or straps which serve either as gusset plates at the joints, or as splice plates, or which may be brought together on a pin to form a pin-connected joint. Evidently, we need a ring connector of only one half the usual depth for this purpose, but there must be a hub provided for bearing against the bolt. The pressed steel or malleable cast iron connectors shown in Fig. 191 fit into precut grooves to lie flush with the timber. Note Table 18.

TABLE 20

ALLOWABLE LOADS IN POUNDS FOR ONE SHEAR-PLATE UNIT AND BOLT IN DOUGLAS FIR OR SOUTHERN PINE (Group B)

Shear Plate Diam.	Ring Depth	Bolt Diam.	Edge Dist.		Depth Timber	Allowable Loads*			
						Parallel to Grain		Perpendicular to Grain	
			Load ∥	Load ⊥		Ring on One Face	Rings on Two Faces	Ring on One Face	Rings on Two Faces
In.	In.	In.	In.	In.	In.	Lb.	Lb.	Lb.	Lb.
					1⅝	2890	2250	2020	1560
2⅝	0.42	¾	1¾	2¾	2		2730		1910
					2⅝ +		2890		2020
					1⅝	4070		2830	
4[a]	0.62	¾	2¾	3¾	1¾	4360	2910	3040	1680
					2		3240		1880
					2⅝		3800		2210
					3		4140		2400
					3⅝ +		4360		2530

*Correct for (1) *wood classification,* (2) *moisture content,* (3) *direction of load,* (4) *margins and spacing,* (5) *metal side plates* by increasing loads 18, 11, 5 and zero per cent, respectively, for A, B, C, and D timber for 4-in. connector and loads parallel-to-grain, but final adjusted load is still limited by †.

† The maximum shear on a 2⅝-in. shear plate is limited to 2900 lb. and for the 4-in. plate to 4970 lb. with ¾-in. bolts even in Group A timber.

Wood Classification. Adjust the values in Table 20 by using the following factors for correction where the timber is classified as different from Group B. (See §210 for the classification of various species of timber.) Group A, 116%; Group B, 100%; Group C, 83%; Group D, 72%.

Moisture Content. This requirement was discussed in §210 for split-ring connectors. The specification for load reduction with increase of moisture content must be applied rigorously for all connectors of fixed diameter.

Direction of Load. Table 20 gives allowable values for load applied parallel and perpendicular to the grain for shear-plate connectors. The values given for load perpendicular and parallel to the grain may be used in Hankinson's formula to determine the value of the connector for a load at any angle from zero to 90 degrees to the grain.

Margins and Spacing. The specifications that were given for split-ring connectors in §210 may be applied with shear-plate connectors.

They are used singly in a timber-to-metal joint or back to back for a timber-to-timber joint. In either case there is a tight fitting bolt which passes through the central hole and bears on the metal plate or hub. They offer ease of assembly and disassembly. They may be installed before shipment, since they are flush with the face of the timber and can be screwed tightly in place if so desired.

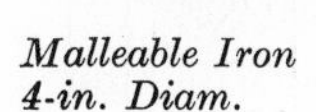

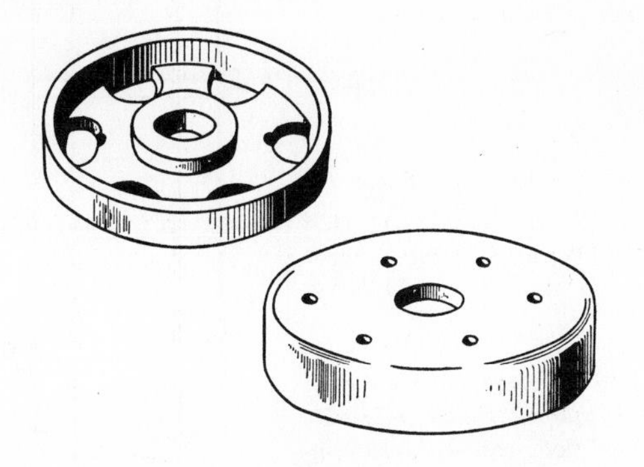

FIG. 191. SHEAR-PLATE CONNECTORS.

The safe load characteristics of shear plate connectors may be obtained by correcting the values given in Table 20. An illustration of the design of a tension member splice using shear plate connectors is given as *DP*35*c*.

TIMBER MEMBERS AND CONNECTIONS

213. Usage. Timber is widely used for all temporary construction, such as concrete form supports, arch centering, trestles, and scaffolding. In the Pacific coast region timber bridge trusses are often used. The heavy timber warehouse designated as "slow burning" or "mill" construction is the most common example of a large timber building. Such structures as elevated bins, mine head frames, wharves, and docks are as commonly constructed of timber as of other materials.

The main structural elements in timber construction are the beam and the post or column. Timber is an excellent material for compression members, since tight knots do not seriously weaken the piece and because *its normal dimensions provide it with proper stiffness* to resist buckling. Timber beams are also satisfactory when they are selected so that only small tight knots are permitted near the extreme fibers. Wood is not ordinarily used for tension members, because steel rods are usually more economical. However, the use of modern connectors has made timber tension members practical.

DP35a. *Design a column splice to transfer 33 per cent of the allowable load through side timbers by the use of split-ring connectors, southern pine, Group B classification timber. Make allowance for 17 per cent moisture content. The splice may have to resist flexure.*

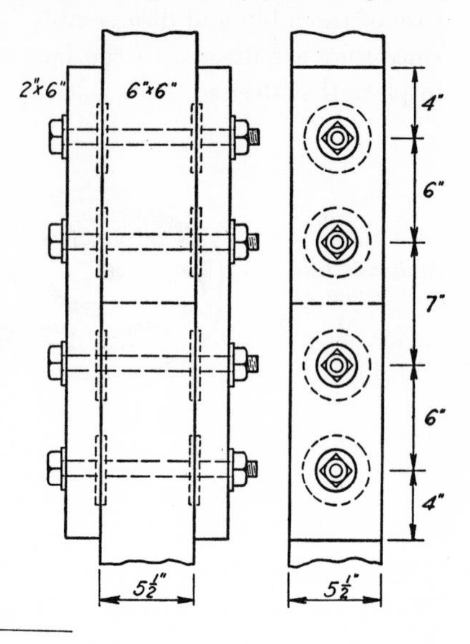

Timber is of 1000c classification. Value of a 6" × 6" post at 1000 psi = 5½ × 5½ × 1000 = 30,200#.

Splice value = 0.33 × 30,200 = 10,000#.

Value of a 4" split ring (Table 16) is 5260#. Reduce to 62.5 per cent for 3½–4" end margins. Splice shown = 4 × 0.625 × 5260 = 13,200# value.

Use two pairs of connectors on each side of the splice. Small moisture change does not weaken split-ring connections.

DP35b. *Redesign the splice of DP35a for use with toothed-ring connectors.*

Diameter. With 4" connectors, edge margins are ¾", or the minimum standard.

Connector value in Group B timber = 3360 × 0.95 = 3200#.

Factor 0.95 is for moisture change, §210.

The sketch shows connectors spaced 1½ diameters apart with full 4" end margins. For these minimum allowances reduce value of toothed-ring splice to 0.67 × 3200 × 4 = 8600#. Three pairs of 4" toothed rings are required.

DP35c. *Design a tension splice for a 3" × 8" redwood timber to develop its net value in tension at 700 psi. Use shear-plate connectors with ¼" steel splice plates.*

Value of timber (¾" bolts) = 2.62(7.5 − 0.81)700 = 12,300#.

Value of 4" connector (Group C timber) = 2 × 3800 × 0.83 = 6300# (pair).

Use two pairs of 4" malleable connectors on each side of the splice. If needed, the connector value for Group C can be increased 5 per cent for steel side plates.

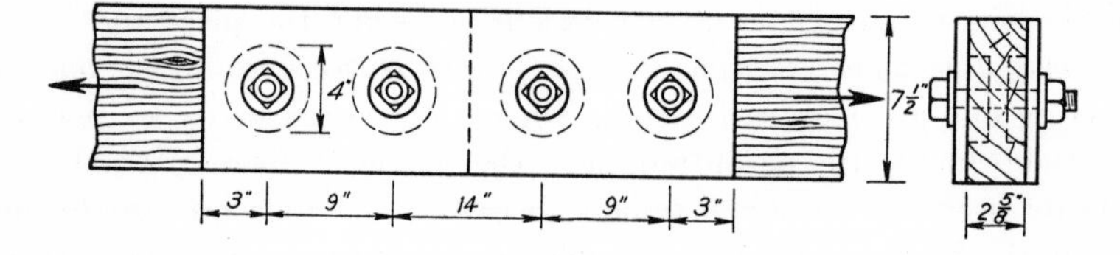

214. Beams and Joists. The important stresses to be considered in the design of timber beams are (1) *fiber stress* in flexure, (2) *beam shear* at the neutral axis, (3) *bearing perpendicular to the grain* at the reactions and under concentrated loads.

Flexural Resistance. The safe moment resistance of a rectangular wood beam may be computed from the ordinary relation

$$M = \frac{fI}{c} = \frac{fbh^2}{6}, \text{ or } bh^2 = \frac{6M}{f}. \tag{6}$$

Of course, f is the allowable stress in flexure of the specified grade of structural timber, and I/c is the section modulus, $bh^2/6$. For design, the value of M is known; the grade of timber is selected tentatively to fix f so that an economical commercial size of timber may be selected. For reasonable economy, the depth of the beam should be at least 50 per cent larger than the breadth, and a greater relative depth is preferred.

Form Relationships. Economy will be obtained by the use of deep narrow timbers. A depth-thickness ratio of from 3 to 6 is common for joists, and a ratio of from 2 to 4 is used for stringers.

Shearing Resistance. The safe shear resistance of a rectangular wood beam may be computed from the *beam-shear formula*

$$H = \frac{VQ}{Ib} = \frac{3}{2}\frac{V}{bh} \text{ (at neutral axis)}, \tag{7}$$

or

$$V = \frac{2}{3}bh. \tag{8}$$

V is the maximum shear or maximum end reaction, and H is the allowable unit shear *parallel to the grain.* Such shear often governs the sizes of wood beams.

Notched Beams. Beams are often notched near the end as shown in Fig. 192. The shearing resistance is reduced thereby not only because the effective depth h in equation (8) must be reduced to d, the remaining depth of the beam, but also to allow for a reduction of the allowable horizontal shear H to H' where

$$H' = Hd/h. \tag{9}$$

This relationship has been established by tests at the Forest Products Laboratory.

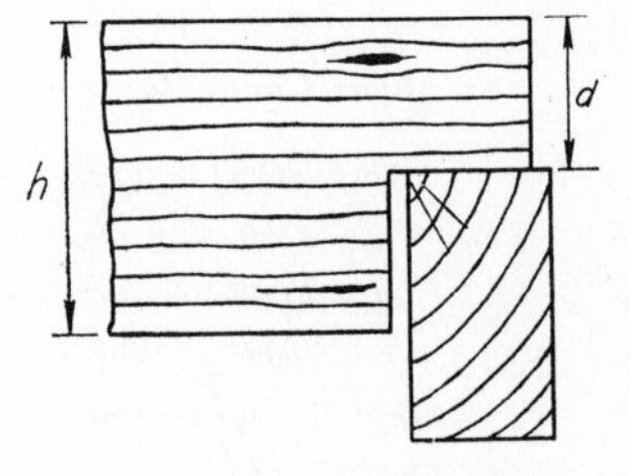

Fig. 192. End Notch.

Bearing Resistance. The normal values of compression perpendicular to the grain apply for end bearing areas and for interior bearing areas more than 6 in. in length. *Shorter interior areas* may be loaded more heavily. The increase in allowable compression perpendicular to the grain may be obtained by multiplying the allowable unit bearing stress by the factor $(L + 0.375) \div L$, where L is the length of bearing. Such formulas as this one and equation (9) cannot be derived from theory. Instead, they are derived empirically to express the results of tests.

DP36. *Design a built-up beam from 6″ × 8″ southern pine timbers (1600f dense structural) to carry a uniform load of 750#/′ on a 20′ span. Timber, being dense, is classified as Group A.*

Beam Section:

Weight of beam	*Estimate weight at 50#/′.*
Bending moment	$M_{max.} = \frac{1}{8} \times 800 \times 20^2 \times 12 = 480{,}000''\#$.
Section modulus	$S = 480{,}000/1600 = 300$.
Dimensions.	*For* $b = 7\frac{1}{2}''$, $h = \sqrt{\frac{6 \times 300}{7.5}} = 15.5''$.
Weight of beam	*Use three 6″ timbers;* $h = 3 \times 5\frac{1}{2} = 16\frac{1}{2}''$. *Nominal size 8″ × 18″, weight = 35#/′.*
Reaction or end shear	$V_{max.} = (750 + 35)10 = 7850\#$.
Horizontal shear.	$H(max.) = \frac{3}{2}\frac{V}{bh} = \frac{3}{2} \times \frac{7850}{7.5 \times 16.5} = 95$ *psi.* (*Allowable shear = 105 psi, Table 9.*)

H on planes of lamination at reaction obtained from beam-shear formula,

$$\frac{VQ}{Ib} = \frac{7850 \times 7.5 \times 5.5 \times 5.5}{\frac{1}{12} \times 7.5 \times 16.5^3 \times 7.5} = 85 \text{ psi.}$$

Shear per lineal foot = $85 \times 12 \times 7.5 = 7650\#$.

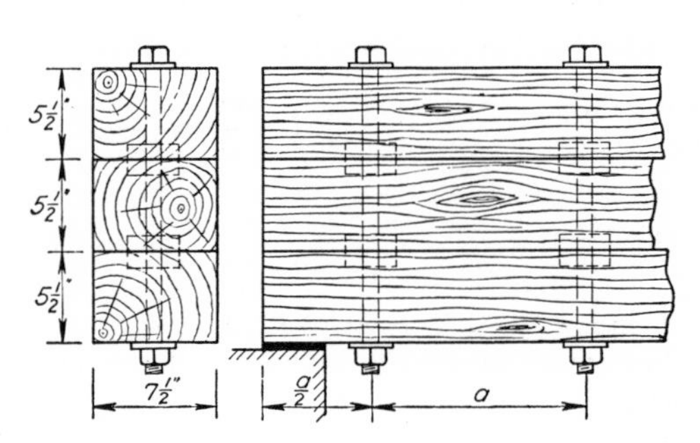

Shear Connectors:

Connectors may be chosen and spaced as follows for use with ¾″ bolts:

(*a*) *Split-ring type*	4″*d.* @	$(1.16 \times 5260 \div 7650)12 = 9\frac{1}{2}''$ *c. to c.*
(*b*) *Toothed-ring type*	4″*d.* @	$(1.10 \times 3360 \div 7650)12 = 6''$ *c. to c.*
(*c*) *Shear-plate type*	4″*d.* @	$(max.\ 4970 \div 7650)12 = 8''$ *c. to c.*

Only the split ring meets standard 9″ spacing. Spacing may be doubled at the quarter point if the uniform load is fixed in position.

End Bearing:

For 1600f dense southern pine, compression perpendicular to the grain is limited to 455 psi.

Bearing length = $7850 \div (7.5 \times 455) = 2.3''$. *Use a 3″ × 7½″ bearing plate attached to beam with countersunk screws.*

215. Built-up Beams. Timber beams may be built up of planks placed side by side and bolted, nailed, or glued together. Figure 193 shows how a beam constructed with vertical laminations (five planks 2 in. by 12 in.) was bolted together for testing in the Forest Products Laboratory. This beam was found to be as strong in flexure as a structural timber of comparable size.

The use of built-up beams is increasing (1) due to the growing shortage of large timber sections that are reasonably free from defects, and (2) because a consistently strong beam section may be manufactured by orienting timber planks for maximum strength as parts of the beam section desired.

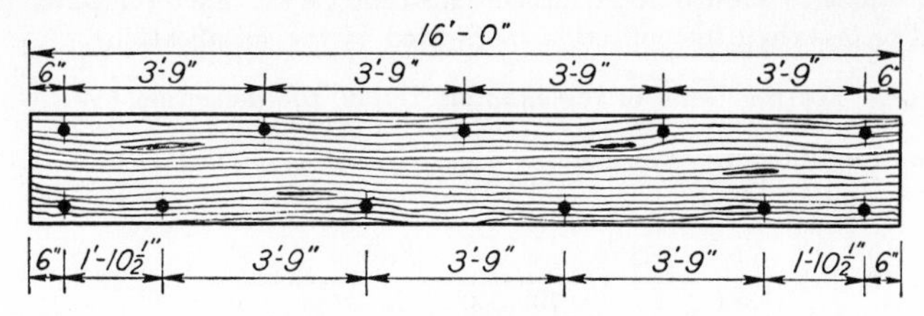

FIG. 193. BOLT SPACING OF LAMINATED BEAMS USED IN TESTS AT THE U.S. FOREST PRODUCTS LABORATORY.

Beams may also be built up with two or more *horizontal laminations.* The use of such beams cannot be recommended unless they are constructed with proper shear developers, such as modern connectors, between successive laminations or are of laminated glued lumber, as described in §201. The design of proper shear developers is not complicated, since the horizontal shear between laminations can be found by use of the beam-shear formula ($H = VQ/Ib$) and the safe load on modern connectors has been given in Tables 16 to 20. This design process is illustrated by the example *DP*36.

216. Buckling and Deflection. Beams that are narrow and deep show a tendency toward lateral buckling and failure by *torsion.* If the compression surface is restrained against lateral deflection, such failure cannot occur. The total *buckling load* for a simply supported beam where the ends are supported laterally, but are not fixed by being "built in" to a wall, is

$$W = \frac{28.3\sqrt{EI'GK'}}{L^2}. \tag{10}$$

In this expression, I' is the moment of inertia of the beam about its vertical axis or $hb^3/12$, G is the torsional modulus of rigidity which is approximately $E/16$, and K' is a factor similar to I' which varies from $hb^3/4$ to $hb^3/3$ as the depth-breadth ratio increases from 2.0 to ∞. Hence, we may write an expression for W', the *safe load with a factor of safety against buckling of about 6 or 7,*

$$W = \frac{2EI'}{L^2} = \frac{hb^3E}{6L^2}. \tag{11}$$

For the example *DP*36, this formula would give a safe total load of

$$W' = \frac{16.5 \times 7.5^3 \times 1{,}600{,}000}{6 \times 240^2} = 32{,}000 \text{ lb.}$$

The actual load is only $785 \times 20 = 15{,}700$ lb. Therefore, the beam will not be endangered by lateral buckling.

Deflections of Wood Beams. The usual formulas for deflection may be applied with the use of the values of E as given in Table 9 or 11. The computed deflection, however, does not represent the result to be expected after *time yield* has taken place. Such yielding will be especially marked for timber which is placed green and which seasons gradually under load. It is common to double the value of the dead loading for use in deflection computations to allow in some measure for time yield. Such computed deflections should then be less than the deflections permitted by the specifications.

Example. For the beam of the example *DP*36, the deflection $\left(\frac{5}{384}\frac{wL^4}{EI}\right)$ will be computed and doubled to represent the approximate ultimate deflection including an allowance for time yielding.

$$\Delta = 2 \times \frac{5}{384} \times \frac{785}{12} \times \frac{240^4}{1{,}760{,}000 \times 1/12 \times 7.5 \times 16.5^3} = 1.13 \text{ in.}$$

Since this deflection is 1/212 times the span while 1/360 is the limitation set for beams, particularly those to which plaster is attached, this deflection would probably need to be decreased by deepening the beam.

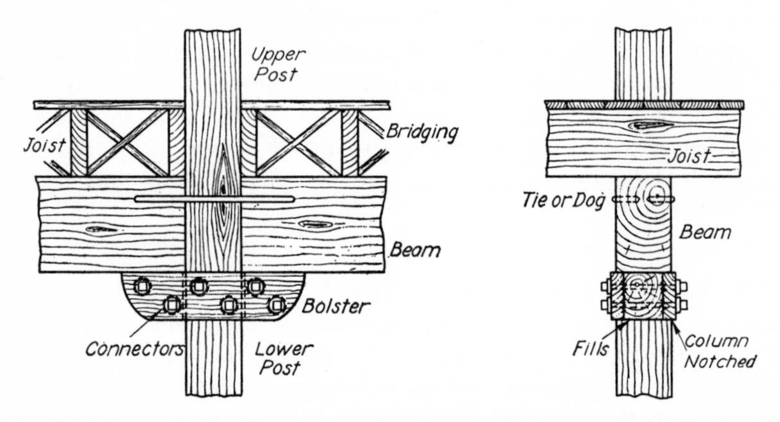

Fig. 194. Satisfactory Structural Detail that is Wasteful of Headroom.

217. Beam and Column Details. Shrinkage occurs in all timber. This influence may be particularly serious where the load is applied perpendicularly to the grain. For instance, Fig. 194 illustrates a beam-to-column connection arranged to let the upper and lower posts bear directly on each other. If, instead, the *bolster* is placed in between the upper and lower post, the bolter is in compression across the grain. Its normal shrinkage and crushing will permit considerable settlement of the upper floor of the building. This objectionable settlement will be exaggerated by bringing the beams together between the upper post and the top of the bolster, since the thickness of wood acting in compression across the grain is thereby increased. The joist hangers of Fig. 195 save headroom equal to the depth of the joists.

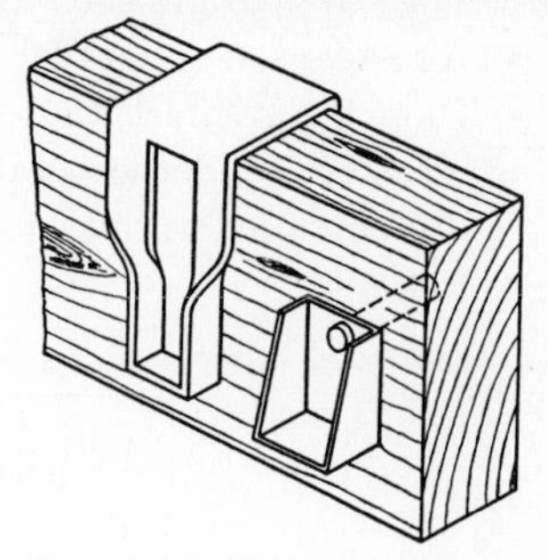

FIG. 195. JOIST HANGERS.

Welded Beam Seat. Simple column caps and beam seats of welded steel can be made as shown in Fig. 196. Patented caps of many types are also available. The steel column cap and beam seat permits direct bearing of the upper and lower posts through the metal cap and provides stability by allowing an adequate seat for the beams. It is advisable to tie the two beams together across the post with a steel *strap or dog* so that the building cannot separate under severe vibration, which might drop a beam from its seat. In the other direction, a tie detail should be arranged between the ends of the joists and the beams, or else tie rods must be run through the building.

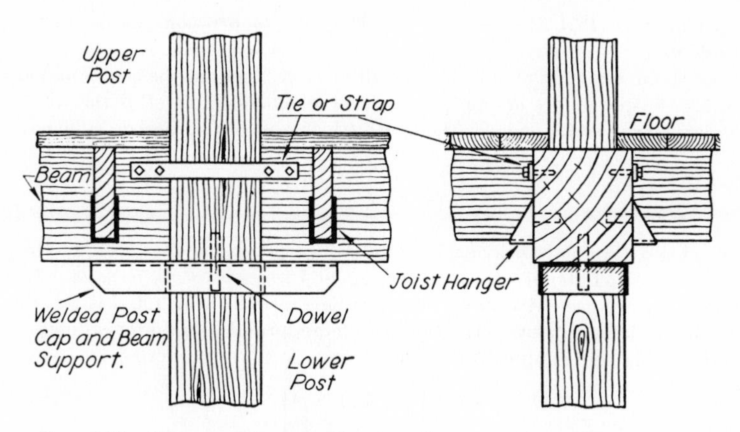

FIG. 196. USE OF WELDED COLUMN CAP AND JOIST HANGERS TO SAVE HEADROOM.

Pintels in Mill Construction. An objection to the use of steel beam seats and exposed ties and joist hangers is that such thin metal is quickly weakened by fire. *Heavy timber construction* with all of the metal connectors enclosed within the timber itself burns very slowly and has an excellent fire rating. The use of a pintel, as illustrated by *DS*37 provides better fire resistance than the detail of Fig. 196 because the cast iron sections are thick and are not fully exposed.

218. Columns and Posts. As has been shown by Table 9, structural timber is classified into stress grades for use as compression members and posts. The stress grade such as 1200c, 1400c, etc., refers to the permissible unit compressive stress parallel to the grain for short compression members; that is, where the greatest length-depth ratio, L/d, is less than 12. For members of greater slenderness ratio, a column formula should be applied. Some early column formulas for wood members that are now seldom used were as follows:

$$\frac{P}{A} = \frac{c}{1 + \dfrac{L^2}{1000d^2}}, \quad \text{and} \quad \frac{P}{A} = c - 10\frac{L}{d}. \tag{12}$$

where c is the allowable compressive stress parallel to the grain for a short strut. The column formula recommended in the *National Design Specification of the National Lumber Manufacturer's Association* is of the Euler type; i.e.,

$$\frac{P}{A} = \frac{\pi^2 E}{2.73(L/r)^2}. \tag{13}$$

For a rectangular cross-section this column formula becomes

$$\frac{P}{A} = \frac{\pi^2 E}{33(L/d)^2} = \frac{0.30E}{(L/d)^2}. \tag{14}$$

The upper limit on P/A is, of course, the allowable compression parallel to the grain from Table 9.

For a column made up of two timbers with spacer blocks at the center and at 0.1 L from each end (spacers are *at* the ends of truss members) where L is the total length between lateral restraints and d is the depth (thickness) of one timber in inches

$$\frac{P}{A} = \frac{0.75E}{(L/d)^2}. \tag{14a}$$

The column formula occurring in standard specifications that was developed by the Forest Products Laboratory is known as a *fourth power parabolic formula.* It is used for columns of intermediate stiffness or slenderness ratio for which L/d is less than the critical value K defined below. Hence, this column formula is used for ordinary design, the Euler formula being applied to slender struts.

$$\frac{P}{A} = c\left[1 - \frac{1}{3}\left(\frac{L/d}{K}\right)^4\right], \tag{15}$$

where
P = total load in pounds,
A = area of cross-section in square inches,
c = allowable unit stress in compression parallel to the grain, Table 9,
L = unsupported length in inches,
d = least dimension of post in inches,

$$K = \frac{\pi}{2}\sqrt{\frac{E}{6c}} \text{ for any grade or species and} \tag{16}$$

E = modulus of elasticity.

For slender columns, where L/d is greater than the critical value K, an Euler formula is applied

$$\frac{P}{A} = \frac{\pi^2 E}{36(L/d)^2}. \tag{17}$$

In *AASHO* specifications the denominator constant is reduced from 36 to 30. It is 33 under *NLMA* specifications. See equation (14) above. The upper limit to be set on slenderness is that L/d shall not exceed 50. The use of these column formulas is illustrated by the example *DP*37.

Column Design. The procedure in designing a timber column is first to choose the stress grade needed, which may be controlled by general requirements; for example, the recommended practice of the *AREA* is as given in Table 21. Then the value of K is obtained from equation (16)

TABLE 21

SPECIFICATION FOR BRIDGE AND CONSTRUCTION TIMBER

(*AREA* Recommendations)

COMBINATION AND HOWE TRUSS SPANS	
(*a*) Compression Members	1200c Structural Posts and Timbers
(*b*) Tension Members	1600*f* or 1400*f* Structural Joist and Plank
(*c*) Diagonals Subject to Reversal of Stress	1200c Structural Posts and Timbers
(*d*) Floor Beams (*e*) Stringers	1800*f* or 1600*f* Structural Beams and Stringers
(*f*) Deck Plank	No. 1 Dimension
(*g*) Bridging	No. 2 or No. 3 Boards
BUILDINGS—HEAVY FRAME CONSTRUCTION	
(*a*) Foundation Timbers (Sleepers)	1400*f* or 1200c Structural Posts and Timbers
(*b*) Posts and Columns	1400*f* or 1200c Structural Posts and Timbers
(*c*) Sills	1400*f* or 1200*f* Structural Joist and Plank
(*d*) Beams, Stringers, Girders, Purlins	
4 inches and thinner	1600*f* or 1400*f* Structural Joist and Plank
5 inches and thicker	1600*f* or 1400*f* Structural Beams and Stringers
(*e*) Joists and Headers	1600*f* or 1400*f* Structural Joist and Plank
(*f*) Bridging	No. 1 or No. 2 Boards or Dimension
(*g*) Subflooring	No. 2 or No. 3 Boards, or No. 2 Dimension

and is substituted into equation (15). Here the factor L/d enters, and it must be approximated by use of the designer's best judgment (enhanced by scratch calculations) as to the approximate area of cross-section that will be required for an estimated value of P/A. The resulting computed value of P/A is the working stress from which an actual cross-sectional area can be selected. This gives rise to an actual value of L/d which makes it possible to revise the value of P/A from equation (15). Thus the design of a timber column becomes a "guess and check" process similar to the

DP37. *Design a column for a ceiling height of 20′ to carry a load of 125,000#. Design a cast iron pintel to pass through a 14″ × 16″ beam and support the 10″ × 10″ column above to avoid compression of beams across the grain.*

Size of Section:

Materials. *Use 1200c timber,* $E = 1{,}650{,}000$.
Use gray cast iron for pintel at 12,000 psi compression.
Column formula. Apply equations (15), (16), and (17).
Approx. column size. At 1000 psi the area required would be 125 in.^{2}
Try nominal dimensions of 12″ × 12″.
Ratio $L/d = 20 \times 12 \div 11.5 = 20.8$.

$$\text{Constant } K = \frac{\pi}{2}\sqrt{\frac{E}{6c}} = 1.57\sqrt{\frac{1{,}650{,}000}{6 \times 1200}} = 23.7. \text{ [Equation (16).]}$$

Since L/d *is less than* K, *the column design is controlled by equation (15).*

$$P/A = c\left[1 - \frac{1}{3}\left(\frac{L/d}{K}\right)^4\right] = 1200\left[1 - \frac{1}{3}\left(\frac{20.8}{23.7}\right)^4\right] = 970 \text{ psi.}$$

Allowable Loads:

$970 \times 11.5 \times 11.5 = 128{,}000\#$.
Load on pintel = value of 10″ × 10″ column.
Ratio $L/d = 20 \times 12 \div 9.5 = 25.3$.
Since L/d *is larger than* K, *equation (17) applies.*

$$P/A = \frac{\pi^2 E}{36(L/d)^2} = 0.275\,\frac{1{,}650{,}000}{25.3^2} = 710 \text{ psi.}$$

Allowable load $= 710 \times 9.5 \times 9.5 = 64{,}000\#$. *This is the pintel load.*

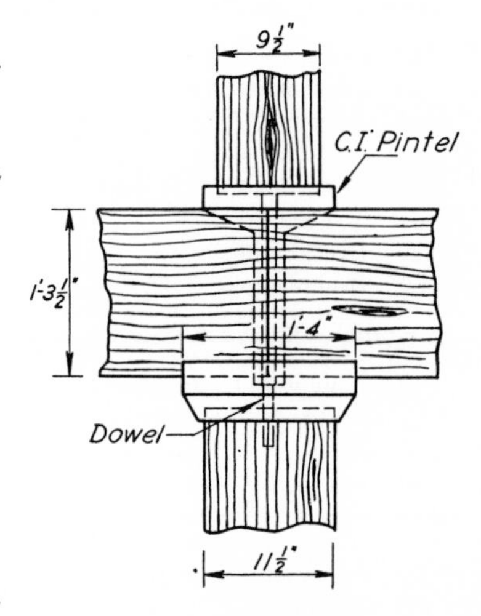

Pintel Design:

$$\text{Area of pintel} = \frac{64{,}000}{12{,}000} = 5.31 \text{ in.}^2$$

Try a pipe stem 3″ O.D. and 1½″ I.D.

$$\text{Area} = \frac{\pi}{4}(3^2 - 1.5^2) = 5.3 \text{ in.}^2$$

The column cap should be flared from 14″ × 14″ to 16″ × 16″ to receive the 14″ beam and bear on the 12″ column to which it should be doweled.

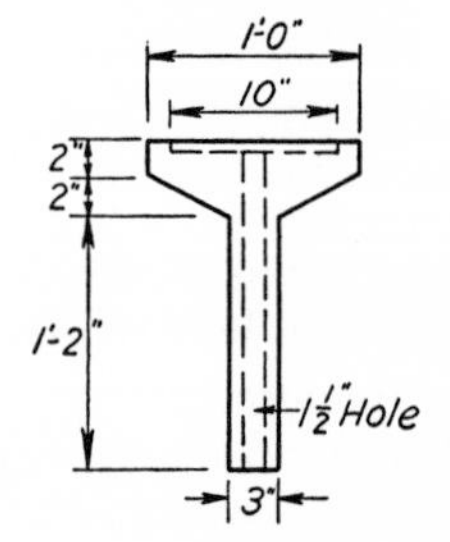

Remark: *By NLMA specifications both columns in this design would be controlled by equation (14)* $P/A = 0.3E/(L/d)^2$.

procedure followed for any long compression member. If the timber is so stiff that $L/d < 12$, a direct design is possible by use of the unreduced working stress for compression parallel to the grain. A relatively great reduction of the allowable stress will be necessary for long slender columns controlled by the Euler formula (14) or (17). By *NLMA* specifications formulas (14) and (14a) are used to control columns of all L/d ratios. This simplifies the process of design. These points are illustrated by the example *DP*37.

219. Tension Resistance of Timber. Since structural joist or stringer timbers are selected for flexural resistance, these classifications can also be used for built-up or even single-piece tension members. The availability of modern connectors makes the use of wood tension members practical. Structural joist or stringer timber is selected so that knots near the edges are limited to small sizes. However, large knots are permitted near the neutral axis of the timber, covering as much as 40 per cent of the face width for some species. (See Table 22.)

TABLE 22

ALLOWABLE PERCENTAGE OF FACE WIDTH COVERED BY KNOT*

	Classification	Joist and Plank	Beam and Stringer
1800*f*	Dense Douglas Fir, Coast or Inland	28%	18%
	Dense Southern Pine, Long or Shortleaf	28	18
1600*f*	Close-grained Douglas Fir, Coast	28	18
	Close-grained Douglas Fir, Inland	25	13
	Dense Southern Pine, Long or Shortleaf	32	25
	Close-grained Redwood	19	5
1400*f*	Tidewater Red Cypress	26	15
	Dense Longleaf Southern Pine	38	32
	Close-grained Redwood	25	14
1200*f*	Douglas Fir, Inland	35	26
	Dense Shortleaf Southern Pine	43	38
	Close-grained Redwood	32	24

* Reduce allowable stresses in flexure by the percentage given to obtain working stresses in tension where timbers cannot be selected to eliminate large knots.

Timber for use as tension members should preferably be restricted as to defects *in any position* in the same way that defects in joists and stringers are limited near the heavily stressed fibers within the middle half of the length. If such selection is not possible, it seems desirable to reduce the allowable stresses in flexure by the percentages given in Table 22 to obtain reasonable working stresses in tension.

Net Section. It is necessary to design tension members upon the basis of the net section after bolt holes have been deducted. The author recommends that *all holes on a zigzag line* be deducted from a right cross-section provided that the slope of the zigzag line is at no point greater than 45 degrees to the right section. The fibrous nature and weak shear resistance of timber *along the grain* dictates a more severe deduction than has been common for steel members.

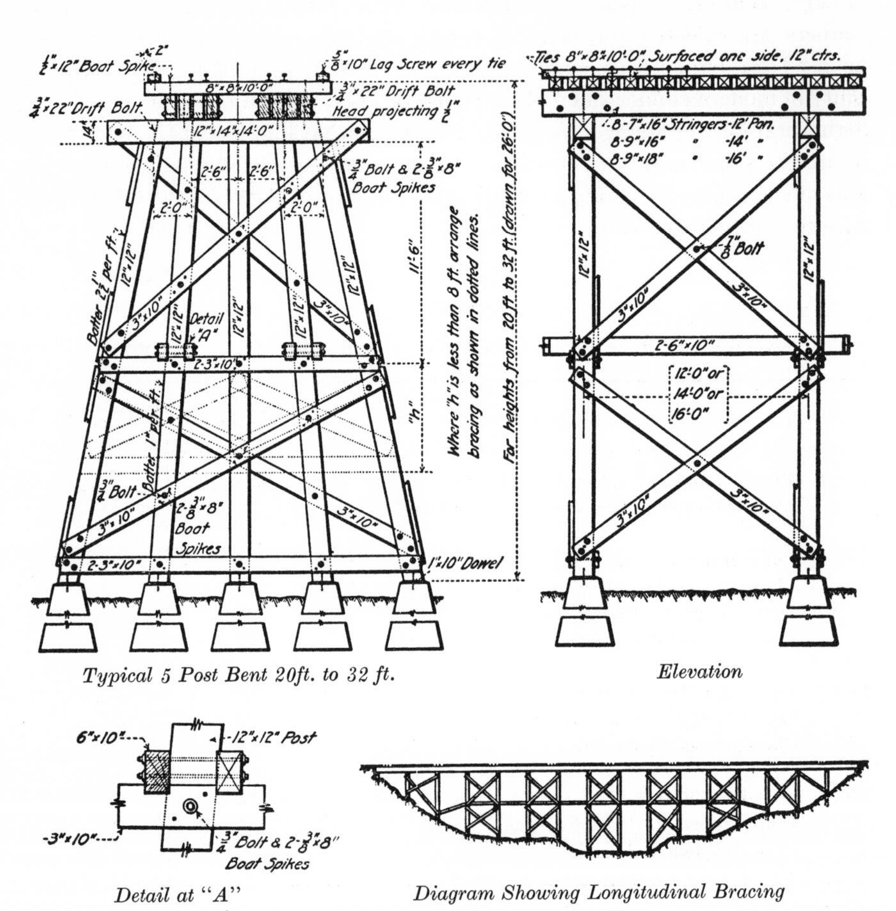

Fig. 197. *AREA*, E-60, 5-Post Bent for Open Deck Framed Trestle.

Structures of Timber

220. Timber Trestles. Perhaps the most common use that has been found for timber as an important modern structural material is in pile trestles for railroad work. The details have been standardized rather carefully by the American Railway Engineering Association. The illustration of Fig. 197 shows the layout for a typical trestle. The two-panel bent is limited to a height of 32 ft. Heights for 6-panels may exceed 80 ft. The members of Fig. 197 are shown merely bolted together. Added strength and stiffness can be provided cheaply by placing toothed-ring or split-ring connectors around those bolts that provide strength.

221. Design of Timber Roof Trusses. Two standard roof-truss designs are shown in Fig. 198. The upper structure is of Howe type for a flat roof span of 60 ft. Its depth is 5 ft.-5 in. at the end and 6 ft.-3 in. at the center of the span. It was designed for a uniform load of 720 lb. per lineal foot of truss including its own weight. This design may be checked by assuming the use of the lowest grade of dense structural southern pine from Table 9 (No. 2 dense SR for 3-in. thickness) and by applying the *NLMA* specifications to determine the strengths of members using equation (14a) for compression. Joints are formed by 4-in. split rings and $\frac{3}{4}$-in. bolts.

Checking the Design of a Howe Roof Truss (Fig. 198). It will be sufficient to check the design of the center member of the upper chord and of the diagonal in the second panel from the end of the truss along with its end connections. The truss depth is 5 ft.-5 in. at the end and 6 ft.-3 in. at mid-span. Its span is 60 ft.-0 in.

Check on Compressive Chord Member at Midspan.

This member is composed of two timbers 3 in. $\times$ 10 in. with spacer blocks.

Moment at mid-span $= 1/8 \times 720 \times 60^2 \times 12 = 3{,}900{,}000$ in-lb.

Stress in chord member at mid-span $= 3{,}900{,}000 \div 6.25 \times 12 = 52{,}000$ lb.

Chord area at mid-span (two timbers 3 in. $\times$ 10 in.) $= 2 \times 2.62 \times 9.5 = 50$ in.^{2}

Unit compressive stress in chord $= 52{,}000 \div 50 = 1040$ psi.

For No. 2 dense stress-rated southern pine the allowable compression parallel to the grain is 1050 psi (Table 9). Assuming that lateral bracing will be attached at panel points through the roof joists, L/d for each individual top chord timber becomes $7.5 \times 12 \div 2.62 = 34.2$. Then by equation (14*a*)

$$\text{Allowable } P/A = \frac{0.75E}{(L/d)^2} = \frac{0.75 \times 1{,}760{,}000}{34.2^2} = 1120 \text{ psi.} \quad (> c = 1050)$$

The actual allowable stress is therefore 1050 psi which checks closely with the working stress of 1040 psi.

Chord Flexure. It will be noted on Fig. 198 that the joint forces at some joints do not intersect at a point, e.g., the center joint of the upper chord. The resulting local bending moment at a point of lateral restraint, acting in the plane of the truss, will not induce lateral buckling but the combined stress should not exceed the allowable flexure stress f, which is 1400 psi for No. 2 dense southern pine. At the center joint of the upper chord the eccentric moment producing chord flexure is at most one half of a panel load times 6 in. or $M_e = 6 \times 2700 = 16{,}200$ in-lb. The resulting flexural stress is

$$16{,}200 \div (\tfrac{1}{6} \times 2 \times 2.62 \times 9.5^2) = 205 \text{ psi.}$$

Hence the maximum fiber stress at mid-span is $1040 + 205 = 1245$ psi (< 1400).

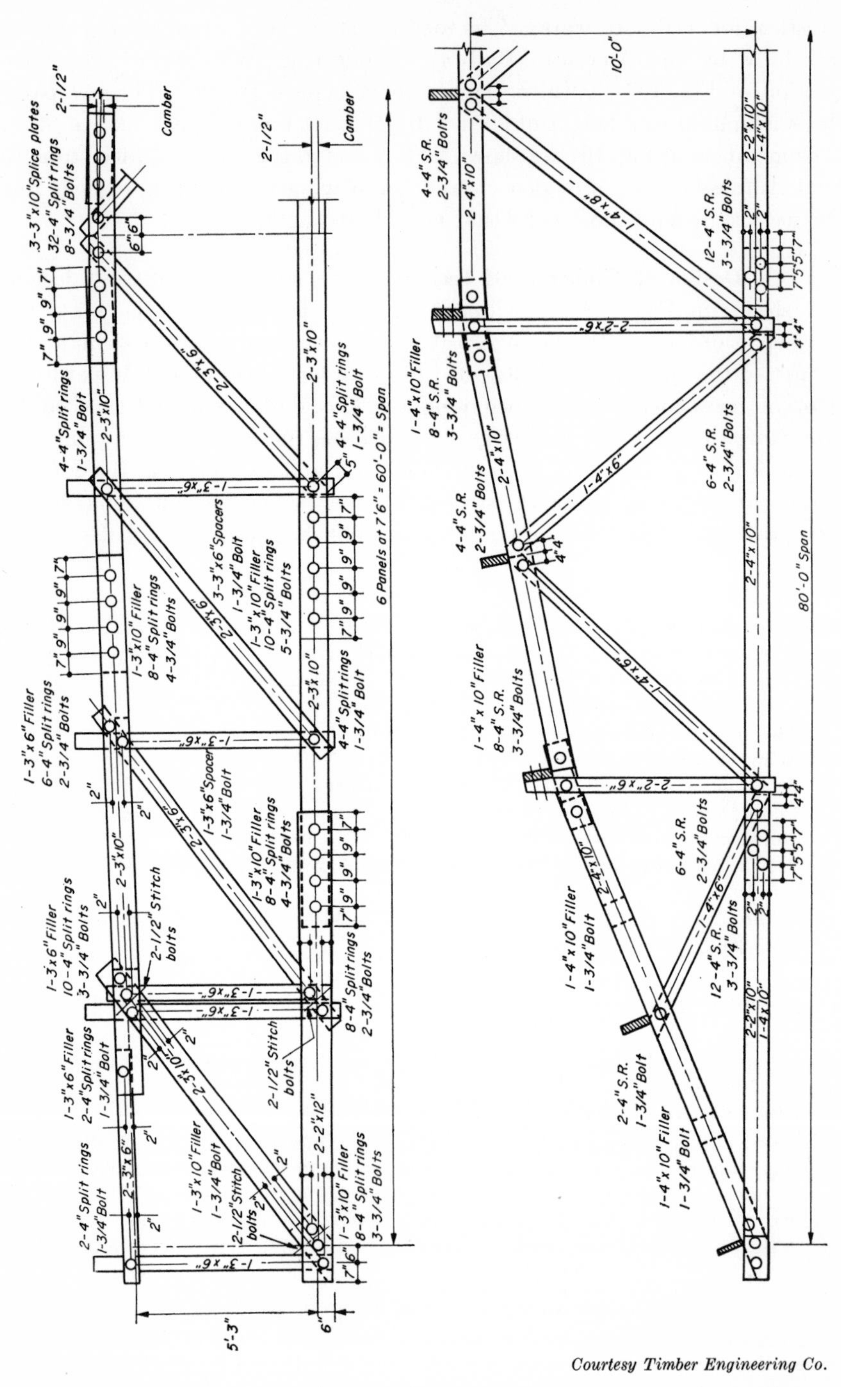

Courtesy Timber Engineering Co.

FIG. 198. FLAT HOWE TRUSS 60-FT. SPAN AND 80-FT. BOWSTRING TRUSS.

Check on Diagonal Member in Panel 2.
This member is composed of two timbers 3 in. × 6 in. with spacer blocks.

Maximum shear in panel 2 = 2.5 × 720 × 7.5 = 13,500 lb.

Force in diagonal = 13,500 × 1.63 = 22,000 lb. This neglects the small shear resisted by the upper chord.

Min. L/d for 3-in. × 6-in. timber for full 9 ft.-6 in. length of the diagonal = 9.5 × 12 ÷ 2.62 = 43.4.
By equation (14*a*)

$$\text{Allowable } P/A = \frac{0.75 \times 1{,}760{,}000}{(43.4)^2} = 705 \text{ psi.}$$

Then by equation (14) for $L/d = 9.5 \times 12 \div 5.5 = 20.7$ (for 5.5-in. width of timber)

$$\text{Allowable } P/A = \frac{0.3 \times 1{,}760{,}000}{(20.7)^2} = 1230 \text{ psi. } (> c = 1050)$$

Actual $P/A = 22{,}000 \div (2 \times 2.62 \times 5.5) = 760$ psi.
Since this member would be 8 per cent overstressed under *NLMA* specifications, it will be noticed that its length has been shortened in Fig. 198 by use of dual end ring connectors. Shortening the length L from 9.5 ft. to 9.0 ft. increases the allowable stress to 780 psi, which is above the actual P/A stress.

Check on Split-ring End Connection for Diagonal in Panel 2.
This member is composed of two timbers 3 in. × 6 in. with spacer blocks.

Force in diagonal = 22,000 lb.

For six 4-in. split rings the load per ring = 3700 lb.
From Table 16 the value of one 4-in. split ring in 2⅝-in. timber of Group B where rings are used on both faces of the timber is 5160 lb. Hence the split-ring connectors will more than develop the value of the diagonal investigated.

Conclusion. From an inspection of the member sizes and their connections it appears that the chord and web members checked are typically stressed as high or higher than other chord and web members. It is concluded therefore that the design of the 60-ft. Howe truss using 1050*c* timber is a reasonably balanced design for a loading of 720 lb. per lineal ft. of span. Depending upon the condition of loading (duration, wet or dry, etc., Table 10) the truss checked might be given a slightly higher or somewhat lower load rating than that computed. Of course, a higher grade of timber might also be chosen to improve the load capacity of the truss, but the advantage gained would be limited by the high L/d ratios of the compressive diagonals which could be strengthened best by use of larger sections.

PROBLEMS

1101. Find the allowable bearing stress for load at 30 degrees to the grain for 1900*f* or 1400*c* select structural beam timber of Douglas fir (coast). *Ans.* 880 psi.

1102. Find the allowable bearing stress for load at 60 degrees to the grain for 2000*f* or 1550*c* dense structural southern pine of 6-in. thickness. *Ans.* 550 psi.

1103. Revise *DP*31 for (*a*) 1400*c*, (*b*) 1550*c* timber. $E = 1{,}760{,}000$.

1104. Determine the required number and size of nails and of lag screws to connect a bent steel plate ¼ in. thick to a 4-in. timber (hardwood, Table 12) to develop a holding power of 2000 lb. Use a length of thread of 2¼ in. for a 4-in. lag screw.

Ans. Use 8 nails 16*d* or 3 lag screws ⁵⁄₁₆ in. × 4 in.

1105. Revise *DP*32 for nails and wood screws only; (*a*) oak, (*b*) redwood timber.

1106. Determine the required number of ⁵⁄₁₆-in × 4-in. lag screws or ½-in. bolts in single shear to develop a lateral shear resistance of 2000 lb. between a ½-in. steel plate and a 4-in. southern yellow pine timber. Permit a 25 per cent increase of safe load where the load is applied through a steel plate. The load is at 30 degrees to the grain.

Ans. 8 lag screws or 3 bolts.

1107. Determine the required number of ½-in. × 6-in. lag screws and also of ½-in. bolts to develop a lateral shear of 3000 lb. between a 3-in. Douglas fir plank and a 6-in. Douglas fir timber. The load is at 45 degrees to the direction of the grain.

1108. Revise *DP*33 for 1300*c* and 1400*f* southern pine for a net tension in the diagonal of 900 psi. Use ¾-in. bolts.

1109. Design and detail a bolted gusset-plate connection of the general type shown to develop a load *P* of 6000 lb. The timber is southern yellow pine. Fulfill all specifications as to edge and end margins and proper spacing. Note eccentricity of load on upper group of bolts which should be eliminated or considered in the design.

1110. Design and detail the bolted splice shown to develop the value of southern pine timber in tension at 800 psi on the net section.

1111. Design and detail the bolted joint shown to develop a total load of 6000 lb. The planks are 3-in. × 12-in. Douglas fir.

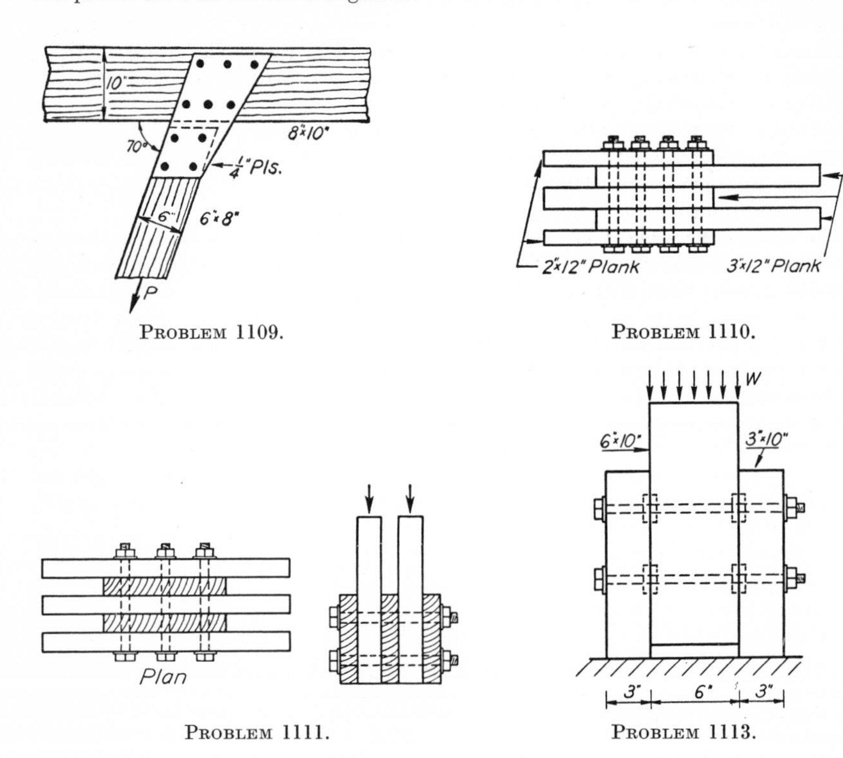

PROBLEM 1109.

PROBLEM 1110.

PROBLEM 1111.

PROBLEM 1113.

1112. Redesign the joint of *DP*34*a* and *b* for southern pine timber and allow for 21½ per cent moisture content. Let the diagonal be stressed to 500 psi.

1113. Select size and number of *pairs of connectors* to resist the load *W* of 30,000 lb. acting parallel to the grain. Timber sizes given are nominal. The timber is seasoned shortleaf southern pine. Carry out the design for (*a*) split ring, (*b*) toothed ring, (*c*) shear plates.

Ans. (*a*) Three 4-in. diam.; ¾-in. bolts.
(*b*) Five 4-in. diam.; ¾-in. bolts.
(*c*) Four 4-in. diam.; ¾-in. bolts.

1114. Redesign the column splice of *DP*35*a* and *b* for fully seasoned Rocky Mountain Douglas fir 1400*c*.

1115. Revise Problem 1113 to account for the following special conditions: load applied at right angles to the grain of seasoned Rocky Mountain Douglas fir with 1-in. end margins.

1116. Revise Problem 1113(*a*) to account for the following special conditions: a tensile load applied parallel to the grain through steel side plates in place of wood side timbers. Use values for Redwood, Group C. Allow for minimum end margin and spacing. *Ans.* 6 pairs of 4 in. *d.*

1117. Solve Problem 1109 by use of flanged plates.

1118. Solve Problem 1109 by use of split-ring connectors for Group B timber. Select plywood gussets of minimum thickness to replace steel plates.

1119. Solve Problem 1111 by use of split-ring connectors. Check required thickness of timber in Table 17. Use a load of 20,000 lb.

1120. Same as Problem 1110, but use (*a*) split rings and (*b*) shear plates.

1121. Same as Problem 1119, but use toothed-ring connectors.

1122. Design a beam to span 22 ft. and carry a uniformly distributed load of 550 lb. per lineal ft.; add in its own weight. Choose a commercial timber, and check shear and necessary length of end bearing. Consider load to be long-term (Table 10).

1123. Design a beam of 15-ft. span to carry a concentrated center load of 30,000 lb. Check shear, and design bearing plates under the load at the reactions. Grade; 1500*f* Douglas fir (coast). Allow for a uniform dead load of 250 lb. per lineal ft. of span.

1124. Revise the design of *DP*36 for 1400*f* southern pine of B classification.

1125. Assume that timbers of all species are available up to size 8 in. × 12 in. Design a built-up beam held together with bolts and timber connectors to carry a fixed load of 1000 lb. per lineal ft. on a span of 21 ft.-6 in. Allow for weight of the beam.

1126. Revise the design of *DP*37 for 1100*c* redwood for which $E = 1{,}320{,}000$. Reduce the load to 115,000 lb. and ceiling heights to 18 ft.

1127. Determine the carrying capacities (equations (15), (16), and (17)) of the following columns: (*a*) 1300*c* dense shortleaf southern pine, 12 in. × 12 in. × 10 ft.-6 in., (*b*) 1200*c* oak, 14 in. × 16 in. × 17 ft.-2 in., for which $E = 1{,}650{,}000$ (*c*) 1000*c* redwood, 6 in. × 6 in. × 11 ft.-3 in., for which $E = 1{,}320{,}000$ (*d*) 1075*c* yellow poplar 6 in. × 8 in. × 15 ft.-0 in. for which $E = 1{,}210{,}000$. Sizes are nominal (reduce each dimension ½ in.)
Ans. (*a*) 164,000 lb.; (*b*) 236,000 lb.; (*c*) 18,300 lb.; (*d*) 12,700 lb.

1128. Compare the answers obtained from the data of Problem 1127, if the design is made by use of equation (14), which is the *NLMA* column formula.

1129. Select and splice a southern pine timber to carry a tension stress of 70,000 lb. Take account of the reduction of allowable stress suggested by the footnote to Table 22. Use flanged connectors and steel side plates.

1130. Repeat Problem 1129 by choosing a built-up section composed of several planks with spacers. Splice by interlocking the planks, adding side planks, and using connectors.

1131. Revise the design of the Howe roof truss of Fig. 198 and §221 to carry a fixed loading of 900 lb. per lineal ft. of truss including its own weight for allowable stresses from Tables 9 and 16. Restrict your computations to three critical members and two or three joints.

1132. If the Howe roof truss of Fig. 198 is constructed of No. 2 SR southern pine timber from Table 9, determine its load rating.

1133. The bow-string truss of Fig. 198 is expected to carry a uniform loading of 860 lb. per lineal ft. of span including its own weight. Check three critical members and two or three joints to determine what grade of southern pine timber should be specified. This truss is 6 ft.-9 in. deep at the hip joint and 10 ft.-0 in. deep at the center. Lateral bracing may be connected at each panel point through the roof joists.

1134. Determine the load rating to be given to the bow-string truss of Fig. 198 if it is constructed of Douglas fir (inland) B. and S. construction grade from Table 9. Note Problem 1133 for other data.

222. Modern Design of Timber Structures. There has been in the past a certain justification for a "rule-of-thumb" approach toward timber design. We realize, of course, that wood is not as uniform as steel. However, modern methods of selection and classification have removed the guesswork from the choice of working stresses. There is little reason to question the fact that the specification of 1750*f* dense Douglas fir (coast) or 1450*c* dense structural southern pine will produce timber fully capable of resisting the working stresses specified for such woods. This eliminates any justification that may have existed for the use of oversafe member sizes selected by "rule of thumb." Scientific methods of design are needed as much in timber as in steel.

Courtesy Florida Architect

Fig. 199. Laminated Timber Bents Frame a Church.

Laminated Timber. A modern wood material has received much study and a great deal of practical use during recent years. The reference is to glued, laminated timber for which, unlike plywood, the grain direction of all layers is practically parallel. As beams, columns, or gusset plates, the built-up material has a greater factor of safety than the plain timber. The reason is that planks can be oriented during assembly so that the weakening effects of knots, shakes, splits, and wanes are reduced to a smaller factor in the built-up member than in a full sized timber. A few such possibilities were suggested by Fig. 186, but this idea has been expanded into built-up arches, rigid frames, continuous beams, etc. Units may be held together by nails, bolts, screws, or connectors, and by waterpoof glue. Two examples are illustrated in Fig. 199 and Fig. 200.

Courtesy Florida Architect

FIG. 200. AUDITORIUM HAS HINGED ARCHES OF LAMINATED TIMBER.

Careful scientific design, the use of modern connectors, and the construction of built-up members have brought timber into greater use than in the recent past. It should be realized that timber lends itself to contemporary metropolitan architecture as well as rustic architectural treatment in harmony with the background of the countryside. When timber is used in thicknesses above 3 in. it takes on a good fire resistance rating because of its slow-burning characteristics.

CHAPTER 12

REINFORCED CONCRETE CONSTRUCTION

223. Specifications. It may be well to review the early uses of reinforced concrete in this country which led up to the organization of the first Joint Committee on Concrete and Reinforced Concrete in 1904. An occasional structure was built of reinforced concrete during the 1870–1890 period, but these were largely experimental. The successful Melan and Hennebique systems were not introduced here until the 1890–1900 decade. A scramble then took place for patents on all possible combinations of concrete and steel. Of course, the wildest claims were made as to strength and economy. The non-homogeneous character of reinforced concrete made an exact analysis of stresses impossible, and successful contradiction of such claims was therefore difficult.

To make order out of this chaos was the job of the first Joint Committee. Its final report, submitted in 1916, took much of the confusion out of the design of reinforced concrete. Further tests and investigations advanced our knowledge of this complex material so rapidly that a second Joint Committee, appointed in 1920, was able to present its final report in 1924. By 1930, further information had accumulated that justified the appointment of the third Joint Committee. However, its deliberations covered ten years so that its final report carried the date 1940. Current specifications are covered by the *Building Code Requirements for Reinforced Concrete* of the American Concrete Institute. A much abbreviated version is given in §311, p. 443. This edition of the *ACI Building Code* includes additional specifications to control design for ultimate strength and for prestressing.

Materials and Mixing

224. Cement. The active ingredient in concrete is the cement. Mixed with fine and coarse aggregates (sand and crushed rock or gravel), it sets and binds the mass together to form concrete. Cements of various compositions have been used to some extent since the time of ancient Rome, but modern Portland cement dates from 1824 when it was produced by Joseph Aspdin in England. Portland cement is a powder made by grinding the clinker formed through burning nearly to fusion a mixture of *shale* and *limestone* or similar natural materials. This standard product is sold everywhere. Special cements having the property of high early strength, or unusual acid resistance, or low heat of setting, are available if needed. Admixtures are available either to improve the workability of the mix or to entrain air which also produces resistance to spalling from repeated freezing.

225. Concrete Mix. Cement, sand, aggregate, and water are mixed to form a plastic workable mass which is then used to fill the forms of wood or steel that determine the shape of the final structure. Since sand and aggregate are local materials of known but not entirely controllable properties, the amounts of cement and water must be varied to obtain immediate workability of the plastic mix and ultimate strength as specified for the cured concrete. The design of a proper mix is a job for a specialist, but certain facts should be known to all who plan concrete structures: (1) *workability* can be improved by adding water or cement and water, by proper grading of the materials, or by the use of rounded aggregate (gravel); (2) *strength* can be increased by adding cement, by proper grading of the materials to reduce voids, or by reducing the amount of water in the mix. Evidently, then, the use of water to improve workability will weaken the concrete unless we add cement at extra cost. Thus the *water-cement ratio* takes on a special significance. The ideal solution is to obtain workability by proper selection, grading, and mixing of materials so that low water and cement contents are acceptable. The time of mixing in the standard rotating batch mixer is usually about 1½ minutes to obtain uniform consistency. This emphasis upon workability or consistency is particularly necessary for *reinforced* concrete. The mix should flow around the reinforcing rods assisted only by ordinary rodding or by vibration of the forms. Otherwise, the result will be a honeycombed structure showing objectionable exposure of the steel bars. To assure flow the maximum size of aggregate is limited to three-fourths of the minimum clear spacing between bars or cables. The approximate amounts of cement and water required per cubic yard of freshly mixed concrete to produce given strengths and medium consistency (4-in. slump) are listed in Table 23.

Slump Test. The slump test for consistency gives the loss of height of a truncated 12-in. cone of freshly mixed concrete when its form bucket is removed. A slump range of from 3 to 6 in. is allowed in building construction. The data of Table 23 refer to concrete for which the anticipated slump is 4 in., the usual definition of medium consistency.

226. Volume and Weight Changes. A significant property of concrete is its change of volume with change of temperature or moisture. Shrinkage cracks are observable in nearly all concrete structures. Expansion makes the introduction of *open joints* necessary both in structures and in pavements. The coefficient of expansion for concrete design is 0.000006 in. per in. per degree F. The coefficient of shrinkage varies from 0.00015 to 0.00045 in. per in. of length, the lower value applying to lean dry mixes. Thus, the average shrinkage of 0.0003 is comparable in magnitude to the expansion or contraction caused by a temperature change of 50 degrees F or the elastic deformation due to a compressive stress of around 1000 psi. Actually, a special cement is patented that expands on setting. It is anticipated that cement mixtures will become commercially available that show essentially no shrinkage from setting. It is even conceived that expanding cement may eventually be used to prestress reinforcing cables by increasing the length of a beam or slab during setting, thus placing the concrete under permanent compression in any direction or directions desired.

Expansion Joints. For concrete trestles, specifications recommend the use of expansion joints not farther apart than 125 ft. The expansion joints in buildings may be spaced from 200 to 500 ft. apart depending upon the degree of exposure. The most severe exposure occurs in the north for unheated, uninsulated buildings. Such structures need expansion joints at 200-ft. intervals across the entire building, and it has often been found that sub-joints at 100-ft. intervals are desirable in the roof.

Weight of Concrete. Although concrete changes in volume with moisture, its weight per unit of volume does not change appreciably. This weight varies from 145 to 150 pcf and is taken for safety as the larger value. Light-weight concretes are made with burned clay or cinder aggregates. They may range in weight from 80 pcf upward.

TABLE 23

GUIDE FOR PROPORTIONING CONCRETE MIXES

SPECIFIED 28-DAY MIN. COMPRESSIVE STRENGTH, PSI f_c'	SACKS OF CEMENT PER CU. YD. CONCRETE (APPROX.)	MAXIMUM PERMISSIBLE WATER-CEMENT RATIO OR U.S. GALLONS PER 94-LB. BAG OF CEMENT*	
		Non-Air-Entrained Concrete	Air-Entrained Concrete†
2000	4.2	8	7¼
2500	4.8	7¼	6¼
3000	5.5	6½	5¼
3500	6.3	5¾	4½
4000	7.0	5	4

* Including free surface moisture on aggregates.

Note: This table applies for a 4-in. slump. For each 1-in. difference in slump, change the cement by ⅛ bag per cu. yd. Increase cement for increased slump.

† Concrete exposed to freezing weather shall contain entrained air and not over 6 gallons of water per bag of cement.

227. Strength of Concrete. Tests show that concrete has excellent resistance to compressive stresses, but that it is weak in tensile strength. An ultimate compressive resistance of 4000 psi for concrete at 28 days can be attained with assurance at reasonable cost. Concrete of this ultimate strength is in common use for building construction. Concrete having an ultimate compressive strength of 5000 psi is commonly used for pavements, and much higher strengths have been allowed in bridge arches and for other special structures. The tensile strength of concrete as measured by tests is variable because it is difficult to produce a tensile failure where both eccentricity of loading and stress concentrations are absent. The tensile strength is commonly measured as the modulus of rupture in flexure. Again, there is considerable variation, and *it seems best not to depend upon this tensile value exceeding 10 per cent of the ultimate compressive strength.* In fact, the *ACI Building Code* specifies the allowable tensile fiber stress in flexure to be $1.6\sqrt{f_c'}$ or 88 psi for 3000 psi concrete and limits this type of resistance to the design of plain concrete footings and walls.

Ultimate Compressive Strength. The ultimate strength of concrete is taken as the crushing strength of a 6-in. concrete cylinder of 12-in. height cured under moist conditions in the laboratory and tested at the end of 28 days. This strength is universally termed f_c', and all working stresses are given as percentages of f_c'. Thus, the allowable compressive stress for a short concrete pedestal is limited to $0.25 f_c'$, while the flexural fiber stress in compression of a reinforced concrete beam may be permitted to reach $0.45 f_c'$ according to the *ACI Building Code* (Table 24). Since concrete may attain in one year a crushing strength one third greater than the 28-day test, there is a reasonable *allowance for retrogression* due to long-time deterioration of any kind. Allowable stresses as specified by the *ACI Building Code* are given in Table 24.[1] Stress-strain curves obtained from the tests of 6-in. cylinders at 28 days are given in Fig. 201.

Shearing Strength. Beam shear is always accompanied by diagonal tension and compression. For the case of "pure shear" illustrated by Fig. 202, the *unit diagonal tension* is the same as the *unit shear*. Hence, shearing resistance in concrete is limited by the weak tensile strength of this material. In Table 24 the allowable average unit shear for beams with no web reinforcement is $1.1\sqrt{f_c'}$. However, this is consistent with $1.6\sqrt{f_c'}$ for tension in plain concrete because the maximum

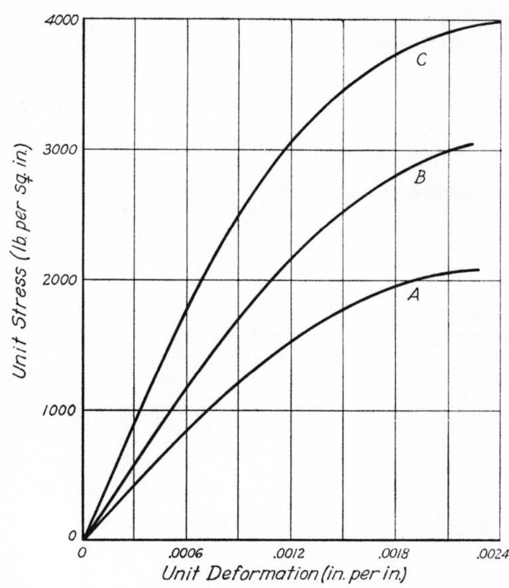

FIG. 201. STRESS-STRAIN DIAGRAMS FOR CONCRETE OF DIFFERENT ULTIMATE STRENGTHS.

[1] Allowable tension, shear, and bond stresses are expressed in terms of $\sqrt{f_c'}$. However, their units are in psi.

TABLE 24

ALLOWABLE UNIT STRESSES FOR REINFORCED CONCRETE

Description	symbol	Allowable Stresses: For any Strength of Concrete	For Strength of Concrete Shown Below: $f_c' = 2500$ psi	$f_c' = 3000$ psi	$f_c' = 4000$ psi	$f_c' = 5000$ psi
Modulus of elasticity ratio; n For concrete weighing 145 pcf	n	$\frac{29{,}000{,}000}{w^{1.5}\, 33\sqrt{f_c'}}$	10	9	8	7
Flexure: f_c						
Extreme fiber stress in compression	f_c	$0.45f_c'$	1125	1350	1800	2250
Extreme fiber stress in tension in plain concrete footings and walls	f_c	$1.6\sqrt{f_c'}$	80	88	102	113
Shear: v (as a measure of diagonal tension at a distance d from the face of the support)						
Beams with no web reinforcement	v_c	$1.1\sqrt{f_c'}$	55	60	70	78
Joists with no web reinforcement	v_c	$1.2\sqrt{f_c'}$	61	66	77	86
Members with vertical or inclined web reinforcement or properly combined bent bars and vertical stirrups	v_c	$5\sqrt{f_c'}$	250	274	316	354
Slabs and footings, peripheral shear	v_c	$2\sqrt{f_c'}$	100	110	126	141
Bond, anchorage: u						
Deformed tension top bar sizes to #11	u	$\frac{3.4\sqrt{f_c'}}{D} < 350$ psi	$\frac{170}{D}$	$\frac{186}{D}$	$\frac{214}{D}$	$\frac{240}{D}$
Other bars	u	$\frac{4.8\sqrt{f_c'}}{D} < 500$ psi	$\frac{240}{D}$	$\frac{262}{D}$	$\frac{303}{D}$	$\frac{338}{D}$
Deformed compression bars	u	$6.5\sqrt{f_c'} < 400$ psi				
Plain bars	u	$\frac{1}{2}$ of above values < 160 psi				
Bearing: f_c						
On full area	f_c	$0.25f_c'$				
On one-third area or less	f_c	$0.375f_c'$				

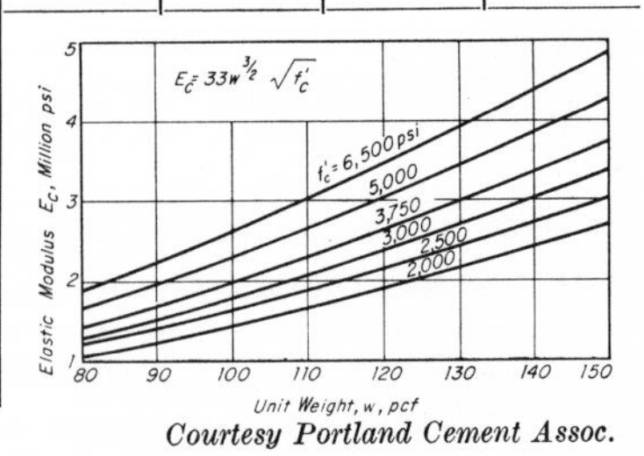

Courtesy Portland Cement Assoc.

shear (or diagonal tension) on a beam web is higher than the average shear. The ratio would be $^3\!/_2$ for a plain concrete section.

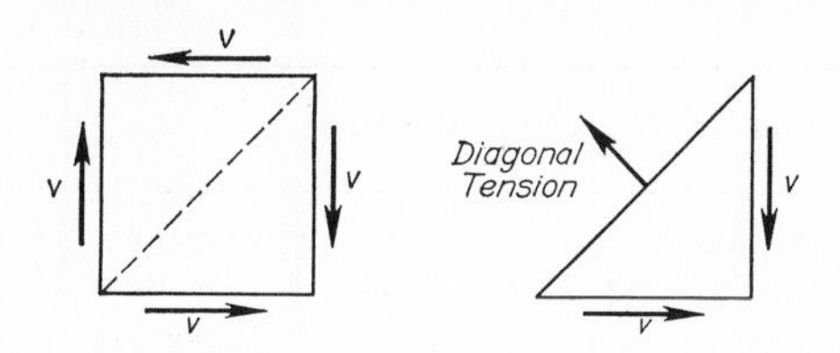

FIG. 202. DIAGONAL TENSION CAUSED BY PURE SHEAR.

REINFORCEMENT

228. Reinforcing Steel. For most purposes, the steel bars used to reinforce concrete beams, slabs, and columns are round rods 1 in. or less in diameter. See Fig. 203. They are available in structural grade, intermediate grade, and hard grade steel. The elastic limit and the allowable stress increase with the carbon content. The allowable steel stresses in tension and compression are given in Table 25.

Courtesy Eng. News-Record

FIG. 203. FLOOR CONSTRUCTION SHOWING BENT RODS.

Reinforcing bars serve three purposes in concrete structures:

(1) They may be placed to resist the tensile stresses which the concrete is unable to resist.

TABLE 25

ALLOWABLE STRESSES FOR STEEL REINFORCEMENT, AND BAR SIZES

TENSION REINFORCEMENT OF FLEXURAL MEMBERS	f_s	BAR NO.	DIAM. IN.	AREA IN.
Structural grade steel bars	18,000 psi	2	0.25	0.05
Deformed bars sizes No. 11 and smaller,		3	0.375	0.11
$f_y = 60{,}000$ psi	24,000 psi	4	0.50	0.20
Main reinforcement sizes No. 3 and smaller in		5	0.625	0.31
one-way slabs of not over 12-ft. span,		6	0.75	0.44
$0.50f_y$ up to	30,000 psi	7	0.875	0.60
Other reinforcement	20,000 psi	8	1.00	0.79
		9	1.128	1.00
COMPRESSION REINFORCEMENT OF FLEXURAL MEMBERS		10	1.27	1.27
$(2n - 1)$ times the compressive stress in the		11	1.41	1.56
concrete at the same level but not more than		14S	1.693	2.25
the allowable stress for the same grade of		18S	2.257	4.00
steel in tension f_s				
COMPRESSION IN VERTICAL RODS OF COLUMNS				
Spiral reinforced columns; $0.40f_y$ up to	30,000 psi			
Tied columns; $0.34\,f_y$ up to	25,500 psi			
*A*7 steel sections in composite columns	16,000 psi			
*A*36 steel sections in composite columns	18,000 psi			
Cast iron sections in composite columns	10,000 psi			

(2) They may be placed to act with the concrete in resisting compression in order to reduce the overall dimensions of the members.

(3) They may be inserted to force the concrete to develop numerous small cracks rather than a few open cracks when the concrete will inevitably be stretched beyond its deformable range. This is the purpose of *temperature steel.*

The illustration Fig. 204(*a*) shows how reinforcing bars are placed near the tension surface of a simple beam to resist the tensile flexural stress. In Fig. 204(*b*) some bars are bent upward near the supports since the sign of the bending moment changes near the ends of restrained beams. The details in (*c*) are for typical 180-degree or 90-degree hooks. The length of hook L is adequate to develop a working stress of 10,000 psi for the bar. The straight parts of the hook may be lengthened to increase the bond or anchorage resistance as needed (§230). The use of compression steel in columns is illustrated by Fig. 205. For slabs where there is double curvature the reinforcing bars are formed into mats or wire mesh by crossing the rods at right angles to each other.

Sizes of Reinforcing Bars. Bars designated #2 to #9 in Table 25 have diameters increasing by ⅛ in. for each successive number. Bars #10 and #11 have the same areas as 1⅛-in. and 1¼-in. square bars. Special bars 14*S* and 18*S* are for massive construction. All are available with surface projections for high bond resistance termed "deformed bars."

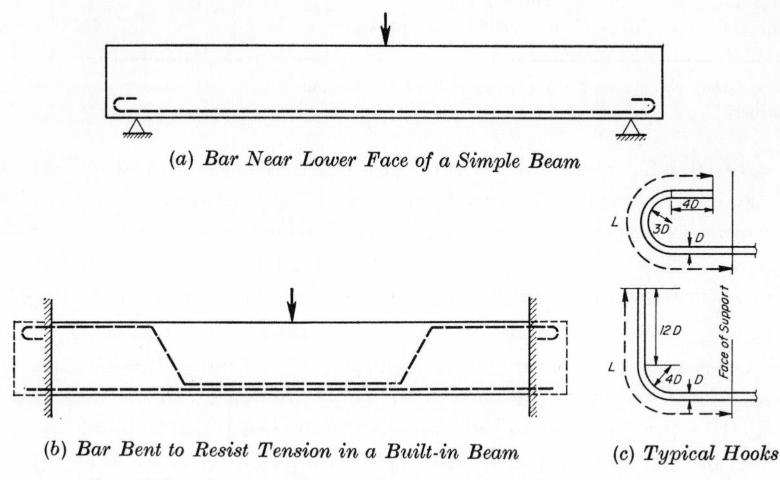

(*a*) *Bar Near Lower Face of a Simple Beam*

(*b*) *Bar Bent to Resist Tension in a Built-in Beam*

(*c*) *Typical Hooks*

FIG. 204. TENSION REINFORCEMENT IN CONCRETE BEAMS.

229. Embedment of Steel Bars. The reinforcing bars must be supported inside the forms so that they will not be displaced when the concrete is worked in around them. Pressed steel seats, wire ties, and patented supports are available for this purpose. For columns, the minimum clear spacing of parallel bars is 1½ diameters. For beams the clear spacing between bars may be as little as one diameter. In order for the aggregate to pass between bars, the open clearance must be 1⅓ times the maximum size of stone aggregate and not less than 1 in. for beams or 1½ in. for columns.

Fireproofing. The thickness of concrete outside of the surface of the steel bars is looked upon as fireproofing. Structures are rated in terms of the hours that they will endure a *standard fire test* without structural failure. The data in Table 26 give the depth of cover to the surface of the steel for varying requirements of fire protection. Ribbed joist floor construction protected underneath by an additional ¾ in. of Portland cement or gypsum plaster requires only the protection of a solid slab. The cover specified for 4-hour fire protection also provides corrosion resistance to weather while 3-hour fire protection resists corrosion for inside construction.

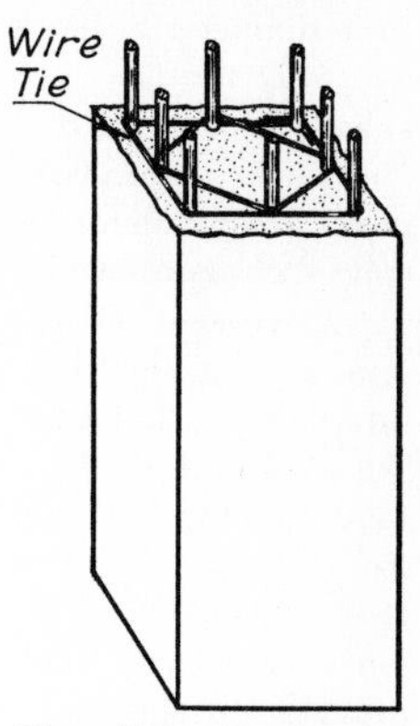

FIG. 205. VERTICAL COMPRESSIVE STEEL IN A SQUARE COLUMN.

TABLE 26

THICKNESS OF FIREPROOFING FOR REINFORCED CONCRETE

TYPES OF MEMBERS	4 HR.*	3 HR.	2 HR.	1 HR.
Columns, beams, girders, and floor joists	2 in.	1½	1½	1
Solid slabs and ribbed floors with ¾ in. of plaster	1 in.	¾	¾	¾

* 4-hour protection should be provided for corrosion resistance for concrete exposed to the weather.

230. Bond. Steel and concrete work together because of the effectiveness of bond. If bars are greased, the bond is destroyed. Ultimate bond resistance is increased by roughening the surface of the bars in the rolling process. Thus *deformed bars* are allowed higher working stresses in bond than plain bars. (See Table 24.) Bond resistance increases with the crushing strength of the concrete. Bond can be expressed in terms of $\sqrt{f_c'}$. Bond resistance may be determined by a simple *pull-out test.* The load necessary to start movement of the embedded bar is divided by the surface area embedded in the concrete to determine the unit resistance to bond slip. The values of u in Table 24 are limits upon computed bond stress at any beam cross-section and of anchorage bond stress computed for the embedded length of bar beyond the face of a support. For tension bars a standard hook as defined by *ACI* specifications may provide full anchorage. (See Spec. 302.)

Bar Splices. Full strength splices for reinforcing bars may be made by butt welding the ends of the bars together for ultimate strength equal to 1.25 times the yield strength of the bar in tension. For compression reinforcement, bars with square cut ends may be aligned by a lightly welded collar and the stress may be transferred by bearing. Tension bars up to No. 11 size may also be spliced by lapping deformed bars 12 in. or more as required for stress transfer by bond at ¾ of the values specified in Table 24. However, for a diameter of bar D the length of overlap shall not be less than $24D$ for $f_y = 40{,}000$ psi, $30D$ for $f_y = 50{,}000$ psi, and $36D$ for $f_y = 60{,}000$ psi. For lapped compression splices in concrete of not less than 3,000 psi strength the minimum length of overlap is $20D$ for $f_y = 50{,}000$ psi, $24D$ for $f_y = 60{,}000$ psi and $30D$ for $f_y = 75{,}000$ psi. All values given are for deformed bars. The specified minimum overlap should be doubled for splices of plain bars.

Example of Design for Bond. Assume that we wish to introduce enough steel in a 3-in. slab of 3000 psi concrete to produce temperature and shrinkage cracks at 10-in. intervals, so that they will be hardly visible. Evidently, then, the bond resistance of the steel in a length of 10 in. must equal the tensile strength of the slab. If the unit tensile strength at rupture is 350 psi, the tensile value of the slab per foot of width is $350 \times 3 \times 12 = 12{,}600$ lb. For steel having an elastic limit of 60,000 psi, we need at least $12{,}600 \div 60{,}000 = 0.21$ sq. in. of steel area per foot of width in order to provide tension steel able to prevent a crack from opening after it has formed. This area will be provided by round bars of ⅜-in. diameter spaced at 6-in. centers.

If the bond strength for such small rods at first slip is 500 psi of embedded area, the bond resistance developed in one rod per inch of length will be $0.375 \times \pi \times 500 = 590$ lb. For a 10-in. length between cracks, each rod will develop 5900 lb. of bond resistance.

Evidently, such bars will need to be spaced about 5½ in. apart in order to provide at least 12,600 lb. of bond resistance per foot width of slab. Since this spacing for bond is closer than the spacing to provide an adequate area of steel, it will control.

231. Modulus of Elasticity. The modulus of elasticity of concrete varies from about 2,000,000 to 5,000,000 psi. The modulus increases with stress approximately as follows,

$$E_c = w^{1.5}\, 33 \sqrt{f_c'} \qquad (1) \quad \text{(Spec. 317).}$$

For normal concrete for which $w = 145$ pcf the modulus is

$$E_c = 57{,}500\sqrt{f_c'}. \qquad (2)$$

For $f_c' = 3000$ psi, $E_c = 3{,}160{,}000$; for $f_c' = 4000$ psi, $E_c = 3{,}630{,}000$; and for $f_c' = 5000$ psi, $E_c = 4{,}060{,}000$.

The modulus of elasticity also changes with the stress as is clearly evident from the stress-strain relationships of Fig. 201. The modulus, being the slope of the stress-strain curve, is only constant or nearly constant for low stresses in the working range. It should be realized that the flattening slope of the stress-strain curve above working stresses (reduction of modulus) permits *inelastic or permanent change of shape* to take place before failure. The result is a redistribution that decreases the relative stress at the overstressed fiber by building up the stress elsewhere. Failure is postponed until a further redistribution would merely overstress other sections.

Ratio n. Since the modulus of elasticity of steel is 29,000,000 psi, the ratio $n = E_s/E_c$ varies through the wide range from 15 to 6. When steel is bonded into concrete, the two must move or deform together (until the bond is disturbed). Hence, in the past, we considered the unit stress in the vertical steel of a concrete column to be n times the unit concrete stress. This will still be true for a temporary or short-time loading, but tests showing the low modulus of concrete under high stress, and *its property of flowing under any stress maintained continuously*, have established the fact that the steel and concrete do not necessarily deform together. Internal adjustments do take place. Therefore, the factor n will not necessarily be considered to define the ratio in compression between the steel stress and the concrete stress, but only the ratio between the moduli of elasticity, that is E_s/E_c.

232. Moment Coefficients. The numbers in Fig. 206 represent the common moment coefficients for continuous beams and building frames. Such moment coefficients of wL^2, where w represents the total uniform $DL + LL$ for the span, can be very useful if it is recognized that they provide only crude approximations of the true moments which may be fully 25 per cent larger or smaller than those obtained from the coefficients. True moments for continuous beams and frames may be calculated by the methods of analysis discussed in Vol. 1 and Vol. 2, *Theory of Modern Steel Structures.* These coefficients are intended to allow for live loading applied to two adjacent spans for producing a large negative moment at the intermediate support and for alternate spans of one floor loaded to produce a maximum positive moment at the middle of an internal span.

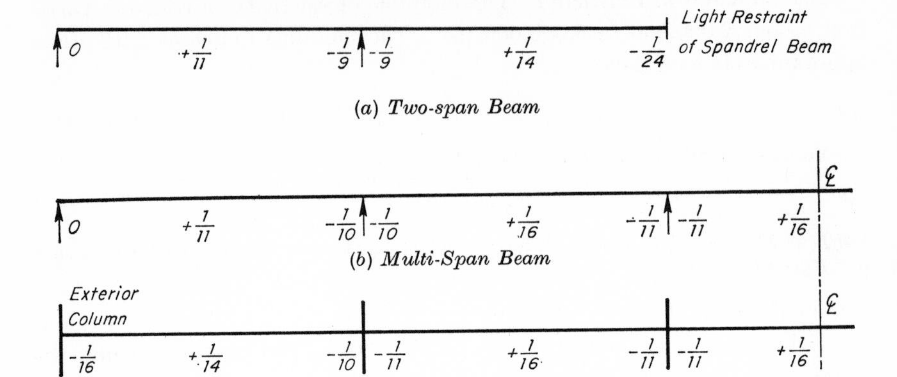

FIG. 206. VALUES OF MOMENT COEFFICIENTS FOR CHECKING CONTINUOUS BEAMS AND FRAMES.

All coefficients are to be multiplied by wL^2. The final moments may be compared with $\frac{1}{8}wL^2$, the simple-span moment. Coefficients in (c) are applicable to frames with light columns and stiff girders for which the I/L value of the end girder is usually equal at least to twice the sum of the I/h values of the wall columns into which it frames. These coefficients apply where the lengths of adjacent spans vary no more than 20 per cent and for a ratio of $LL \div DL < 3.0$. Shear at a support $= wL/2$, except use 1.15 $wL/2$ for the shear in the end member at the first interior support.

The span length L of members that are not built integrally with their supports shall be considered to be the clear span plus the depth of the beam or slab but not to exceed the distance between centers of supports.

For continuous frames the moments are to be computed from values of L that represent center-to-center distances but the computed moments may be reduced for the design of beams and girders to the moments at the faces of the supports.

Slabs of not more than 10-ft. clear spans built integrally with their supports may be designed for knife-edge supports using the clear spans for moment computation.

CHAPTER 13

REINFORCED CONCRETE BEAMS AND SLABS

Working Stress Design

233. Flexure of Beams. The theory of flexure of homogeneous beams, such as steel I-beams or rectangular timber sections, has been discussed in detail. It is assumed that the reader is able to apply the standard beam formulas to the investigation of homogeneous cross-sections of any kind. The beam formulas are : (1) the flexure formula, $f = Mc/I$, and (2) the shear formula, $v = VQ/Ib$. Their terms do not need redefinition here since they were defined in Chapter 7. It will be useful, however, to restate the basic assumptions upon which these formulas depend so that we may determine whether revised formulas are needed for the investigation of reinforced concrete beams.

General Assumptions of Analysis for Homogeneous Beams.

1. A plane cross-section before bending remains a plane cross-section after bending; hence, strain or deformation is proportional to distance from the neutral axis.
2. Stress is proportional to strain; therefore, from (1) we conclude that the stress increases linearly from the neutral axis either way to the extreme fiber.

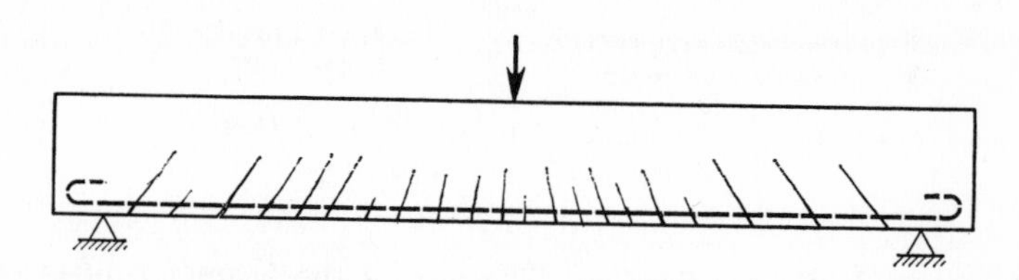

Fig. 207. Direction of Cracks in a Reinforced Concrete Beam.

234. Flexure of Reinforced Concrete Beams. It should now be clear that reinforcing rods must be added to concrete beams to supplement or replace the weak tensile resistance of the concrete. As shown in Fig. 207, cracks are seldom vertical, but are inclined in a direction normal to the direction of maximum diagonal tension which is the resultant of a horizontal tension caused by flexure and a 45-degree tension due to shear. Later, we will investigate how to bend bars or add stirrups to resist effectively the diagonal tension, but, first, it is necessary to determine the steel requirement to resist the longitudinal tension caused by beam flexure.

Special Assumptions of Reinforced Concrete Beam Analysis. In addition to the assumptions involved in the analysis of all beams, as stated in §233, there are three other assumptions that are necessary for the investigation of beams of reinforced concrete:

1. The tensile resistance of the concrete is negligible for working loads and is assumed to be zero. Evidently, since this is neglect of a definite, even though small, resistance, this assumption is on the side of safety in design.

2. Temperature and shrinkage stresses are neglected. Such stresses actually are important, and they would not be neglected if they were determinable. However, they are like the cooling and straightening stresses that are neglected in the analysis of steel members. We allow for all undeterminable internal strains through a reduction of allowable working stresses by specification.

3. Plastic flow is not to be considered for working stress design. It is known, of course, that concrete flows or deforms continuously under stress. The plastic deformations are not large at working stresses, and fortunately, they tend to hold down the development of high stress concentrations, as, for example, at the extreme compressive fiber of the beam. Thus, neglect of plastic flow in concrete is ordinarily expected to act on the side of safety. (See Fig. 208.) Plastic flow will be considered in §247 with reference to compressive reinforcement. Plastic design for ultimate loading will be investigated in Chapter 15.

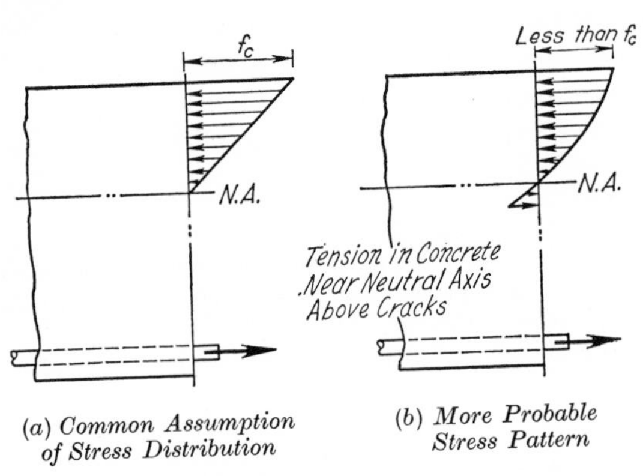

(*a*) *Common Assumption of Stress Distribution*

(*b*) *More Probable Stress Pattern*

FIG. 208. ASSUMED AND PROBABLE DISTRIBUTION OF COMPRESSIVE CONCRETE STRESS AT WORKING LOADS.

235. The Transformed Section. The use of the beam formulas assumes the existence of a beam of homogeneous material. In such a beam, the neutral axis passes through the center of gravity of the cross-section. For a composite beam of steel and concrete, this convenient relationship would no longer hold true. Hence, it is desirable to picture a substitute homogeneous cross-section composed entirely of concrete, which has exactly the same properties as the actual concrete-steel section. This *transformed section* is shown in Fig. 209. It consists of the same area of compressive concrete (A_c) above the neutral axis that exists as a part of the real cross-section. Below the neutral axis there is only an imaginary area of tensile concrete (A_t) which replaces the reinforcing steel. Its area is n times the tensile steel area or nA_s. The area A_t is determined on the basis that this imaginary tensile concrete would elongate n times as much as steel for the same unit stress (where $n = E_s/E_c$). Therefore, to maintain the same deformations for the transformed section as for the real cross-section, one must provide n times as much tensile concrete as tensile steel so that the unit stress in the imaginary tensile concrete will be only $1/n$ times as great as the real steel stress.

Using the Mc/I Formula. As soon as the transformed section has been determined, its moment of inertia about its gravity axis can be calculated, and either extreme fiber stress may be obtained by use of the Mc/I formula. The extreme fiber distance to the compressive side of the beam is designated as kd in Fig. 209, and the corresponding value measured to the steel is d-kd. When the fiber stress at the level of the steel, f_t, has been determined for the imaginary tensile concrete, its value is multiplied by n to give the correct steel stress, f_s. This method as outlined is in common use; it is sometimes varied, however, by treating I/c as the section modulus, or more explicitly, the two values of I/c are used as section moduli. Then the bending moment divided by the proper section modulus gives the corresponding fiber stress for the transformed section.

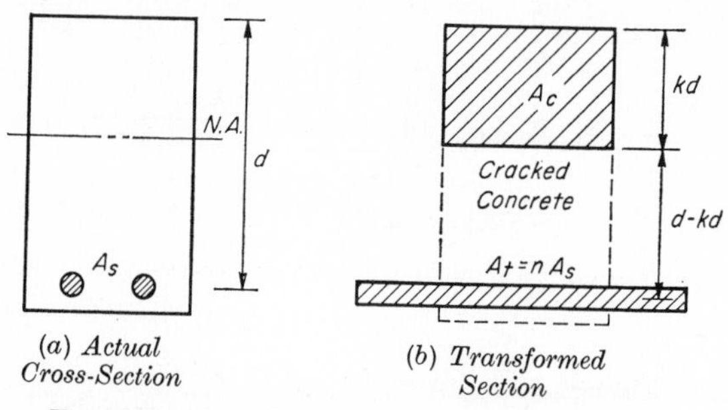

(a) *Actual Cross-Section* (b) *Transformed Section*

FIG. 209. TRANSFORMING THE CROSS-SECTION.

Using the Lever Arm from T to C. In the design of the steel plate girder, analysis was simplified by estimating the *effective depth* from the line of action of the tensile force T to the line of action of the compressive force C. Whenever physical conditions are such that one can compute or closely estimate the value of this lever arm, its use will simplify analysis. In Fig. 210 the total tension T is assumed to be concentrated at the level of the tensile steel, and the centroid of the compressive forces (based upon linear stress variation) is taken at ⅓ the distance down from the compressive face of the beam to the neutral axis or to the center of gravity of the transformed section. It will be seen in Fig. 210 that the depth to the neutral axis is marked kd and that the depth to the steel is shown as d. The lever arm from C to T is marked jd. These are the common designations in all literature on reinforced concrete, j and k being decimal fractions smaller than 1. Based upon the use of the effective depth, one may compute the total tension T (which, since $\Sigma H = 0$, is equal to the total compression C) by dividing the bending moment M by the effective depth $d - kd/3$. Then, obviously, the unit steel stress will be

(1) $$f_s = \frac{M}{\left(d - \frac{kd}{3}\right) A_s} = \frac{M}{A_s jd}.$$

Again, for the concrete stress, bending moment may be divided by the effective depth to obtain C. The maximum unit compressive stress in the concrete for linear variation is twice the average compressive stress. Hence, if b is the breadth of the beam, we may write

(2) $$f_c = \frac{2M}{\left(d - \frac{kd}{3}\right) A_c} = \frac{2M}{\left(d - \frac{kd}{3}\right) b(kd)} = \frac{2M}{jkbd^2}.$$

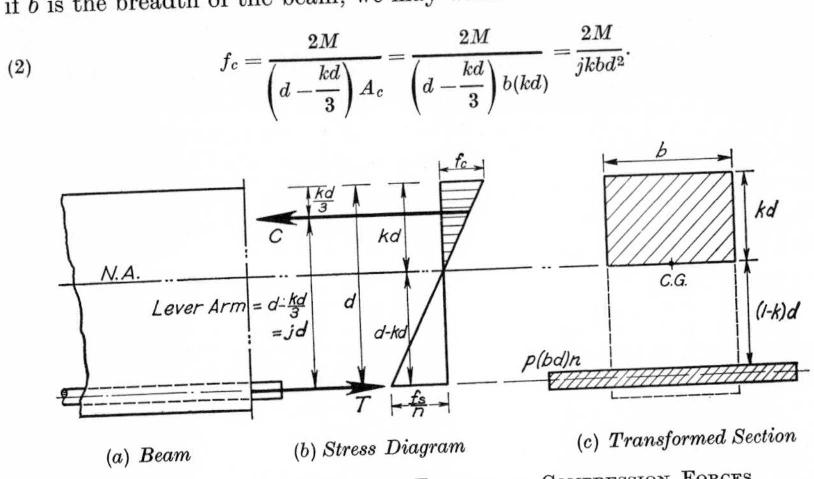

(a) *Beam* (b) *Stress Diagram* (c) *Transformed Section*

FIG. 210. LEVER ARM FROM TENSION TO COMPRESSION FORCES.

236. Use of Symbols and Formulas. Formulas (1) and (2) are widely used, and it is possible to derive numerous special formulas for determining the stresses for every shape of reinforced concrete section. However, the simple numerical use of the effective depth, or of the lever arm from T to C, makes the remembrance of formulas unnecessary. After the common problems in the design of reinforced concrete beams, slabs, and columns have been solved by use of the transformed section and the effective depth, we will list the common formulas for reference. It seems doubtful, however, whether most students will find them necessary or even very useful. At times, in the design problems, steps in the computations may be explained by giving the corresponding symbolic language. For example, the computation of the total tension or compression by dividing the flexural moment by the effective depth is explained in engineering shorthand by the expression $C = T = M/jd$. As an aid in following such explanations, each symbol is defined below.

Symbols Used in the Language of Reinforced Concrete Beam Flexure.

A_c area of compressive concrete
A_s area of tensile steel

A_t area of transformed steel $= nA_s$
b breadth of beam
c extreme fiber distance
C total compression in concrete
d depth to center of reinforcing rods
E_c modulus of elasticity of concrete
E_s modulus of elasticity of steel
f_c compressive unit stress at extreme fiber of concrete beam
f_c' ultimate compressive unit stress for concrete
f_s tensile unit stress in steel
f_t tensile unit stress in imaginary tension concrete (transformed section)
jd effective depth or lever arm from T to C
kd depth from extreme compressive fiber to neutral axis
M bending moment or resisting moment of section
n E_s/E_c
p percentage of steel or (A_s/bd)

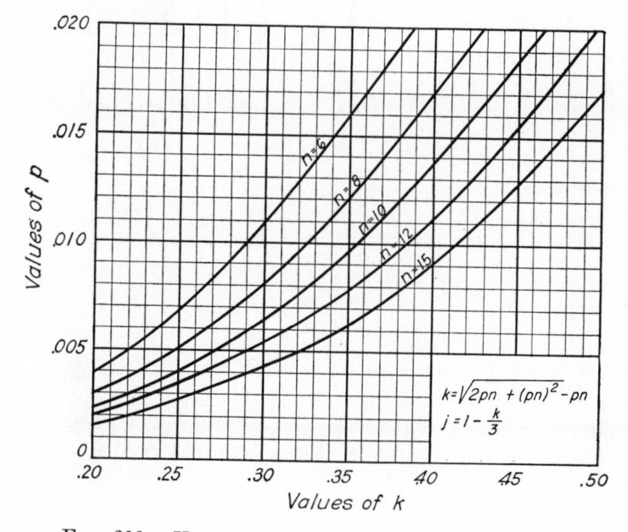

FIG. 211. VALUES OF k FOR RECTANGULAR BEAMS.

237. Use of Charts for Reinforced Concrete Design. The main function of a chart or table in the analysis or design of a concrete beam of any type is to give the designer quickly and conveniently the values of k and j. Other information is largely superfluous.

Rectangular Beams. The curves of Fig. 211 provide values of k for values of p and n. Since j for the simple rectangular section is always $1 - k/3$, which may be obtained by mental arithmetic, it seems unnecessary to have a chart for determining its value.

Formula for k. In Fig. 210(c) the area above the neutral axis may be expressed as of width b and depth kd. The transformed area of steel may be designated as $(pbd)n$, where p is the percentage of steel. If the statical moments about the c.g. of the

DP38a. *Compute by use of the transformed section and the effective depth the maximum fiber stresses in the reinforced concrete beam for the section illustrated. The bending moment is 470″k. Let $f_c' = 2500$ psi. $w = 145$ pcf. Use ACI spec.*

Transformed Section:

Ratio of moduli $= n = E_s/E_c = 10$. $E_c = 3{,}000{,}000$ *when* $f_c' = 2500$ *psi (Spec. 317).*

Area of transformed steel is $2 \times 10 = 20$ *in.*^{2}

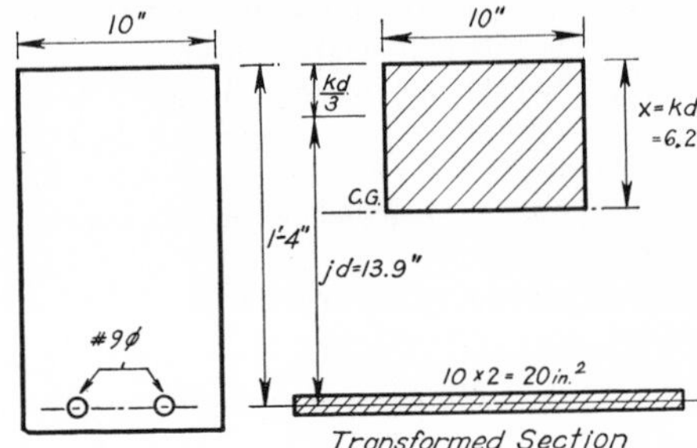

Center of Gravity: *Take moments about the c. g.*

$$10x\left(\frac{x}{2}\right) = 20(16 - x).$$

$$x^2 + 4x + 4 = 64 + 4.$$

$$x + 2 = \sqrt{68}.$$

$$x = kd = 6.2'';$$

$$jd = 16 - \frac{6.2}{3} = 13.9''.$$ *(This is the effective lever arm from T to C.)*

Fiber Stresses:

$$T = C = \frac{M}{jd} = 470{,}000 \div 13.9 = 33{,}800\#.$$

$$f_s = \frac{T}{A_s} = 33{,}800 \div 2 = 16{,}900 \text{ psi}.$$

$$f_c = \frac{2C}{bkd} = 2 \times 33{,}800 \div 10 \times 6.2 = 1090 \text{ psi}.$$

DP38b. *Determine the maximum allowable bending moment for the beam of DP38a when* $f_s = 18{,}000$ *psi and* $f_c = 0.45 \times 2500 = 1125$ *psi. Assume that* $kd = 6.2''$ *and* $jd = 13.9''$ *as in DP38a.*

Maximum value of $T = f_sA_s = 18{,}000 \times 2 = 36{,}000\#.$

Maximum value of $C = \frac{f_c}{2}\,bkd = \frac{1125}{2} \times 10 \times 6.2 = 35{,}000\#.$

Controlling Moment:

The smaller value (35,000#) controls the resistance to moment.
Resisting moment $= Tjd = 35{,}000 \times 13.9 = 487{,}000''\#.$

Remarks: *This beam represents balanced design in that the maximum steel stress is reached at nearly the same time as the maximum allowable concrete stress. The beam is about 4 per cent stronger than needed to carry the bending moment of 470,000″#. This beam is rather shallow for its width, but, if headroom is limited, it may represent a proper design.*

transformed section for the concrete area and the transformed steel area are equated, it will be found that the terms b and d may be cancelled out, leaving the expression

$$k = \sqrt{2pn + (pn)^2} - pn. \tag{3}$$

The formula for k is plotted in Fig. 211. This graph will be found convenient for checking calculations made by numerical use of the transformed section. However, in the examples to be presented neither formulas nor the chart for k are needed or used. All calculations are made quite simply by direct use of the transformed section.

Rectangular Beams

238. Investigation of Rectangular Cross-Sections. This problem occurs frequently in one of several ways: (*a*) A finished structure must be studied to determine its load capacity, perhaps under new specifications. (*b*) A completed design is to be checked before it is accepted for construction. (*c*) A cross-section has been *guessed at* as a preliminary step in design, and must then be analyzed as a final step. In each case, the problem is to compute either the fiber stresses or the moment resistance of a rectangular cross-section of fixed dimensions reinforced by a known area of tensile steel.

Examples *DP*38*a* and *DP*38*b*. This beam, which is 10 in. wide and 16 in. deep to the steel, is represented by a compressive area 10 in. wide by kd deep above the neutral axis and by a transformed steel area $10 \times 2 = 20$ sq. in. below the neutral axis at the level of the steel ($n = 10$ for $f_c' = 2500$ psi). The simplest way to locate the neutral axis (or to determine the value of kd) is to equate the statical moments about the neutral axis of the compressive area above and the transformed steel area below the axis. The equation obtained will be of second degree in x, where $x = kd$. After the first experience in writing such equations, the reader will probably drop the conventional use of x to represent the unknown and write such equations directly in terms of kd. The quadratic equation in *DP*38 is solved for x or kd by completing the square. Then jd is obtained as $d - kd/3$ which is 13.9 in. A simple division of the bending moment by this effective depth (M/jd) gives the value of the total tension or the total compression, $C = T = 33{,}800$ lb. This value of the total tension when divided by the steel area gives rise to the unit steel stress, $f_s = T/A_s = 16{,}900$ psi. The average compressive stress is, of course, the value of the total compression divided by the compressive area of concrete. This value when doubled will equal the maximum compressive fiber stress f_c, which is found to be 1090 psi.

In *DP*38*b* the maximum values of T and C are determined for limiting fiber stresses. Then the minimum resisting moment (Tjd or Cjd) is computed as the controlling moment of resistance of the section. In this case the maximum concrete stress controls the resisting moment.

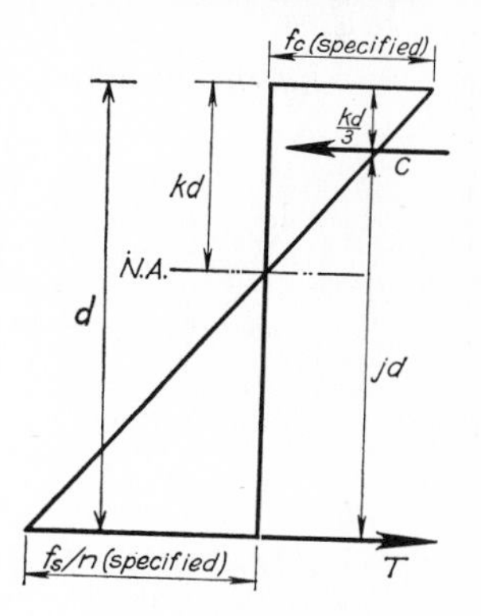

Fig. 212. Stress Diagram for Balanced Reinforcement.

239. Design of a Rectangular Cross-Section. More important than the investigation of a given section is the design of a cross-section to resist a

DP39a. *Design a beam section to resist a bending moment of 556,000″#. Make the depth approximately twice the breadth to the nearest inch. The allowable stresses are to be selected from the ACI specifications for 2500 psi concrete weighing 145 pcf.*

Fiber Stresses:

Working stress for steel bars (structural grade) = 18,000 psi.
Working stress at extreme fiber in compression = 0.45 × 2500 = 1125 psi.
Ratio $n = E_s/E_c = 10$ *for concrete weighing 145 pcf when* $f_c' = 2500$ *psi.*
Stress diagram is as shown.

Neutral Axis: *(located from similar triangles)*

$$\frac{1125}{kd} = \frac{1125 + 1800}{d}.$$

$$kd = \frac{1125d}{2925} = 0.38d.$$

$$jd = d - \frac{1}{3}\,0.38d = 0.87d.$$

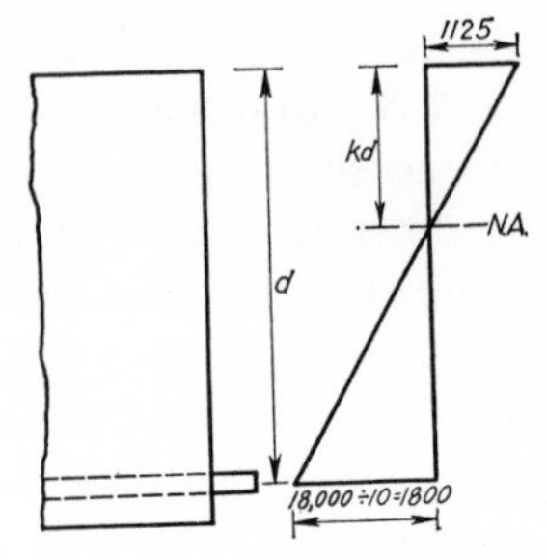

Design: *Resisting moment based upon concrete stress is set equal to the bending moment of 556,000″#.*

$$556{,}000 = \left(\frac{1125 \times 0.38d \times b}{2}\right)0.87d = 186bd^2.$$

$bd^2 = 2980$ *or, if* $b = d/2$, $d^3 = 5960$; *hence* $d = 18.1''$, $b = 9.05''$.
To the nearest inch, $d = 18''$, $b = 9''$.

Steel area, $A_s = \dfrac{M}{jd} \div f_s = \dfrac{556{,}000}{(0.87 \times 18)18{,}000} = 1.97$ in.^{2}

The area furnished by two No. 7 bars and one No. 8 bar is 1.99 in.^{2}

DP39b. *Repeat the calculations of DP39a for the case of a fixed breadth of 8″. Use intermediate steel for which* $f_s = 20{,}000$ *psi.* $n = 9$ *for concrete weighing 145 pcf when* $f_c' = 3000$ *psi.*

Effective Depth:

$$f_c = 0.45f_c' = 1350 \text{ psi.}$$

$$f_t = f_s/n = 20{,}000 \div 9 = 2220 \text{ psi.}$$

$$kd = \left(\frac{1350}{1350 + 2220}\right)d = 0.38d.$$

$$jd = \left(1 - \frac{0.38}{3}\right)d = 0.87d.$$

Cross-Section:

$$556{,}000 = \frac{1350}{2} \times 0.38d \times 8.0 \times 0.87d = 1780d^2.$$

$d = \sqrt{312} = 17.7''$. *Use a beam 8 × 18″.*

$$A_s = \left(\frac{M}{jd}\right) \div f_s = \frac{556{,}000}{(0.87 \times 18)20{,}000} = 1.78 \text{ in.}^2$$

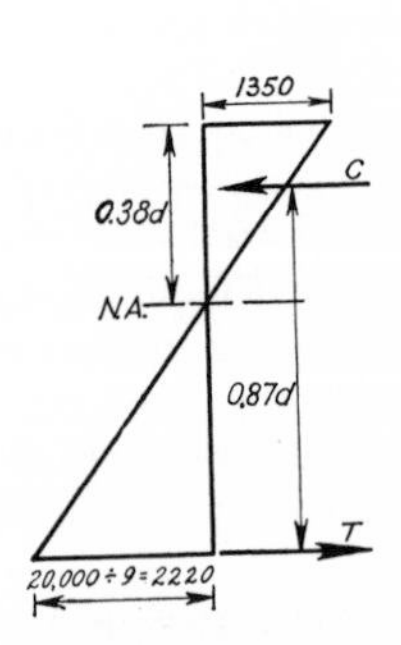

Use 3-No. 7 bars of ⅞″ D. giving 1.8 in.^{2} *of tensile steel area.*

known bending moment. The specifications controlling the design determine the maximum compressive stress in the concrete, the maximum tensile stress in the steel, and the ratio n. Thus the ideal stress diagram for the transformed section is determined in its entirety as indicated in Fig. 212.

Balanced Reinforcement. The design of a cross-section so arranged that the concrete will be stressed to its maximum allowable value just when the steel reaches its maximum working stress is termed design for balanced reinforcement. Under these conditions, as mentioned above, the stress diagram (Fig. 212) is fixed in size and shape, and the location of the neutral axis is determined by computing the value of kd from similar triangles. The most convenient proportion is as follows: $kd : f_c = d : (f_c + f_s/n)$. As soon as kd is known, we determine the effective depth jd as $d - (kd)/3$. Note, therefore, that it is not necessary to use the transformed section or the Mc/I formula to design for balanced reinforcement. Balanced reinforcement can seldom be achieved exactly because steel bars are only available in a limited number of commercial sizes. However, the values of k and j determined for balanced reinforcement may be used without appreciable error for slightly different conditions. Balanced reinforcement usually ranges from 1.0 to 1.5 per cent of the concrete area bd.

Courtesy Portland Cement Association

FIG. 213. BENDING AND WELDING REINFORCING BARS.

EXAMPLES *DP*39*a* and *b*. The first of these examples illustrates the selection of a cross-section for a depth equal to twice the breadth, a common ratio for reasonable economy. Since breadths and depths are usually not chosen in fractions of an inch, the final dimensions are given as 9×18 in. The second example illustrates the choice of a depth when the breadth is fixed. It is evident that beams will become more economical as they are made deeper and narrower until the width becomes insufficient to hold the steel bars in one layer. The proper minimum width for holding the three ⅞-in. bars of *DP*39*b* should be $3 \times \frac{7}{8} + 2 \times 1 + 2 \times 1\frac{1}{2} = 7\frac{5}{8}$ in. (Spec. 303.) This allows 1 in. of clear space between bars and 1½ in. of clear fireproofing on each side.

OVERSIZED BEAMS

240. Steel Requirement for Oversized Beam. This is one of the more troublesome problems in the design of reinforced concrete beams. Since

DP40a. *In DP39b a beam 8 × 18″ was found to be adequate. Suppose that for architectural reasons this beam should be 12 × 20″ in order to match up with other beams. Determine the required area of steel. Follow ACI spec.*

Data: $f_c' = 3000;\ f_s = 20{,}000$ *psi.* $w = 145$ *pcf.* $n = 9.$ $M = 556{,}000''\#.$

Approximate Solution: *Since the concrete will be lightly stressed, the lever arm to the center of gravity of the compressive stresses will be greater than usual.*

Hence, assume $jd = 0.9d$.

Lever arm $= jd = 0.9 \times 20 = 18.0''$.

$$\text{Steel area} = A_s = \frac{T}{f_s} = \left(\frac{M}{jd}\right) \div f_s = \frac{556{,}000}{18 \times 20{,}000} = 1.55 \text{ in}^2.$$

Use $2 - 1''\ \phi s;\ A_s = 2 \times 0.785 = 1.57 \text{ in}^2$.

Check on Effective Depth: *(Locate center of gravity.)*

$$1.57 \times 9(20 - kd) = \frac{12(kd)^2}{2}.$$

$$(kd)^2 + 2.4(kd) + 1.2^2 = 47.2 + 1.2^2, \text{ from which}$$

$$kd = 7.0 - 1.2 = 5.8''.\quad jd = 20.0 - \frac{5.8}{3} = 17.95'' \text{ (check).}$$

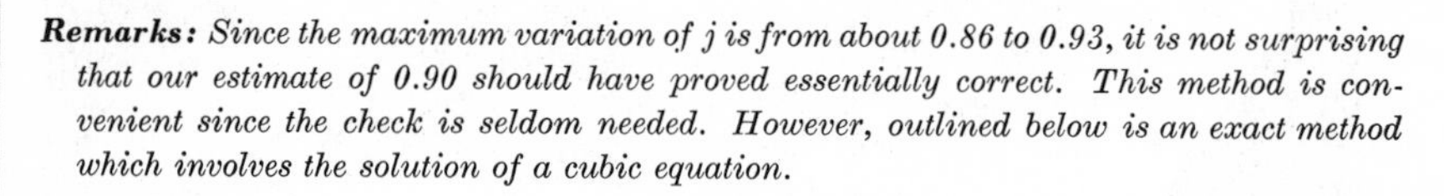

Remarks: *Since the maximum variation of j is from about 0.86 to 0.93, it is not surprising that our estimate of 0.90 should have proved essentially correct. This method is convenient since the check is seldom needed. However, outlined below is an exact method which involves the solution of a cubic equation.*

DP40b. *Rework problem DP40a by an exact method without assuming a value for the effective depth. Write an equation involving kd by equating the internal resisting moment in terms of concrete stress to the bending moment. Change* f_s *to 18,000 psi.*

Let $f_c' = 3000;\ f_s = 18{,}000$ *psi.;* $n = 9;$

$M = 556{,}000''\#;\ b = 12'';\ d = 20''.$

$$556{,}000 = \frac{1}{2}\left(2000\,\frac{kd}{20 - kd}\,12kd\right)\left(20 - \frac{kd}{3}\right).^*$$

$$kd = 6.0''.\quad jd = 20.0 - \frac{6.0}{3} = 18.0''.$$

$$A_s = \frac{556{,}000}{18 \times 18{,}000} = 1.72 \text{ in.}^2$$

$$f_c = 2000 \times \frac{6}{20 - 6} = 860 \text{ psi.}$$

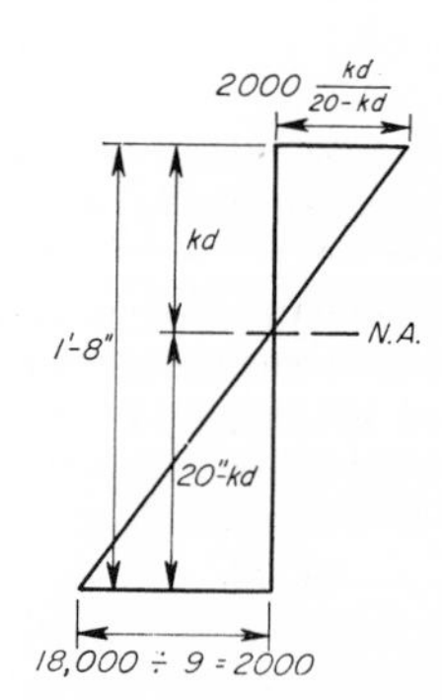

Remarks: *The cubic equation* can be solved by trial rather easily because the value of kd can be guessed quite closely.*

the concrete section is larger than needed, only the fiber stress in the steel is known at the start. The fiber stress in the concrete is low; hence, the value of kd is smaller than normal, and the value of jd is larger than with balanced reinforcement. Three cases will be discussed: (1) *The beam is often only slightly oversized.* In this case, the same values of j and k may be used as for balanced reinforcement without appreciable error. This procedure is well illustrated in the calculation of the required steel area for *DP39b*. Although the depth was increased from 17.7 to 18 in., j was retained as 0.87. (2) *The value of jd may be approximated* in most cases without serious error since the maximum variation for j is only from about 0.86 to 0.93 with a much narrower range around 0.87 representing balanced reinforcement for the usual variations of working stresses. This procedure is illustrated by *DP40a*. (3) *An exact analysis may be made* by equating the internal resisting moment, expressed in terms of the concrete stress, to the external bending moment. This procedure, resulting in a cubic equation, is illustrated by *DP40b*.

Approximate Method of Steel Selection—*DP40a*. In the first study, *DP40a*, the value of jd is assumed to be $0.9d$ or 18 in. Of course, it is then possible to solve directly for the total tension and the required area of steel. The method of checking the accuracy of our assumption regarding the value of jd is to calculate the values of kd and jd by the usual procedure of determining the center of gravity of the new fixed cross-section. It happened in *DP40a* that the check calculation showed our assumption of jd to be nearly exact. If there had been an error of 2 or 3 per cent (and one can almost always estimate the value of j within this accuracy), probably a revision of steel area would not have been considered necessary. In fact, it is seldom possible to provide the exact steel area with an accuracy of 2 per cent from commercial bar sizes. Of course, excess rather than insufficient area of steel is provided.

Exact Method, *DP40b*. An exact solution to the problem of determining the area of steel needed for an oversized beam is worked out in *DP40b*. The proper starting place is to express the compressive stress in terms of the known steel stress by use of similar triangles; whence,

$$f_c = \frac{f_s}{n}\left(\frac{kd}{d - kd}\right). \tag{4}$$

Then, the resisting moment is set up in terms of this expression for f_c and is equated to the applied bending moment. The value of kd follows from the solution of the resulting cubic equation. Incidentally, since one can almost guess the value of kd, this equation can be solved quickly *by trial*. Usually, a solution can be obtained on the second trial. With known values of kd and jd, one can readily compute the area of steel and the concrete fiber stress.

PROBLEMS

ACI specifications given in §311 are to be followed.

1301. A small beam 4 in. wide and 6 in. deep to the steel must resist a maximum bending moment of 30,000 in-lb. It is reinforced with a single ½-in. round bar.

Determine the controlling stresses if $f_c' = 3500$ psi and $n = 8.5$. $A_s = 0.2$.
Ans. $f_s = 28{,}000$; $f_c = 1500$ psi.

1302. A large concrete beam 20 in. wide and 60 in. deep to the steel is reinforced with 1.4 per cent of steel. $w = 130$ pcf. If the value of n is 9, find the controlling moment of resistance. $f_c = 1500$; $f_s = 20{,}000$ psi. *Ans.* $M = 17{,}500{,}000$ in-lb.

1303. Compute the maximum moment resistance for the beam of Problem 1301 if fiber stresses are limited to 24,000 psi for the steel and 1350 psi for the concrete, $n = 9$.
Ans. $M = 25{,}600$ in-lb.

1304. Determine the maximum unit compressive stress in the concrete and the maximum unit tensile stress in the steel for the beam of Problem 1302 when the applied bending moment is 1350 ft-kips. Let $n = 8$. *Ans.* $f_s = 18{,}300$; $f_c = 1380$ psi.

1305. Design a beam section to resist a bending moment of 2,000,000 in-lb. for balanced reinforcement at unit stresses of 20,000 psi for the steel and 900 for the concrete. $n = 11$. Let the depth be 2.5 times the breadth, and select both dimensions to the nearest inch. *Ans.* $d = 34$ in.

1306. Repeat Problem 1305 with the breadth fixed at 16 in. *Ans.* $d = 31$ in.

1307. Repeat Problem 1305 with the depth fixed at 24 in. *Ans.* $b = 26$ in.

1308. A beam is 12 in. wide and 32 in. deep to the steel. Determine the required area of reinforcing steel by the use of jd for balanced reinforcement. $f_c' = 4000$ psi, $n = 8$, $f_s = 24{,}000$ psi. *Ans.* $A_s = 5.4$ sq. in.

1309. If the beam of Problem 1308 is made 14 in. wide and 36 in. deep to the steel, determine the required steel area by estimate of the value of j, and check by an exact method. $M = 300$ ft-kips. *Ans.* $A_s = 4.7$ sq. in.

1310. Design a beam section to resist a moment of 2,500,000 in-lb. for balanced reinforcement at unit stresses of 18,000 and 1350 psi for $n = 9$. (*a*) First determine A_s when $d/b = 3.0$. (*b*) Then choose d and b in whole numbers and recompute A_s and f_c.
Ans. to (*a*). $A_s = 5.0$ sq. in.

1311. Let b equal the width of a 10-in. form board, or 9½ in., for Problem 1310. Compute the depth for $f_c = 1350$ psi. Set the depth to the nearest ½ in. above the computed value of d and determine A_s. *Ans.* $A_s = 4.8$ sq. in.

241. Beam Cross-Sections. Whenever a floor slab or a roof slab is poured integrally with its supporting beams, T-beam cross-sections are formed. Thus, the T-beam becomes the common form of cross-section in building construction, and also for the construction of bridge floors. There are many uses, however, for the simple rectangular beam section. Rigid frames for bridges, buildings, and industrial structures are composed of rectangular sections. Columns must often resist flexure, and their cross-sections are frequently rectangular. Continuous beams of buildings and bridges, commonly poured integrally with slabs, act as T-beams when they resist positive moment. However, at sections of negative moment (near supports) the slab is on the tension side of the cross-section where its usefulness is considered to be negligible. For flexure of columns and negative flexure of continuous beams there is compressive as well as tensile steel reinforcement to be considered. Such beams are termed *doubly reinforced*. They will be studied separately.

T-BEAMS

242. T-Beam Specifications. Specifications in the past have varied somewhat concerning the width of slab that may be considered to form the flange of a T-beam. Now, however, the recommendations of the *ACI* Code given below, have definitely established a standard practice in this regard. This specification is illustrated by Fig. 214. Also read Spec. 307.

(1) The effective flange width used in the design of symmetrical T-beams should not exceed (*a*) ¼ of the span length of the beam, (*b*) 16 times the slab thickness plus the width of the stem, (*c*) the spacing from center to center of beam stems.

(2) For unsymmetrical beams having a flange on one side only the effective flange width should not exceed (*a*) 1/12 of the span length of the beam plus the width of the stem, (*b*) 6 times the flange thickness plus the width of the stem, (*c*) ½ of the clear distance to the next beam plus the width of the stem.

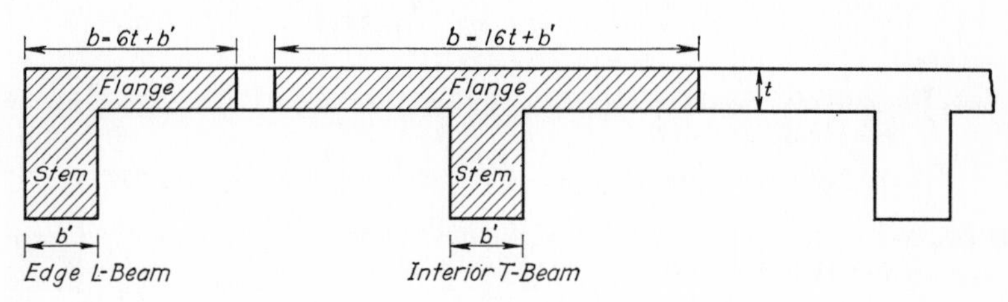

FIG. 214. LIMITATIONS UPON FLANGE WIDTHS OF T-BEAMS.

This figure illustrates only the limitations due to flange thickness. See §242 for limitations based upon span length and stem spacing.

243. Procedures of Analysis. As in the case of rectangular beams, the moment resistance of concrete below the neutral axis of a T-beam is completely neglected. This means that the main function of the stem is in resisting shear, and, in fact, the rectangular section of depth equal to the depth of the T-beam and of width equal to the stem width of the tee will later be treated for shear resistance just like the cross-section of a rectangular beam section.

For the purpose of analysis we will distinguish between three procedures:

CASE 1. The neutral axis lies in the flange. (See Fig. 215(*a*).) Hence, the analysis is identical with the analysis of a rectangular section having the same depth and a width equal to the flange width of the T-beam. This is obviously true because the tensile concrete below the neutral axis is always neglected anyhow. The proper method of analysis is to follow the procedure already studied for rectangular sections.

DP41a. *The cross-section shown is a part of a typical concrete floor system. Find the moment resistance of the section when $f_s = 20{,}000$ psi; $f_c = 1125$; $n = 10$. The beam stems of 24′-0″ length are spaced 8′-0″ on centers. Follow ACI spec.*

Effective Flange Width: *Spec. 307.*

(a) $16 \times 6'' + 12'' = 9'\text{-}0''$.
(b) $\frac{1}{4} \times 24'$ span $= 6'\text{-}0''$ (controls).
(c) Beam spacing $= 8'\text{-}0''$.

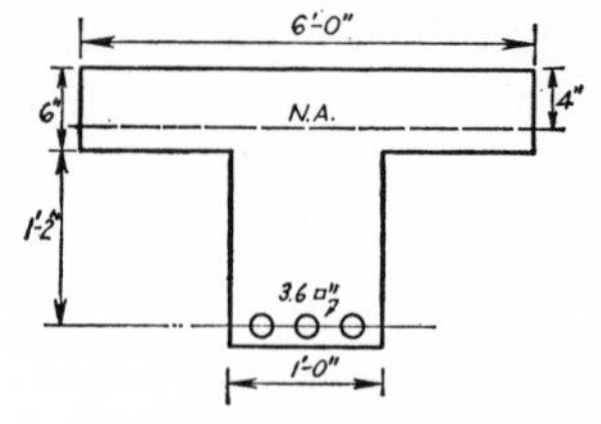

Concrete Stress: *The concrete fiber stress f_c will be low and the steel stress will clearly control the moment of resistance.*

Neutral Axis: *Obtain by statical moments.*

$$3.6 \times 10 \times (20 - kd) = 72\,\frac{(kd)^2}{2}, \text{ or}$$

$$20 - kd = (kd)^2.$$

$$kd = 4.0''; \; jd = 20 - \frac{4}{3} = 18.67''.$$

Rectangular Section: *Since the neutral axis lies within the slab, this is a rectangular section.*

Resisting moment $= A_s f_s jd = 3.6 \times 20{,}000 \times 18.67 = 1{,}340{,}000''\#$.

DP41b. *Repeat the study in DP41a by approximating the effective depth. Change the slab thickness to 3″.*

Effective Depth: *Estimate at 19″ (from steel to ½″ above center of slab). Approximate moment resistance* $= 3.6 \times 20{,}000 \times 19.0 = 1{,}370{,}000''\#$.

Check Investigation: *(Neglect compression resisted by stem.)*

Flange width $= 16 \times 3'' + 12'' = 5'\text{-}0''$.

Neutral axis. $60 \times 3(kd - 1.5) = 3.6 \times 10(20 - kd)$.

$kd = 4.6''$; $d - kd = 15.4''$.

$$I = 36 \times 15.4^2 + \frac{1}{12} \times 60 \times 3^3 + 180 \times 3.1^2 = 10{,}300 \text{ in.}^4$$

$$M_s = \frac{fI}{c} = \frac{f_s I}{d - kd} = \frac{(20{,}000/10) \times 10{,}300}{15.4} = 1{,}340{,}000''\#.$$

$$f_c = \frac{Mc}{I} = \frac{M_s kd}{I} = \frac{1{,}340{,}000 \times 4.6}{10{,}300} = 600 \text{ psi}.$$

Conclusion: *The resisting moment based upon the estimated effective depth was satisfactory for practical use. Neglect of the compression resisted by the stem was found to influence only the 4th significant figure of M_s.*

CASE 2. The neutral axis lies below the flange. As shown in Fig. 215(*b*) the exact transformed area consists of a shallow T-section above the neutral axis and a long narrow tensile area at the level of the steel. The analysis is slightly complicated by the shape of the compressive area. Therefore, the direct use of the Mc/I formula is recommended.

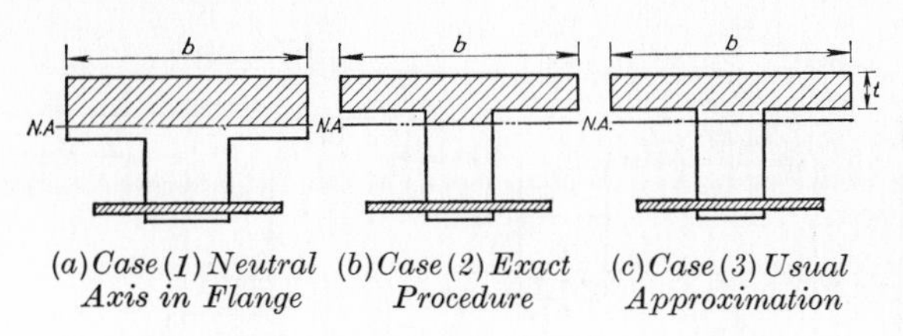

(*a*) *Case* (*1*) *Neutral Axis in Flange* (*b*) *Case* (*2*) *Exact Procedure* (*c*) *Case* (*3*) *Usual Approximation*

FIG. 215. TRANSFORMED SECTIONS FOR T-BEAMS.

CASE 3. The usual approximation when the neutral axis lies below the slab is illustrated in Fig. 215(*c*). The compression in the stem above the neutral axis is neglected, a procedure that is on the safe side in design. Then the compressive area becomes a simple rectangle of width b and depth t. Since the line of action of the total compression C is slightly above the mid-depth of the thin concrete slab, the effective depth jd can be approximated rather accurately, and the analysis is quite simple.

INVESTIGATION OF A T-BEAM WITH A THICK SLAB, *DP*41*a*. The problem is to determine the moment resistance of a reinforced T-beam with a relatively thick 6-in. slab. Since the beam is only 20 in. deep to the steel and has only 3.6 sq. in. of reinforcing steel, which is exactly 0.25 per cent of $b \times d$, we know that the concrete stress will be low. At least 1 per cent of steel is usually needed for balanced reinforcement. Hence, it is fairly evident that the neutral axis will lie above the bottom of the slab and that the controlling moment will depend upon the total tension T. The calculations of kd, jd, and M_s follow the procedure of *DP*38*a*. A check upon the value of f_c shows it to be only 500 psi.

INVESTIGATION OF A T-BEAM WITH A THIN SLAB, *DP*41*b*. The slab of problem *DP*41*a* is reduced from 6 in. to 3 in., which reduces the effective width of flange to 60 in. (Spec. 307) and places the neutral axis in the stem. This is now a T-section rather than a rectangular section.

The Effective Depth. It is common to estimate the effective depth as the distance from the center of the tensile steel reinforcement to ½ in. above the mid-depth of the slab. Of course, the designer will vary this rule of thumb as conditions warrant. However, it is usually possible to estimate the effective depth closely. In *DP*41*b* the effective depth is estimated to be 19 in.

Check Analysis. The section in *DP*41*b* was checked by computing the effective moment of inertia and the resisting moment from the beam-flexure formula. If the correct value of M_s is divided by the total steel stress, the result is the true value of the effective depth. Thus $jd = 1{,}340{,}000 \div (20{,}000 \times 3.6) = 18.7$ in. Hence, our estimate of 19 in. was in error by 0.3 in. This error would not be of serious consequence in design.

DP42. *Design a T-beam floor panel 20 ft. square to the center lines of the girders to carry a live and dead loading of 200 psf plus a wall load of 300#/′ on the edge beam. The 3½″ slab will span 5′–11″ between beams. Let $f_s = 18{,}000$ psi, $f_c = 1350$, $n = 9$. Use ACI spec.*

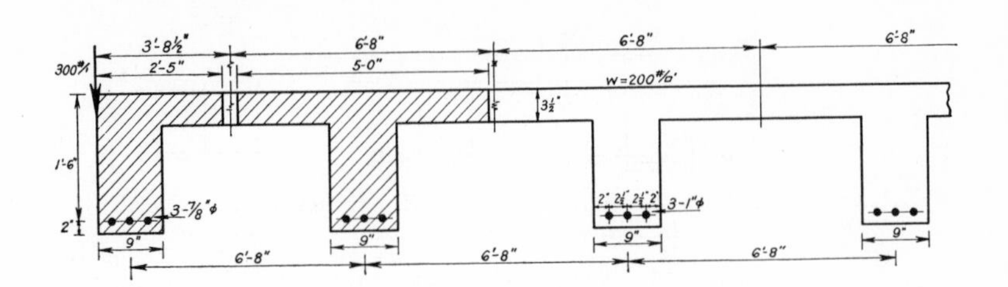

Layout: *The arrangement shown seems the best practical layout.*

Stem area for shear. Without calculation, it will be stated that the shear requires an area b′d equal to 162 in.² in the stem.

Dimensions of stem. For a depth of twice the breadth, d = 18″; b′ = 9″.

Effective Width of Flange: *(See §242 or Spec. 307.)*

Inside T-beam	*Edge L-beam*
(a) 16 × 3.5″ + 9″ = 5′–5″	*(a) 6 × 3.5″ + 9″ = 2′–6″*
(b) ¼ × 20′–0″ = 5′–0″	*(b) 1/12 × 20′ + 9″ = 2′–5″*
(c) Spacing (6′–8″) = 6′–8″	*(c) ½(6′–8″) + 4½″ = 3′–8½″*
Use b = 5′–0″.	*Use b = 2′–5″.*

The smallest value of (a), (b) or (c) controls the effective width of flange.

Bending Moments: *End restraint reduces simple span moment to $1/10wL^2$.*

T-beam $\frac{1}{10}(6.67 \times 200) \times 20^2 \times 12 = 640{,}000''\#$.

L-beam $\frac{1}{10}(3.70 \times 200 + 300) \times 20^2 \times 12 = 500{,}000''\#$.

Selecting Reinforcements:

Approximate effective depth (to ½″ above center of slab) = 16.75″.

Approximate steel areas.

T-beam $640{,}000 \div (16.75 \times 18{,}000) = 2.12$ *in.² Use 3–1″ φs.*

L-beam $500{,}000 \div (16.75 \times 18{,}000) = 1.66$ *in.² Use 3–⅞″ φs.*

Check: *An analysis shows that the neutral axis for the T-section is in the slab at 3.2″ below the surface. Hence, the effective depth is 16.9″ and the design is slightly conservative. The neutral axis of the L-beam is in the stem at 4.0″ below the top surface. In fact, the moment resistance of the L-beam with 3-⅞″ φ rods is found to be 535,000″#.*

244. Use of T-C Couples for T-Beams. If it is desired to avoid the use of the Mc/I formula and base all calculations upon known lever arms for internal stress couples, one can analyze a T-beam section with a thin slab by the use of *two stress couples* as indicated in Fig. 216. Whenever a single couple can be used to represent the stress situation, that method is preferred, but the use of two couples, as in Fig. 216, has no particular advantage over the use of the flexure formula. This device of two internal couples can also be used to investigate beams with steel reinforcement in both the tension and compression faces, but the method will not be emphasized here.

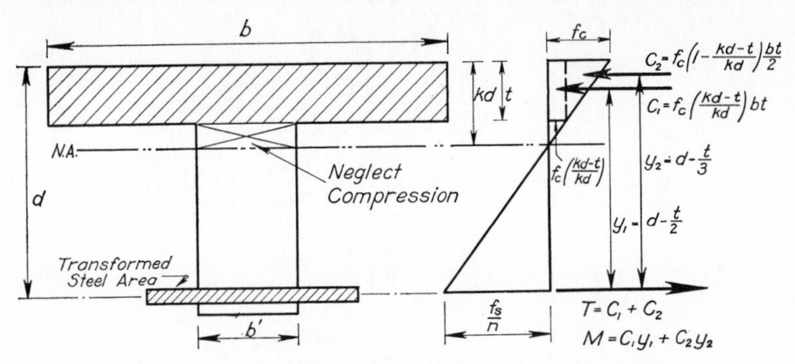

FIG. 216. T-BEAM ANALYSIS BY USE OF TWO T-C COUPLES.

245. Design of T-Beams. The design of a T-beam floor panel involves three steps beyond the design of the slab, which is a separate problem. (1) The effective width of flange must be determined from the specifications given in §242 or Spec. 307. (2) The size of the stem must be chosen to resist the maximum vertical shear. This problem will be treated in §250. (3) The area of steel reinforcement must be determined by one of the methods of §243. The proportions of the stem are usually such that the depth to the steel d is about twice b', the stem width. An increase of depth and a decrease of width would produce economy in the floor itself, but the *extra height* added to the building would increase the total cost of the structure. A shallow floor system is always preferred.

EXAMPLE OF FLOOR SYSTEM DESIGN, *DP*42. This design includes the selection of an interior T-beam and a wall L-beam for known loads. The effective flange widths are taken at the minimum values according to the three specified limitations of §242. Bending moments are computed for a span length of 20 ft. since no data are available as to the reduction of moment due to the width of the edge girder. However, it is assumed that edge conditions provide sufficient restraint to reduce the simple-span bending moments from $1/8wL^2$ to $1/10wL^2$. The design is made upon the basis of the rather common assumption that the effective depth is from the center of the steel to ½ in. above the center of the slab. Steel areas furnished (in order to use bars of a single size in each beam) are about 10 per cent greater than those needed. In the T-beam, we could use 2 No. 8 bars and 1 No. 7 bar, while, for the L-beam, 2 No. 7 bars and 1 No. 6 bar would be adequate.

T-Beam Charts. The Charts for determining values of k and j for T-beams are quite useful. These ratios may be obtained from Fig. 217 for any values of pn and of t/d. Remember that p is A_s/bd, where b is the width of the flange or slab, t being the slab thickness. The diagonal line in the chart for k of Fig. 217 is the limit of T-beam action, where $t = kd$. These data for T-beams were first published in the form of pn curves by R. A. Caughey. They may be used to check your calculations for the transformed section.

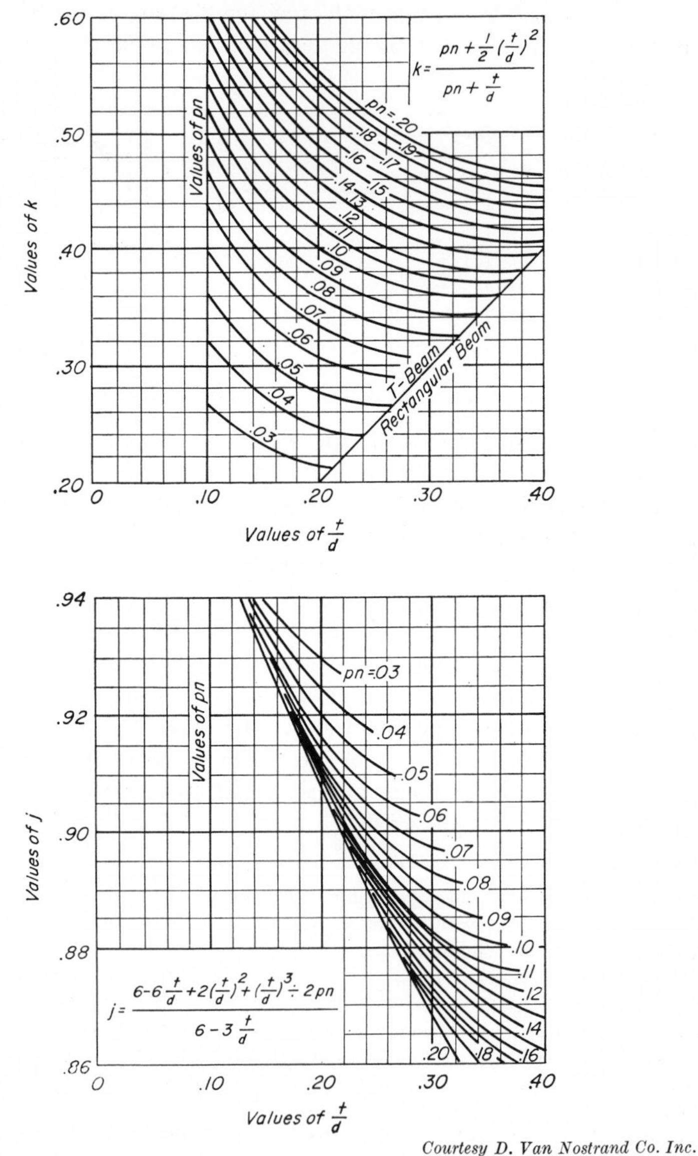

Courtesy D. Van Nostrand Co. Inc.

FIG. 217. VALUES OF k AND j FOR T-BEAMS. ENTER CHART WITH VALUES OF pn AND t/d.

PROBLEMS

1312. A T-beam has the following dimensions: $b = 3'-4''$; $t = 7$ in.; $d = 24$ in.; $b' = 10$ in.; $A_s = 3$ sq. in. Determine the fiber stresses when $M = 1{,}334{,}000$ in-lb. by locating the neutral axis. $n = 10$. *Ans.* $f_s = 20{,}000$; $f_c = 570$ psi.

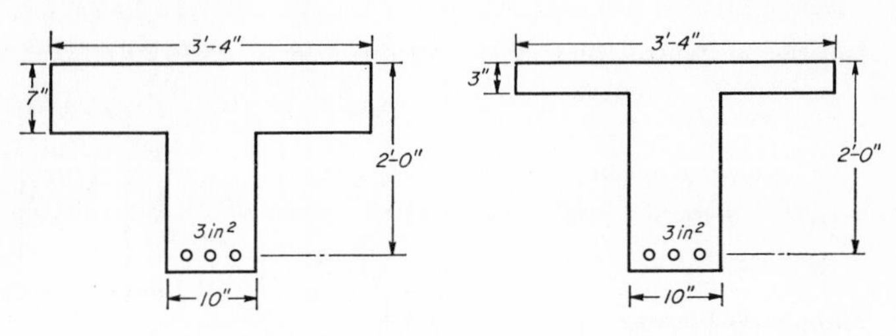

PROBLEM 1312. PROBLEM 1313.

1313. A T-beam has the following dimensions: $b = 3'-4''$; $t = 3$ in.; $d = 24$ in.; $b' = 10$ in.; $A_s = 3$ sq. in. Determine the controlling resisting moment first by estimating the effective depth and second by locating the neutral axis and using the fI/c formula; $f_s = 20{,}000$ psi.; Neglect the compression in the web. (*a*) Let $n = 10$; (*b*) $n = 8.5$. *Ans.* to (*a*) $M_s = 1{,}360{,}000$ in-lb.

1314. Check either (*a*) or (*b*) of Problem 1313 by use of an exact effective depth determined by locating the centroid of the compressive stress acting on the section of the slab. Neglect compression in the web. Revise by considering the compression in the web.

1315. Design a T-beam and an edge L-beam for a floor panel 24 ft. by 30 ft. Span the beams in the shorter direction. The slab is 3¼ in. thick. It can span 5½ ft. clear between beams and carry the uniform dead and live loading of 275 psf. There is an additional wall load of 400 lb. per ft. acting on the edge beam. Consider this to be a single panel so that the simple-span moments control the design. Let $f_s = 20{,}000$ psi, $f_c = 1350$, $n = 9$. Assume that shear requires the area $b'd$ to be at least 180 sq. in. for 24-ft. beams spaced about 6 ft. on centers. Follow *ACI* spec.

1316. Redesign the panel of Problem 1315 for $f_c' = 2500$ psi, $n = 10$. Use a 3-in. slab; allow edge restraint that reduces moment to $1/10\ wL^2$. Let the uniform $DL + LL$ be 180 psf.

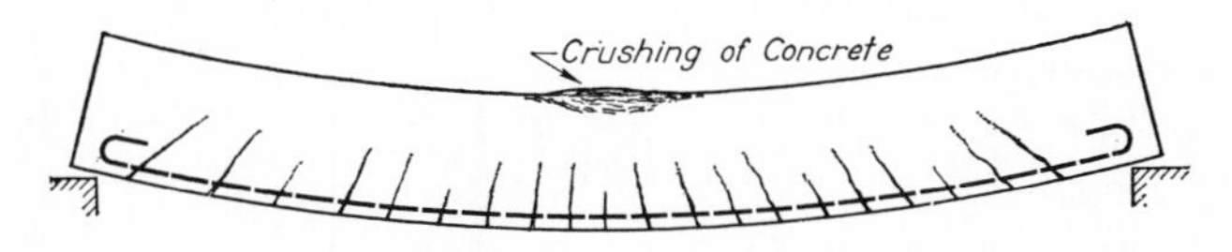

FIG. 218. FAILURE BY CRUSHING OF CONCRETE. WEB REINFORCEMENT NOT SHOWN.

BEAMS WITH COMPRESSIVE REINFORCEMENT

246. Doubly Reinforced Beams. Concrete beams tend to be overly large in appearance and their depths use up valuable head-room when spans are rather long. If a rectangular beam is reinforced heavily to reduce its depth, the concrete may become overstressed in compression at the extreme fiber. The type of failure under such conditions is illustrated by Fig. 218. Of

DP43. *The doubly reinforced beam shown must resist a bending moment of 150,000"#. Determine the fiber stresses. Let $n = 10$ for normal weight concrete when $f_c' = 2500$ psi; $f_s = 20{,}000$ psi. Use $2n - 1 = 19$ to transform the compressive steel.*

Location of Neutral Axis: *Equate statical moments about the neutral axis.*

$$8.8(10 - kd) = \frac{6(kd)^2}{2} + 3.8(kd - 2).$$

$$(kd)^2 + 4.1(kd) + 2.05^2 = 35.9.$$

$$kd = 3.93''.$$

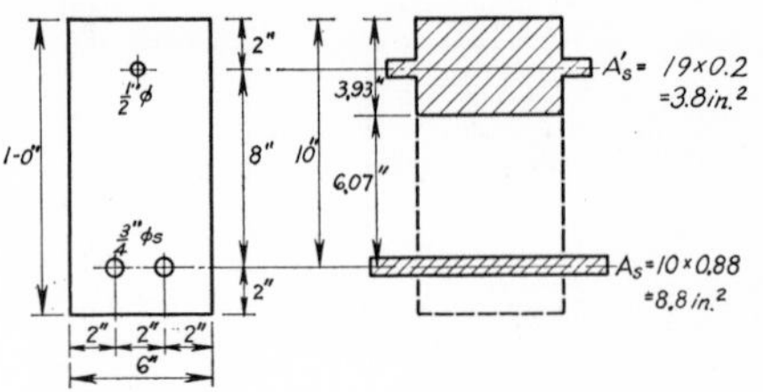

Moment of Inertia:

$$I = 8.8 \times 6.07^2 + 3.8 \times 1.93^2 + \tfrac{1}{3} \times 6 \times 3.93^3 = 458.$$

Fiber Stresses (Mc/I):

$f_c = 150{,}000 \times 3.93 \div 458 = 1290$ psi (exceeds allowable of 1125).

$f_s = (150{,}000 \times 6.07 \div 458)10 = 19{,}900$ psi (under 20,000).

$f_s' = (2 \times 150{,}000 \times 1.93 \div 458)10 = 12{,}600$ psi (under 20,000).

Conclusion: *f_c' would be increased above 2500 psi in preference to increasing A_s'.*

DP43b. *The beam with compressive reinforcement shown is constructed with structural grade steel for which $f_s = 18{,}000$ psi and with concrete for which $f_c' = 2500$ psi and $n = 10$. Hence, $f_c = 0.45 \times 2500 = 1125$ psi. If the area of tensile steel is proper for balanced reinforcement at 18,000 psi, determine the resisting moment of the doubly reinforced section by ACI spec.*

Compression in Steel: *Twice the computed steel stress in compression would exceed 18,000 psi. Hence, the effective compressive stress in the steel for moment resistance is* $18{,}000 - 1125 \dfrac{6.2}{8.7} = 17{,}200$ *psi. (Spec. 317.)*

Moment Resistance:

Moment resisted by $A_s' = 1.0 \times 17{,}200 \times 20.0 = 344{,}000''\#$.

Moment resisted by concrete $= \dfrac{1125}{2} \times 8 \times 8.7\left(22.5 - \dfrac{8.7}{3}\right) = 766{,}000''\#$.

Total resisting moment $= 344{,}000 + 766{,}000 = 1{,}110{,}000''\#$.

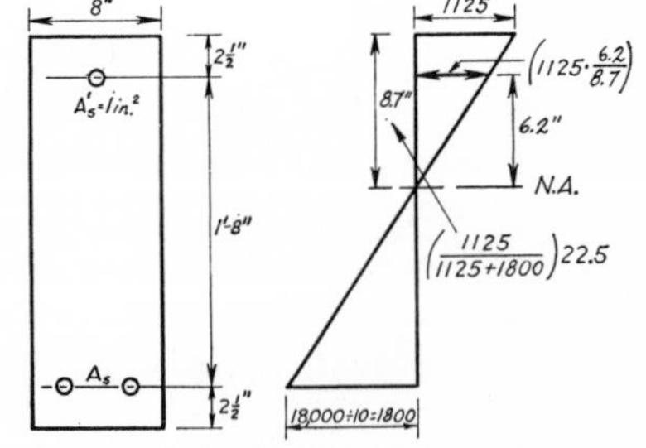

Remarks: *The area of tensile steel found by dividing the total compression C of 56,300# by 18,000 psi is 3.13 in². A_s is so large that a higher strength steel may be needed.*

course, we can always increase the breadth of the beam to reduce the compressive stresses, but it may be more economical to provide *compressive steel.* This is particularly true since there are several arrangements of reinforcement that provide steel in both faces of the beam anyway. For example, when a T-beam is continuous over several panels, it must resist negative moment over each support. At these sections the lower fibers of the beam are in compression, the T-section becomes a rectangular section, and the reinforcing bars that were designed at the mid-span as tensile steel now act as compressive steel. This situation will be clarified by Fig. 219.

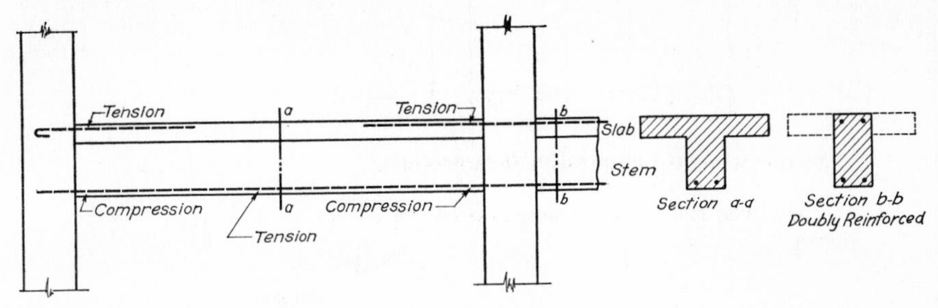

FIG. 219. ACTION OF A CONTINUOUS T-BEAM FLOOR SYSTEM.

247. Specification Regarding Compressive Reinforcement. The standard specification in regard to the use of compressive reinforcement in beams may be summarized as follows:

Compressive reinforcement in girders or beams should be secured against buckling by ties or stirrups of not less than ¼-in. diameter adequately anchored in the concrete and spaced not more than 16 bar diameters or 48 tie diameters apart. Where compressive reinforcement is used, its *effectiveness in resisting bending may be taken at twice the value indicated by the calculations*, assuming a straight-line relationship between stress and strain and the proper value of n, but not greater than the allowable stress in tension (Spec. 317). Hence the compressive steel is transformed by use of the factor $2n - 1$.

Explanation of Specification. It is a relatively simple matter of analysis to compute the stress in compressive reinforcement on the basis of a straight-line variation of stress over the cross-section. The *ACI Building Code*, however, permits the compressive steel to be twice as effective (up to the allowable stress in tension) as this calculation would suggest. The reason is that plastic creep of the concrete has been demonstrated to produce greater steel stresses in compressive reinforcement than is indicated by the simple theory of straight-line stress distribution. Hence, the higher stress developed by the steel can be depended upon to help resist the external bending moment.

248. Investigation of Doubly Reinforced Sections. Since compressive steel displaces an equal area of useful concrete, its theoretical addition to the transformed section is $(n-1)A_s'$, where A_s' is the area of compressive steel.

DP44. *The beam shown (taken from DP39a) was designed according to ACI specifications for 2500 psi concrete of 145 pcf., i.e.,* $f_c = 1125$ *psi,* $f_s = 18{,}000$, $n = 10$. *The bending moment was 556,000″#. Assume that it becomes necessary for a beam of this size to resist a bending moment of 860,000″#. Compute the increase in tensile steel area and the area of compressive steel needed, if working stresses are raised to* $f_c = 1500$; $f_s = 24{,}000$; *and* $n = 9$,

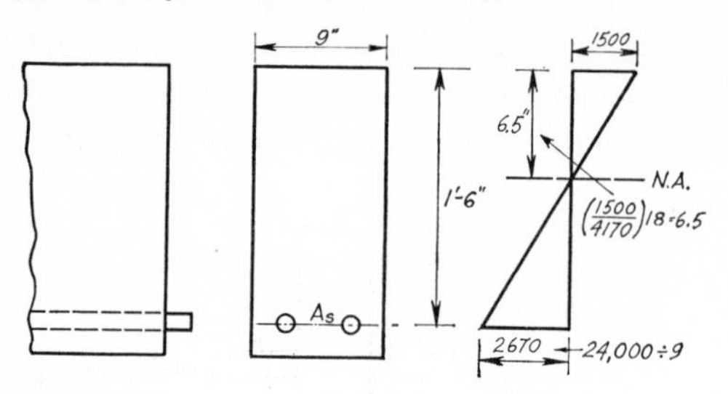

Section without Compressive Reinforcement:

$$\text{Resisting moment from concrete stress} = \left(\frac{1500 \times 6.5 \times 9.0}{2}\right)\left(18 - \frac{6.5}{3}\right) = 690{,}000''\#.$$

$$\text{Steel area to balance concrete resistance} = \frac{690{,}000}{24{,}000[18 - (6.5/3)]} = 1.82\ in^2.$$

$$\text{Resisting moment remaining} = 860{,}000 - 690{,}000 = 170{,}000''\#.$$

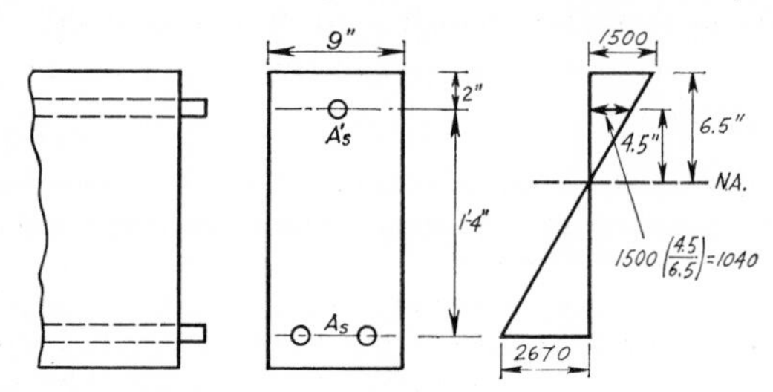

Compressive Reinforcement: *Placed where* $f_c = 1040$ *psi.*

Compressive steel stress $= 2 \times 1040 \times 9 = 18{,}800$ *psi. The effective stress is limited to* $18{,}800 - 1040 = 17{,}760$ *psi.*

$$A_s' \text{ to resist the moment of } 170{,}000''\# = \frac{170{,}000}{17{,}760 \times 16} = 0.60\ in^2.$$

Use 1–⅞″ϕ. No. 7 bar.

$$A_s \text{ to equalize } A_s' = 0.60 \times \frac{17{,}760}{24{,}000} = 0.44\ in^2.$$

Total area of tensile steel needed $= 1.82 + 0.44 = 2.26\ in^2$.

Use 2–#10 ϕs; area furnished $= 2 \times 1.27 = 2.54\ in^2$.

Remarks: *The transformed section was not used here. It is not needed in design for balanced reinforcement either with or without compressive steel.*

However, by Spec. 317 the effectiveness of compressive steel is increased by a factor of 2 if its calculated compressive stress does not then exceed the allowable tensile stress for the grade of steel used. Accordingly, if we are reasonably certain that twice the computed compressive steel stress will be less than the allowable compressive stress (which is identical with the allowable tensile stress for the grade of steel being used), the simplest way to allow for the increased effectiveness of compressive steel is to give it a fictitious area in the transformed section of $(2n - 1)A_s'$.

Determination of Fiber Stresses, *DP*43*a*. This example illustrates the common method of investigating a doubly reinforced section. For shallow beams (less than say 18 in. deep) it is usually found that the compressive steel stress computed as $2n$ times the compressive concrete stress at the level of the compressive steel is less than the limiting upper value for the steel. For such beams, we transform the tensile steel as nA_s and the compressive steel as $(2n - 1)A_s'$. From here on the procedure has already been standardized, that is, (*a*) locate the neutral axis (by statical moments) as the c.g. of the transformed section, (*b*) compute the moment of inertia of the transformed section about its c.g., (*c*) determine fiber stresses by use of the Mc/I formula.

Compressive Steel Stressed to Maximum, *DP*43*b*. The limit on compressive steel stress according to the *ACI* spec. is 18,000 psi for structural grade steel. However, the fact that the steel displaces an equal area of compressive concrete will be taken into consideration if the effective steel stress is reduced to $18{,}000 - f_c''$ where f_c'' is the concrete stress at the level of the compressive steel. This procedure is followed in *DP*43*b* for determining the moment resisted by the compressive steel. To this moment is added the resisting moment based upon compression in the concrete in order to obtain the total resisting moment of the doubly reinforced section.

249. Design of Doubly Reinforced Sections. It should be clear from the preceding discussion that one approaches the analysis or design of a doubly reinforced beam by setting up the moment resistance of the regular concrete-steel section and by adding to this resisting moment a couple developed by the compressive steel and an equivalent area of tensile steel. The "equivalent area" will be determined so that the corresponding values of C' and T' will be identical.

If the compressive steel stress was limited by elastic analysis to $n - 1$ times the stress in the concrete that it displaces, we would have to balance A_s' by adding an area of tensile steel such that the neutral axis would not be shifted. However, the acceptance of a compressive steel stress of $2n - 1$ times the stress in the concrete that it displaces involves acceptance of incompatibility of compressive strains in the concrete and the compressive steel. Hence, instead of the refinement of balancing added steel areas by use of their distances from the neutral axis we merely need to provide a tensile steel area to resist T' at the allowable stress f_s where $T' = C'$ the force resisted by A_s'.

Strengthening a Section by Compressive Steel, *DP*44. In this example, the resisting moment of the section is determined first without compressive steel but with balanced tensile steel of 1.82 sq. in. The difference between this resisting moment and the bending moment is the moment of the couple to be developed by the compressive steel and by an equivalent area of tensile steel. The equivalent area of tensile steel, found in this way, is 0.44 sq. in. The final value of A_s is, therefore, $1.82 + 0.44 = 2.26$

sq. in. Again, as in previous examples, the most convenient method of handling a doubly reinforced beam is to consider it as a regular rectangular section without compressive steel strengthened by a couple developed by use of compressive steel and the *addition of an equivalent area of tensile steel.* Notice that the neutral axis of such a doubly reinforced beam may not pass exactly through the center of gravity of the transformed section. This would only be true if the steel and concrete acted together elastically in compression. Instead, an increase in the compressive steel stress caused by plastic flow has been assumed.

PROBLEMS

1317. A beam of 10-in. width and 30-in. depth (to the c.g. of the steel) carries 2 per cent of tensile steel or 6 sq. in. in two layers as shown. Find the area of compressive steel to permit the value of $f_s = 20{,}000$ psi to be developed. $f_c = 1350$; $n = 9$. Use *ACI* spec. *Ans.* $A_s' = 2.6$ sq. in.

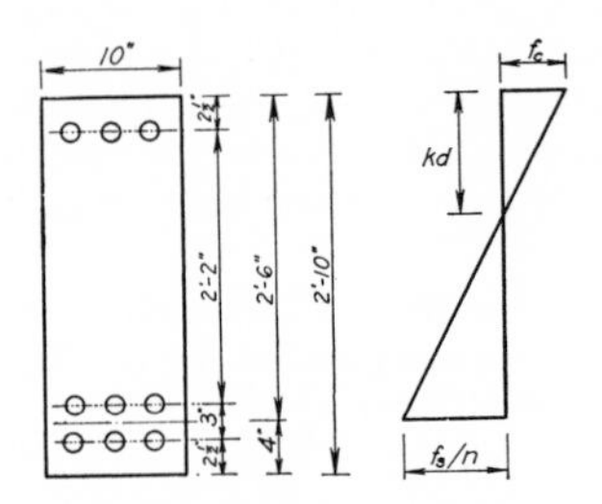

PROBLEM 1317.

1318. Add compressive steel to the beam of Problem 1302 to increase the moment resistance from 17,500,000 to 21,000,000 in-lb. The level of the compressive steel is 3 in. below the top surface. Limit f_s' to $2n - 1$ times the unit concrete stress at the level of the compressive steel to allow for its reduction in effective area of concrete. $f_c = 1500$ psi; $f_s = 24{,}000$; $n = 9$. Is additional tensile steel needed? *Ans.* 3.2 sq. in.

1319. In Problem 1308, the beam of 12-in. breadth and 32-in. depth to the steel resists a moment of 4,500,000 in-lb. when $n = 8$, $f_c = 1800$, $f_s = 24{,}000$ psi. First determine the value of A_s for balanced reinforcement, and then determine the change in A_s and the area of compressive steel to resist the increased moment. The compressive steel is 2.5 in. below the surface. *Ans.* $A_s' = 1.35$ sq. in.

1320. If the dimensions of the cross-section of Problem 1317 cannot be increased and if three round bars per layer are the greatest number permitted for $b = 10$ in. for the size of the aggregate used, determine whether a 10 per cent necessary increase in moment above the full resistance of the section can best be achieved by improving the strength of the concrete or by increasing the area of compressive steel above 2.6 sq. in. and of tensile steel as needed. Assume that a 10 per cent increase in the strength of the concrete costs the same as a 10 per cent increase in the area of longitudinal steel bars.

SHEAR

250. Unit Shear in Concrete Beams. The *average* unit vertical shear on the cross-section of a rectangular reinforced concrete beam would be the total shear V divided by the area of the effective cross-section $(b \times d)$. We know that the maximum unit shear for a plain rectangular cross-section is $\frac{3}{2}$ times the average, or $\frac{3}{2}(V/bd)$. Therefore, we might expect to find the maximum unit shear for the reinforced cross-section to be greater than V/bd.

Isolate a short length x of the beam as shown in Fig. 220. This part of the beam is in equilibrium under the forces shown. Since the only horizontal forces below the neutral axis are T_1 and T_2 (tension in the concrete being neglected) the expression $T_1 - T_2$ represents the total horizontal shear on any horizontal plane below the neutral axis. The corresponding unit horizontal shear is $(T_1 - T_2) \div bx$. Above the neutral axis, the unit shear has parabolic variation as shown in Fig. 220(b) just as would be true for the compression side of a plain concrete section.

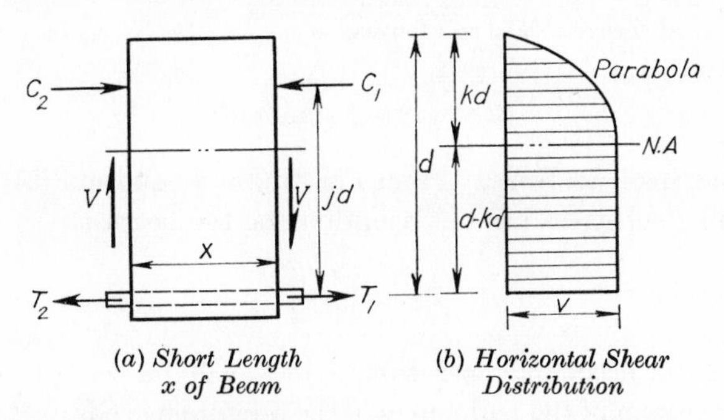

(a) *Short Length x of Beam* (b) *Horizontal Shear Distribution*

FIG. 220. SHEAR DISTRIBUTION ACROSS THE SECTION.

By equating the horizontal and vertical couples in Fig. 220(a), we obtain

(5) $$(T_1 - T_2)jd = Vx.$$

or

(6) $$\frac{T_1 - T_2}{x} = \frac{V}{jd}.$$

Since our interest is in the *unit* horizontal shear, each side of equation (6) may be divided by the breadth b to give

(7) $$v = \frac{T_1 - T_2}{bx} = \frac{V}{bjd}.$$ (See Spec. 318 where j is omitted.)

It is also possible to derive this relationship from the area of the shear distribution curve of Fig. 220(b).

Unit Shear in T-Beams. It is the common practice, as justified by tests, to treat the stem of a T-beam cross-section as a rectangular beam of depth equal to the depth of the T-beam and of width equal to the width b' of the stem of the tee. Other cross-sections may also be handled by substitute rectangular sections. Evidently, the analysis of shearing stresses by neglect of the tension resistance of the concrete is rather crude. Therefore it is unnecessary to determine the exact value of j. It has been common practice to set j for shear calculation at 0.9. However, by *AISC* specifications, j is merely omitted from formula (5), which is equivalent to giving it a value of 1.0. If allowable values of unit shear are reduced in proportion to the change in j, there is no influence upon the design.

Working Stresses in Shear. According to the *ACI Building Code* shearing unit stresses allowable in reinforced concrete beams as a measure of resistance to diagonal tension are those given in Table 24 which are used with a value of j of unity. (See Spec. 318.)

(a) Beams without web reinforcement .... $1.1\sqrt{f_c'}$

(b) Joists without web reinforcement .... $1.2\sqrt{f_c'}$

(c) Members with vertical or inclined web reinforcement or a proper combination.. $5.0\sqrt{f_c'}$

(d) Peripheral shear in slabs and footings........................ $2.0\sqrt{f_c'}$

Bond and Anchorage

251. Bond Stress on Rods. From Fig. 220 and equation (5), we see that the change in steel stress per unit length along the beam is

$$T_1 - T_2 = \frac{V}{jd}. \tag{8}$$

The bond stress in pounds per square inch will be $u = (T_1 - T_2) \div \Sigma 0$, where $\Sigma 0$ is the sum of the perimeters of the reinforcing rods. Hence we may write

$$u = \frac{V}{\Sigma 0 jd}. \quad \text{(See Spec. 323.)} \tag{9}$$

This formula defines the bond stress caused by changes of steel stress that tends to slide the steel bars through the concrete. However, since cracks disturb the ideal action considered here, we should consider this formula merely as a measure of bond stress for comparisons between test beams and designed beams.

Working Stresses in Bond. According to the *ACI Building Code* the following unit bond stresses are allowable in reinforced concrete beams. (See Spec. 315 and Table S-9.)

(a) Top bars in tension, up to No. 11 size .... $\dfrac{3.4\sqrt{f_c'}}{D} < 350$ psi.

(b) Other bars in tension, up to No. 11 size............... $\dfrac{4.8\sqrt{f_c'}}{D} < 500$ psi.

(c) Bars in compression, all sizes .... $6.0\sqrt{f_c'} < 400$ psi.

(d) Plain bars .... ½ of values above < 160 psi.

Note: Top bars are those below which the depth of concrete is 12 in. or more. Since end anchorage of longitudinal bars influences the resistance of a beam to both shear and bond, anchorage requirements will be considered next.

252. End Anchorage of Reinforcing Bars. It is commonly assumed that the embedded end of a longitudinal bar beyond the face of the support provides an anchorage resistance equal to the product of the allowable unit bond resistance times the surface area of the embedded bar, or bars. The length of embedment may be straight or curved. A typical hook as shown in Fig. 204 is sufficient anchorage to resist a stress in the hooked bar equal to 10,000 psi. The standard 180-degree hook has an inside radius of bend increasing with bar size from $2.5D$ to $5D$ plus an extension of $2\frac{1}{2}$ in. (or $4D$ for large bars) at the free end of the bar, where D is the diameter of the bar. A 90-degree hook usually has a radius of bend of $4D$ plus a straight extension at the free end of $12D$. Stirrups are often anchored by 135-degree hooks with a radius of $3D$ and an extension of $2\frac{1}{2}$ in. or $6D$ at the free end of the stirrup. The full semi-circular bend is the most common hook. Plain bars in tension must terminate in standard hooks except that hooks are not required on the positive reinforcement of continuous beams at interior supports where the negative bending moment reverses the sign of the steel stress.

Minimum Anchorage by Extension of Bars. The many different anchorage problems of simple beams, cantilevers, continuous beams, and rigid frames may be treated under the concept that each bar must be extended for minimum anchorage at least $12D$, or the depth of the member beyond the point where it is no longer needed to resist stress. A bottom tension bar may be anchored by bending it across the web at an angle of 15 degrees or more with the longitudinal direction and making it continuous with bars in the top of the beam. It is not permitted to cut off a tension bar in a tension zone unless either the shear stress, bond stress, or tension steel stress just beyond the point of cut-off is only 50 per cent of the corresponding allowable stress. One third of the top bars resisting negative moment at a support of a continuous beam must be extended beyond the point of zero moment, the larger distance of either $\frac{1}{16}$ of the clear span or the depth of the member. The positive reinforcement of continuous beams is lightly anchored by extending one fourth of the bars into the support a distance of 6 in. This fraction of the positive steel to be extended into the support is increased to one third for simple spans or at a simply supported end of a continuous beam.

Anchoring Web Reinforcement. When longitudinal bars are bent across the member they are anchored by being welded to or made continuous with the bars in the opposite face or by bond resistance, with or without hooks, in the opposite half of the beam to develop the bar. Stirrups, either simple or multiple U-shape, are usually anchored either by welding to the longitudinal bars or by hooking around these bars with 135-degree or 180-degree hooks. Anchorage is computed by bond stress in the compressive half of the depth of the beam if less than a 180-degree hook is used.

Stirrups and Bent Bars

253. Diagonal Tension Reinforcement. Wherever shears exist, there are also unit tensile stresses of the same value at 45 degrees. (See Fig. 202.) These tensile stresses combine with the horizontal tension caused by flexure to produce diagonal tensions of varying slope throughout the length and depth of the beam. The result is the diagonal tension cracks shown by Fig. 207. Evidently, the most effective reinforcement would be the use of sloping web bars crossing these cracks at as near 90 degrees as possible. However, since there are horizontal bars near the lower surface of the beam, the web reinforcement can be designed effectively as vertical stirrups. Vertical web reinforcement will resist the vertical components of the diagonal tension stresses and leave the horizontal components to be resisted by the horizontal bars. See Fig. 221, where a complete failure could have been prevented by a vertical stirrup crossing the diagonal crack along *a*-*a*. This is the most common form of web reinforcement.

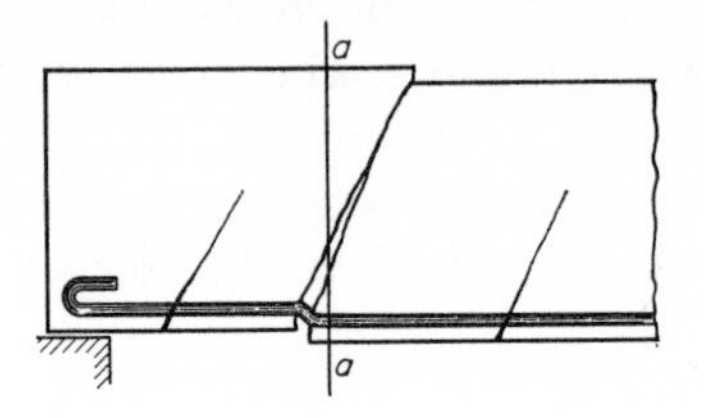

FIG. 221. DIAGONAL TENSION FAILURE PREVENTABLE BY VERTICAL STIRRUP ALONG *a*-*a*.

254. Stirrup Spacing Formulas. In Fig. 222 the diagonal tension will be considered to act at 45 degrees at all points (as for pure shear) since we have consistently neglected horizontal tension in the concrete.

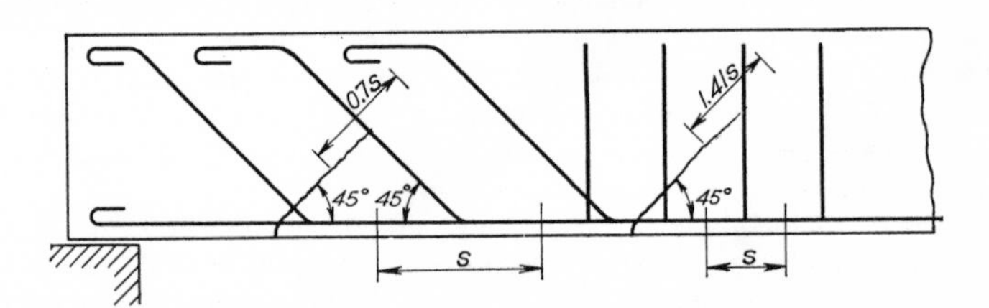

FIG. 222. SPACING OF STIRRUPS AND BENT BARS.

Bars at 45 *Degrees.* For bars bent at 45 degrees, the total diagonal tension resisted per bar will be

$$v'b(0.7s) = A_v f_v,$$

where f_v is the allowable stress for the web steel which by *ACI* specifications is the same as f_s, the allowable tension in the longitudinal steel.

$$s = \frac{A_v f_v}{0.7v'b}. \quad \text{(Diagonal bars at 45 degrees.)} \tag{10}$$

Significance of Terms. In these formulas each symbol has the following meaning:

A_v cross-sectional area of bent bar or stirrup. If several bars or stirrups occur in one plane, A_v is the sum of their cross-sectional areas.
b breadth of beam that carries the shear, *i.e.*, stem width b' for a T-beam.
d depth of beam to the reinforcing steel.
f_v allowable unit stress in stirrups or bent bars, usually the same as f_s.
s horizontal distance between stirrups or bent bars.
v' unit vertical shear in excess of the unit shear resisted by the concrete. (Unit diagonal tension resisted by the web reinforcement is also equal to v'.)
V' total vertical shear in excess of that resisted by the concrete section or $v'bjd$.
α angle between a sloping bar and the direction of the longitudinal rods.

Vertical Stirrups. For vertical stirrups the diagonal tension per bar is $v'b(1.41s)$. (See Fig. 222.) Only the vertical component of this force or $v'bs$ is resisted by the vertical stirrup. Hence, we write

$$v'bs = A_v f_v,$$

or

(11)
$$s = \frac{A_v f_v}{v'b}, \quad \text{or by } ACI, \quad A_v = \frac{V's}{f_v d}.$$

Bent Bars. For slopes between 15 and 90 degrees an empirical formula (Spec. 321) is commonly used,

(12)
$$s = \frac{A_v f_v(\cos \alpha + \sin \alpha)}{v'b}, \quad \text{or by } ACI, \quad A_v = \frac{V's}{f_v d(\sin \alpha + \cos \alpha)}.$$

In the *ACI* formulas j is again omitted or given a value of unity. If the bars bent up are in a single plane of inclination α, the term s has no meaning and the following empirical formula is used.

(13)
$$A_v = \frac{V'}{f_v \sin \alpha}.$$

Spacing of Bars. Where web reinforcement is needed the minimum area provided shall be 0.15 per cent of $b \times s$, or $b' \times s$ for a T-section. The horizontal length of web reinforced by bent bars in one plane should not exceed that covered by the middle ¾ of the bent portion of the bar. Web reinforcement is to be spaced so that any 45-degree crack in the tension half of the beam will be intersected by at least one web bar. (Spec. 319.) At least two bars (in different planes) should intersect each possible 45-degree crack when the unit shear exceeds $3\sqrt{f_c'}$.

Bending Bars for Web Reinforcement. If the moment diagram for the entire beam is known, one can readily determine the points where bars may be bent up (usually in pairs) without weakening the flexural resistance of the beam. The procedure is simply to calculate the effective moment resistance of the cross-section with reduced area of tensile steel, and then to bend the bars at that point beyond which the moment resistance of the

DP45. *Design the cross-section and reinforcement of a rectangular beam of length 24′–0″ for which the center moment is 1,660,000″# and the end shear is 33,000#. The shear reduces to 27,500# at 2 ft. from the support. Allow* $f_s = 20{,}000$ *psi,* $f_v = 18{,}000$ *psi;* $f_c = 0.45 \times 3500 = 1580$ *psi,* $n = 8.5$. *Follow ACI spec.*

Moment Requirements: *Use balanced reinforcement.*

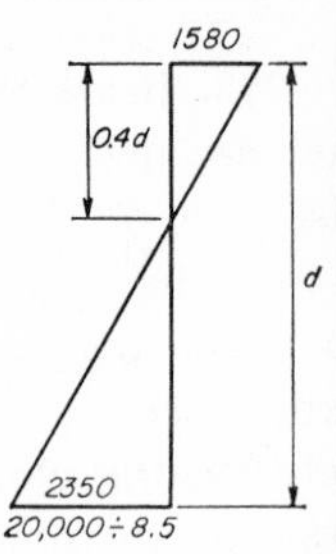

$$k = \frac{1580}{1580 + 2350} = 0.4;\ j = 1 - \frac{0.4}{3} = 0.87.$$

$$C = T = \left(\frac{1580}{2}\right) bkd = 316\ bd.$$

$M_c = Cjd = (316 \times 0.87)bd^2 = 275\ bd^2.$
For $b = d/3$, $M_c = 1{,}660{,}000 = 275\ d^3/3$, or $d = 26.3''$.
Let $b = 9''$, $d = 26.5''$, as shown.
$A_s = 1{,}660{,}000 \div (26.5 \times 0.87 \times 20{,}000) = 3.62\ in^2.$
This area is provided by 6 ⅞-in. No. 7 bars of intermediate grade.

Bond Stress: *Assume 3 bars continue into the support.*

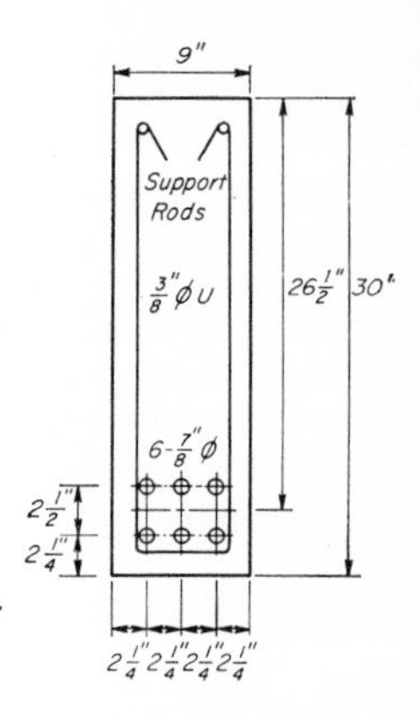

$$u = \frac{V}{\Sigma 0 jd} = \frac{33{,}000}{3 \times 3.14 \times 0.875 \times 0.87 \times 26.5} = 174\ \text{psi}.$$

Allowable u for deformed bars $= (4.8\sqrt{3500}) \div 0.875 = 325$ *psi.*

Shear Stress: *(By AISC spec. use reduced V at d from support)*

$$v = \frac{V}{bd} = \frac{27{,}500}{9 \times 26.5} = 115\ \text{psi}.$$

Allowable v_c *of* $1.1\sqrt{f_c'} = 65$ *psi (occurs at 6′–4″ from support).* $v'_{max} = 115 - 65 = 50$ *psi.*
Shear reinforcement should extend 6′–4″ + d = 102.5″ from support.

Bent Bars: *Two bars may be bent up at one location and one at a second location determined from the moment diagram. However, since this arrangement will not cover the length needing shear reinforcement, stirrups will be used instead.*

Stirrups: *A ⅜″ single loop stirrup furnishes* $A_v = 0.22\ in^2$ *at a section.*
At 2.0 ft. from support

$$s = \frac{A_v f_v}{v'b} = \frac{0.22 \times 18{,}000}{(115 - 65) \times 9} = 8.8''\ \text{(constant for length } d).$$

At 3.5 ft. from support v reduces to 100 psi.

$$s = \frac{0.22 \times 18{,}000}{(100 - 65) \times 9} = 12.5''.$$

This spacing is close enough so that each 45-degree crack in the lower half of the beam will intersect one stirrup. Stirrup spacing may be 3 @ 8″, 2 @ 10″, and 5 @ 12″ from each end of the beam.

Specification: *Minimum stirrup area* $= 0.15\% \times (bs) = 0.0015 \times 9 \times 12 = 0.16\ in^2$; $0.22\ in^2$ *provided.*

emainder of the section equals or exceeds the bending moment. It is not ιecessary to locate these points with great accuracy.

Design of Reinforced Concrete Beams

255. Beam Design. The complete design of a reinforced concrete beam ıcludes not only the choice of the breadth, depth, and area of steel, but lso the design of web reinforcement. For long beams, where flexure s more important than shear, it may be possible to design the cross-section o resist shear without the need for web reinforcement. The common xperience, however, is to find that the web is adequate to resist the shear etween the quarter points and the center of the beam, but that bent-up ars, or stirrups, or both are needed from near the quarter points to the nds of the beam.

Design of a Beam, *DP*45. The cross-section of this beam is first chosen for alanced design, that is, allowable fiber stresses in steel and concrete are both to be ealized under the maximum moment. The cross-section chosen contains six ⅞-in. ϕ ods in two layers. The effective depth is taken to the mid-depth between the two yers of steel. Since the beam is 9 in. wide, clearances between bars can be greater ıan the minimum of one diameter.

Bond resistance is found to be satisfactory if three of the six deformed rods are ontinued into the support. The allowable unit shear for 3500 psi concrete leaves 50 si to be resisted by web reinforcement within 2 ft. of the support. Single loop stirrups of o. 3 rod (⅜-in. diameter) are found to be adequate at 8.8-in. spacing near the support nd at 12.5-in. spacing at 3.5 ft. from the support. Bent bars could be used to reduce ıe length of the span to be covered by stirrups.

PROBLEMS

Follow *ACI* specifications as given in §311, p. 443.

1321. Redesign the beam of *DP*45 for use with bent bars and stirrups for $b = d/2$. rrange the longitudinal steel in a single layer if possible.

1322. Design completely a rectangular beam of 28-ft. span uniformly loaded with)00 lb. per lineal ft. including its own dead weight and carrying a concentrated load of 00 lb. 5 ft. from the left support. Let $f_s = 24{,}000$, $f_c' = 4000$, $f_v = 20{,}000$ psi, and llow *ACI* specifications. Use web reinforcement as needed with deformed longitudinal ırs.

1323. Check the T-beam and L-beam designs of *DP*42 and determine whether the ems would need web reinforcement. Also check the bond stress in the main reinforcing ds on the assumption that two rods will be bent upward near the support. Allow orking stresses for plain bars (unless higher bond is needed) and for $f_c' = 3000$ psi.

1324. Rows of columns 24 ft. apart in two directions support a parking deck. A eck slab 6 in. thick will span between joists. The joist webs weigh 120 lb. per lineal ft. ıd are spaced 6 ft. on centers. They provide concentrated loads on the main girders hich span 23 ft. clear between columns. Compute the dead load acting on a girder and low an overall superimposed fixed loading of 100 psf for stored cars. Design a T-beam rder section [for moments from Fig. 206(c)] meeting *ACI* spec., and include bond and ear calculations. Choose all materials.

256. Formulas for Reinforced Concrete Beam Design. If symbols had been used in place of numbers in the numerical problems that have been solved in Chapter 13 by use of the transformed section, the standard formulas of reinforced concrete design would have resulted. These formulas will be given without comment or explanation of their usefulness since it is assumed that they will be used primarily for checking calculations made by the methods already studied. The symbols used are given significance by Fig. 210 and the notation given in the front matter.

FOR ORDINARY RECTANGULAR SECTIONS:

(14) $$p = \frac{A_s}{bd} = \frac{1/2}{\frac{f_s}{f_c}\left(\frac{f_s}{nf_c} + 1\right)}.$$ (Balanced reinforcement.)

(15) $$k = \sqrt{2pn + (pn)^2} - pn.$$

(16) $$\frac{kd}{d} = \frac{f_c}{f_c + f_s/n}.$$

(17) $$j = 1 - \frac{k}{3}.$$

(18) $$jd = d - \frac{kd}{3}.$$

(19) $$M = Tjd = f_sA_sjd = f_spjbd^2.$$

(20) $$M = Cjd = 1/2 f_ckjbd^2.$$

(21) $$f_s = \frac{M}{A_sjd} = \frac{M}{pjbd^2}.$$

(22) $$f_c = \frac{2M}{kjbd^2}.$$

(23) $$bd^2 = \frac{M}{f_spj}.$$

(24) $$bd^2 = \frac{M}{1/2 f_ckj}.$$

FOR T-BEAMS (COMPRESSION IN WEB NEGLECTED):

(25) $$k = \frac{pn + \frac{1}{2}\left(\frac{t}{d}\right)^2}{pn + \frac{t}{d}}.$$

(26) $$k = \frac{f_c}{f_c + f_s/n}.$$

(27) $$jd = d - z \quad \text{where}$$

(28) $$z = \frac{t}{3}\left(\frac{3kd - 2t}{2kd - t}\right).$$

(29) $$f_s = \frac{M}{A_s jd}.$$

(30) $$f_c = \frac{f_s}{n}\left(\frac{kd}{d - kd}\right) = \frac{f_s}{n}\left(\frac{k}{1 - k}\right).$$

FOR DOUBLY REINFORCED BEAMS: The following formulas are based upon elastic action; that is, the compressive steel stress f_s' is n times the concrete stress at the same level. By *ACI* specifications, this value of f_s' may be doubled in computing moment resistance if the new value of f_s' is still less than the allowable compressive stress which is the same as f_s. In the following formulas, this result will be achieved if the term $(n-1)$ is changed to $(2n - 1)$ in formulas (31) and (32).

(31) $$k = \sqrt{2pn + 2p'(n - 1)d'/d + (pn + p'[n - 1])^2} - (pn + p'[n - 1]).$$

(32) $$jd = d - z, \quad \text{where } z = \frac{dk^3/3 + 2(n - 1)p'd'(k - d'/d)}{k^2 + 2(n - 1)p'k - d'/d)}.$$

(33) $$f_s = \frac{M}{A_s jd}.$$

(34) $$f_c = \frac{f_s}{n}\left(\frac{k}{1 - k}\right).$$

(35) $$f_s' = nf_c\left(\frac{kd - d'}{kd}\right) \quad (\leq \text{allowable } f_s \text{ for bars}).$$

FOR SHEAR OR DIAGONAL TENSION:

(36) $$v = \frac{V}{bjd} \quad \text{or} \quad \frac{V}{b'jd} \quad \text{for T-beams.} \quad (\textit{ACI} \text{ Code omits } j.)$$

(37) $$s = \frac{A_v f_v}{v'b} \quad \text{(vertical stirrups).}$$

(38) $$s = \frac{A_v f_v}{0.7v'b} \quad \text{(bars at 45 degrees).}$$

(39) $$s = \frac{A_v f_v (\cos \alpha + \sin \alpha)}{v'b} \quad \text{(bars at a slope } \alpha).$$

FOR BOND:

(40) $$u = \frac{V}{\Sigma Ojd} \quad \text{(unit bond stress).}$$

(41) $$L = \frac{T}{\Sigma Ou} \quad \text{(length for anchorage).}$$

DP46. *The slab of this T-beam floor panel of light cinder concrete, for which* $f_c' = 2000$ *psi, must span between joists and carry a uniform live load of 150 psf. Dead load including floor and ceiling = 75 psf. The end spans are fixed by walls so that the interior panel controls the design. Working stresses are controlled by local Building Code.*

Working Stresses:

$f_s = 25{,}000$ psi; $f_c = 0.45 \times 2000 = 900$ psi; $n = 15$ for low-grade cinder concrete.

$v = 55$ psi; $u = 160$ psi for 3/8″ plain bars.

Bending Moments:

Length-width ratio $= 24 \div 8 = 3.0$.

Treat as a one-way slab.

Interior span.

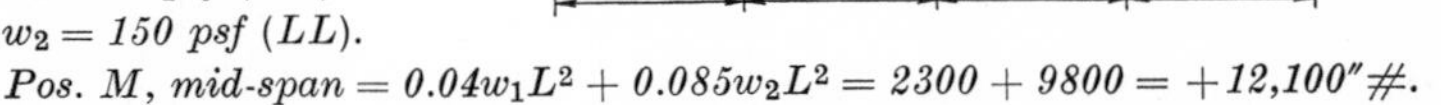

$w_1 = 75$ psf (DL);

$w_2 = 150$ psf (LL).

Pos. M, mid-span $= 0.04 w_1 L^2 + 0.085 w_2 L^2 = 2300 + 9800 = +12{,}100''\#$.

Neg. M, mid-span $= 0.04 w_1 L^2 - 0.045 w_2 L^2 = 2300 - 5200 = -2900''\#$.

Neg. M, support $= -\,0.08 w_1 L^2 - 0.115 w_2 L^2 = -4600 - 13{,}200$

$= -17{,}800''\#$.

Depth: $k = 0.35$; $j = 0.88$ for balanced reinforcement at the support.

$$M = Cjd = \frac{f_c}{2} b(kd)(jd), \text{ or } 17{,}800 = \left(\frac{900}{2} \times 12 \times 0.35 \times 0.88\right) d^2.$$

$d = \sqrt{10.7} = 3.26''$. Depth to steel will be $3\frac{1}{4}''$.

Use $4\frac{1}{4}''$ thickness. With 3/8″ ϕs, fireproofing $= 4.25 - 3.26 - 0.19 = 0.80''$.

Steel Requirements:

Neg. area at support. $A_s = M \div f_s jd = 17{,}800 \div (25{,}000 \times 2.86)$

$= 0.25$ in² per ft.

$$\text{Spacing of } 3/8'' \ \phi\text{s} = \left(\frac{0.11}{0.25}\right) 12 = 5.3''.$$

$$\text{Spacing of positive bars at mid-span} = \frac{17{,}800}{12{,}100} \times 5.3'' = 7.8''.$$

Temperature steel $= 0.2\% \times bt = 0.002 \times 12 \times 4.25 = 0.10$ in² per ft.

$$\text{Spacing of } 3/8'' \ \phi \text{ temperature bars} = \left(\frac{0.11}{0.10}\right) 12 = 13''.$$

Shear and Bond: (at support) $v = \dfrac{V}{bd} = \dfrac{225 \times 4}{12 \times 3.25} = 23$ psi; $\quad u = \dfrac{V}{\Sigma O jd} = \dfrac{225 \times 4}{2.65 \times 2.86}$

$= 119$ psi.

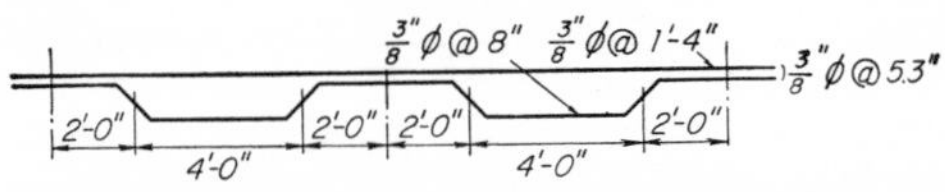

Remarks: *From Table 27 it can be seen that the negative DL moment over the support overbalances the corresponding positive LL moment even for a 2:1 ratio of LL to DL. Therefore, no steel is needed at the support in the bottom of the slab. By ACI Code 1/4 of the positive steel should extend through the supports and be replaced by short bars over the supports.*

$$\frac{(w^{\#})\ \ell^2}{3} = \frac{4\,349^{\#\text{-}FT}}{3} \quad 13{,}047$$

$$W\ell^2 = 13{,}047$$

$$\frac{P}{A}$$

$$\frac{W\ \ell}{3} \qquad \frac{w\ \ell^2}{3}$$

$$\frac{4800\ \ell^2}{3} =$$

$$\ell^2 = \frac{\left(\frac{52\,080}{12}\right) 3}{4800} \quad (4340)$$

$$= \sqrt{2.7125}$$

$$= 1.6469$$

"9"

59.25

80

4772

4740
4800
9540

4770

4ow
4775
9525

11"

4762

083

"10"

59.17.

80

4733.60
4800

2)9533
4766.

× .833

4050.

.92

Slab Design

257. One-Way Slabs. If the slab spans from one support to another as a simple beam, its design is essentially the same as the design of a rectangular beam of reinforced concrete. The bending moment may be computed per foot of width, and, if the loading is uniform, each foot of width will be made identical. (See Fig. 223.) Slabs are usually reinforced with small round rods—probably ½-in. round bars are the most common. The requirement for *fireproofing* is that there shall be ¾ in. of clear concrete below the bars. Hence, for ½-in. bars the overall depth equals the depth to the center of the steel plus 1.0 in.

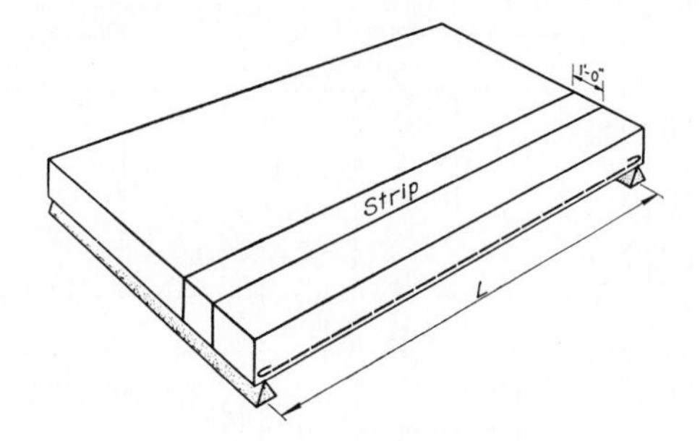

Fig. 223. One-Way Slab on Simple Supports.

Bending Moments. Of course, the positive bending moment at the center of a span such as Fig. 223 is $\frac{1}{8}wL^2$, where w is the load per sq. ft. acting on the strip of 1-ft. width and L is the span from center to center of the supports. More frequently, however, the slab is poured integrally with its supports and is continuous across several panels. Usually, the spans are all of the same length, and the live and dead loadings are identical in all panels. For this special case, bending moments, positive at the centers of the panels and negative over the supports, are given by Table 27.

Design of a Continuous One-Way Slab, *DP*46. The slab of the T-beam floor panel shown here is continuous for several spans. Since each panel has a length of 3.0 times its width, the load is almost entirely carried in the short direction, and the slab may be treated as a one-way slab. The design is made for a typical 1-ft. strip. In the long direction, a small amount of temperature steel should be introduced near the upper surface of the slab to prevent the opening of shrinkage cracks and to resist a small amount of negative moment over the edge supports. It is reasonable to compute the temperature steel as 0.18 to 0.25 per cent of the gross cross-sectional area of the slab. The lower value applies for high elastic limit bar steel or wire fabric with welded cross wires 12 in. apart.

TABLE 27

MAXIMUM MOMENT COEFFICIENTS FOR MULTI-SPAN ONE-WAY SLABS

The coefficients given in the table below are for the special case of equal spans and uniformly distributed loads. They are based on the assumption of continuity over the supports with negligible restraints at end and at intermediate supports. The numerical values given are coefficients of w_1L^2 and w_2L^2, respectively, in which w_1 equals the dead load, and w_2 equals the live load per unit of area.

No. Spans	End Span					Interior Span			
	End Support Neg.	Mid-Span		First Int. Support		Mid-Span		Typical Support	
		Pos.	Neg.	Pos.	Neg.	Pos.	Neg.	Pos.	Neg.
Dead Load									
1	−0.040	0.125							
2	−0.040	0.075			−0.125				
3	−0.040	0.085			−0.100	0.030			
4 or more	−0.040	0.080			−0.110	0.040			−0.080
Live Load									
1	−0.040	0.125	0.000						
2	−0.040	0.100	−0.030	0.000	−0.125				
3	−0.040	0.105	−0.025	0.017	−0.120	0.080	−0.050		
4 or more	−0.040	0.105	−0.020	0.015	−0.120	0.085	−0.045	0.036	−0.115

258. Two-Way Slabs. Slabs are usually supported on all four edges, and, unless the length is about three times the width, they should be reinforced to span in both directions. Complete moment coefficients are given in the *ACI Building Code* for two-way slabs (poured monolithically with their supporting beams) that are continuous with identical slabs in any or all directions. We will limit our consideration to *two-way slabs that are simply supported on all four edges.*

If we consider two crossing center strips of a two-way slab, as in Fig. 224, we conclude that they must have equal center deflections under the action of those parts of the uniform load carried by each. Also, we know that the deflection of a simple beam acting under a uniform loading is (5/384) wL^4/EI. Hence, for equal values of all terms except w and L, we may write

$$\frac{w_1}{w_2} = \frac{L_2{}^4}{L_1{}^4}. \tag{42}$$

This relationship is limited in use to unrestrained, knife-edge supports. It provides a simple procedure for subdividing the total uniform load w into loads w_1 and w_2 to be applied to the simple spans L_1 and L_2. Note that for $L_1 = 2L_2$, $w_2 = 16w_1$. Hence for any span ratio beyond 2.0 the slab will act essentially as a one-way slab.

PROBLEMS

1325. Design a one-way slab as a simple span to rest on masonry walls spaced 18 ft-6 in. center to center. The slab must carry a superimposed uniform live load of 200 psf. Let $f_c = 3500$ psi, $f_s = 24{,}000$ psi, and follow *ACI* working stresses.

1326. Redesign the slab of Problem 1325 as a ribbed slab with tees spaced 6 ft. apart spanning 18 ft.-6 in. between supports. The slab now spans across several ribs. Moment coefficients are given in Table 27.

1327. Redesign the slab of *DP*46 for these changed conditions: (1) There are only two instead of three interior ribs; (2) The concrete has a value of $f_c' = 3000$ psi. $n = 9$.

1328. Redesign the slab of *DP*46 for four interior ribs spaced 6 ft.-0 in. on centers. Design both an interior span and an end span. Reduce the span of the slab for 6 in. ribs.

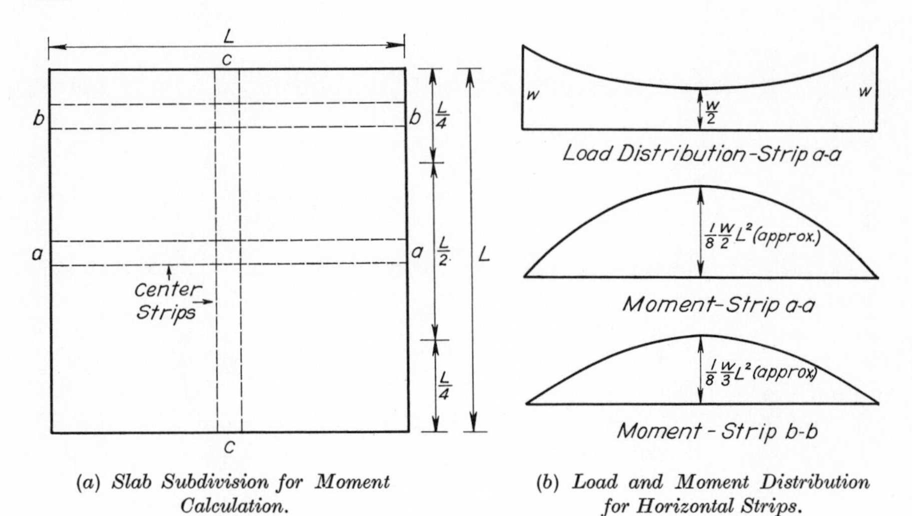

(*a*) *Slab Subdivision for Moment Calculation.* (*b*) *Load and Moment Distribution for Horizontal Strips.*

FIG. 224. MOMENTS FOR A TWO-WAY SLAB WITH ZERO EDGE RESTRAINTS.

259. Moments Controlled by Statics. It is well to emphasize that statics controls the design moments in two-way slabs and continuous slabs just as it controls the design moment for a simple span beam. For any uniformly loaded one-way span, the total moment (sum of positive and negative moments) will be the same as the moment in a simple beam carrying a uniform load, that is, $\frac{1}{8}WL$. If the panel forms a square two-way slab, we can properly use $W/2$ to be carried in each direction. However, we may conclude that it is best to design for $\frac{2}{3}(W/2)$ in one direction for the center half of the panel and only $\frac{1}{3}(W/2)$ for the two outer quarters. Nevertheless, when total moments for all strips in two directions including both negative and positive moments are summed for a square panel, *the total moment should equal not less than* $\frac{1}{8}WL$ where L is the span and W is the total panel loading. In fact, because there is considerable guess-work in dividing the load or moment between strips, it is evident that, for safety, the total of all moments should be greater than $\frac{1}{8}WL$. If the total of all moments as specified is less than $\frac{1}{8}WL$, it is evident that the result has the effect of raising working stresses. This procedure is objectionable because it confuses a very important distinction. Total moments are controlled by statics—specification committees set allowable stresses.

CHAPTER 14

REINFORCED CONCRETE COLUMNS AND FOOTINGS

Working Stress Design

260. Structural Action. The columns of a tall building are of the greatest importance because the failure of a single column near the bottom of the building might possibly mean a complete collapse of the structure. In contrast, the failure of a floor panel would most likely result in only a repair job. The effective section of a reinforced concrete column consists of an area of concrete, usually square or round, containing a number (four or more) of longitudinal rods protected by at least $1\frac{1}{2}$ in. of concrete outside of the steel. Since the load divides itself between the concrete and these vertical steel rods, the latter would buckle outward and *spall* the concrete encasement if they were not restrained by regularly spaced wire ties or by a continuous helix of wire known as the *spiral*. (See Fig. 225 and Fig. 226.)

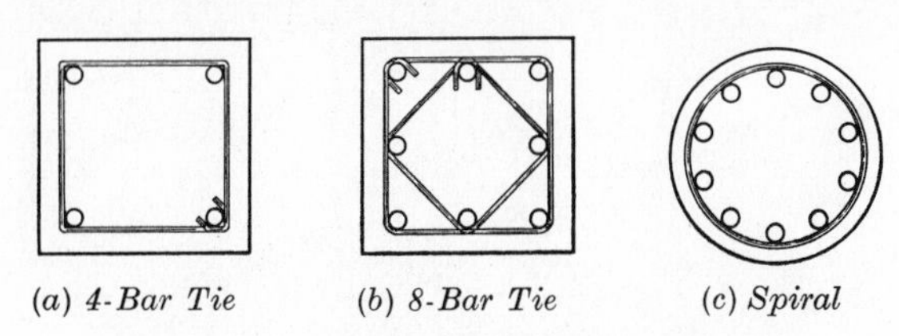

(*a*) *4-Bar Tie* (*b*) *8-Bar Tie* (*c*) *Spiral*

Fig. 225. Ties and Spiral Reinforcement.

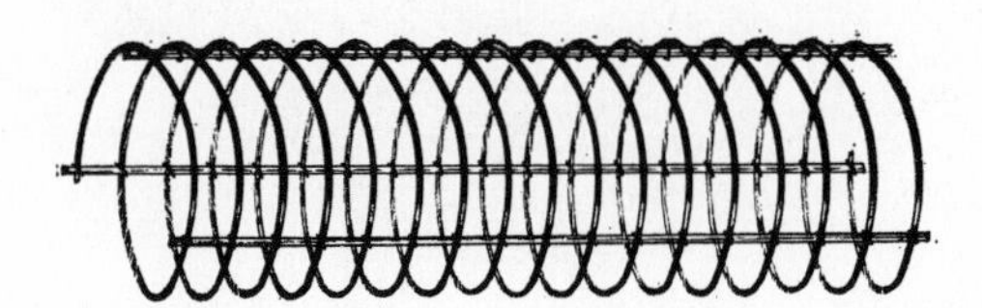

Fig. 226. Large Spiral with Spacer Bars Before Erection.

Vertical steel rods overlap from story to story and are bonded together by the concrete. Therefore, in effect, the columns are continuous from the basement to the top of the building.

Short and Long Columns. A short pedestal, no more than three times its least dimension in height, does not need steel reinforcement and may be designed of plain concrete. The range of length from three to fourteen times the diameter, or least dimension, is considered the normal range of column design, and to this range the usual allowable column stress formulas apply. Above a length of fourteen times the minimum dimension (better expressed as $h/r = 50$) we find the range of *long columns* for which the working stress must be reduced for safety. The common formula (*ACI*) for the allowable load on a long column is

$$P' = P\left(1.32 - 0.006\frac{h}{r}\right). \tag{1}$$

In this formula, P' is the allowable load for the long column, P is the allowable load on a standard short column, h is the unsupported or clear column height, and r is the least radius of gyration which may be taken as $0.3d$ where d is the depth of a rectangular section or $0.25d$ where d is the outside diameter of a circular section. It is assumed that the column is totally restrained at its ends against lateral motion and has sufficient rotational restraint at its ends so that rotation of one end will produce an internal point of contraflexure within the length h. Other cases of end restraint are covered in the *ACI Building Code.*

Courtesy Portland Cement Association

FIG. 227. SPIRAL COLUMN CONSTRUCTION.

Note spiral, wood framing to form column cap and vertical rods bent inward to permit a reduction of the diameter of the column.

261. Ties and Spirals. As previously mentioned, the vertical rods must be restrained against outward buckling by ties at regular intervals or by a continuous wire helix, the spiral. The minimum requirements are as follows:

Lateral Ties. Lateral ties should be at least of 1/4-in. diameter and should be spaced apart not over 16 bar diameters, 48 tie diameters, or the least dimension of the column. When there are more than four vertical bars, additional ties should be provided so that every longitudinal bar is held firmly in its designated position. (See Spec. 304.)

Spirals. Spiral reinforcement should consist of evenly spaced continuous spirals held firmly in place and true to line by at least two vertical spacer bars. See Fig. 226 and Fig. 227. The minimum diameter of spiral bars should be 1/4 in. The center-to-center spacing of spirals should not exceed 1/6 of the core diameter. The clear spacing between spirals should not exceed 3 in. nor be less than 1 3/8 in. or 1 1/2 times the maximum size of coarse aggregate used. (See Spec. 304.) The required amount of spiral steel will be covered later.

Fireproofing. For columns, the minimum coverage is 1 1/2 in. beyond the outer face of the steel ties or outside of the spiral and 1 1/2 times the maximum size of coarse aggregate.

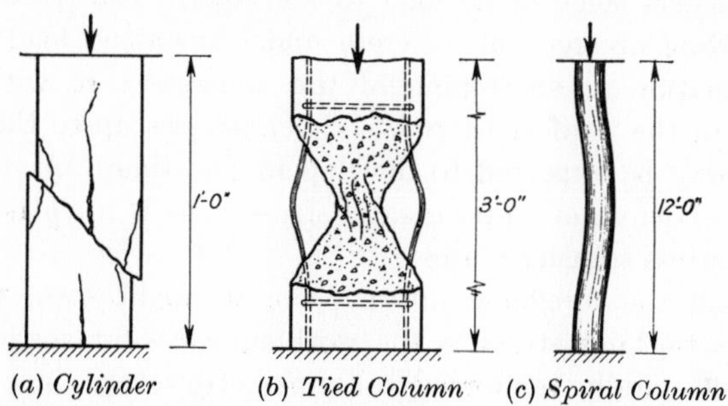

(*a*) *Cylinder* (*b*) *Tied Column* (*c*) *Spiral Column*

FIG. 228. FAILURES OF CONCRETE AND OF CONCRETE COLUMNS.

262. Column Failures. When a plain concrete cylinder is crushed in a testing machine, the failure is by shear along a diagonal plane. The fracture is sudden and is best described by the word "brittle." Some fractures amount almost to minor explosions. The failure of a tied column is similar to the failure of a cylinder since it is almost an unrestrained compression-shear failure between ties. On the other hand, the spiral column shows a toughness quite unlike plain concrete. Even after it has buckled sidewise and developed a lateral deflection of several inches, it will sustain a heavy load. Of course, in the earlier stages of failure its fireproof covering outside of the spiral spalls off and this area is lost. The resistance of the spiral then comes into play due to the internal lateral swelling of the disintegrating core, and the tough characteristics of the spiral column become evident. (See Fig. 228.)

In the early days, it was the practice to ignore the strength of the fireproof covering for all columns. Modern specifications base strength upon the gross area, including the fireproofing. This is reasonable since the fireproofing is not consumed and is seldom damaged by fire. For the spiral column, there was long discussion as to whether both the gross area and the strength added by the spiral should be considered effective. Since the spiral cannot become fully effective until the outside cover has spalled, one or the other, but not both, are properly considered in the design. Tests by Consideré, in the early part of this century, indicated an additional strength from spiral steel equal to 2.4 times the strength added by an equal weight of vertical steel. This relationship even appeared in early specifications, but today we use the gross concrete area and neglect the direct influence of the spiral. However, because of their lack of toughness, the working stresses for tied columns are 15 per cent smaller than for spiral columns. (Spec. 325.)

263. Effectiveness of Vertical Steel. For nearly forty years it was the common practice to allow a working stress in vertical column steel equal to n times the working stress for the concrete. Finally, it became clear that concrete and steel do not act together elastically, but that the concrete gradually transfers some of its load to the steel. The reason is found in the time yielding or creep of concrete under sustained load that permits plastic deformation or shortening of the concrete core with consequent overstressing of the reinforcing rods. Steel stresses up to the elastic limit of the steel may be expected to develop in due time. At this point the increase in steel deformation for greater stress exceeds the plastic flow of the concrete and stress transfer ceases.

Based upon the foregoing information, it might seem reasonable to accept the elastic limit stress as the working stress for vertical steel rods, particularly in spirally reinforced columns. However, since there is still much to be learned of plastic flow in reinforced concrete, present specifications permit a design stress for the steel of only 40 per cent of the elastic limit. (See Spec. 314.)

Specification for Percentages of Vertical Steel. The spirally reinforced column may include an area of vertical steel from 0.01 to 0.08 times the *gross area* of the concrete section. (Spec. 310.) For the tied column, the range of the percentage of vertical steel is from 0.01 to 0.04. A minimum allowance of vertical steel equal to 1 per cent of the gross area of concrete has been found desirable to prevent undue shrinkage and plastic flow. The maximum allowance is greater for the spirally reinforced column than for the tied column because only a spiral can properly restrain a large amount of vertical steel from buckling and spalling the concrete fireproofing. Thus it becomes evident that specifications should define strictly the amount of spiral reinforcement to be used. [Equation (5)].

Bar Spacing and Column Size. Spacing of bars (clear distance) shall be at least 1½ diameters, 1½ in., and 1½ times the maximum size of aggregate. (Spec. 303). The smallest allowable bar is of ⅝-in. diameter. At least four bars are required in a tied column and six bars for a spiral column. To accommodate the vertical steel properly, a minimum column diameter of 10 in. or a minimum thickness of 8 in. for a rectangular section is considered necessary. A 6-in. diameter is allowed for one-story columns or posts carrying very small loads.

264. Allowable Load. The *ACI Building Code* has specified the allowable load for reinforced concrete columns very simply. The procedure is merely to sum the strength of the concrete section and that of the vertical steel.

Column with Spirals. (Spec. 324.) (Spiral requirements will be specified later.)

$$P = 0.25 f_c' A_g + f_s A_s'. \tag{2}$$

where P = the allowable column load,
f_c' = the 28-day strength of the concrete,
f_s = 40 per cent of the minimum elastic limit of the steel; or 16,000 psi for intermediate grade, 20,000 psi for hard grade and 30,000 psi maximum,
A_g = gross area of concrete including fireproofing,[1]
A_s' = area of vertical reinforcing steel. A_{st} is used in *ACI* specifications.

Tied Columns. (Spec. 325.) (85 per cent of the load allowed for spirally reinforced columns.)

$$P = 0.85(0.25 f_c' A_g + f_s A_s'). \tag{3}$$

Composite Columns. (Spec. 326.) (Reinforced with vertical rods, spirals, and a metal core.)

$$P = 0.225 f_c' A_g + f_s A_s' + f_r A_r, \tag{4}$$

where A_r = area of steel or cast-iron core limited to 20 per cent of A_g,
f_r = allowable unit stress for metal core; 18,000 psi for *A*36 steel or 10,000 psi cast iron.

265. Spiral Requirement. If the percentage of spiral steel p' or p_s is expressed in terms of the area of the concrete core A_c out-to-out of the spiral (Spec. 310),

$$p_s = p' = 0.45\left[\frac{A_g}{A_c} - 1\right]\frac{f_c'}{f_y}. \tag{5}$$

The term f_y is the elastic limit strength of the spiral, or 40,000 psi for intermediate grade steel wire, 50,000 psi for hard grade, and 60,000 psi for cold drawn wire. (Spec. 310.) The diameter of the spiral wire may be ¼ in. or larger to meet the spacing requirements of §261.

Column Design

266. Design of Concrete Columns. The design of a concrete column for a heavy load often becomes a problem of obtaining the smallest possible

[1] Note that A_g should be reduced by A_s' the area of the compressive reinforcing bars. The use of the full value of A_g corresponds to the use of $2n$ rather than $2n - 1$ for transforming steel which is also quite common. The result is a small increase in allowable stress. The matter is more serious when a metal core, which may replace as much as 20 per cent of the concrete, is used. No deductions are made on *DS*47 from gross concrete areas.

DP47a. *Design a tied column to carry a load of 720,000#. Use 4000 psi concrete and $f_s = 20{,}000$ psi; $n = 8$. Obtain minimum dimensions by using the maximum percentage of steel. Follow ACI Spec. 325.*

$p_g = 0.04A_g$ *for minimum dimensions.*

$P = 0.85(0.25f_c'A_g + p_gA_gf_s)$

$\qquad 0.85(1000 + 800)A_g.$

$A_g = 720{,}000 \div 1530 = 470$ in^2.

$b = d = \sqrt{470} = 21.7''$; use $22''$.

$A_s' = 0.04 \times 470 = 18.8$ in^2. Use, $18.8 \div 1.56 = 12$-#11ϕs; $D = 1.41''$.

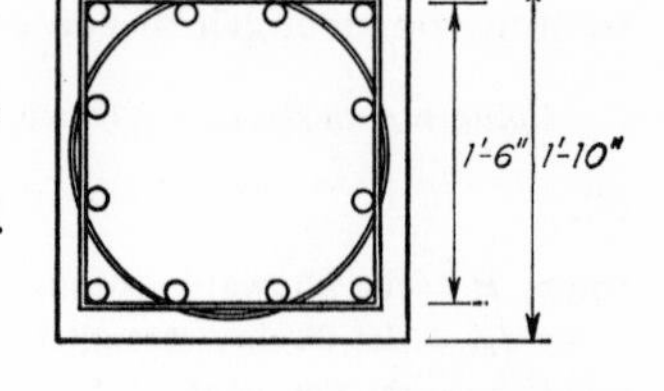

Ties are ½″ ϕ rods spaced 20″ apart $(16 \times 1.41 = 22''$; $48 \times \frac{1}{2} = 24'')$. *(Spec. 304.)*

Alternate circular and square ties at 10″ spacing as indicated on sketch. Other arrangements of ties may be equally effective.

DP47b. *Redesign the column of DP47a as a circular section with spiral steel in order to reduce the wasted floor area. f_y for spiral = 50,000 psi. (See Specs. 304 and 324.)*

$p_g = 0.08$ *for minimum dimensions.*

$P = 0.25f_c'A_g + p_gA_gf_s = (1000 + 1600)A_g.$

$A_g = 720{,}000 \div 2600 = 277$ in^2. $d = 19.0''$, d' (spiral) $= 15''$.

$A_s' = 0.08 \times 277 = 22.2$ in^2. Use 10-#14Sϕ rods.

For a 15″ spiral, rod spacing $= \pi \times 15 \div 10 = 4.7''$.

The diameter of a #14S rod is 1.69″. $2\frac{1}{2}D = 4.2''$.

The spacing is adequate.

Percentage of spiral $p_s = 0.45\left(\dfrac{277}{176} - 1\right)\dfrac{4000}{50{,}000} = 0.02.$ *(Spec. 310).*

Pitch of ½″ $\phi = [0.2(15\pi)] \div \left[\dfrac{\pi \times 15^2}{4} \times 0.02\right] = 2.7''.$

DP47c. *Determine whether the introduction of a cast iron pipe core of 6″ outside diameter and 1″ thickness ($A = 17.3$ in^2.) would reduce the spiral of DP47b to 12″ diameter. Column diameter = 16″. (See Spec. 326.)*

$A'_s = 0.08 \times \pi \times 16^2/4 = 16.1$ in^2.

Use 10-#11 ϕs; $A_s = 15.6$ in^2.

$P = 0.225 \times 4000 \times 201 + 15.6 \times 20{,}000 + 17.3 \times 10{,}000.$

$P = 181{,}000 + 312{,}000 + 173{,}000 = 666{,}000\#.$

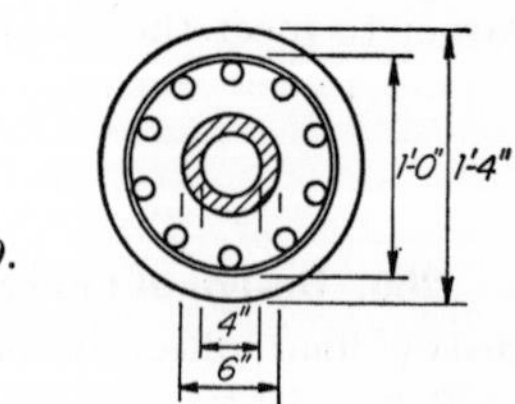

Remarks: *Since this capacity is smaller than the load, even when the maximum percentage of vetrical steel is used, the diameter of the column cannot be reduced to 16″ without excessive overstress. A 17″ diameter could be used.*

section since large columns are wasteful of floor area. The devices available for reducing column cross-sections are: (1) use of high strength concrete, (2) use of spirals and the maximum allowable percentage ($0.08\ A_g$) of vertical steel, (3) use of a steel or cast-iron core.

EXAMPLES OF COLUMN SELECTION, *DS*47. A column section to carry a load of 640,000 lb. is first chosen with 4 per cent of vertical steel restrained by steel ties. The required outside dimensions of the section are 22×22 in. By introducing a spiral and by increasing the vertical steel to 8 per cent, the section can be reduced to an outside diameter of 19 in., the spiral being of 15 in. diameter. Finally, it is found that a further reduction in outside diameter is possible if a cast-iron pipe core, 6 in. O.D. and 1 in. thick, is used as a part of the section. For most purposes, the standard spirally reinforced section of *DP*47*b* would be selected. In these examples, the designs work out rather easily. We ordinarily expect to make one or two trial arrangements before a section is obtained having acceptable characteristics from all points of view and meeting all specifications.

267. Column Flexure and Direct Stress. Eccentric loads, and continuity between girders and columns, produce flexure as well as direct load on a column cross-section. It is not common for the flexural moment to be high enough to reverse one fiber stress to tension, but the compression along one face of the column may be increased significantly. The conception of the transformed section is a convenient tool for the investigation of flexure and direct stress when compression exists over the entire cross-section. By the *ACI Building Code* the column must be proportioned to meet the simple interaction formula

$$\frac{f_a}{F_a} + \frac{f_b}{F_b} \leqq 1.0. \tag{6}$$

This formula for maximum loading is equivalent to

$$\frac{P/A_{tr}}{F_a} + \frac{Mc/(A_{tr}r^2)}{F_b} = 1.0. \tag{7}$$

and is also equivalent to

$$P = \frac{A_{tr}F_a}{1 + \dfrac{ec}{r^2}\left(\dfrac{F_a}{F_b}\right)}. \tag{8}$$

Here A_{tr} is the total area of the transformed cross-section and e is the equivalent eccentricity of the load P for $M = P \times e$. Of course, r is the radius of gyration of the transformed cross-section.

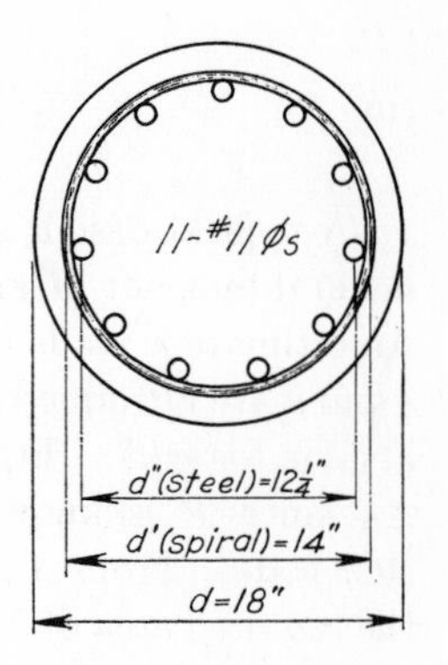

FIG. 229. SPIRALLY REINFORCED SECTION.

Checking a Column Section for an Eccentric Load. The column section of Fig. 229 will be checked to determine its load capacity for a load P applied with an eccentricity e of 2 in. from the center of the column. Let $f_c = 4000$ psi, $n = 8$, $f_s = 20{,}000$ psi, and $A'_s = 17.2$ in^2. for eleven No. 11 bars.

For the area of the total transformed section we have the following relation:

$$A_{tr} = \frac{\pi \times 18^2}{4} + (2 \times 8)1.72 = 530 \text{ in}^2.$$

$$I_{tr} = \frac{\pi \times 18^4}{64} + 1/2(2 \times 8) \times 17.2 \times 6.1^2 = 10{,}250 \text{ in}^4.$$

$$r = \sqrt{I/A} = \sqrt{10{,}250 \div 530} = 4.4 \text{ in.}$$

For the purpose of this analysis F_a will be the unit stress permitted on the transformed section if P is a central load, that is,

$$P = 0.25f'_c A_g + f_s A'_s = 1000 \times 255 + 20{,}000 \times 17.2 = 599{,}000 \text{ lb.},$$

$$F_a = P/A_{tr} = 599{,}000 \div 530 = 1130 \text{ psi},$$

and

$$F_b = 0.45 f_c' = 1800 \text{ psi.}$$

Therefore, by equation (8)

$$P = \frac{530 \times 1130}{1 + \dfrac{2 \times 9}{4.4^2}\left(\dfrac{1130}{1800}\right)} = 376{,}000 \text{ lb.}$$

If equation (6) is used directly the *ACI* code permits use of $F_a = 0.34f_c'$ (approximately) which increases the value of P_c to 425,000 lb. Either value of P represents a large decrease from the central load value of 599,000 lb.

268. Approximation of r and Procedure for Design. Before a section has been chosen, one cannot calculate the exact value of the radius of gyration for use in the expression ec/r^2. As a satisfactory approximation use $r = 0.29 \times$ the depth t of a square section and $\frac{1}{4} \times$ the diameter d for a circular section. Then

(9) $$\frac{ec}{r^2} \text{ for a square section (reinforced)} = \frac{6e}{t},$$

(10) $$\frac{ec}{r^2} \text{ for a circular section (reinforced)} = \frac{8e}{d}.$$

A typical design situation is one for which the central load P and the flexural moment M are known and from which $e = M/P$ may be calculated. An estimate is made of the outside diameter of the column and the values of e and d are introduced into the appropriate expression above, which provides a value for ec/r^2. Equation (8) may then be solved for the transformed area A_{tr} since P is known, $F_b = 0.45f_c'$ and $F_a = 0.34f_c'$ (approximately) by *ACI* code. From A_{tr} and the assumed column dimensions one can compute the required area of compressive steel as $(A_{tr} - A_g) \div 2n$ and then determine whether the cross-section is acceptable. If not, the direction of necessary change in the column diameter will be indicated and a redesign can be made.

PROBLEMS

1401. Compute the allowable central load for the column of Fig. 229 for working stresses as follows: $f_c' = 3000$ psi; $f_s = 20{,}000$ for vertical rods; $f_y = 50{,}000$ for spiral steel. Use 13 vertical bars of 1-in. diameter.

1402. Revise *DS*47 for a central load of 860,000 lb. Let $f_c' = 5000$, and $f_s = 24{,}000$ psi.

1403. Design a spiral column for a load of 400,000 lb. when $f_c' = 3000$ psi; $f_y = 50{,}000$ for spiral; $f_s = 20{,}000$ for vertical steel. Repeat for a tied column. Compare these designs from the viewpoint of economy.

1404. A circular column with the same diameters as Fig. 229 must resist a vertical load of 440,000 lb. and a flexural moment of 490,000 in-lb. Determine the percentage of vertical steel when $f_c' = 4000$; $f_s = 24{,}000$ psi.

1405. Design the cross-section for a spirally reinforced column to carry a load of 500 kips at an eccentricity of 2 in. Let the percentage of vertical steel p be 0.06, $f_c' = 4000$, $f_s = 20{,}000$, psi.

Tension over Part of Section. If the bending moment is sufficiently large to produce a resultant tension at one edge of the column section, either exact analysis or design becomes complicated. The study of this unusual problem is beyond the limitations of this textbook. The reader is referred instead to any standard text dealing entirely with the subject of reinforced concrete.

Wall and Column Footings

269. Wall Footing. Wall footings are sometimes constructed of plain concrete. Such footings undergo bending as simple cantilevers. The flexural stress in tension, computed on a section at the face of the wall, is limited to $1.6\sqrt{f_c'}$. This is also the limit set upon the *maximum* shear, but, since the *average* shear for an unreinforced section is $\frac{2}{3}$ of the maximum shear, specifications limit the average shear to $1.1\sqrt{f_c'}$ instead. (See Table 24.) Shear is computed on a section at a distance $d - 2$ in. from the face of the wall because the lower 2 in. of the depth is neglected because the concrete in contact with the soil may be poor.

Example of Plain Wall Footing. In Fig. 230, let the width of wall be 12 in. and the combined wall and footing load be 17,000 lb. per lineal foot. If the allowable bearing value of the soil is 2400 psf, the width of the footing would need to be 7 ft., the projection beyond the face of the wall being 3 ft. Let $f_c' = 2000$ psi. Assume the net upward pressure (soil pressure minus the weight of the footing slab) to be 2000 psf.

Moment at face of wall $= (2000 \times 3 \times 1.5)12 = 108{,}000$ in-lb.

Allowable tensile stress $= 1.6\sqrt{2000} = 72$ psi.

Section modulus $= 108{,}000 \div 72 = 1500 = \frac{1}{6} \times 12 \times d^2$.

$d = \sqrt{750} = 28$ in. Overall depth $= 28 + 2 = 30$ in. (Wt. $= 370$ psf.)

Shear at section 2-2 of Fig. 230, which is only 21 in. from the edge of the footing slab, is negligible for this footing.

Example of Reinforced Wall Footing. If the footing designed above is reinforced with structural steel bars, for which $f_s = 18{,}000$ psi, its depth can be greatly reduced. Even allowing for a 3-in. cover, a depth of 9 in. to the steel or 12 in. overall can be maintained. Hence, there would be no advantage in using higher strength concrete except for the unreinforced footing.

270. Column Footings. Unlike the wall footing, the column footing undergoes double flexure. The reinforcing steel will be designed for flexure

DP48. *Design a two-way column footing to support a 20″ × 20″ column (3,000 psi) carrying a load of 400,000#. Estimate weight of footing at 20,000#. The soil will support a load of 4000 psf. Let $f_c' = 2500$, $f_s = 20{,}000$ psi, $n = 10$, $v = 100$ psi for periferal shear, $u = 240$ psi for deformed bars. Follow ACI spec.*

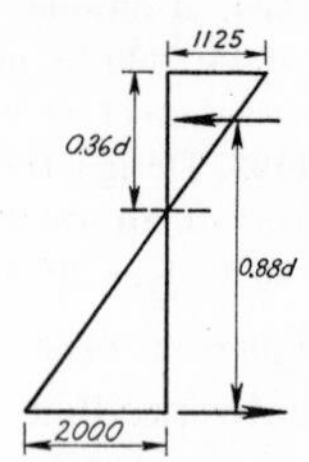

Size: *$A = 420{,}000 \div 4000 = 105$ ft.²*

Use a footing 10′–3″ square.

Projection beyond column = (123 − 20) ÷ 2 = 4′-3½″.

Depth assumed at 16″; weight = 200 psf.

Net upward pressure = 4000 − 200 = 3800 psf.

Moment on Section 1-1: *(Spec. 322.)*

$$M = 3800 \times 10.25 \times 4.29^2 \div 2 = 359{,}000'\#.$$

Design moment per ft.

$$= 359{,}000 \times 12 \div 10.25 = 420{,}000''\#.$$

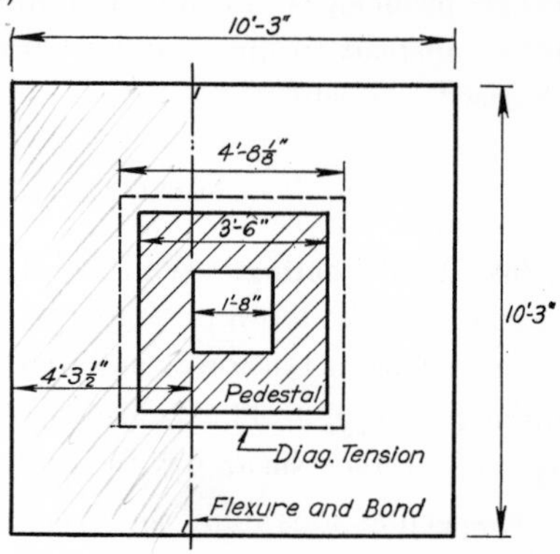

$$M = \frac{f_c}{2} b(kd)(jd)$$

$$= 562 \times 12 \times 0.36 \times 0.88d^2 = 420{,}000''\#.$$

$$d = \sqrt{196} = 14.0''.\ \text{Overall } d = 14.0 + 0.9 + 3 = 17.9''.$$

Use an 18″ slab. Thus we are allowing 3″ cover below ⅞″ϕ bars.

Steel Area:

$$A_s = 420{,}000 \div (0.88 \times 14.1 \times 20{,}000) = 1.69 \text{ in}^2. \text{ per ft.}$$

Try ⅞″ ϕs @ 4¼″ spacing for which $A_s = 1.69$ in². per ft.

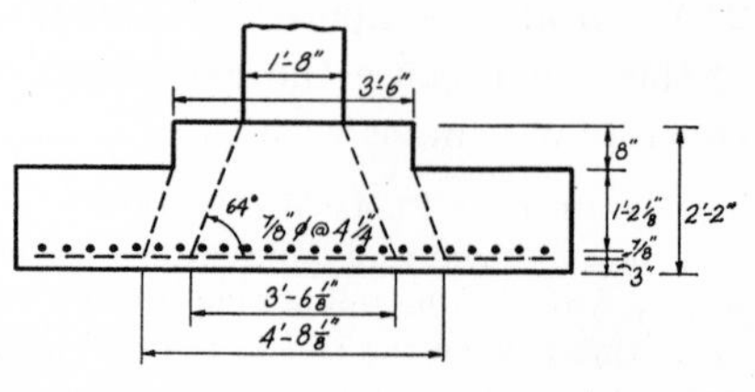

Bond: *(Use section 1–1, Spec. 322.)*

$$u = V/\Sigma O jd = 3800 \times 4.29 \div 2.8 \times \pi \times 0.875 \times 0.88 \times 14.1 = 170 \text{ psi}.$$

Pedestal: *By specification, $A_{ped.} = 3.0A_{col.} = 1200$ in².*

Minimum size = 36″ × 36″.

Pedestal will actually be made 3′–6″ square for diagonal tension.

Diagonal Tension: *(Spec. 322.) Allowable v = 100 psi.*

Thru pedestal, $v = 3800(10.25^2 - 3.51^2) \div (4 \times 42.1 \times 22.1) = 95$ psi.

Thru slab, $v = 3800(10.25^2 - 4.68^2) \div (4 \times 56.1 \times 14.1) = 99$ psi.

Remarks: *This design is economical of concrete, and the spacing of the reinforcing bars is satisfactory.*

in one direction, and, then, identical reinforcing will also be provided in a perpendicular direction. Hence, we find two layers of steel bars at right angles to each other in the bottom of the footing.

Moments by Statics. Despite the fact that the load causes flexure in two directions, the total moment across the footing along the face of the column on the section 1-1 or along the center line on the section 2-2 in Fig. 231 is determinable by statics.[2] Tests have shown that the critical section for moment is across the face of the column, section 1-1 of Fig. 231. This total moment is equal to the net pressure (soil pressure minus weight of concrete) on the cross-hatched area times $a/2$, the moment arm. It is common to assume that the soil pressure is uniformly distributed over the area of the footing, although we know that it reduces somewhat toward the edges. If the conservative assumption of uniform pressure is used in computing the bending moment acting on the section 1-1 in Fig. 231, any possible moment acting on section 2-2 will be resisted properly.

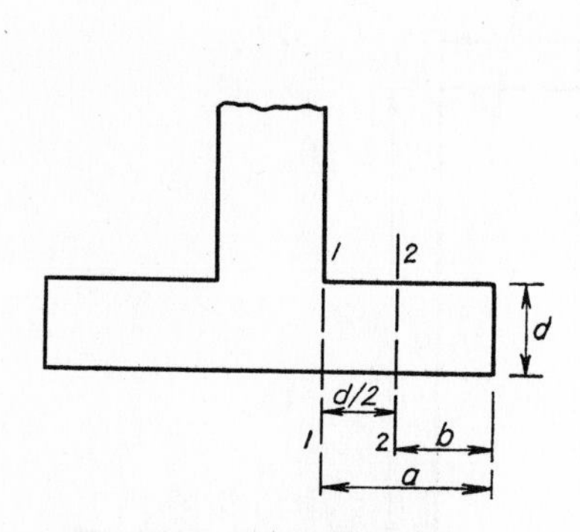

FIG. 230. WALL FOOTING OF PLAIN CONCRETE.

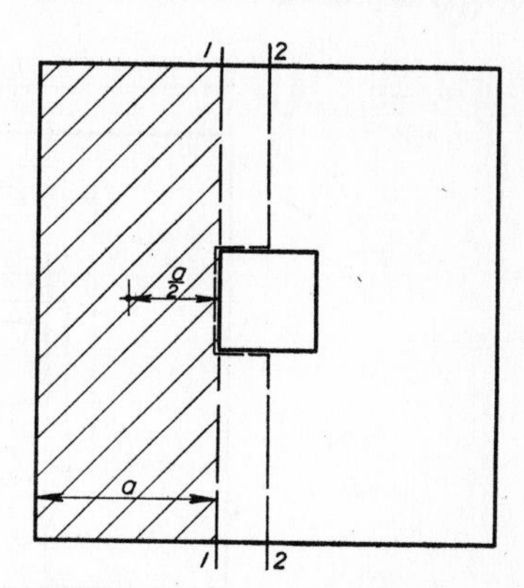

FIG. 231. COLUMN FOOTING.

Moment Distribution across Footing. It is reasonably evident that the total moment determined by statics will not be uniformly distributed across the section 1-1 of Fig. 231. More than one half of this moment will occur within the middle half of the footing. It is therefore not unusual to find a closer spacing of the reinforcing bars across the middle half than across the outside quarters of the footing. On the other hand, the ability of the concrete to transfer moment assures us that all bars will come into proper action before failure even if they are uniformly spaced over the entire width of the footing. Only for large footings does it seem important to consider the concentration of the moment in the central strips.

Design of a Pedestal Footing, *DP48*. High diagonal tension and bond stresses in a footing of uniform thickness require an uneconomical depth. One device for reducing

[2] The classical publication that emphasizes this point is by A. N. Talbot, Bulletin No. 67, University of Illinois Engineering Experiment Station.

the volume of concrete is to step down the depth of the footing by use of a pedestal under the column. The pedestal serves another purpose in distributing the column stress from the high-strength concrete of the column into the lower strength concrete of the footing. For this reason, the area of the pedestal is controlled by the following formula

$$A_{ped.} = A_{col.} \frac{0.25 f_c' \text{ for column}}{0.375 f_c' \text{ for footing}}. \tag{11}$$

In this equation, the factor 0.375 is based upon the pedestal having one third or less of its area loaded. Also, all of the steel stress is to be transferred into the pedestal by bond through extension of the reinforcing rods or by lapped and bonded dowels.

In the determination of the area of steel required in *DP*48, the bending moment for the cantilever projection beyond the face of the column is used. (Spec. 322.) The depth to the steel is taken to the *bottom of the upper layer of bars*, which is the centroid of the area of crossing bars.

Bond is computed on the same section as moment. Diagonal tension or shear is checked on two sections defined by lines extending downward from the face of the column and from the face of the pedestal at an angle from the vertical having a tangent of 0.5. The pedestal reduces the diagonal tension to an allowable value.

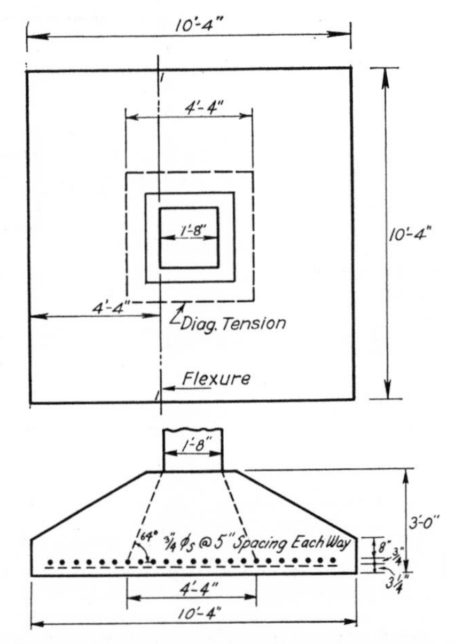

FIG. 232. COLUMN FOOTING WITH SLOPED SURFACES.

Design of a Sloped Footing. This design illustrated by Fig. 232 was made in order to reduce the number and the size of bars needed in the pedestal footing of *DP*48. A sloped footing may be made quite deep near the face of the column to control diagonal tension and still the volume of concrete can be kept within reasonable limits. The average depth of the footing in Fig. 232 is 24 in., or 20 in. to the steel. This depth controls the steel stress and the bond stress, while the depth of 36 in., or 32 in. to the steel, at the face of the column, controls the diagonal tension stress. For this design No. 6 bars may be spaced 5 in. on centers as contrasted to No. 7 bars 4.25 in. on centers for the stepped footing of *DS*48

TABLE 28

BALANCING FOOTING AREAS*

	COL. A	COL. B	COL. C	COL. D
Dead load	200,000 lb.	270,000 lb.	500,000 lb.	400,000 lb.
Weight of footing	30,000	20,000	50,000	40,000
Live load	300,000	120,000	390,000	180,000
Total load	530,000	410,000	940,000	620,000
A = Total ÷ 3000 psf	177 sq. ft.	137 sq. ft.	313 sq. ft.	207 sq. ft.
$DL + Wt. + \frac{1}{3}LL$	330,000 lb.	330,000 lb.	680,000 lb.	500,000 lb.
Soil pressure	1870	2410	2170	2410
A for soil pressure of 1870 psf	330,000/1870 =177 sq. ft.	330,000/1870 =177 sq. ft.	680,000/1870 =363 sq. ft.	500,000/1870 =267 sq. ft.
Dimensions	13′-4″ sq.	13′-4″ sq.	19′-0″ sq.	16′-4″ sq.

* For another procedure, see Sheiry's *Elements of Structural Engineering*

SIZE OF FOOTING

271. Balancing Footing Areas. Settlement of column footings of a building, bridge, or industrial structure is not objectionable if all footings settle the same amount. Unequal settlement stresses and usually cracks the structure. The dead load remains continuously on the footing, and therefore, the dead load produces the greatest settlement. Live loading is temporary and produces little settlement. Hence, in balancing footing areas, we will discount the live load 67 per cent and balance the footing areas for $DL + \frac{1}{3} LL$. Of course, each individual footing must be large enough to support not only the entire dead load including its own weight but also the full live loading. The procedure of determining final footing sizes for equal soil pressures under all footings for the combination of DL + weight of footing + $\frac{1}{3} LL$ is illustrated by Table 28.

PROBLEMS

1406. Redesign the wall footing of §269 using reinforcing bars to reduce the overall depth to 12 in. if possible. Let, $f_s = 20.000$ psi and follow the *ACI* specifications.

1407. Design a footing of a constant depth to support the column load of *DP*48. Let $f_c' = 3000$ psi, $f_s = 24{,}000$, $n = 9$.

1408. Make a redesign for the footing of *DP*48 of the sloping type shown in Fig. 232.

1409. Design a footing in two of four ways by using materials of your own choice: (*a*) plain concrete, (*b*) constant depth to the steel, (*c*) stepped or pedestal type, (*d*) sloping type. The column is of 16-in. diameter and its load is 360,000 lb. Column $f_c' = 3500$ psi.

1410. Balance footing areas from Table 28 when the allowable bearing pressure is 4000 psf for $DL + Wt. + LL/2$.

TABLE 29

SAFE BEARING POWER OF SOILS—*AREA*

MATERIAL	MINIMUM TONS PER SQ. FT.	MAXIMUM TONS PER SQ. FT.
Alluvial soil	½	1
Clays	1	4
Sand confined	1	4
Gravel	2	4
Cemented sand and gravel	5	10
Rock	5	—

272. Bearing Power of Soils. For foundation design, the unit bearing stresses of Table 29 may be assumed if definite information on bearing power is not available. Actually, of course, the allowable *unit bearing pressure* should depend upon size and shape of footing as well as depth of excavation, moisture content, and composition of the soil. However, the bearing pressures listed in Table 29 are considered to be conservative.

Soil Mechanics. Much attention has been given during the past few years to the scientific study of soils and to the field testing of foundations and footings. These data are available in the literature of soil mechanics. Great advances have been made in our understanding of the action of soils under continuous loading. Nevertheless, in its present state of development, this new science is so dependent upon practical observations and experience that it cannot be taught effectively to students other than those who are specializing in the subject of foundations. Other engineers should realize that no structure will be satisfactory unless it has a properly designed foundation and that expert advice in this regard is often necessary.

CHAPTER 15

ULTIMATE STRENGTH DESIGN OF REINFORCED CONCRETE MEMBERS

273. Load Resistance above Working Stresses. In Chapter 13, the design of beams and slabs of reinforced concrete was based upon anticipated working loads and allowable stresses, specifically $0.45f_c'$ for concrete in compression and $0.40f_y$ to $0.50f_y$ for steel reinforcement depending upon the grade of steel used. Evidently then, the design loading might be exceeded considerably, probably by 100 per cent, before the steel would reach its yield strength or before the concrete might be expected to crush or spall by compressive overload. Test beams and slabs have fully confirmed this range of strength or extra load capacity between working stresses and ultimate strength. The

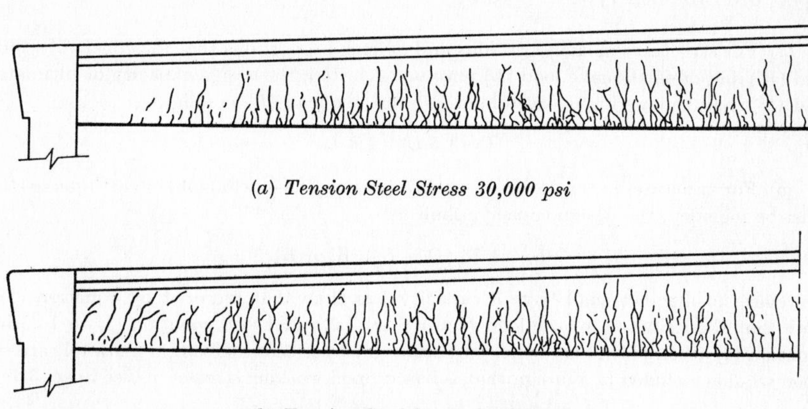

(a) *Tension Steel Stress 30,000 psi*

(b) *Tension Steel Stress 62,000 psi*

FIG. 233. CRACK PATTERNS FOR ROOF T-GIRDER OF SPAN 57 FT.-8 IN.

Girder test by Gaston and Hognestad of Portland Cement Association demonstrating high load capacity of girder of high concrete compressive strength reinforced with bars of $f_y = 83,000$ psi.

analyses in Chapter 10 demonstrated a comparable range of strength for steel beams between working loads and collapse loads corresponding to the development of plastic hinges. However, the illustration in Fig. 233 which shows the actual crack pattern of a full scale T-beam girder of span 58 ft.-7 in. at steel stresses of 30,000 psi and 62,000 psi indicates clearly that the related problems of plastic design of a steel girder and of ultimate load design for a reinforced concrete girder are of a somewhat different character. The fact is that concrete is a brittle material that cracks under a low tensile stress and which has no well-defined compressive yield point but merely a gradually reducing tangent modulus of elasticity with increase of compressive strain. Research has led to adoption of a limited procedure of design for reinforced concrete members based upon ultimate strength, but it has not as yet provided us with a reliable procedure for designing continuous frames of reinforced concrete for ultimate loading comparable to the plastic design of welded frames of structural steel.

Load Factors. The objective of ultimate strength design is not particularly the concept that smaller sections may be used to achieve economy although this sometimes occurs and is a desirable by-product. The main attraction is the expectation that better balanced design may be achieved. It is not really significant that a certain limit of stress be attained under working loads, but it is quite important that the engineering designer knows what maximum load a member may be expected to resist before failure because he can then establish an appropriate allowable load for the member based upon a specified factor of safety. Thus the *ACI Building Code* specifies the ultimate load for design by applying appropriate load factors (Spec. 331) to each type of loading.

(*a*) For structures in such locations and of such proportions that the effects of wind load (W) and of earthquake load (E) may be neglected, the design capacity or ultimate load (U) shall be based upon dead load (D) and live load (L) as follows

$$U = 1.5\,D + 1.8\,L. \tag{1}$$

(*b*) For structures in the design of which a loading due to wind (W) or earthquake (E) must be included, the design capacity shall be

$$U = 1.25\,(D + L + W \text{ or } E). \tag{2}$$

However, no member shall have a capacity less than that required by equation (1). Note that the reduction of the load factor from 1.5 and 1.8 in equation (1) to 1.25 in equation (2) accomplishes the same purpose as a 33 per cent increase in allowable stress when wind is included in a design that is based upon working stresses. (See Spec. 316.)

Strength and Serviceability. Ultimate strength design provides a method of proportioning reinforced concrete members based upon computations of ultimate strength. However, a member may be sufficiently strong but be too flexible under working loads or it may develop objectionably wide tension zone cracks. Hence working load deflections must be computed and compared to maximum limitations of the *ACI Building Code.* (Spec. 332.) To limit the width of cracks, deformed bars are used for main tension reinforcement and the value of f_y is limited to 60,000 psi unless full scale tests demonstrate that cracks will not exceed 0.01 in. in width for exterior members or 0.015 in. for interior members. (Spec. 333.)

ULTIMATE STRESS ANALYSIS

274. Stress Distributions at Ultimate Loading. In early tests of plain concrete and reinforced concrete members the lack of strain gages made the breaking strength in terms of the ultimate load capacity the main test objective. Hence experimenters were forced to picture the stress and strain distributions over the cross-section in terms of ultimate load capacity. It gradually became recognized that strains in a reinforced concrete beam or a plain concrete specimen in flexure vary linearly from a neutral axis but that stress variation in the concrete near ultimate loading is far from linear. Simple compressive cylinder tests showed non-linear variation of strain with applied load somewhat as indicated by Fig. 234(a). Hence it had to be

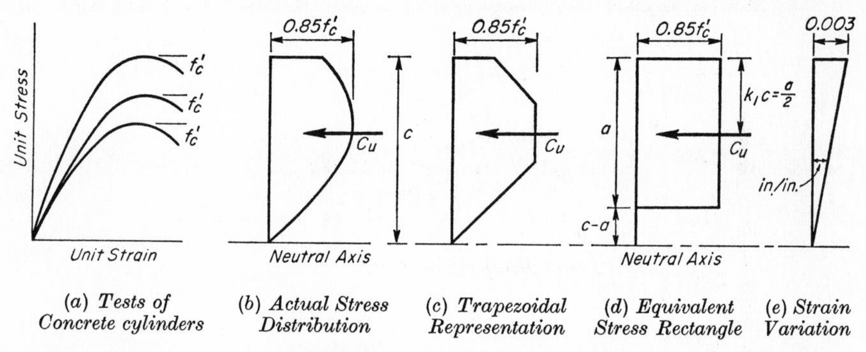

(a) *Tests of Concrete cylinders* (b) *Actual Stress Distribution* (c) *Trapezoidal Representation* (d) *Equivalent Stress Rectangle* (e) *Strain Variation*

FIG. 234. ULTIMATE STRESS DISTRIBUTION ABOVE NEUTRAL AXIS FOR BEAM.

recognized that a similar variation of stress near ultimate loading based upon linear variation of strain was the necessary pattern for compressive stress above the neutral axis of a reinforced concrete beam as shown in Fig. 234(b). The conclusion from many tests is that the maximum compressive concrete stress in a plain or reinforced concrete beam at failure approximates $0.85f_c'$, where f_c' is the average crushing strength of test cylinders of the same concrete mix and age of curing.

Because stress-strain test diagrams of concrete vary considerably in shape, a conventional diagram is needed for ultimate load to replace the conventional straight-line stress variation above the neutral axis that was used in Chapter 13 for working stress calculations. Evidently, a parabola could be used to represent the shape of stress-strain diagram of Fig. 234(b), but the relationships involved might be more involved than would be justified by the fact that the shape of the actual stress distribution diagram varies from beam to beam. For the same reason the trapezoidal representation of Fig. 234(c) has had little use. Instead, the less accurate but more convenient "equivalent stress rectangle" has been adopted in the *ACI*

Building Code as the basis for ultimate strength design of beams and slabs of reinforced concrete.

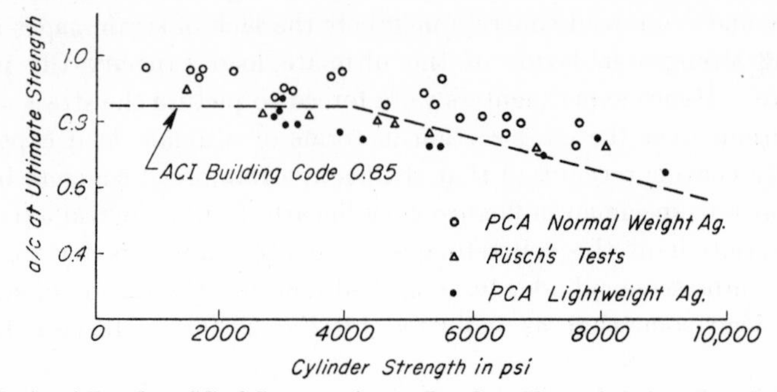

(*a*) *Ratio of Depth to CG of Compression to Depth to Neutral Axis—Test Data.*

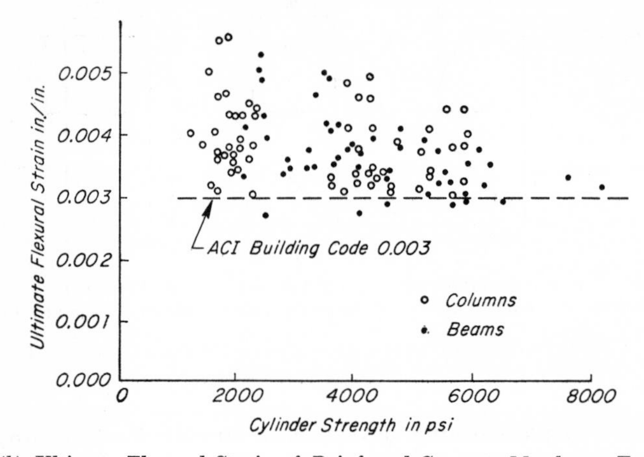

(*b*) *Ultimate Flexural Strain of Reinforced Concrete Members—Test Data.*

(Data from article by Mattock, Kirz, and Hognestad, Vol. 32, *Journal of the ACI*.)

FIG. 235. TEST DATA JUSTIFYING EQUIVALENT ULTIMATE STRESS RECTANGLE.

Dimensions of Equivalent Stress Rectangle. The equivalent stress rectangle has a maximum stress value of $0.85f_c'$, which represents about the minimum ultimate stress of beams and of columns of normal h/r values as contrasted to f_c' for cylinder tests. The maximum strain in the concrete at ultimate loading was established at the conservative value of 0.003 in. per inch based upon extensive tests. (See Fig. 235(*b*).) Then the ratio of the depth of the stress rectangle to the depth of the neutral axis below the top fiber, that is, the ratio a/c from Fig. 234, had to be established. Mattock, Kriz, and Hognestad[1] correlated test data (Fig. 235(*a*)) and showed that the

[1] "Rectangular concrete distribution in ultimate strength design," *Journal of the American Concrete Institute*, Vol. 32.

ratio a/c might be set at 0.85 for concrete up to $f_c' = 4000$ psi, 0.80 for $f_c' = 5000$ psi, 0.75 for $f_c' = 6000$ psi, etc. With all dimensions thus defined, the location of C_u at $a/2$ below the top fiber and its magnitude of $0.85f_c'ab$ depend merely upon the value of c or the location of the neutral axis which will be shown below to be dependent upon the strain in the tensile steel.

275. Assumptions Involved in Ultimate Stress Analysis. It is desirable to restate the assumptions which must be fulfilled for rectangular cross-sections, doubly reinforced sections, T-beam sections, etc.

1. Tensile strength of the concrete is neglected exactly as for working stresses.

2. Force equilibrium and compatibility of strains must be satisfied. The latter does not apply at a tensile crack or near the end of a bar within its anchorage length.

3. Strain in the concrete above and below the neutral axis shall be assumed to be directly proportioned to distance from the neutral axis with a maximum compressive strain of 0.003 in. per inch.

4. Steel strain is to be taken as equal to the concrete strain at the same location. Steel stress below the yield strength shall be computed by multiplying the steel strain by E_s. For steel strain beyond the yield point strain (or stress) the steel stress is independent of its strain and may be taken at f_y the design yield strength.

5. Concrete stress at ultimate load is not proportional to strain. The total compressive stress may be represented for computation of ultimate resisting moment as an equivalent stress rectangle.

6. The equivalent stress rectangle has a maximum stress value of $0.85f'_c$ and a depth a that is $0.85c$ for $f'_c = 4000$ psi. The factor 0.85 reduces by $0.05c$ for each increment of f'_c of 1000 psi.

SPECIAL NOTATION FOR ULTIMATE DESIGN.

a depth of the equivalent stress rectangle.
A_{st} area of reinforcement to develop compressive strength of overhanging flanges for I and T-sections
c depth below the top fiber to the neutral axis
C_u total compression resisted by concrete above the neutral axis
f_c' design strength of the concrete based upon cylinder tests
f_y yield strength of the steel
j_u ultimate value of j when jd is arm from T to C
k_1 where $k_1c = a$, the depth of the equivalent stress rectangle
k_u where $k_ud = c$, the depth to the neutral axis
M_u ultimate resisting moment of a section
p_b percentage of tensile steel for balanced reinforcement
q pf_y/f_c'
T_u total tension resisted by the steel at ultimate load
U ultimate loading for design
v_c unit shear resisted by an unreinforced concrete web
v_u unit shear resisted by the concrete of a reinforced web for ultimate load

V_u total shear at a section for ultimate loading
V_u' total shear resisted by web steel at ultimate load
ϕ capacity reduction factor, 0.90 for flexure, 0.85 for shear or bond
Note: Also see Notation on pages xv, xvi, and xvii.

Design Equations

276. Rectangular Sections Reinforced in Tension.

Ultimate Strength. One may equate the ultimate compression C_u and the ultimate tension T_u on the cross-section illustrated by Fig. 236(a), to obtain a value of a, the depth of the stress rectangle.

$$A_sf_y = 0.85f_c'ab \qquad \text{or} \qquad a = \frac{A_sf_y}{0.85f_c'b}. \tag{3}$$

For a known cross-section all terms on the right-hand side of the expression for a will be known if the yield stress in the steel is reached simultaneously with the ultimate concrete stress, because f_y may then be used for the steel stress. The ultimate resisting moment may be computed by multiplying T_u or C_u by the arm from T_u to C_u which is $d - a/2$. The resulting equations are

$$M_u = \phi A_sf_y\left(d - \frac{a}{2}\right) = \phi A_sf_yd(1 - 0.59q), \tag{4}$$

$$M_u = \phi bd^2f_c'q(1 - 0.59q). \tag{5}$$

where $q = pf_y/f_c'$, $a = A_sf_y/0.85f_c'b$, and ϕ is a "capacity reduction factor" introduced by *ACI* to improve safety and specified as 0.90 for flexure, 0.85 for bond or diagonal tension, 0.75 for spirally reinforced members with axial load, and 0.70 for tied members with axial load. The *ACI Building Code* restricts the percentage of steel to 3/4 of that for balanced reinforcement so that the steel stress will reach f_y and all beams will obey equations (4) and (5). For balanced reinforcement the yield stress in the steel would be reached simultaneously with the ultimate concrete stress of $0.85f_c'$. The percentage of steel for balanced reinforcement p_b may be obtained by equating T_u and C_u as follows.

$$A_sf_y = 0.85f_c'ab,$$

or

$$p_bbdf_y = 0.85f_c'(k_1c)b = 0.85f_c'(k_1k_ud)b. \tag{6}$$

Then from the linear strain diagram of Fig. 236(b), k_u (where $k_ud = c$) is written as

$$k_u = \frac{\epsilon_u}{\epsilon_u + \epsilon_y} = \frac{\epsilon_uE_s}{\epsilon_uE_s + \epsilon_yE_s} = \frac{90{,}000}{90{,}000 + f_y}. \tag{7}$$

Substituting this value of k_u into equation (6) gives the percentage of steel for balanced reinforcement.

$$p_b = \frac{0.85f_c'\,k_1}{f_y}\left(\frac{90{,}000}{90{,}000 + f_y}\right). \tag{8}$$

Numerical Calculations versus Use of Equations. In general, it has been the objective of this text to make the use of formulas unnecessary. Since space does not permit the presentation of numerical examples for all of the many variations of cross-sections and steel ratios that may occur in beam design for ultimate strength the next sections will present the *ACI* specifications for doubly reinforced beams and for T-beams. These specifications cover only the most common cases and include the usual equations for balanced reinforcement and ultimate resisting moment M_u. One can readily apply such equations to situations where they will produce incorrect results. It is recommended therefore that the designer use numerical calculations based upon the dimensions of the cross-section, the equating of numerical expressions for T_u and C_u, the equating of moments expressed in terms of T_u and C_u, and the use of equation (7) which is the strain compatibility relationship for linear variations of strains. The latter must be introduced whenever the steel stress has just initially reached f_y. Stress in the steel in such cases is directly proportioned to strain. These elementary relationships may each contain a single unknown or they may need to be solved simultaneously, but they are adequate to complete an analysis or to provide the design factors being sought. One example of a numerical design for a beam of rectangular cross-section that is handled without use of the formulas will be presented on Design Sheet 49.

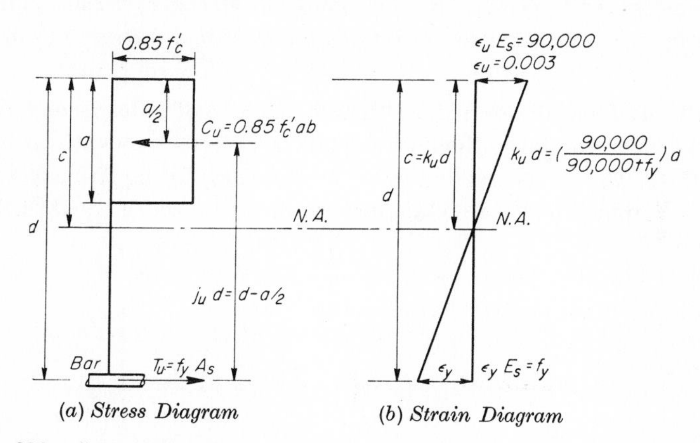

(*a*) *Stress Diagram* (*b*) *Strain Diagram*

FIG. 236. STRESS AND STRAIN DISTRIBUTIONS FOR ULTIMATE LOADING.

SPECIFICATIONS

277. *ACI* Specifications for Ultimate Strength of Beams with Double Reinforcement.

(*a*) The ultimate load resisting moment in rectangular beams with compression reinforcement shall be calculated by

(9) $$M_u = \phi\left[(A_s - A_s')\,f_y\left(d - \frac{a}{2}\right) + A_s'f_y(d - d')\right]$$

where $a = (A_s - A_s')f_y/0.85f_c'b$.

(*b*) Equation (9) is valid only when the compression steel reaches the yield strength f_y at ultimate strength. This is satisfied when

(10) $$p - p' \geq 0.85\,k_1\frac{f_c'd'}{f_yd}\left(\frac{90{,}000}{90{,}000 - f_y}\right).$$

(*c*) When $(p - p')$ is less than the value given by equation (10), so that the compression steel stress is less than the yield strength f_y or when effects of compression steel are neglected, the calculated ultimate moment shall not exceed that given by equations (4) and (5), except when a general analysis is made on the basis of the assumptions given in §275.

(*d*) The quantity $(p - p')$ shall not exceed 0.75 of the value p_b given by equation (8). When the compression steel does not yield at ultimate strength, or when effects of compression steel are neglected, p shall not exceed 0.75 p_b, except when it is shown by a general analysis that the tension steel ratio p does not exceed 75 per cent of that corresponding to balanced conditions.

(*e*) Balanced conditions exist when, at ultimate strength of a member, the tension reinforcement reaches its yield strength stress f_y just as the concrete in compression reaches its assumed ultimate strain of 0.003.

278. *ACI* Specifications for Ultimate Strength of I-Beams and T-Beams.

(*a*) When the flange thickness equals or exceeds the depth to the neutral axis ($1.18\,qd/k_1$), the section may be designed by equations (4) and (5), with q computed as for a rectangular beam with a width equal to the overall flange width.

(*b*) When the flange thickness is less than $1.18\,qd/k_1$, the ultimate moment shall not exceed that given by

(11) $$M_u = \phi\left[(A_s - A_{sf})f_y\left(d - \frac{a}{2}\right) + A_{sf}f_y(d - 0.5t)\right],$$

in which A_{sf}, the steel area necessary to develop the compressive strength of overhanging flanges, is

(12) $$A_{sf} = 0.85\,(b - b')\,tf_c'/f_y,$$

and

(13) $$a = (A_s - A_{sf})f_y/0.85f_c'b'.$$

(*c*) The quantity $(A_s - A_{sf})/b'd$ shall not exceed 0.75 of the value p_b given by equation (8).

Other Cross-Sections.

(*d*) For other cross-sections and for cases of non-symmetrical bending, the ultimate moment shall be computed by a general analysis based on the assumptions given in §275.

(*e*) The amount of tension reinforcement shall be so limited that the steel ratio p does not exceed 75 per cent of that corresponding to balanced conditions as defined by §277(*e*).

279. Shear and Bond Design for Ultimate Strength. Generally speaking, no new procedures of analysis for shear or bond are required merely because ultimate loads rather than allowable loads are used in design. In each instance that the total shear V or V' occurs in a formula for shear or bond or stirrup spacing it is replaced by V_u or V_u', the ultimate shear. Also, the "capacity reduction factor" ϕ is introduced either in the numerator or denominator of the formula where its value of 0.85 will increase the factor of safety of the member. For stirrup design or anchorage calculation f_y replaces f_s since the design objective is to work the steel to its yield value at ultimate loading. The shear and bond stresses in the concrete may be computed from the following formulas.

(14) $$v_u = \frac{V_u}{bd}, \text{ or for } T \text{ beams } v_u = \frac{V_u}{b'd},$$

and

(15) $$u_u = \frac{V_u}{\Sigma O jd}.$$

Ultimate Shear and Bond Stresses for Use in Design. The following increased stresses are permitted by the *ACI Building Code* for design based upon ultimate loads.

Limit upon Shear as a Measure of Diagonal Tension. For concrete weighing 145 pcf.

(16) $v_c = 2\phi\sqrt{f_c'}$ unreinforced web.

(17) $v_u = 10\phi\sqrt{f_c'}$ reinforced web.

(18) $v_c = 4\phi\sqrt{f_c'}$ slab or footing unreinforced for shear.

Limiting Bond Stresses for Deformed Bars.

(19) $$u = \frac{6.7\phi\sqrt{f_c'}}{D} < 560 \text{ psi}$$ *A*305, top bars.

(20) $$u = \frac{9.5\phi\sqrt{f_c'}}{D} < 800 \text{ psi}$$ *A*305, other bars.

(21) $u = 13\phi\sqrt{f_c'} < 800$ psi deformed compressive bars.

Shear stresses greater than the allowable values given in (16) to (18) must be resisted by stirrups or bent bars. Note $\phi = 0.85$ for shear and bond.

DP49. *A simply supported beam of 26-ft. span carries a uniform loading of 1500#/′ from a water tank and a uniform dead load of 600#/′. Since the bottom of the tank is self-supporting for a span of 4′–0″, beams 12″ wide will be tried at 5′–0″ center to center.*

Let $k_1 = 0.80$ *for* $f_c' = 5000$ *psi;* $f_y = 60{,}000$ *psi;* $\phi = 0.90$ *for flexure and 0.85 for shear and bond. By equation (1),*

$U = 1.5D + 1.8L = 1.5 \times 600 + 1.8 \times 1500 = 3600\#/'$.

$M_u(\text{for } D + L) = \frac{1}{8} \times 3600 \times 26^2 \times 12 = 3{,}650{,}000''\#$ *req'd.*

V_u *at 18″ from support (assuming* $d = 18''$*)* $= 11.5 \times 3600 = 41{,}400\#$.

For linear strain distribution

$$c = k_u d = \left(\frac{90{,}000}{90{,}000 + 60{,}000}\right) d.$$

Therefore

$c = 0.6 \times 18 = 10.8''$,

$a = 0.8c = 8.64''$.

For $T_u = C_u$ *with balanced reinforcement,* $A_s f_y = (0.85 f_c') b a$.

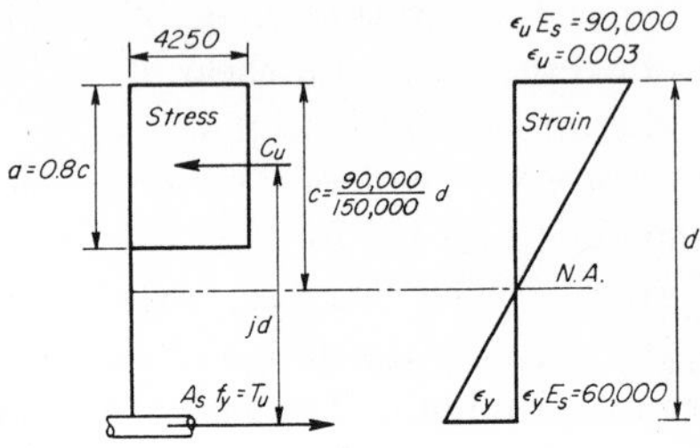

Steel Area: $A_s = \dfrac{4250 \times 12 \times 8.64}{60{,}000} = 7.34 \text{ in.}^2$

$T_u = A_s f_y = 7.34 \times 60{,}000 = 440{,}000\#$.

$M_u = T_u(d - a/2) = 440{,}000(18 - 8.64/2) = 6{,}040{,}000''\#$.

$M_u(\text{for } D + L) = 0.61 M_u(\text{for } p_b)$. *ACI permits* $p = 0.75 p_b$ *but applies* $\phi = 0.90$.

Provide steel for $0.61 M_u \div \phi = 0.61 \times 6{,}040{,}000 \div 0.9$.

$A_s = 4{,}070{,}000/60{,}000 = 6.8 \text{ in.}^2$

Use 7-No. 9 deformed bars, $A_s = 7.00 \text{ in.}^2$, $D = 1.13''$.

Bend up 4 bars leaving 3 for bond.

Bond: $u_u = V_u/\Sigma O jd = 41{,}400 \div (\pi \times 1.13 \times 3)(18 - 8.63/2)$. (*Spec. 342.*)

$u_u = 285$ *psi; limiting* $u_u = 9.5\phi\sqrt{f_c'}/D = 9.5 \times 0.85 \times \sqrt{5000}/1.69 = 505$ *psi.*

Shear: $v_u = \dfrac{V_u}{bd} = \dfrac{41{,}400}{12 \times 18} = 192$ *psi.*

Limiting $v_c = 2\phi\sqrt{f_c'} = 2 \times 0.85 \times \sqrt{5000} = 120$ *psi.* (*Spec. 336.*)

Difference to be carried by stirrups $= 192 - 120 = 72$ *psi.*

(*Specs. 337 and 340.*)

For a maximum stirrup spacing of $d/2$ *or 9″,* $A_v = \dfrac{72 \times 12 \times 9}{0.85 \times 60{,}000} = 0.15 \text{ in.}^2$

A single loop ⅜″ *wire provides* $A_s = 0.22$. *Four bars can be bent up at 30 degrees to reinforce a length of web* $s = 2d$ *adequately near the support.*

Unit Shear = 120 psi at 5.8′ from support. Discontinue stirrups at $5.8 + d = 7.3'$ *from support.*

Remarks: *The use of 7-No. 9 bars requires placement of bars in two layers which deepens the beam by 2½″ overall.*

Beam Design for Ultimate Load

280. Example of Design Calculations without Use of Formulas. *DP*49. The following example is that of a simple span beam having a rectangular cross-section that carries the weight of a tank filled with water. The sketches show the equivalent stress rectangle for balanced ultimate stresses and the linear strain diagram that controls the location of the neutral axis for balanced reinforcement. The maximum concrete strain is specified by *ACI* at 0.003 in. per inch which may be converted into an imaginary steel stress at the top of the beam of 90,000 psi. Hence, for $f_y = 60{,}000$ psi at the level of the tensile steel the neutral axis is below the mid-depth and

$$c = \left(\frac{90{,}000}{90{,}000 + 60{,}000}\right) d = 0.6d.$$

Since $a = 0.8c$ for $f_c' = 5000$ psi, it follows that $a = 0.8 \times 0.6d = 0.48d$. Therefore, when values for T and C are equated for balanced reinforcement only one unknown A_s will occur in the equation which leads to $A_s = 7.34$ sq. in. Actually, the balanced steel area provides a larger value of M_u than is needed. Hence the steel area is reduced to that required to provide for the ultimate dead load plus live load moment including an allowance for the *ACI* "capacity reduction factor" (safety increment factor) of $\phi = 0.9$ for flexure. No revision of the calculations is necessary because the steel strain will change as needed to permit reduction in the concrete stress block to fit the reduced moment. We simply know that the steel stress will not exceed 60,000 psi and the maximum concrete stress will not exceed $0.85 f_c$ for the reduced bending moment.

For bond and shear the author used the standard formulas without including the *ACI* capacity reduction factor ($\phi = 0.85$), which was used instead to reduce the limiting bond and shear stresses for the concrete. (Spec. 329.) Again for determining stirrup spacing the factor ϕ was used to reduce the value of f_y for the stirrup steel which is a consistent use of this factor. Of course, ϕ could be introduced to increase the computed shear and bond requirements due to the loading rather than to reduce limiting stresses, but a consistent procedure should be adopted for all such calculations. Specifications are not always consistent in this regard.

The choice of seven No. 9 bars placed in two layers was dictated by the economical 12-in. width of the beam. Since four (or even five) bars can be bent up without excessive bond stress on the remaining bars, it would be possible to carry all web shear without stirrups if bars are bent up individually rather than symmetrically in pairs. (Spec. 339.) For a 30-degree slope the maximum required area for a single bar for a spacing of 20 in. horizontally (s) would be

$$A_v = \frac{V_u's}{\phi f_y d(\sin\alpha + \cos\alpha)} = \frac{72 \times 12 \times d \times 20}{0.85 \times 60{,}000 \times d(0.5 + 0.866)} = 0.25 \text{ sq. in.}$$

One No. 9 reinforcing bar provides 1.0 sq. in. Because the maximum spacing is ¾ of the sloping length of bar or 20 in., (Spec. 339) it would require five bars bent up individually to cover the length of 7.3 ft. determined in *DP*49. Spacing of bends could be reduced to 18 in. throughout or to 16 in. near the support and 20 in. elsewhere.

PROBLEMS

1501. If the water loading of *DP*49 cannot be exceeded because of limited depth of the tank, it can be treated as dead load in equation (1). Make this change and revise the design for the reduced ultimate loading.

1502. Revise *DP*49 for $f_c' = 4000$ psi, $f_y = 50{,}000$ psi, and for an increased span of 31 ft.-6 in. There is also a load concentration of 35,000 lb. at 5 ft. from each end of the span.

1503. Design a simple span beam of rectangular cross-section to support a fixed loading of 750 lb. per lineal ft., including its weight, and a live loading of 1350 lb. per lineal ft. for a span of 40 ft.-0 in. Use $f_c = 6000$ psi and $f_y = 75{,}000$ psi. Follow *ACI* specifications.

1504. A precast concrete joist for a span of 24 ft. has a depth to the steel of 14 in. and a breadth of 5½ in. The steel is two No. 8 bars. If $f_c' = 5000$ psi and $f_y = 60{,}000$ psi, what ultimate uniform fixed loading can be sustained? There is no web reinforcement.

1505. Revise Problem 1504 for balanced reinforcement and web reinforcement as considered economical when $f_y = 75{,}000$ psi.

281. Development of Ultimate Load Design of Reinforced Concrete Structures. There is much yet to be learned about ultimate load design of reinforced concrete structures. First, as we have noted in this chapter, the stress distribution over any cross-section is non-linear. By the device of initially analyzing the cross-section for balanced reinforcement you have formulated a relatively simple procedure for design that provides a safe estimate of the ultimate resisting moment for reduced percentages of reinforcing steel. However, the calculations provide inadequate knowledge of the accompanying concrete stresses. When such a cross-section is considered as a part of a continuous frame it becomes necessary to know its inelastic deformations, which control the moment distribution throughout the structure. No concept comparable in simplicity to the plastic-hinge procedure of analysis and design for steel structures appears adequate for reinforced concrete frames. When any reinforced concrete section becomes "plastic" a considerable length of the member of which it is a part has concrete stresses well beyond the assumed elastic range for working stresses. This fact must be considered along with the picture of the highly cracked area of tensile concrete illustrated by Fig. 233. The latter involves the acceptance of discontinuity between such highly cracked concrete and the tensile reinforcement. Such considerations lead to a cautious viewpoint regarding the simple application of the plastic hinge concept to reinforced concrete frames. Additional tests of large scale reinforced concrete frames near ultimate loading must precede the development and acceptance of a useful theory of inelastic action that could lead to improved design.

CHAPTER 16

PRESTRESSED CONCRETE

282. The Concept of Prestress. Cannon in early days were made of brittle cast metal prestressed with external circumferential steel bands. The bands could be heated and then shrunk onto the gun barrel to produce prestress. The gun barrel resisted the tension in the circumferential steel bands by internal circumferential compression as shown in Fig. 237 (*a*) or (*b*). When a charge of powder was exploded in the barrel the circumferential compression might be reduced to zero by the internal pressure as illustrated by Fig. 237(*c*). Under the condition of an internal pressure just sufficient to reduce the initial compression C_1 to zero the tension in a steel band T_2 would equal the initial prestress T_1. This simple analysis neglects reduction in diameter or deformation of the barrel due to initial prestress.

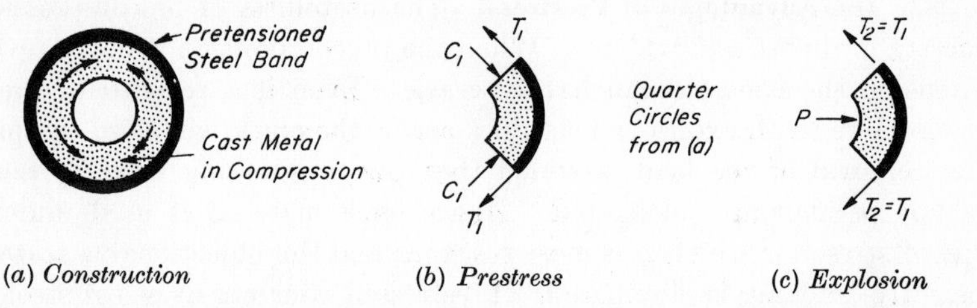

FIG. 237. ACTION OF A PRESTRESSED GUN BARREL BEFORE AND DURING EXPLOSION.

Early attempts to prestress concrete whether as circular tanks by external steel rods or as concrete beams with internal longitudinal rods pretensioned by tightening the end nuts were not successful. A simple calculation based upon the relation $E = f/\varepsilon$, where E is the modulus of elasticity, f is the unit stress, and ε is the unit strain, will establish the reason. Available steel rods in the period before 1900 provided an elastic limit around 30,000 psi. Even if prestressed to this value the unit deformation in the steel would be only 30,000/30,000,000 or 0.001 in. per inch of length. When such rods were tightened against concrete having an elastic modulus of 2,000,000 psi and an area 50 times the cross-sectional area of the steel, the concrete was stressed to 600 psi and the corresponding deformation should be 600/2,000,000 or 0.0003 in. per inch of length. Hence the initial compressive deformation of the concrete might be as much as one third of the deformation of the steel which would release one third of the steel stress. This might be corrected by further tightening of the steel rods, but thereafter a continuing release of the pretension stress would occur from a gradual plastic shortening or creep and shrinkage of the concrete. These effects were found to be sufficient to release a large fraction if not all of the pretension in the steel since under the worst conditions shrinkage and creep of concrete can equal 0.001 in. per inch, which is equivalent to the steel deformation corresponding to a unit stress of 30,000 psi. This explains why modern prestressing wires have a yield strength well above 150,000 psi so that they may be pretensioned to this stress, and then the stress will not drop below 120,000 psi after shrinkage and creep have occurred in the concrete.

The use of high strength wires for prestressing concrete developed first in France and Belgium following the research of Freyssinet and Magnel upon devices for anchoring the wires. Friction anchorages based upon wedges that bind the ends of the wires after they have been jacked to the required pretension were devised to eliminate the loss of strength due to any type of threaded tightener. In this country prestressed circular concrete tanks were constructed widely after 1935 but the first prestressed bridges and buildings date from about 1950. At present essentially any concrete member or structure that can be built of reinforced concrete could also be prestressed although prestressed structures are not always economical.

283. The Advantages of Prestress. The usefulness of precompression in concrete is almost self-evident. When the precompression is never reversed to tension the concrete can hardly crack. Even if a reversal of precompression due to an excessive load does occur, the crack will close completely after removal of the load provided that the prestressing wires or tendons are not permanently elongated. Hence each material is used under the type of stress for which it is most resistant and the objectionable feature of unsightly cracking is eliminated. Prestressed concrete uses less steel than reinforced concrete because the prestressed wires are worked to five or six times the stress permitted for medium steel bars. Also, the concrete area can be reduced by use of high strength concrete, which is usually desirable with prestress. The volume of concrete is further reduced by the fact that the entire cross-section of a prestressed beam resists compression rather than the part above the neutral axis of a reinforced concrete section. Also, longitudinal precompression in a beam will be found to counteract diagonal tension due to shear thus permitting a considerable reduction of stirrup steel. Hence all beam materials are reduced by prestressing which makes possible greatly increased spans for prestressed girders. Costs are not directly related to weight, however, because prestressing usually increases labor costs and also requires more expensive materials.

284. Precast, Pretensioned Beams. Precasting yards usually provide pretensioned beams in standard sizes to compete with steel or wood beams. The simplest procedure of manufacture is to construct a trough several hundred feet long to cast a series of beams of one size. The prestress wires or strands are placed in the trough and tensioned against heavy abutments at the ends of the trough. Diaphragms at intervals separate the individual beams when the trough is filled with concrete. After the concrete has set sufficiently to anchor the wires by bond the wires are cut at each diaphragm and the shortening of the wires prestresses the concrete. This is the least expensive method of prestressing. It is an effective method of producing prestressed beams, but larger girders are usually tensioned individually. The multiple system of precasting works best with straight wires although the wires can be pulled downward and anchored to a heavy concrete slab before pouring the concrete. Wires anchored by bond are usually less than $3/16$ in. diameter unless mechanical corrugations, and end buttons or clamps are added to improve the anchorage. Strands of seven wires are in common use.

285. Post-Tensioning of Beams and Girders. Large precast girders, and most beams, girders and slabs that are cast in place on the job, must be post-tensioned after the concrete has developed its design strength. Because the bond of post-tensioned steel is relatively unimportant, groups of wires or twisted cables an inch or more in diameter may be used. Elaborate patented devices are used to anchor the wires either with frictional wedges or by cold forming rivet heads on the ends of straight wires or by splaying the wires of a twisted cable and casting them into a metal cone. Tensioning devices include hydraulic jacks that grip the wires or cables and pull them to the required stress by reacting against metal bearing plates on the end of the girder. Because design of the cross-section of the girder is not influenced by the type of anchorage bidders may be permitted to propose different anchorage systems.

For post-tensioning it is necessary that the wires or cables be protected from initial bonding to the concrete either by greasing or other coating or more commonly by use of conduits. If a final bond between the post-tensioned steel and the concrete is desired, the conduit must be of metal and of adequate size for grout to be forced around the wires from one end of the conduit to the other. For ultimate loading it is desirable that the wires be bonded. Otherwise, the first crack that develops in the concrete due to overload will continue to open as the load increases and the concrete above the top of the crack may crush. With bonded steel many small cracks will be produced with less possible damage to the concrete. Small hair-cracks are more likely to close completely when the overload is removed. Also, grouting provides corrosion protection for the tensioned wires or cables.

Achieving Effective Prestress

286. High-Strength Materials. While 3000 psi concrete is adequate with standard bar reinforcing 5000 psi concrete may be required for economy in a prestressed girder. For example, if 1 per cent of steel that is stressed to

150,000 psi is placed at one third of the depth from the bottom of a rectangular beam, it will produce a triangular compressive stress diagram varying from zero at the top to 3000 psi at the bottom. Since 5000 psi concrete may be stressed to only 2250 psi (for $0.45f_c'$) it is clear that the prestress in the steel should be below 150,000 psi or that the area of steel must be less than 1 per cent of the concrete cross-section. Concrete with an ultimate strength well above 5000 psi is difficult to produce consistently. Therefore, it becomes clear why the area of prestressing steel for typical installations is usually somewhat less than 1 per cent of the cross-section of the concrete.

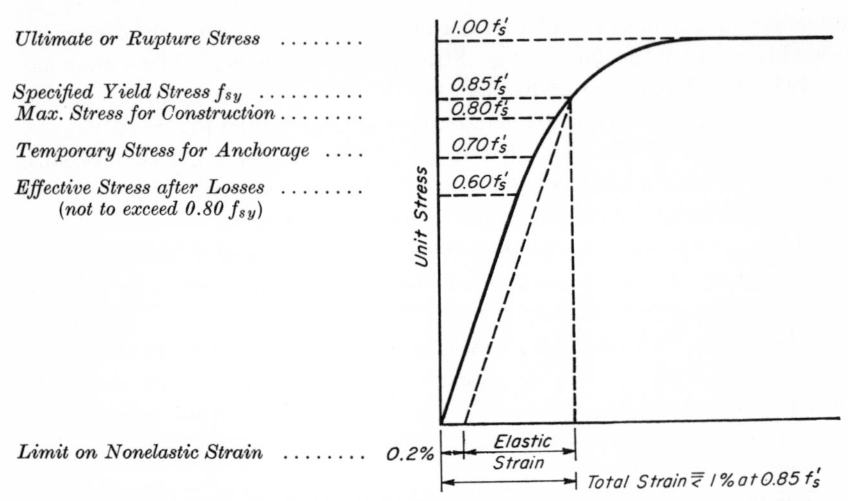

FIG. 238. *ACI* REQUIREMENTS OF STRESS-STRAIN DIAGRAM FOR PRESTRESS WIRE OR STRAND.

Prestressing steel is obtainable either as plain or galvanized wires or as twisted strands of multiple wires. The latter have been increasing in use. The ultimate strength of the wires varies from 200,000 psi to 300,000 psi, the highest strength being for wires under $\frac{1}{16}$ inch in diameter which are used only in twisted strands. Straight wires are often of 0.25-in. or 0.196-in. diameter although many gages have been used. Strands range from $\frac{1}{4}$ in. to 1 in. or more in diameter and may contain from seven wires upward. The steel used for prestressing wires is cold drawn and then stress relieved by stretching or by time-temperature treatment. The result is a wire having an elongation of at least 4 per cent and a 30 per cent reduction of cross-section at rupture. Its yield stress must be 85 per cent of its specified ultimate strength at 1 per cent total elongation or 0.2 per cent permanent elongation as illustrated by Fig. 238. For prestress steel of these properties the working prestress after all losses may be 60 per cent of the ultimate stress f_s' or 80 per cent of the specified yield stress, whichever is smaller. However, during construction the wires or strands may be pulled for a short time up to $0.80f_s'$ to reduce creep in the steel. The stress when the wires are released into the anchorage may be $0.70f_s'$. Hence the prestress steel is more heavily stressed during construction than later in its life even though the structure may be considerably overloaded. This point will be clarified later.

287. Loss of Prestress from Elastic Deformations. Consider a concrete beam section 10 in. wide by 24 in. deep symmetrically prestressed by 0.67 per cent of steel initially stressed to 150,000 psi. The applied prestressing force is $150,000 \times 240 \times 0.0067 = 240,000$ lb. The initial unit stress in the concrete is $240,000 \div 240 = 1,000$ psi. The concrete will shorten elastically. If $E_c = 4,000,000$, the unit concrete strain will be $1,000/4,000,000 = 0.00025$ in. per inch. The corresponding reduction of prestress in the steel will be $0.00025 \times 30,000,000 = 7500$ psi. There are two small factors neglected in this analysis. The net area rather than the gross area of the concrete section might have been used, and the final prestress rather than the initial prestress is the true force producing strain in the concrete. The total error involved is small. Actually for multiple wires or cables that are tightened in succession the average loss of prestress will be about one half of that computed above. The first cable tightened will lose prestress as each successive cable is tightened, but the last cable tightened will produce very little shortening of the concrete and will lose almost none of its prestress. There is also the deformation of the anchorages to be considered, but this movement of about a tenth of an inch is usually allowed for by overtensioning the steel.

288. Creep in Concrete and Steel. Both concrete and high strength wires will permanently change dimensions due to stress. This plastic flow is usually termed creep. For concrete the creep deformation is assumed to be about 1.5 times the corresponding elastic deformation due to prestress. Shrinkage of concrete has a similar effect of equal or greater magnitude. Creep in the prestressing wires or cables is usually of somewhat less significance. It may also be overcome by overtensioning the steel slightly and holding this overstress for a couple of minutes or by retensioning the wires or cables after a few weeks. When the latter can be done it also will eliminate much of the loss of prestress due to shrinkage and creep of the concrete. The combined factors of elastic strain in the concrete, creep in concrete and steel, and shrinkage of concrete will reduce the prestress about 20 per cent unless the steel is retensioned. A joint specification committee has recommended an allowance of 25,000 psi for loss of prestress for post-tensioned wires when the individual factors involved are not determinable for greater accuracy. However, this allowance does not cover frictional loss which should be estimated separately.

289. Frictional Losses. A greased wire or strand in a straight hole should have no significant loss of prestress due to friction. However, some damage to the shield around the post-tensioned steel during construction is probable and besides much prestressing is done with curved cables. If the steel is later to be grouted for corrosion resistance and development of bond, a lubricant may be undesirable. Hence there is usually a significant loss of prestress due to friction at some distance from an anchorage. Overtensioning the steel followed by a backward movement as the tension is reduced is considered the most effective friction reducer. For a cable placed in a circular arc α the friction reduces the cable force from T_o at the end of the arc nearest the anchorage to T_x at a distance x along the arc depending upon the coefficient of friction μ as follows.

$$T_x = T_o(2.72^{-\mu\alpha}). \tag{1}$$

Consider a long cable curved over several supports for which we will assume that $\Sigma\alpha =$ 1.0 radian. Then if $\mu = 0.33$,

$$T_x = T_0 \div 2.72^{1/3} = 0.72\,T_0.$$

The loss of prestress due to cable friction would be 28 per cent, which would require a 39 per cent increase in the area of steel to equal the prestress effect of a straight cable. An economic study would be required to determine whether the reduction of bending moment and steel area due to curving the cable would more than offset the increase of steel area to overcome friction. Some allowance is usually made in specifications for a small friction loss due to lack of perfect straightness of conduit or sheathing in which wire cables or strands are strung (wobble coefficient, Spec. 407).

Analysis of Beam Sections for Working Loads

290. Special Definitions for Prestressed Concrete. The most common letters and subscripts used in the analysis of prestressed sections are listed here for convenient reference.

A_b area in bearing; A_b' related concentric area
A_c area of concrete; A_n net; A_g gross; A_u ultimate area
A_s area of prestress steel, either bars, wires, or cable
A_t transformed area of concrete and steel section
A_v area of web steel, area of stirrups over a length of beam s
b width of beam or of flange for a T-section or I-section
b' width of web for a beam of T-section or I-section
C compressive force, lb; C_u ultimate value
d depth of beam to center of prestress steel
e any eccentricity
f_c concrete stress, psi; f_{ci} at transfer; f_{ce} effective; f_{cb} bearing
f_c' ultimate, 28-day cylinder strength, psi; f_{ci}' ultimate strength at transfer
f_s unit steel prestress, psi; f_{si} before or at transfer; f_{se} effective after losses
f_s' breaking strength of prestress steel, psi
f_{su} $0.80f_s'$ approx.; prestress for ultimate strength design; see Spec. 408(*c*)
f_{sy}, specified yield strength or stress of prestress steel
f_y' yield strength of unprestressed steel or stirrups, psi;
F prestress force, lb; F_i initial; F_e after all losses

h	overall depth of beam as contrasted to d
I_c	moment of inertia of concrete section; I_g gross; I_n net; I_t transformed section
jd	lever arm from center of compression to steel
kd	depth of compressive area
M	bending moment; M_g gravity moment; M_u ultimate moment
n	ratio of moduli of elasticity, E_s/E_c
p	percentage of steel computed as A_s/bd even for T-section
s	stirrup spacing
T	tension in steel, lb; T_e effective; T_i initial; T_x at x from T_o
T_u	ultimate tension
u	bond stress in psi; u_u ultimate bond resistance in psi
V	total shear at a section, lb; v is unit shear, psi; v_c allowable unit shear; $v' = v - v_c$
V_u	ultimate-load shear to be reduced by concrete shear and cable v — component
y	vertical distance from axis or vertical deflection

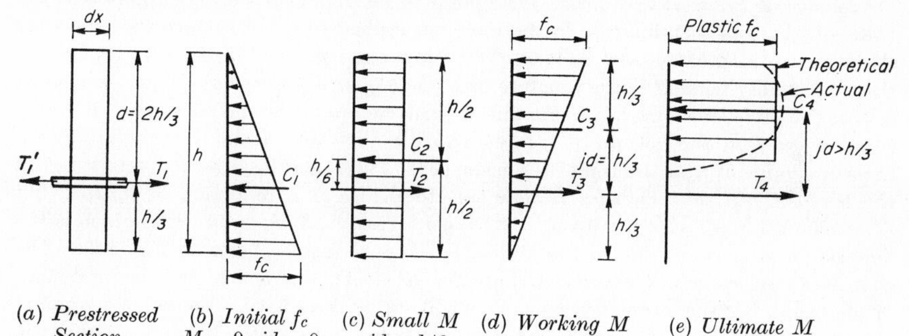

(a) *Prestressed Section* (b) *Initial* f_c $M = 0$; $jd = 0$ (c) *Small M* $jd = h/6$ (d) *Working M* $jd = h/3$ (e) *Ultimate M* $jd > h/3$

FIG. 239. GROWTH OF jd WITH INCREASE OF APPLIED MOMENT; STEEL AT $h/3$ FROM BOTTOM.

291. Variation of Concrete Stress with Bending Moment. We will consider first a section for which the prestress cable is located one third of the height h from the bottom of the section as in Fig. 239(a). The triangular stress distribution (b) provides a compressive force C_1 that is collinear with the steel prestress T_1 so that the lever arm jd is zero, which agrees with the initial condition of zero loading or zero applied bending moment. Let f_c be the maximum elastic resistance of the concrete. As the beam is loaded, or a moment is applied to the section, compression increases at the top and tension reduces the precompression at the bottom of the section. Hence, for elastic stress distribution the condition of Fig. 239(c) will develop under a small, determinable applied moment. Note that jd has increased to $h/6$. As the applied moment is increased jd will also increase up to the value of $h/3$ shown in (d), which is its maximum value for elastic stress distribution if tension is not permitted in the concrete and the location of the prestressing steel is at $h/3$ above the bottom of the section.

If f_c is the maximum elastic resistance of the concrete, further increase in applied moment will produce plastic deformation of the concrete at the top of the beam and will initiate cracks starting at the bottom surface ultimately resulting in the plastic stress distribution of Fig. 239(*e*). The rectangular stress distribution of Fig. 239(*e*) is used for simplifying ultimate load calculation, as in Chapter 15. The curved broken line represents the more probable shape of the plastic stress distribution based upon the typical stress-strain diagram obtained from concrete cylinder tests. It is also based upon the observation that plane sections remain plain in flexure so that the concrete strain has a straight-line variation from the upper limit of the cracked area to the top of the beam. Because the average tensile strain in the concrete over a few inches at the level of the steel is a better measure of the steel strain than the micro-strain in the concrete near a crack, theoretical straight-line variation of strain is even applicable to the cracked zone.

Change in Prestress with Load. The point to be emphasized in Fig. 239 is that the value of jd grows with increase in the moment applied to the section so that the steel stress for working loads need increase only a few per cent from T_1 to T_3. As long as the steel is fully bonded to the concrete its change in stress must be n times the change in f_c at the same level or $n f_c$. From initial prestress producing the maximum allowable compression f_c at the bottom of the beam to the allowable elastic moment producing the same value of f_c at the top of the beam [Fig. 239 (*b*) and (*d*)], the concrete stress at the level of the steel changes from $0.66f_c$ to $0.33f_c$ or a reduction of $0.33f_c$. Let $f_c' = 5000$ psi, $n = 7$, and $f_c = 0.45f_c' = 2250$ psi. Then $0.33\ nf_c = 4970$ psi, which is the increase in steel stress due to the allowable moment for the beam of Fig. 239. The change of steel stress will be somewhat greater for steel placed nearer the bottom surface of the beam, but the stress increment is not likely to exceed twice the value computed above or 10,000 psi. If the effective prestress before loading the beam is 120,000 psi, an increment of 10,000 psi is 8.3 per cent. This is considerably less than the loss of prestress caused by creep and shrinkage. Hence the increase of steel stress due to load is not a factor that usually limits the elastic strength of a prestressed concrete beam. With unbonded cables the change in steel stress is even less significant because it is produced by the average moment for the span rather than the maximum moment at the most highly stressed section of the beam.

292. Use of the Transformed Section for Bonded Steel. If the prestress steel is bonded, the elastic stress computations may be made on the basis of the transformed section and the usual straight-line formula

$$f_c = \frac{T}{A_t} \pm \frac{Tey}{I_t} \pm \frac{My}{I_t}. \tag{2}$$

T is the effective tensile preload and e is its eccentricity from the c.g. of the transformed area A_t which has a moment of inertia I_t about its c.g. M is the applied moment due to loads and y is the distance from the c.g. of the transformed section to the point at which the stress is desired. Because compression exists over the whole section of the beam at working loads the transformed section includes the entire area of concrete and $(n - 1)$ times the area of *bonded* steel. If the beam is post-tensioned and then grouted, the first two terms in equation (2) and the dead load moment in the third term are to be based upon the *net* concrete section. Use of the transformed section applies to bonded steel.

In Fig. 240 the prestress steel amounts to 0.7 per cent of the 10-in. $\times$ 30-in. cross-section or 2.1 sq. in. For $n = 5.0$, $(n-1)A_s = 8.4$ sq. in., which is 2.8 per cent of the cross-section.[1] Hence, if the gross concrete area rather

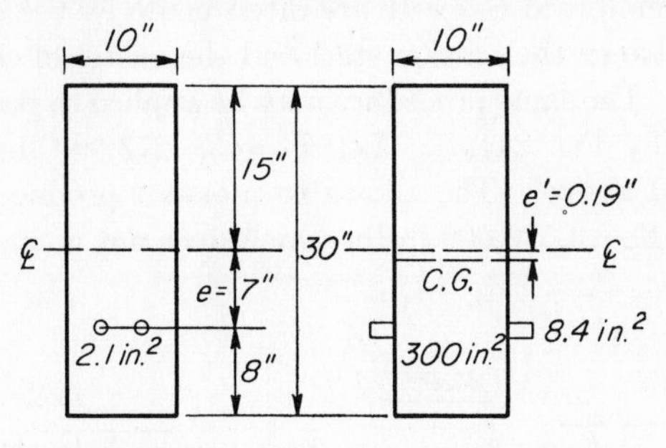

(*a*) *Beam Section* (*b*) *Transformed Section*

FIG. 240. MINOR INFLUENCE OF TRANSFORMED SECTION OF PRESTRESSED BEAM.

than the transformed section is used, somewhat conservative stresses will be obtained. Let the effective prestress be $0.6f_s' = 0.6 \times 217{,}000 = 130{,}000$ psi, and determine the allowable moment due to loads when f_c max $= 2400$ psi.

$$T = 0.7\% \times 300 \times 130{,}000 = 273{,}000 \text{ lb.}$$

$$Te = 273{,}000 \times 7 = 1{,}911{,}000 \text{ in-lb.}$$

$$A_c = 10 \times 30 = 300 \text{ in}^2;\ I_c = \tfrac{1}{12} \times 10 \times 30^3 = 22{,}500 \text{ in}^4.$$

For an upper fiber stress of 2400 psi we may compute the allowable moment from equation (2).

$$f_c = -2400 = \frac{-273{,}000}{300} + \frac{1{,}911{,}000 \times 15}{22{,}500} - \frac{M \times 15}{22{,}500}.$$

$$M = (2400 - 910 + 1270)\,\frac{22{,}500}{15} = 4{,}140{,}000 \text{ in-lb.}$$

This moment will produce a lower fiber stress of

$$f_c = -910 - 1270 + 4{,}140{,}000 \times \frac{15}{22{,}500} = -2180 + 2760 = +580 \text{ psi}$$

Since 600 psi is approximately the modulus of rupture in tension of 5000 to 6000 psi concrete the above computations are valid. However, in practice the permissible tension for working loads would be reduced to about 200 psi, which would reduce the allowable moment to 3,570,000 in-lb. and the upper

[1] By *ACI* specifications the range of n for stress calculations is from 6 to 10, (Spec. 317). However, concrete can vary from light-weight cinder concrete of poor quality and very low elastic modulus to nuclear shielding concrete, using steel punchings or heavy mineral aggregate, which is of highest quality and very high modulus. Hence the author presents examples in which $n = E_s/E_c$ varies from 5 to 15 for stress calculations in the elastic range.

fiber stress to −2020 psi as may be determined by introducing new values into the equations for f_c and M.

293. Use of the T-C Lever Arm for Stress Calculation. Stress and moment calculations for reinforced concrete are often made by use of a determinable lever arm (jd) between the tension steel and the center of compression above the neutral axis. The same procedure may be applied to prestressed concrete as is illustrated by Fig. 241(a). Let $T = C = 273{,}000$ lb. for the beam of Fig. 240 analyzed above. The allowable moment produced by the loading will be taken as $M = 3{,}570{,}000$ in-lb. which does not include the moment of eccentricity, Te.

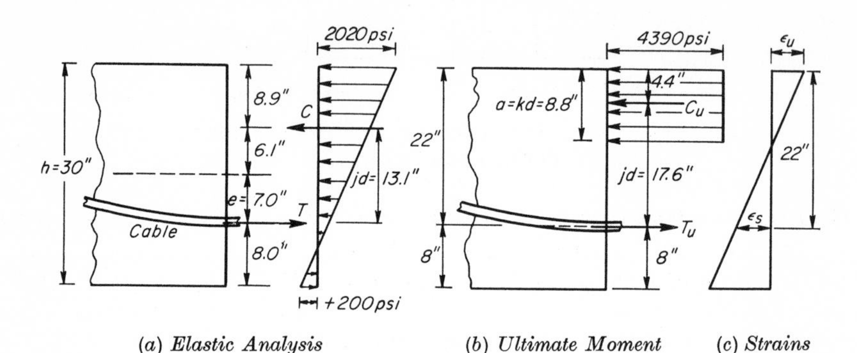

(a) *Elastic Analysis* (b) *Ultimate Moment* (c) *Strains*

FIG. 241. USE OF T-C COUPLE TO COMPUTE ELASTIC AND ULTIMATE MOMENTS.

Then

$$jd = M/T = 3{,}570{,}000 \div 273{,}000 = 13.1 \text{ in.} \tag{3}$$

The compressive force C therefore acts at 6.1 in. above the mid-height of the rectangular section. Accordingly, for straight-line stress distribution [Fig. 241(a)] we may write

$$f_c = \frac{C}{A_n} \pm \frac{Cey}{I_n} = \frac{273{,}000}{300} \pm \frac{273{,}000 \times 6.1 \times 15}{22{,}500} \tag{4}$$

$$= -910 \pm 1110 = -2020 \text{ or } +200 \text{ psi.}$$

A_n and I_n refer to the net concrete section, but gross-section values are used here. The error is less than 1 per cent. Observe that this method reduces the three-term stress equation (2) to the two-term equation (4). The reason for this simplification is that the three-term equation contains the values of T, Te, and M, which are the external force and the moments that give rise to the stresses of the transformed section. However, in the two-term equation we use the internal eccentric concrete force C and then merely compute its distribution over the concrete cross-section. Hence, theoretically we should use A_n and I_n for the net concrete section.

294. Stress Analysis for Unbonded Steel. An unbonded prestressed beam is properly analyzed as a plain concrete section under the system of vertical loads and horizontal forces indicated in Fig. 242. The concrete cross-section to be used is the net cross-section although the change from the gross section may be negligible. However, use of the transformed section for unbonded steel would be incorrect since the prestress steel acts merely to produce longitudinal forces applied at the ends of the beam. It is assumed in Fig. 242 that the cables are straight. Curved cables of parabolic shape place an additional upward uniform load on the concrete of w lb. per ft. where

$$w = \frac{8yT_e}{L^2}. \tag{5}$$

T_e is the total effective prestress, y is the sag of the cable, and L is the length of span. This relation is developed in the author's, *Theory of Modern Steel Structures*, Vol. II, revised edition, page 222.

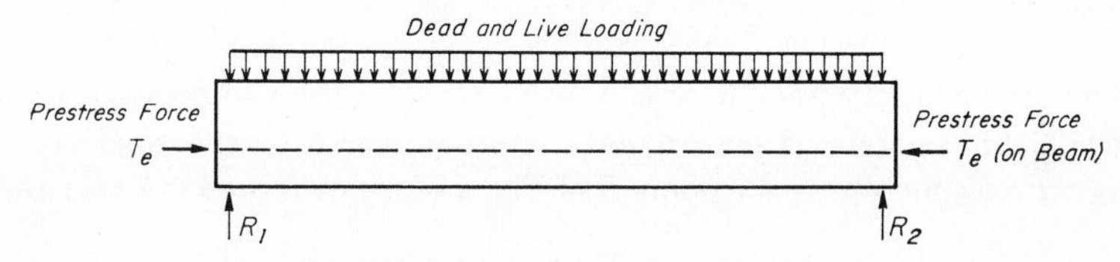

FIG. 242. FORCES APPLIED TO UNBONDED PRESTRESSED CONCRETE BEAM.

ULTIMATE STRENGTH

295. Stress Analysis for Ultimate Loading. Increased attention is being given to the ultimate strength of concrete structures. Actually, it would be logical to design all structures for conditions just preceding collapse and then to set the working loads at a safe value, perhaps one half of the ultimate resistance. Hence we will investigate the beam section of Fig. 240, already analyzed elastically, to determine what overload it should resist with safety before spalling occurs. The load factor is defined as the ratio of the ultimate load or "near-ultimate" load to the working load. It usually ranges from 1.8 to above 2.0 for gravity loads. Hence if we multiply the allowable moment of 3,570,000 in-lb. for the beam analyzed above in §293 by a load factor of say 1.9 we obtain the desired plastic or "near ultimate" moment resistance M_u under a severe type of overload.

$$M_u = 1.9 \times 3{,}570{,}000 = 6{,}780{,}000 \text{ in-lb.}$$

The effective prestress for elastic action was $0.6 \times 217{,}000 = 130{,}000$ psi acting on an area of 2.1 sq. in., or 273,000 lb. for the value of T. The elastic prestress is $0.60f_s'$ while by Fig. 238 the limit of theoretical elastic strain or the beginning of plastic strain is set at $0.85f_s'$. The ratio $(0.85f_s' \div 0.6f_s')$ is $\sqrt{2}$ which is convenient to remember. Hence the plastic or "near ultimate" value of T or T_u becomes

$$T_u = C_u = \sqrt{2}(130{,}000 \times 2.1) = 386{,}000 \text{ lb.}$$

Based upon a required ultimate moment of 6,780,000 in-lb. and a corresponding prestress force of 386,000 lb. one can determine the necessary arm between T_u and C_u, which has been termed *jd*.

$$jd = \frac{6,780,000}{386,000} = 17.6 \text{ in.}$$

From Fig. 241(*b*) it is clear that the assumption of ultimate strength is based upon a rectangular stress diagram above the cracked lower part of the cross-section.[2] It follows that the depth of the rectangle is

$$a = k_u d = (30 - 8 - 17.6) \times 2 = 8.8 \text{ in.}$$

Therefore, the area of concrete near ultimate stress is

$$A_u = 8.8 \times 10.0 = 88.0 \text{ sq. in.}$$

Accordingly, the required resistance of the concrete is

$$f_c = \frac{C_u}{A_u} = \frac{386,000}{88.0} = 4390 \text{ psi.}$$

Since the computed value of f_c is 73 per cent of the compressive strength for 6000 psi concrete it corresponds approximately to the relative stress acting on the concrete at the point *B* of Fig. 243 which represents a test beam.

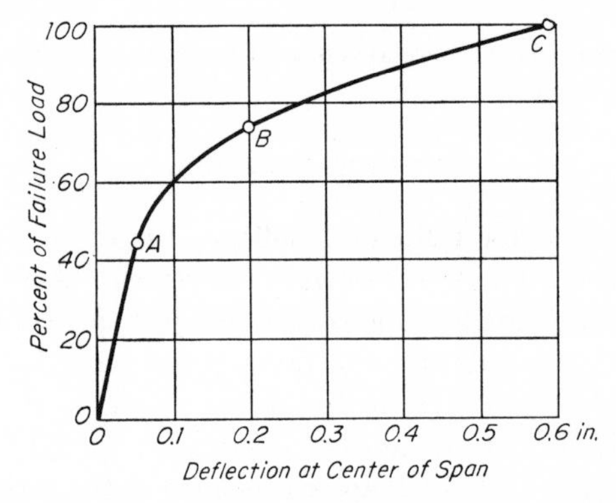

FIG. 243. TYPICAL LOAD DEFLECTION CURVE OF A PRESTRESSED BEAM FAILING BY COMPRESSION AND SHEAR.

In comparison the point *A* represents the normal working stress for concrete at about $0.45f_c'$ and the point *C* represents collapse. The deflection at mid-span of the test beam corresponding to the point *B* is 0.2 in., which is four times the fully recoverable deflection. The writer considers this amount of non-recoverable or plastic deformation to approach the "ultimate loading" because tests of a large group of beams of concrete always show variations in strength from above point *C* down toward point *B* in Fig. 243 due to imperfect control of construction.

[2] For a method of analysis based upon the actual shape of the stress-strain diagram for concrete in compression, see *Journal of the American Concrete Institute*, Proceedings, Vol. 57, pp. 737–766 and pp. 875–928.

296. Specified Ultimate Load *versus* Collapse. The *ACI Building Code* limits plastic or ultimate-load stresses more specifically than we have above. The maximum concrete stress is limited to $0.85\,f_c'$ and the ultimate prestress is approximately $f_s'(1 - 0.5pf_s'/f_c')$ for ultimate load design. [Spec. 408(*c*).]

If one reduces the maximum steel stress in §295 by this formula it becomes 190,000 psi and $T_u = C_u = 400{,}000$ lb. For $f_c = 0.85 \times 6000$ or 5100 psi, $A_u = 400{,}000/5100 = 78.4$ sq. in, $kd = 7.84$ in., and $jd = 18.09$ in. Then

$$M_u = 400{,}000 \times 18.09 = 7{,}200{,}000 \text{ in-lb.}$$

For comparison, the use of formulas from the *ACI* Code (Spec. 408) give a plastic moment of 6,500,000 in-lb. which is conservatively designated as M_u, the "ultimate load" moment.

Compatibility of Strains. In order to determine the acceptability of the simple ultimate load analysis performed above, one may check for consistency of the strains involved. The limiting strain for concrete in beam tests was established by Fig. 235(*b*) at 0.003 in. per inch. From the previous calculation in this section, $kd = 7.84$. Hence for straight-line variation of strain as pictured in Fig. 241(*c*), the steel strain ε_s at 22.0 in. below the top surface would be $(0.003 \div 7.84) \times (22.0 - 7.84) = 0.0054$. Even if the steel were still wholly elastic this strain would produce a steel stress of only $0.0054E = 162{,}000$ psi rather than 190,000 psi. Hence it seems doubtful that the neutral axis can be as low as 7.84 in. For a value of kd of 7.4 in., the value of C_u would be $5100 \times 7.4 \times 10 = 377{,}000$ lb.; $f_{su} = 377{,}000 \div 2.1 = 180{,}000$ psi; $\varepsilon_s = 180{,}000 \div 30{,}000{,}000 = 0.006$; and kd for straight-line variation of strains would be $0.003 \div (0.003 + 0.006) \times 22.0 = 7.33$ in. This value is close enough to the estimate of 7.4 in. to confirm the value of $C_u = 377{,}000$ lb. Hence

$$M_u = 377{,}000 \times (22.0 - 7.33/2) = 6{,}920{,}000 \text{ in-lb.}$$

Thus it is possible to refine an analysis by trial and error to make the position of the neutral axis obtained from strain distribution agree with its required position to produce equal values of C and T as determined by statics. However, the reader should not be overly impressed with the refinement because it contains two approximations.

(1) The value of 0.003 as the ultimate strain for concrete at the extreme fiber of a beam is a lower limit. From Fig. 235 it is seen that the median value is more nearly 0.004 and the range of test values is great.

(2) Because the steel at ultimate load should have passed beyond initial yield the computation of steel strain by use of E is an equally rough approximation.

Nevertheless, because both concrete and steel strains are taken at conservative values in the compatibility calculations above, the value of 6,920,000 in-lb. is also a conservative estimate of M_u. This value of M_u is a refinement over the value of 7,200,000 in-lb. computed earlier in this section by statics without aid from the straight line compatibility relation. The *ACI* formulas for M_u in Spec. 408 also fail to consider compatibility.

297. Moment of Collapse. If one is interested in estimating the theoretical ultimate or collapse load that the beam of Fig. 240 should sustain at a deflection comparable to point C in Fig. 243, the ultimate steel stress which is 1.67 times the effective prestress may be used.

$$T_u = 1.67 \times 130{,}000 \times 2.1 = 456{,}000 \text{ lb.}$$

The ultimate useful concrete stress is believed to be limited to $0.85f_c'$. Hence the ultimate stress rectangle would have a depth equal to

$$kd = 456{,}000 \div (10 \times 0.85 \times 6000) = 9.0 \text{ in.}$$

It follows from Fig. 241(*b*) that

$$jd = 30 - 8 - (9.0/2) = 17.5 \text{ in.}$$

Accordingly, the ultimate or collapse moment becomes

$$M_u = 456{,}000 \times 17.5 = 7{,}980{,}000 \text{ in-lb.}$$

The load factor at the ultimate collapse load would therefore be $7{,}980{,}000 \div 3{,}570{,}000 = 2.23$.

Of course, this calculation assumes that the concrete will be sufficiently strong to force the steel stress to approach the ultimate tensile strength with compatibility of strains. Note that "ultimate moment" as defined in the *ACI* Code is not the collapse moment but is a considerably lower moment corresponding to an earlier stage of plastic action.

298. Ultimate Strength of T- or I-Sections. The computation of the collapse moment or ultimate strength of a section is not greatly complicated by a non-rectangular shape. Because the entire area of concrete in compression is assumed to be stressed to a limiting value such as $0.85f_c'$, and since the value of C_u may be equated to T_u or the ultimate strength of the steel, the total compressive area is obtained simply by dividing C_u or T_u by $0.85f_c'$. The area of concrete acting in compression is therefore independent of the shape of the cross-section for ultimate moment resistance. The position of C_u may be located at the c.g. of the compressive area, or alternately C_u may be subdivided into C_1 and C_2, each of which may be located at the centroid of a compressive area as shown in Fig. 244.

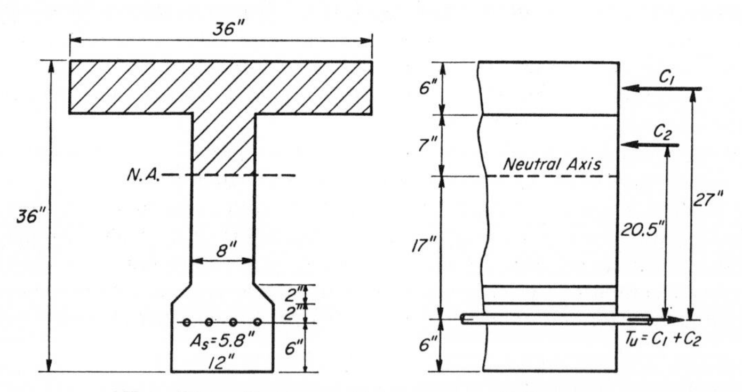

FIG. 244. ULTIMATE MOMENT OF A T-SECTION.

Example. In Fig. 244 the T-shaped cross-section is reasonably typical of a heavy post-tensioned girder. Let the ultimate resistance of the concrete be $0.85f_c'$ for 5000 psi concrete, which is 4250 psi. The ultimate usable strength of the steel is 200,000 psi. $A_s = 5.8$ sq. in. Hence we may write for the ultimate tensile force

$$T_u = 5.8 \times 200{,}000 = 1{,}160{,}000 \text{ lb.}$$

It follows that

$$A_c = \frac{1{,}160{,}000}{4250} = 272 \text{ sq. in.}$$

$$A_{\text{flange}} = 36 \times 6 = 216 \text{ sq. in.}$$

$$A_{\text{web}} = \text{difference} = 56 \text{ sq. in. (Area} = 8 \text{ in. by } 7 \text{ in.)}$$

$$\text{Arm to } C_1 = 36 - 6 - 3 = 27.0 \text{ in.}$$

$$\text{Arm to } C_2 = 36 - 6 - 6 - 7/2 = 20.5 \text{ in.}$$

$$C_1 = 216 \times 4250 = 918{,}000 \text{ lb.} \quad M_1 = 918{,}000 \times 27.0 = 24{,}790{,}000 \text{ in-lb.}$$

$$C_2 = 56 \times 4250 = 238{,}000 \text{ lb.} \quad M_2 = 238{,}000 \times 20.5 = 4{,}880{,}000 \text{ in-lb.}$$

$$\text{Ultimate moment, } M_u = 29{,}670{,}000 \text{ in-lb.}$$

One may revise this computation for M_u to meet more conservative *ACI* specifications by introducing the capacity reduction factor $\phi = 0.90$ giving $M_u = 26{,}700{,}000$ in-lb. (Spec. 329.)

299. Subjective Factors. The determination of the ultimate strength of a prestressed section involves an element of judgment. The computations for the T-section in §298 place the neutral axis, or the lower edge of the compressive area, at 13 in. below the top of the beam. Cracks therefore may extend upward 23 in. from the bottom of the beam for the conditions assumed. However, for lower strength concrete or a larger area of steel, the compressive area might extend so far downward that the calculated ultimate moment could not be developed. It appears that this condition will usually be avoided if kd, the distance from the top of the beam to the neutral axis, is restricted to no more than one third of the depth to the steel for computing M_u. In the example above, the neutral axis may be raised 5.0 inches with a reduction of the value of M_u of only 11 per cent. Fortunately, the value of M_u is not highly sensitive to the position of the neutral axis and particularly so for a T-section. Hence, strain compatibility may be achieved without significant change in M_u.

It is useful to note the differences between the conventional stress diagrams used for ultimate strength analysis of reinforced concrete and prestressed concrete sections. The difference is observed by comparing the depth $c = k_u d$ of the equivalent stress rectangle for a prestressed section with $k_1 c = k_1 k_u d$ as the depth of the stress rectangle for a reinforced concrete section. Note that k_1 varies from 0.85 downward with increase in f_c'. The introduction of k_1 for bar reinforcement is necessary because the elastic strain for $f_y < 75{,}000$ psi with balanced reinforcement corresponds to a position of the neutral axis below the mid-depth of the section. A stress rectangle of such depth would usually give an ultimate compressive stress well below $0.85 f_c'$. The relatively high position of the neutral axis with ultimate prestress ($f_y > 150{,}000$ psi) provides a stress rectangle of smaller depth that predicts the ultimate compressive stress reasonably well for a value of

$k_1 = 1.0$. However, both procedures are conventional because the actual compressive stress distribution follows an unsymmetrical curve above the neutral axis.

PROBLEMS

1601. Determine the position of a prestress cable for a rectangular beam section to produce a maximum tensile stress of $0.10f_c'$ and a maximum compressive stress of $0.45f_c'$ when gravity loads are neglected.

Suggestion. For simplicity use kern moment equation, p. 278 *Theory of Modern Steel Structures*, Vol. 2, revised edition. Compute ratio of extreme fiber stresses to eliminate undesired terms. *Ans.* $d = 0.76h$ from top of beam.

1602. Determine the position of a prestress cable for a rectangular beam section to produce a maximum tensile stress of $0.05f_c'$ and a maximum compressive stress of $0.45f_c'$. Allow for a dead-load moment producing a compressive stress of $0.15f_c'$ at the top and an equal tension at the bottom of the section.

Suggestion. Use kern moment equation referred to in Problem 1601.

Ans. $d = 0.83h$ from top of beam.

1603. Same as Problem 1602 but let the dead load stresses be increased to $0.25f_c'$.

Ans. $d = 0.92h$ from top of beam.

1604. Compute the loss of prestress in a cable of 0.8 sq. in. area, pulled to an initial prestress of 160,000 psi, due to elastic deformation of a concrete beam of 120 sq. in. cross-section. Let $E_s/E_c = 7$. Assume that the steel is placed at the centroid of the cross-section. Use the transformed area. *Ans.* 7210 psi.

1605. Compute the frictional loss of prestress for a cable that is turned 180 degrees in a single circular arc. The coefficient of friction is 0.25. *Ans.* Loss of 11.5 per cent.

1606. In Fig. 240 let the width and depth be unchanged but increase e to 8 in. and reduce the steel area to 1.8 sq. in. Using an upper fiber stress of -2000 psi compute the gravity moment M_g and the lower fiber stress for bonded steel. Let $f_{se} = 120{,}000$ psi.

Ans. $f_c = +560$ psi.

1607. Reduce the tensile value of f_c to $+200$ psi in Problem 1606. Recompute M_g and the maximum compression stress using equation (2). *Ans.* $f_c = -1640$ psi.

1608. Check the answer to Problem 1607 by use of a *T-C* couple for an applied moment M_g of 3,100,000 in-lb. Do the same for Problem 1606 using an applied moment of 3,650,000 in-lb.

1609. In Fig. 240 reduce the area of steel to 1.8 sq. in., the effective prestress to 120,000 psi, and limit the allowable compressive stress f_c to no more than 2000 psi. Compute the elastic resisting moment of the section for (*a*) zero tension and (*b*) 200 psi tension. *Ans.* (*a*) 2,600,000 in-lb. (*b*) 2,900,000 in lb.

1610. A prestressed beam section is 12 in. wide and 26 in. deep. It is prestressed with 0.5 per cent steel located 5 in. above the bottom and stressed to 125,000 psi after loss of prestress. Find the elastic moment resistance for a maximum tensile fiber stress of $6\sqrt{f_c'}$ and alternately, for maximum compressive stress of $0.45f_c'$ for 5000 psi concrete. Which controls? *Ans.* 2,970,000 in-lb.

1611. Revise the overload computations of §295 to determine the required concrete stress to resist the overload moment if the load factor is changed to 1.8 and the concrete strength to 5000 psi. *Ans.* 3600 psi.

1612. Revise the ultimate-load computation of §296 by changing the crushing strength of the concrete from 6000 to 7000 psi. Adjust the ultimate moment for compatibility of strains.

1613. Compute the resisting moment for the T-section of Fig. 244 at the initial development of a plastic cross-section. Let the steel stress corresponding to point B

of Fig. 243 be $\sqrt{2} \times 120{,}000 = 170{,}000$ psi, and let the concrete stress for the same stage of plasticity be 72 per cent of 5000 or 3600 psi. *Ans.* $M_p = 25{,}200{,}000$ in-lb.

1614. Compute the ultimate resisting moment of the T-section of Fig. 244 if the neutral axis is at $0.25h$ from the top of the slab. Let the ultimate prestress be 225,000 psi and let $f_c' = 6000$ psi for the concrete. Limit the concrete stress to $0.80\,f_c'$. Determine the changed area of steel to agree with these conditions. *Ans.* $A_s = 5.1$ sq. in.

1615. Determine the elastic moment of resistance for the T-section of Fig. 244 for the following conditions. $f_s = 120{,}000$ psi, $f_c = -2250$ or $+300$ psi, $n = 6$. Compare this moment with the ultimate moment computed in §298 and determine the load factor. *Ans.* Load factor $= 1.95$.

1616. Follow the *ACI* Code and compute the ultimate resisting moment for the T-section of Fig. 244. Using $A_s = 6.75$ sq. in., find the position of the neutral axis. Let $f_c' = 7000$ psi and $f_s' = 240{,}000$ psi.

Shear Resistance

300. Shear Strength of Prestressed Beams. A prestressed beam does not require shear reinforcement until it begins to develop cracks. Cracking is initiated by excessive moment but the horizontal unit tension in the concrete will be less than the diagonal unit tension due to the combined effect of vertical shear with horizontal tension. See equation 25(*a*), Table 1, §38. When thin concrete webs are used this equation may be applied to determine the maximum web tension at each critical point. All values of diagonal tension computed should be within a reasonable working stress in tension of $3\sqrt{f_c'}$. If not, a thicker web may be desirable or web reinforcement may be used. See Spec. 412 for greater detail.

At ultimate load a prestressed beam without web reinforcement could be expected to fail in a sudden or brittle manner. Toughness will be increased by web reinforcement due to a curved cable supplemented by vertical stirrups in the areas of excessive shear. Again as for reinforced concrete it is reasonable to assume that the horizontal steel will resist the horizontal tension leaving the vertical component of the diagonal tension to be resisted by the concrete assisted by the vertical component of the cable stress and the stirrups. The design of stirrups must be made for ultimate loading because a prestressed beam is not expected to develop cracks under working loads, and stirrups do not function until rather deep cracks have appeared. This is the essential difference from stirrup action in ordinary reinforced concrete where cracks appear under working loads.

301. Stirrup Spacing. Using a load factor determined from §273 one should compute the vertical shear in the beam for ultimate loading at a point where it is desired to determine the spacing of stirrups. The critical section is at $d/2$ from a support. (Spec. 413.) Let A_v be the area of one single or double stirrup chosen to fit the thickness of the concrete web. Then $A_v f_y'$ will be the yield strength of a stirrup which will be taken as its ultimate strength because diagonal cracks must not be permitted to open due to stirrup elongation. At ultimate load one may transform equation (11) of §254 to give the stirrup spacing.

$$s = \frac{A_v f_y'}{v'b'}, \quad \text{or} \quad A_v = \frac{v'b's}{f_y'}. \tag{6}$$

As elsewhere, v' is the unit shear to be resisted entirely by the stirrups and b' is the web thickness. However, by equation (7), §250, $v' = V_u'/b'jd$, where of course V_u' is the shear due to the ultimate loading reduced by the vertical component of the tension in the curved prestressed cable and further reduced by the ultimate shear resisted by the cracked concrete, which may be taken safely as $V_c = 3\sqrt{f_c'}\, b'jd$. The value of j may be set at 0.90. The revised formula for stirrup spacing becomes

$$s = \frac{A_v f_y' jd}{V_u - V_c}, \quad \text{or} \quad A_v = \frac{(V_u - V_c)s}{f_y' jd}. \tag{7}$$

The use of this formula for A_v is believed to be conservative for prestressed concrete design because the prestress force reduces diagonal tension in the concrete at all loads.

The *ACI* formula for A_v includes the factor ϕ and drops j (Specs. 411 and 412).

$$A_v = \frac{(V_u - \phi V_c)s}{\phi d f_y'} \tag{7a}$$

Minimum Web Reinforcement. The spacing of minimum stirrups of ¼-in. diameter should not exceed three quarters of the depth of the beam, 24 in., or the depth of the web of a T- or I-section. Web reinforcement is provided for a length d beyond the point where it might theoretically be terminated. (Spec. 413.) The end stirrups may be designed for the shear at a distance from the support equal to one half the depth of the beam. These rules (Spec. 413) seem reasonable for a beam with straight prestressing cables. For parabolic draped cables of maximum sag y prestressed by a total force $wL^2/8y$ the shear at all points due to the uniform load w on the span L is fully resisted by the vertical component of the stress in the cable so that the concrete resists no vertical shear. For a derivation of this formula see the author's Theory of Modern Steel Structures, Vol. II, revised edition, page 222. Of course, there is usually a possibility of concentrated or unsymmetrical loads so that shear resistance of the concrete is essential to safety.

Bond and Anchorage

302. Bond of Prestressing Steel. The procedure of computing bond stress is the same for prestressing steel as for bars in reinforced concrete. However, bond stress in reinforced concrete beams is usually more critical than in prestressed beams. The explanation follows directly from Fig. 245. Because the steel stress in (*a*) does not change in proportion to the applied moment the expression $T_1 - T_2$ is much smaller for prestressed concrete than for reinforced concrete, and therefore the bond stress u which is $T_1 - T_2 \div (\Sigma O)x$ is not a significant stress for an uncracked prestressed beam. At the ultimate load the steel stress does increase in direct proportion to the bending moment because the maximum adjustment of the center of compression has already taken place. [Note constant jd in Fig. 245(b).] Under ultimate load the bond stress u may be computed by adjusting the usual formula for reinforced concrete, to allow for the low bond requirement at normal loading.

$$u = \frac{V_u - \frac{2}{3}V}{\Sigma O jd}, \tag{8}$$

where V is the shear at the section due to working loads and V_u is the shear at ultimate loading.

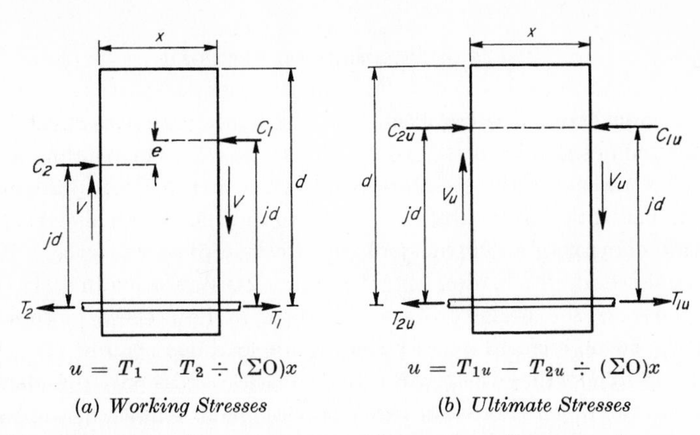

$u = T_1 - T_2 \div (\Sigma O)x$ $\quad$ $u = T_{1u} - T_{2u} \div (\Sigma O)x$

(a) *Working Stresses* $\quad$ (b) *Ultimate Stresses*

FIG. 245. BOND COMPUTATION FOR PRESTRESSED CONCRETE SECTION.

Note in (a) that jd increases from left to right with increase of bending moment while in (b) jd is constant. Accordingly, T_1 and T_2 in (a) vary less greatly than the bending moments while in (b) T_{1u} and T_{2u} vary directly with M.

Bond at Anchorage. For pretensioned steel the anchorage is formed by bond for a short length of steel at the end of the beam. This length is determined by the simple relationship

$$x = \frac{T_u}{u_u \Sigma O}, \tag{9}$$

where u_u is the bond stress at ultimate permissible slip. For a wire of 0.2 in. diameter let $T_u = 212{,}000 \times 0.0314 = 6700$ lb. Using an ultimate bond value of 500 psi for 4000 psi concrete gives $x = 6700 \div (500 \times 3.14 \times 0.20) = 21.4$ in. This value is about midway in the range from 10 to 30 in. that tests have shown to be necessary for adequate anchorage of prestressed wires or strands of varying diameters.

The *ACI* requires anchorage length of $(f_{su} - \frac{2}{3}f_{se})D$, where f_{su} and f_{se} are in kips per sq. in. (Spec. 414). This expression comes from equation (9) for post-tensioned steel for which T_u may be replaced by $T_u - T_e$ (or more conservatively by $T_u - \frac{2}{3}T_e$), bond stress being zero at initial prestress transfer before grouting.

303. Bearing at Anchorage. For post-tensioned wires, strands, or rods the main anchorage stress occurs between a metal bearing block and the concrete. The area in bearing is determined by dividing the prestress at transfer by an allowable bearing stress f_{cp}, where

$$f_{cp} = 0.6f_{ci}' \times 3\sqrt{A_b'/A_b} \leq f_{ci}'. \tag{10}$$

A_b is the bearing area of the anchor plate and A_b' is the largest concentric area to A_b on the end of the beam as defined by the *ACI* Code. Of course, f_{ci}' is the reduced compressive strength of the concrete at the time of post-tensioning the steel which will usually be less than the 28-day strength. To prevent splitting of the concrete horizontally due to bearing pressure at the anchorage a vertical stirrup may be placed within six inches of the bearing plate.

Design of Prestressed Sections

304. General Principles Involved. Two critical conditions must be considered for the design of a prestressed beam section, (1) the bending moment produced by transfer of the prestress load to the concrete and (2) the greatest bending moment in service due to the maximum dead and live loading as well as the moment of eccentricity of the effective prestress force. We will select a trial section for loading (2), check its stresses for loading (1), and, if necessary, revise the design. As an example of how these factors work, consider the economical shape of a section for loadings (1) and (2). Under full dead and live loading the compressive concrete stress will be a maximum at the top of the beam and either zero or a very small tension at the bottom. The ideal section for this loading should be a T-section. However, at first transfer of prestress the stress diagram is essentially inverted with the result that the narrow web of a T-section may be overstressed in compression at its lower edge. Hence the final shape of the section may have to change to an I-section or a T-section with a widened area around the bottom steel as in Fig. 246. A rectangular section is used only for shallow or narrow beams where the cost of framing a non-rectangular cross-section would not be compensated by the saving of concrete. Large girders usually have a narrower web than flange because the diagonal tension stresses are reduced by the prestress force and a web of the full width of the flange is not needed.

305. Depth of Section. There are charts and tables available that provide guides for estimating the economical depth of a reinforced concrete beam of given span and loading. Compared to reinforced concrete, prestressed concrete uses stronger materials, permits a reduced width of web, and provides a better distribution of stress on the concrete with the result that the dead load is reduced considerably. Hence the required depth is often no more than ¾ of the depth of a reinforced concrete beam. As a first estimate of required depth the following formula may be useful.

$$h = \frac{9000}{f_c'}\sqrt{M_g}, \tag{11}$$

where the gravity moment M_g is the maximum live load plus dead load moment in kip feet to be resisted by the section and h is the overall depth in inches.

Depth to Prestressing Steel. Since the main purpose of the prestressing steel is to produce a high initial compression at the lower edge of the concrete it would seem advantageous to place the prestressing cable near the bottom of the section with only enough cover to resist corrosion. However, with the cable placed in this position a high tensile stress may be computed at the top of the section due to the high moment of eccentricity of the prestress force. Fortunately, this moment of eccentricity curves the beam upward until it is free of its forms over most of its length so that its own dead weight develops a resisting moment of considerable magnitude which produces a determinable reduction of the tensile stress for the upper fiber. However, if a tensile stress in excess of $3\sqrt{f_{ci}'}$, based upon the concrete strength at the time of transfer still occurs, the choice is either to raise the level of the prestress steel, to deepen the section, or to add ordinary reinforcing bars near the top of the section to resist the tension caused by transfer of the prestress. Such bars also serve a useful purpose if the beam is precast and must be transported because the handling of a beam may increase the tension at the upper fiber unless the beam is provided with end connections for crane hooks.

306. Design Problem. Design the cross-section for a 30-ft. beam that carries a uniform live load of 1580 lb. per lineal ft. plus dead load estimated at 400 lb. per lineal ft. Let f_{si} at transfer be 130,000 psi and f_{se} at working load be 120,000 psi. Use 5000 psi concrete for which the strength at transfer f_{ci}' is to be 4000 psi. Let $n = 6$ or $n-1 = 5$. Allowable stresses are to be restricted to the following:

$-f_{ci}$ = temporary compressive stress $= 0.60 \times 4000 = -\ 2400$ psi.

$+f_{ci}$ = temporary tensile stress $= 3\sqrt{4000} = +190$ psi.

$-f_{ce}$ = effective compressive stress $= 0.45 \times 5000 = -2250$ psi.

$+f_{ce}$ = effective tensile stress $= 6\sqrt{5000} = +\ 420$ psi.

M_e = effective bending moment $= 1/8 \times 1980 \times 30^2 \times 12 = 2{,}660{,}000$ in-lb.

Estimated depth h by equation (11) $= \dfrac{9000}{5000}\sqrt{\dfrac{2660}{12}} = 26.7$ in. Try $h = 26.0$ in.

Estimated T-C arm for T-section $= 2/3(26.0) = 17.3$ in.

$T_e = C = 2{,}660{,}000 \div 17.3 = 153{,}000$ lb.

$A_s = T_e/f_{se} = 153{,}000 \div 120{,}000 = 1.28$ sq. in.

Concrete Section. For triangular stress distribution and zero stress at the bottom fiber

$$A_c = 2C/f_{ce} = 2 \times 153{,}000 \div 2250 = 136 \text{ sq. in.}$$

It may be wise to lay out a section providing somewhat more than 136 sq. in. of concrete area because the weight of this beam will be only 10 per cent of the total load which indicates that the temporary stresses due to prestress transfer may not be sufficiently compensated by the stresses from the initial gravity moment unless some excess moment of inertia is provided. A section will be selected as in Fig. 246 which provides a gross area of 177 sq. in. The c.g. of the transformed section is at 12.25 in. below the top of the section, the transformed area being 183.4 sq. in.

e of steel = 10.75 in. from c.g. of transformed section.
I_t of transformed area = 16,800 in^4.

Stress Calculations.
The top fiber stress for dead and live load is

$$-\frac{153{,}000}{183.4}+\frac{153{,}000\times 10.75\times 12.25}{16{,}800}$$

$$-\frac{2{,}660{,}000\times 12.25}{16{,}800}=-1580 \text{ psi.}$$

The bottom fiber stress for dead and live load is

$$-\frac{153{,}000}{183.4}-\frac{153{,}000\times 10.75\times 13.75}{16{,}800}$$

$$+\frac{2{,}660{,}000\times 13.75}{16{,}800}=\text{zero.}$$

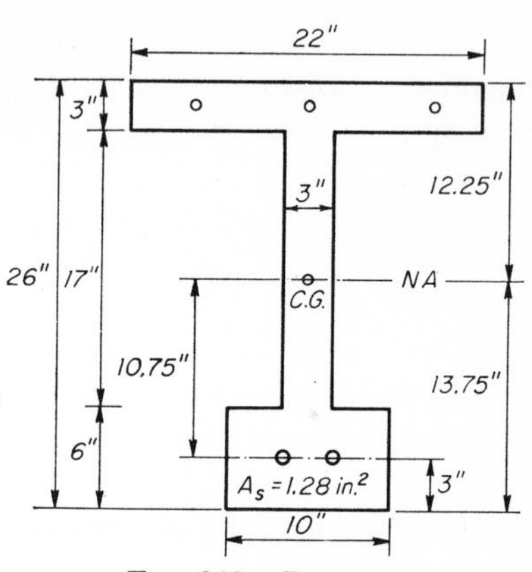

FIG. 246. DESIGN OF A PRESTRESSED SECTION.

These fiber stresses are below the allowable stresses but are close enough to justify a check on the stresses just after prestress transfer when $f_{si}=130{,}000$ psi and $T_i=1.28\times 130{,}000=166{,}000$ lb. The gravity moment at transfer is due merely to the weight of the concrete section or 185 lb. per ft.

$$M_g = 1/8\times 185\times 30^2\times 12 = 250{,}000 \text{ in-lb.}$$

The top fiber stress at transfer is

$$-\frac{166{,}000}{183.4}+\frac{166{,}000\times 10.75\times 12.25}{16{,}800}-\frac{250{,}000\times 12.25}{16{,}800}=+210 \text{ psi.}$$

The bottom fiber stress at transfer is

$$-\frac{166{,}000}{183.4}-\frac{166{,}000\times 10.75\times 13.75}{16{,}800}+\frac{250{,}000\times 13.75}{16{,}800}=-2170 \text{ psi.}$$

If the beam is to be cast in place, most designers would accept this section as satisfactory even though the temporary tensile stress of +210 psi is 20 psi over the allowable stress as specified. However, if the girder is precast and transported to the site, the entire tension in the upper slab, which for straight-line variation is found to be 5600 lb., can be resisted by three, 3/8-in. unprestressed round bars placed at the mid-depth of the slab as shown on Fig. 246.

Web Stirrups. The web of the beam of Fig. 246 may be considered to be a concrete rectangle of 3-in. by 26-in. cross-section.

$$A_{\text{web}} = 3.0 \times 26.0 = 78.0 \text{ sq. in.}$$

Allowing for a load factor of 1.8 at ultimate load, we find the shear at a distance from the end of the span equal to one half the depth of the beam to be $V_u = 50{,}000$ lb. The *ACI* stirrup spacing formula recommends vertical stirrups at a spacing s of area A_v, where

$$A_v = \frac{(V_u - \phi V_c)s}{\phi f_y' d}, \text{ or } s = \frac{A_v \phi f_y' d}{V_u - \phi V_c}. \tag{12}$$

b' is the width of the web, 3 in.
d is the depth to the prestress steel, 23 in.
f_y' is the yield stress of the stirrup steel, 50,000 psi; $0.85\, f_y' = 42{,}500$ psi.
$\phi V_c = 3\sqrt{f_c'}\, b'\, d = 3\sqrt{5000} \times 3.0 \times 23.0 = 14{,}500$ lb.
$V_u - \phi V_c = 50{,}000 - 14{,}500 = 35{,}500$ lb.

Hence we may compute the stirrup spacing for No. 4, ½-in. round bars, as

$$s = \frac{0.196 \times 42{,}500 \times 23.0}{35{,}500} = 5.4 \text{ in.}$$

At 8.0 ft. from the end of the span the shear is reduced to $V_u = 25{,}000$ lb.

$$s = \frac{0.196 \times 42{,}500 \times 23.0}{25{,}000 - 14{,}500} = 18.2 \text{ in.}$$

Since this value of s approaches $0.75h$, a maximum spacing of $s = 18.0$ in. is recommended through the middle 14 ft. of the span. For the 3-in. web a continuous stirrup as shown in Fig. 247 may be chosen. If a standard loop stirrup is used, a 6-in. web would be desirable.

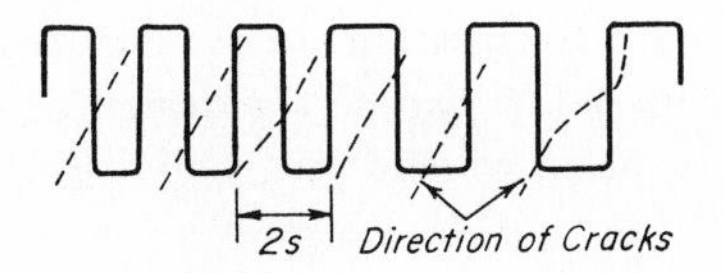

FIG. 247. CONTINUOUS STIRRUPS—VARIABLE SPACING

PROBLEMS

1617. Determine the percentage increase in the live and dead loading permissible within the specified allowable stresses for the beam of §306 and Fig. 246.

Ans. +19 per cent without and +34 per cent with tension reinforcement.

1618. Revise the design of the T-beam of §306 using the allowable stresses of the *ACI* Code. Try reducing the widths of flanges in Fig. 246 by 10 per cent and add reinforcement if excessive tensile stress occurs. Let $n = 7$.

1619. Redesign the stirrups for the T-beam of §306 to fulfill the requirements of the *ACI* Code for V_c.

1620. Determine the maximum possible reduction of depth of the 17-in. web between the flanges of the cross-section of Fig. 246 and §306 without exceeding the allowable working stresses for f_{ce} of -2250 and $+420$ psi for $LL + DL$. Then compute the temporary stresses at prestress transfer for the reduced section. How could overstress be avoided if the beam is cast in place?

1621. Redesign the cross-section for the beam of Fig. 246 and §306 for 6000 psi concrete and determine the required strength of the concrete at the time of prestress transfer. Use tensile reinforcement if needed.

1622. Design a rectangular section to replace the T-section of Fig. 246 for the beam of §306. Try a ratio of h/b of 3.5 approximately.

1623. Design a symmetrical I-section prestressed beam for the working stresses used in the *ACI* Code. The simple span is 35 ft. The loading covers the entire span and amounts to 1700 lb. per lineal ft. including an allowance of 200 lb. per lineal ft. for the beam itself. Let $f_c = 5500$ for 6500 psi concrete and $f_{se} = 0.60f_s' = 140{,}000$ psi.

1624. Design an I-section by the *ACI* Code for a bending moment (elastic) of 3,600,000 in-lb. Let the initial prestress of 145,000 psi be reduced to 120,000 psi by elastic and plastic strains. Use 6500 psi concrete.

1625. Design the I-section of Problem 1623 by using an ultimate load factor of 1.8 applied to the total moment and an ultimate stress distribution. Allow $0.85f_c'$ in compression for 6500 psi concrete, and $f_{su} = 0.85f_s' = 200{,}000$ psi. Let $h = 36$ in. Follow the *ACI* Code.

307. Structures of Other Materials. This book has presented briefly and in an introductory manner procedures of analysis and design for structures of three basic materials, steel, timber, and reinforced or prestressed concrete. Designs have been based upon working stresses and also upon ultimate strength. Engineers design structures, large and small, of a variety of materials, aluminum, cast iron, titanium, plastics, glass, rubber, ceramics, fiber glass, and many others. If the properties of a material are fully known, the principles of analysis and design presented here will be adequate in most cases for completing a practical design. The main complexities not treated in this book are those involved in statically indeterminate structures and in internal stress analysis by the theories of elasticity and plasticity. After informing himself in regard to these theories and their applications to design, the engineer will be prepared to handle the design of structures used in any of the rapidly advancing areas of modern technology.

CHAPTER 17

SPECIFICATIONS

AMERICAN INSTITUTE OF STEEL CONSTRUCTION

308. Abbreviated[1] *AISC* Building Code Requirements.

DEFINITIONS AND ASSUMPTIONS

1. Types of Construction. Three basic types of construction and associated design assumptions are permissible under the respective conditions stated hereinafter, and each will govern in a specific manner the size of members and the types and strength of their connections.

Type 1, commonly designated as "rigid frame" (continuous frame), assumes that beam to-column connections have sufficient rigidity to hold virtually unchanged the original angles between intersecting members.

Type 2, commonly designated as "conventional" or "simple" framing (unrestrained, free-ended), assumes that the ends of beams and girders are connected for shear only, and are free to rotate under load.

Type 3, commonly designated as "semi-rigid framing" (partially restrained), assumes that the connections of beams and girders possess a dependable and known moment capacity intermediate in degree between the complete rigidity of Type 1 and the complete flexibility of Type 2.

Elastic versus Plastic Theory. Type 1 construction is unconditionally permitted under this Specification. Two different methods of design are recognized. Within the limitations laid down, members of continuous frames, or continuous portions of frames, may be proportioned, on the basis of their maximum predictable strength, to resist the specified design loads multiplied by the prescribed load factors. Otherwise Type 1 construction shall be designed to resist the stresses produced by the specified design loads, assuming moment distribution in accordance with the elastic theory.

LOADS AND FORCES

2. Dead Load and Live Load. The dead load to be assumed in design shall consist of the weight of steelwork and all material permanently fastened thereto or supported thereby.

The live load, including snow load if any, shall be that stipulated by the Code under which the structure is being designed or that dictated by the conditions involved. Snow load shall be considered as applied either to the entire roof area or to a portion of the roof area, and the arrangement of loads resulting in the highest stresses in the supporting member shall be used in the design.

[1] For complete specifications, consult the most recent *AISC Manual, Steel Construction,* revised annually.

3. Impact. For structures carrying live loads which induce impact, the assumed live load shall be increased sufficiently to provide for same.

If not otherwise specified, the increase shall be:

For supports of elevators	100%
For travelling crane support girders and their connections	25%
For supports of light machinery, shaft or motor driven, not less than .	20%
For supports of reciprocating machinery or power driven units, not less than	50%
For hangers supporting floors and balconies	33%

4. Crane Runway Horizontal Forces. The lateral force on crane runways to provide for the effect of moving crane trolleys shall, if not otherwise specified, be 20% of the sum of the weights of the lifted load and of the crane trolley (but exclusive of other parts of the crane), applied at the top of rail, one half on each side of the runway; and shall be considered as acting in either direction normal to the runway rail.

The longitudinal force shall, if not otherwise specified, be taken as 10% of the maximum wheel loads of the crane applied at the top of rail.

5. Wind and Other Forces. Proper provision shall be made for stresses caused by wind both during erection and after completion of the building. The wind pressure is dependent upon the conditions of exposure, geographical location, and shape of the structure. Structures in localities subject to earthquakes, hurricanes, and other extraordinary conditions shall be designed with due regard for such conditions.

6. Minimum Loads. In the absence of any applicable building code requirements, the loads referred to above shall be not less than those recommended in the *American Standard Building Code Requirements for Minimum Design Loads in Buildings and Other Structures* ASA *A*58.1, latest edition.

Material

7. Structural Steel. Structural steel shall conform to one of the following specifications, latest edition:

*Steel for Bridges and Buildings, ASTM A*7
*Structural Steel for Welding, ASTM A*373
*Structural Steel, ASTM A*36
*High-Strength Structural Steel, ASTM A*440
*High-Strength Low-Alloy Structural Manganese Vanadium Steel, ASTM A*441
*High-Strength Low-Alloy Structural Steel, ASTM A*242

8. Rivet Steel. Rivet steel shall conform to one of the following specifications, latest edition:

*Structural Rivet Steel, ASTM A*141
*High-Strength Structural Rivet Steel, ASTM A*195
*High-Strength Structural Alloy Rivet Steel, ASTM A*406

9. Bolts. High strength steel bolts shall conform to one of the following specifications, latest edition:

*High Strength Steel Bolts for Structural Joints, ASTM A*325
*Quenched and Tempered Alloy Steel Bolts and Studs with Suitable Nuts, ASTM A*354, Grade *BC*

Other bolts shall conform to the *Specification for Low-Carbon Steel Externally and Internally Threaded Standard Fasteners, ASTM A*307, latest edition, hereinafter designated as *A*307 bolts.

10. Filler Metal for Welding. Welding electrodes for manual shielded metal-arc welding shall conform to the *E*60 or *E*70 series of the *Specification for Mild Steel Arc-Welding Electrodes, ASTM A*233, latest edition.

Bare electrodes and granular flux used in the submerged-arc process shall conform to the provisions of Spec. 52.

ALLOWABLE UNIT STRESSES

11. Structural Steel, Tension.
On the net section, except at pin holes $F_t = 0.60F_y$.
On the net section at pin holes in eyebars, pin-connected plates or built-up members $F_t = 0.45F_y$.

12. Shear. On the gross section of beam and plate girder webs $F_t = 0.40F_y$.
(See Spec. 29 for reduction required for thin webs.)

13. Compression.[2] On the gross section of axially loaded compression members when L/r, the largest slenderness ratio of any unbraced segment as defined in Spec. 23, is less than C_c

$$F_a = \frac{\left[1 - \frac{(L/r)^2}{2C_c^2}\right]F_y}{\text{F.S.}} \qquad \text{Formula (1)}$$

where

$$\text{F.S.} = \text{factor of safety} = \frac{5}{3} + \frac{3(L/r)}{8C_c} - \frac{(L/r)^3}{8C_c^3}, \text{ and } C_c = \sqrt{\frac{2\pi^2 E}{F_y}}.$$

Note $C_c = 132$ for $A7$, 127 for $A36$, and 107 for $A440$–441 steels. Also C_c = value of L/r at which column would collapse (F.S. = 1.0) when $F_a = 0.5F_y$.

On the gross section of axially loaded columns when L/r exceeds C_c

$$F_a = \frac{149{,}000{,}000}{(L/r)^2}. \qquad \text{Formula (2)}$$

On the gross section of axially loaded bracing and secondary members, when L/r exceeds 120

$$F_{as} = \frac{F_a \text{ (by Formula 1 or 2)}}{1.6 - \frac{L}{200r}}. \qquad \text{Formula (3)}$$

On the gross area of plate girder stiffeners $F_a = 0.60F_y$.
On the web of rolled shapes at the toe of the fillet (crippling) $F_a = 0.75F_y$.

14. Bending. Tension and compression on extreme fibers of rolled shapes and built-up members having an axis of symmetry in the plane of loading and proportions meeting the requirements for a "compact section" when the member is supported laterally at intervals no greater than 13 times its compression flange width. (For a full definition of a "compact section" refer to *Manual of Steel Construction.*)
$F_b = 0.66F_y$.

Continuous Beams and Frames. Beams and girders which meet the requirements of the preceding paragraph and are continuous over supports or are rigidly framed to columns by means of rivets, high strength bolts or welds, may be proportioned for 9/10

[2] See Table S-1 for numerical values of allowable compressive stresses for various grades of steel corresponding to provisions of this Section.

TABLE S-1

Allowable Stresses for Compression Members by *AISC* Specifications

ALLOWABLE STRESS (KSI)
FOR COMPRESSION MEMBERS OF 33 KSI SPECIFIED YIELD POINT STEEL

Main and Secondary Members l/r not over 120						Main Members l/r 121 to 200				Secondary Members l/r 121 to 200			
$\frac{l}{r}$	F_a (ksi)	$\frac{l}{r}$	F_a (ksi)	$\frac{l}{r}$	F_a (ksi)	$\frac{l}{r}$	F_a (ksi)	$\frac{l}{r}$	F_a (ksi)	$\frac{l}{r}$	F_a (ksi)	$\frac{l}{r}$	F_a (ksi)
1	19.77	41	17.64	81	14.32	121	9.96	161	5.76	121	10.01	161	7.25
2	19.73	42	17.57	82	14.23	122	9.84	162	5.69	122	9.94	162	7.20
3	19.69	43	17.50	83	14.13	123	9.72	163	5.62	123	9.87	163	7.16
4	19.66	44	17.43	84	14.03	124	9.59	164	5.55	124	9.79	164	7.12
5	19.62	45	17.36	85	13.93	125	9.47	165	5.49	125	9.71	165	7.08
6	19.58	46	17.29	86	13.84	126	9.34	166	5.42	126	9.63	166	7.04
7	19.54	47	17.22	87	13.74	127	9.22	167	5.35	127	9.55	167	7.00
8	19.50	48	17.14	88	13.64	128	9.09	168	5.29	128	9.47	168	6.96
9	19.46	49	17.07	89	13.53	129	8.96	169	5.23	129	9.38	169	6.93
10	19.41	50	16.99	90	13.43	130	8.83	170	5.17	130	9.30	170	6.89
11	19.37	51	16.92	91	13.33	131	8.70	171	5.11	131	9.21	171	6.85
12	19.32	52	16.84	92	13.23	132	8.57	172	5.05	132	9.12	172	6.82
13	19.28	53	16.76	93	13.13	133	8.44	173	4.99	133	9.03	173	6.79
14	19.23	54	16.68	94	13.02	134	8.32	174	4.93	134	8.94	174	6.76
15	19.18	55	16.60	95	12.92	135	8.19	175	4.88	135	8.86	175	6.73
16	19.13	56	16.52	96	12.81	136	8.07	176	4.82	136	8.78	176	6.70
17	19.08	57	16.44	97	12.71	137	7.96	177	4.77	137	8.70	177	6.67
18	19.03	58	16.36	98	12.60	138	7.84	178	4.71	138	8.62	178	6.64
19	18.98	59	16.28	99	12.49	139	7.73	179	4.66	139	8.54	179	6.61
20	18.93	60	16.20	100	12.38	140	7.62	180	4.61	140	8.47	180	6.58
21	18.88	61	16.12	101	12.28	141	7.51	181	4.56	141	8.39	181	6.56
22	18.82	62	16.03	102	12.17	142	7.41	182	4.51	142	8.32	182	6.53
23	18.77	63	15.95	103	12.06	143	7.30	183	4.46	143	8.25	183	6.51
24	18.71	64	15.86	104	11.95	144	7.20	184	4.41	144	8.18	184	6.49
25	18.66	65	15.78	105	11.83	145	7.10	185	4.36	145	8.12	185	6.46
26	18.60	66	15.69	106	11.72	146	7.01	186	4.32	146	8.05	186	6.44
27	18.54	67	15.61	107	11.61	147	6.91	187	4.27	147	7.99	187	6.42
28	18.48	68	15.52	108	11.50	148	6.82	188	4.23	148	7.93	188	6.40
29	18.42	69	15.43	109	11.38	149	6.73	189	4.18	149	7.87	189	6.38
30	18.36	70	15.34	110	11.27	150	6.64	190	4.14	150	7.81	190	6.36
31	18.30	71	15.25	111	11.15	151	6.55	191	4.09	151	7.75	191	6.35
32	18.24	72	15.16	112	11.04	152	6.46	192	4.05	152	7.69	192	6.33
33	18.18	73	15.07	113	10.92	153	6.38	193	4.01	153	7.64	193	6.31
34	18.11	74	14.98	114	10.80	154	6.30	194	3.97	154	7.59	194	6.30
35	18.05	75	14.89	115	10.69	155	6.22	195	3.93	155	7.53	195	6.28
36	17.98	76	14.80	116	10.57	156	6.14	196	3.89	156	7.48	196	6.27
37	17.92	77	14.70	117	10.45	157	6.06	197	3.85	157	7.43	197	6.26
38	17.85	78	14.61	118	10.33	158	5.98	198	3.81	158	7.39	198	6.24
39	17.78	79	14.51	119	10.21	159	5.91	199	3.77	159	7.34	199	6.23
40	17.71	80	14.42	120	10.09	160	5.83	200	3.73	160	7.29	200	6.22

TABLE S-1 (*Continued*)

ALLOWABLE STRESSES FOR COMPRESSION MEMBERS BY *AISC* SPECIFICATIONS

ALLOWABLE STRESS (KSI)
FOR COMPRESSION MEMBERS OF 36 KSI SPECIFIED YIELD POINT STEEL

Main and Secondary Members l/r not over 120						Main Members l/r 121 to 200				Secondary Members l/r 121 to 200			
$\frac{l}{r}$	F_a (ksi)	$\frac{l}{r}$	F_a (ksi)	$\frac{l}{r}$	F_a (ksi)	$\frac{l}{r}$	F_a (ksi)	$\frac{l}{r}$	F_a (ksi)	$\frac{l}{r}$	F_a (ksi)	$\frac{l}{r}$	F_a (ksi)
1	21.56	41	19.11	81	15.24	121	10.14	161	5.76	121	10.19	161	7.25
2	21.52	42	19.03	82	15.13	122	9.99	162	5.69	122	10.09	162	7.20
3	21.48	43	18.95	83	15.02	123	9.85	163	5.62	123	10.00	163	7.16
4	21.44	44	18.86	84	14.90	124	9.70	164	5.55	124	9.90	164	7.12
5	21.39	45	18.78	85	14.79	125	9.55	165	5.49	125	9.80	165	7.08
6	21.35	46	18.70	86	14.67	126	9.41	166	5.42	126	9.70	166	7.04
7	21.30	47	18.61	87	14.56	127	9.26	167	5.35	127	9.59	167	7.00
8	21.25	48	18.53	88	14.44	128	9.11	168	5.29	128	9.49	168	6.96
9	21.21	49	18.44	89	14.32	129	8.97	169	5.23	129	9.40	169	6.93
10	21.16	50	18.35	90	14.20	130	8.84	170	5.17	130	9.30	170	6.89
11	21.10	51	18.26	91	14.09	131	8.70	171	5.11	131	9.21	171	6.85
12	21.05	52	18.17	92	13.97	132	8.57	172	5.05	132	9.12	172	6.82
13	21.00	53	18.08	93	13.84	133	8.44	173	4.99	133	9.03	173	6.79
14	20.95	54	17.99	94	13.72	134	8.32	174	4.93	134	8.94	174	6.76
15	20.89	55	17.90	95	13.60	135	8.19	175	4.88	135	8.86	175	6.73
16	20.83	56	17.81	96	13.48	136	8.07	176	4.82	136	8.78	176	6.70
17	20.78	57	17.71	97	13.35	137	7.96	177	4.77	137	8.70	177	6.67
18	20.72	58	17.62	98	13.23	138	7.84	178	4.71	138	8.62	178	6.64
19	20.66	59	17.53	99	13.10	139	7.73	179	4.66	139	8.54	179	6.61
20	20.60	60	17.43	100	12.98	140	7.62	180	4.61	140	8.47	180	6.58
21	20.54	61	17.33	101	12.85	141	7.51	181	4.56	141	8.39	181	6.56
22	20.48	62	17.24	102	12.72	142	7.41	182	4.51	142	8.32	182	6.53
23	20.41	63	17.14	103	12.59	143	7.30	183	4.46	143	8.25	183	6.51
24	20.35	64	17.04	104	12.47	144	7.20	184	4.41	144	8.18	184	6.49
25	20.28	65	16.94	105	12.33	145	7.10	185	4.36	145	8.12	185	6.46
26	20.22	66	16.84	106	12.20	146	7.01	186	4.32	146	8.05	186	6.44
27	20.15	67	16.74	107	12.07	147	6.91	187	4.27	147	7.99	187	6.42
28	20.08	68	16.64	108	11.94	148	6.82	188	4.23	148	7.93	188	6.40
29	20.01	69	16.53	109	11.81	149	6.73	189	4.18	149	7.87	189	6.38
30	19.94	70	16.43	110	11.67	150	6.64	190	4.14	150	7.81	190	6.36
31	19.87	71	16.33	111	11.54	151	6.55	191	4.09	151	7.75	191	6.35
32	19.80	72	16.22	112	11.40	152	6.46	192	4.05	152	7.69	192	6.33
33	19.73	73	16.12	113	11.26	153	6.38	193	4.01	153	7.64	193	6.31
34	19.65	74	16.01	114	11.13	154	6.30	194	3.97	154	7.59	194	6.30
35	19.58	75	15.90	115	10.99	155	6.22	195	3.93	155	7.53	195	6.28
36	19.50	76	15.79	116	10.85	156	6.14	196	3.89	156	7.48	196	6.27
37	19.42	77	15.69	117	10.71	157	6.06	197	3.85	157	7.43	197	6.26
38	19.35	78	15.58	118	10.57	158	5.98	198	3.81	158	7.39	198	6.24
39	19.27	79	15.47	119	10.43	159	5.91	199	3.77	159	7.34	199	6.23
40	19.19	80	15.36	120	10.28	160	5.83	200	3.73	160	7.29	200	6.22

of the negative moments produced by gravity loading which are maximum at points of support, provided that, for such members, the maximum positive moment shall be increased by 1/10 of the average negative moments. This reduction shall not apply to moments produced by loading on cantilevers. If the negative moment is resisted by a column rigidly framed to the beam or girder, the 1/10 reduction may be used in proportioning the column for the combined axial and bending loading, provided that the unit stress f_a, due to any concurrent axial load on the member, does not exceed $0.15F_y$.

Tension on extreme fibers of other rolled shapes, built-up members and plate girders $F_b = 0.60F_y$.

Compression on extreme fibers of rolled shapes, plate girders, and built-up members having an axis of symmetry in the plane of their web (other than box-type beams and girders), the *larger value* computed by Formulas (4) and (5), but not more than $0.60F_y$

$$F_b = \left[1.0 - \frac{(L/r)^2}{2C_c^2C_b}\right]0.60F_y. \qquad \text{Formula (4)}$$

$$F_b = \frac{12{,}000{,}000}{Ld/A_f}, \qquad \text{Formula (5)}$$

where L is the unbraced length of the compression flange; r is the radius of gyration of a tee section comprising the compression flange plus 1/6 of the web area, about an axis in the plane of the web; A_f is the area of the compression flange; C_c is defined in Spec. 13 and C_b, can conservatively be taken as unity.[3] It involves end moments not considered here. Refer to *Manual of Steel Construction.*

Tension and compression on extreme fibers of large pins under flexure $F_b = 0.90F_y$.

Tension and compression on extreme fibers of rectangular bearing plates $F_b = 0.75F_y$.

15. Bearing (on contact area).[4] Milled surfaces including bearing stiffeners and pins in reamed, drilled or bored holes, pounds per square inch $F_p = 0.90F_y$.

Expansion rollers and rockers, pounds per linear inch

$$F_p = \left(\frac{F_y - 13{,}000}{20{,}000}\right)660d$$

where d is the diameter of roller or rocker[4] in inches.

16. Rivets and Bolts. Allowable unit *tension* and *shear* stresses on rivets, bolts, and threaded parts (pounds per square inch of area of rivets before driving or unthreaded body area of bolts and threaded parts) shall be as given in Table S-2.

Allowable *bearing stress* on projected area of bolts in bearing-type connections and on rivets where F_y is the yield point of the connected part $F_p = 1.35F_y$. (Bearing stress not restricted in friction-type connections assembled with *A*325 and *A*354, Grade *BC* bolts.)

17. Welds (stress in pounds per square inch of throat area).

Fillet, Plug, Slot, and Partial Penetration Groove Welds

Fillet, plug, slot and partial penetration groove welds made with *A*233 Class *E*60 series electrodes or by submerged arc welding Grade *SAW*-1 or by *E*70 or *SAW*-2 on *A*7 and *A*373. 13,600 psi

Fillet, plug, slot and partial penetration groove welds made with *A*233 Class *E*70 series electrodes or by submerged arc welding Grade *SAW*-1 on *A*36, *A*242 and *A*441 steels. 15,800 psi

[3] Where $L/r < 40$ stress reduction by Formula (4) may be neglected.

[4] When parts in contact have different yield points, F_y shall be the smaller value.

TABLE S-2

ALLOWABLE RIVET AND BOLT STRESSES

DESCRIPTION OF FASTENER	TENSION (F_t) PSI	SHEAR (F_v) PSI	
		FRICTION-TYPE CONNECTIONS	BEARING-TYPE CONNECTIONS
*A*141 hot-driven rivets	20,000		15,000
*A*195 and *A*406 hot-driven rivets	27,000		20,000
*A*307 bolts and threaded parts of *A*7 and *A*373 steel	14,000		10,000
Threaded parts of other steels	$0.40F_y$		$0.30F_y$
*A*325 bolts when threading is *not* excluded from shear planes	40,000	15,000	15,000
*A*325 bolts when threading is excluded from shear planes	40,000	15,000	22 ,000
*A*354, Grade *BC*, bolts when threading is *not* excluded from shear planes	50,000	20,000	20,000
*A*354, Grade *BC*, when threading is excluded from shear planes	50,000	20,000	24,000

Complete Penetration Groove Welds. On complete penetration groove welds the allowable tension, compression, bending, shear, and bearing stresses shall be the same as those allowed in the connected material. (See Spec. 51 for electrodes to be employed on various grades of steel.)

18. Masonry Bearing. In the absence of Code regulations the following unit stresses in pounds per square inch shall apply:

On sandstone and limestone .... $F_p = 400$ psi
On brick in cement mortar .... $F_p = 250$ psi
On the full area of a concrete support .... $F_p = 0.25f_c'$
On one third of this area .... $F_p = 0.375f_c'$

where f_c' is the specified compression strength of the concrete at 28 days.

19. Wind and Seismic Stresses. Allowable stresses may be increased one third (⅓) above the values provided in previous specifications when produced by wind or seismic loading, acting alone or in combination with the design dead and live loads, provided the required section computed on this basis is not less than that required for the design dead and live load and impact (if any) etc., computed without the ⅓ stress increase, nor less than that required by Spec. 22, if it is applicable.

COMBINED STRESSES

20. Axial Compression and Bending. Members subject to both axial compression and bending stresses shall be proportioned to meet the requirements of both Formula (6) and Formulas (7) and (7*a*).

When $f_a/F_a \leq 0.15$

$$\frac{f_a}{F_a} + \frac{f_b}{F_b} \leq 1.0; \qquad \text{Formula (6)}$$

when $f_a/F_a > 0.15$

$$\frac{f_a}{F_a} + \frac{C_m f_b}{\left(1 - \frac{f_a}{F_e'}\right) F_b} \leq 1.0. \qquad \text{Formula (7a)}$$

$$\frac{f_a}{0.6F_y} + \frac{f_b}{F_b} \leq 1.0 \text{ (applicable only at braced points).} \qquad \text{Formula (7b)}$$

where

F_a = axial stress that would be permitted if axial stress alone existed

F_b = bending stress that would be permitted if bending stress alone existed

$F_e' = \frac{149{,}000{,}000}{(L/r_b)^2}$ (May be increased one third in accordance with spec. 19.)

L = actual unbraced length in the plane of bending

r_b = radius of gyration about axis of bending

f_a = computed axial stress

f_b = computed compressive bending stress at the point under consideration

C_m = 0.85 for frames. Refer to *Manual of Steel Construction.*

21. Shear and Tension. Rivets and bolts subject to combined shear and tension due to force applied to the connected parts, shall be so proportioned that the tension stress produced by the force shall not exceed the following:

For *A*141 rivets .... $F_t = 28{,}000 - 1.6f_v \leq 20{,}000$ psi
For *A*195 and *A*406 rivets .... $F_t = 38{,}000 - 1.6f_v \leq 27{,}000$ psi
For *A*307 bolts .... $F_t = 20{,}000 - 1.6f_v \leq 14{,}000$ psi
For *A*325 bolts in bearing type joints .... $F_t = 50{,}000 - 1.6f_v \leq 40{,}000$ psi
For *A*354, Grade *BC* bolts in bearing-type joints. .... $F_t = 60{,}000 - 1.6f_v \leq 50{,}000$ psi

REPEATED VARIATION OF STRESS

22. Members and Connections Subjected to Repeated Variations of Stress.

TABLE S-3

REPEATED LOADS—ALLOWABLE STRESSES

NO. OF VARIATIONS OF STRESS	DESIGN STRESS	ALLOWABLE STEELS	ALLOWABLE RIVETS	ALLOWABLE WELDS
0–10,000	f_{max}	All steels	All rivets	All welds
10,000–100,000	$f_{max} - \frac{2}{3} f_{min}$†	All steels	All rivets	All welds
100,000–2,000,000	$f_{max} - \frac{2}{3} f_{min}$†	*A*7 steel	*A*141 rivets	*E*60, *SAW*-1
over 2,000,000*	$f_{max} - \frac{3}{4} f_{min}$†	*A*7 reduced to ⅔ value	*A*141 reduced to ⅔ value	*E*60, *SAW*-1 at ⅔ value

* 200 applications per day for 25 years.

† This combination is meaningful only when f_{max} and f_{min} are of opposite signs. With design stresses exceeding f_{max} avoid sharp corners or reduce allowable stresses 25 per cent. Friction bolted connections are designed for f_{max} at allowable stresses of Specs. 16 and 21.

Slenderness and Thickness Ratios

23. Maximum Slenderness Ratios. The slenderness ratio of compression members shall not exceed 200.

The slenderness ratio of tension members, other than rods, preferably should not exceed:

For main members	240
For bracing and other secondary members	300

24. Projecting Elements Under Compression—Width-Thickness Ratios. Projecting elements of members subjected to axial compression or compression due to bending shall have ratios of width-to-thickness not greater than the following:

Single-angle struts; double-angle struts with separators	$2{,}400/\sqrt{F_y}$
Struts comprising double angles in contact; angles or plates projecting from girders, columns or other compression members; compression flanges of beams; stiffeners on plate girders	$3{,}000/\sqrt{F_y}$
Stems of tees	$4{,}000/\sqrt{F_y}$

The width of plates shall be taken from the free edge to the first row of rivets, bolts, or welds; the width of legs of angles, channels, and tees, and of the stems of tees, shall be taken as the full nominal dimension; the width of flanges of beams and tees shall be taken as one half the full nominal width.

Plate Girders and Rolled Beams

25. Proportions. Riveted and welded plate girders, cover-plated beams, and rolled beams shall in general be proportioned by the moment of inertia of the gross section. No deduction shall be made for shop or field rivet or bolt holes in either flange, except that in cases where the reduction of the area of either flange by such holes exceeds 15% of the gross-flange area, the excess shall be deducted.

26. Web. The clear distance between flanges in inches, shall not exceed

$$\frac{14{,}000{,}000}{\sqrt{F_y(F_y + 16{,}500)}}$$

times the web thickness.

27. Flanges. The thickness of outstanding parts of flanges shall conform to the requirements of Spec. 24.

Each flange of welded plate girders shall in general consist of a single plate rather than two or more plates superimposed. The single plate may comprise a series of shorter plates, laid end-to-end and joined by complete penetration butt welds.

Rivets, high strength bolts, or welds connecting flange to web, or cover plate to flange, shall be proportioned to resist the total horizontal shear resulting from the bending forces on the girder. The longitudinal distribution of these rivets or intermittent welds shall be in proportion to the intensity of the shear. But the longitudinal spacing shall not exceed the maximum permitted, respectively, for compression or tension members in Spec. 58 or 61. Additionally, rivets or welds connecting flange to web shall be proportioned to transmit to the web any loads applied directly to the flange unless provision is made to transmit such loads by direct bearing.

28. Bearing Stiffeners. Bearing stiffeners shall be placed in pairs at unframed ends on the webs of plate girders and at points of concentrated loads. Such stiffeners shall have a close bearing against the flange, or flanges, through which they receive their loads or reactions, and shall extend approximately to the edge of the flange plates or flange angles. They shall be designed as columns subject to the provisions of Spec. 13

assuming the column section to comprise the pair of stiffeners and a centrally located strip of the web whose width is equal to not more than 25 times its thickness at interior stiffeners or a width equal to not more than 12 times its thickness when the stiffeners are located at the end of the web. The effective length shall be taken as not less than ¾ of the length of the stiffeners in computing the ratio L/r. Only that portion of the stiffener outside of the angle fillet or the flange-to-web welds shall be considered effective in bearing.

TABLE S-4

Allowable Shear Stresses for Plate Girders by *AISC* Specifications

ALLOWABLE SHEAR STRESSES (F_v) IN PLATE GIRDERS (KSI)
FOR 33 KSI SPECIFIED YIELD POINT STEEL
(Required Gross Area of Intermediate Stiffeners, as per cent of web area, shown in *italics*)

Slenderness ratios h/t: web depth to web thickness	Aspect ratios a/h: stiffener spacing to web depth													
	0.5	0.6	0.7	0.8	0.9	1.0	1.2	1.4	1.6	1.8	2.0	2.5	3.0	over 3
70								13.0	13.0	13.0	13.0	13.0	13.0	12.6
80						13.0	13.0	12.9	12.5	12.2	12.0	11.6	11.5	11.0
90					13.0	12.9	12.1	11.5	11.3	11.1	11.0	10.7	10.6	9.8
									0.4	*0.7*	*0.8*	*0.9*	*0.9*	
100				13.0	12.4	11.6	11.2	11.0	10.7	10.5	10.4	10.0	9.8	8.4
							0.8	*1.3*	*1.6*	*1.7*	*1.8*	*1.7*	*1.6*	
110			13.0	12.2	11.4	11.2	10.8	10.5	10.2	9.8	9.5	9.0	8.6	6.9
					0.3	*1.2*	*2.0*	*2.4*	*2.7*	*2.9*	*3.0*	*2.9*	*2.7*	
120		13.0	12.3	11.4	11.1	10.8	10.4	9.8	9.4	9.0	8.7	8.2	7.8	5.8
				0.5	*1.6*	*2.3*	*3.2*	*3.9*	*4.2*	*4.3*	*4.2*	*3.9*	*3.5*	
130		12.7	11.5	11.1	10.8	10.4	9.8	9.2	8.8	8.4	8.1	7.5	7.1	5.0
			0.3	*1.6*	*2.6*	*3.6*	*4.8*	*5.3*	*5.4*	*5.3*	*5.2*	*4.6*	*4.1*	
140	13.0	11.8	11.2	10.9	10.5	10.0	9.3	8.8	8.3	7.9	7.6	7.0	6.5	4.3
			1.3	*2.6*	*3.9*	*5.1*	*6.1*	*6.3*	*6.3*	*6.2*	*5.9*	*5.2*	*4.6*	
150	12.8	11.4	11.0	10.6	10.1	9.6	8.9	8.4	7.9	7.5	7.2	6.6	6.1	3.7
		0.7	*2.2*	*3.8*	*5.3*	*6.4*	*7.1*	*7.2*	*7.1*	*6.8*	*6.5*	*5.7*	*5.0*	
160	12.0	11.2	10.9	10.3	9.8	9.3	8.6	8.1	7.6	7.2	6.9	6.2	5.8	
		1.5	*3.1*	*5.1*	*6.5*	*7.4*	*7.9*	*7.9*	*7.7*	*7.4*	*7.0*	*6.1*	*5.3*	
170	11.5	11.1	10.6	10.0	9.5	9.1	8.4	7.8	7.3	6.9	6.6	5.9		
	0.3	*2.3*	*4.4*	*6.3*	*7.5*	*8.2*	*8.6*	*8.5*	*8.2*	*7.8*	*7.4*	*6.4*		
180	11.3	10.9	10.3	9.8	9.3	8.8	8.2	7.6	7.1	6.7	6.4			
	1.1	*3.0*	*5.6*	*7.2*	*8.3*	*8.9*	*9.2*	*9.0*	*8.6*	*8.2*	*7.7*			
200	11.1	10.5	9.9	9.4	8.9	8.5	7.8	7.3	6.8	6.4				
	2.3	*5.2*	*7.4*	*8.7*	*9.5*	*10.0*	*10.1*	*9.8*	*9.3*	*8.8*				
220	10.8	10.2	9.6	9.1	8.7	8.3	7.6	7.0						
	4.0	*6.8*	*8.7*	*9.8*	*10.5*	*10.8*	*10.7*	*10.3*						
240	10.5	9.9	9.4	8.9	8.5	8.1	7.4							
	5.5	*8.1*	*9.7*	*10.6*	*11.2*	*11.4*	*11.2*							
260	10.3	9.7	9.2	8.8	8.3	7.9								
	6.8	*9.0*	*10.4*	*11.3*	*11.7*	*11.9*								
280	10.1	9.6	9.1	8.6	8.2									
	7.7	*9.8*	*11.1*	*11.8*	*12.2*									
300	10.0	9.4	9.0	8.5										
	8.5	*10.4*	*11.6*	*12.2*										
320	9.8	9.3	8.9											
	9.2	*10.9*	*12.0*											
340	9.7	9.3												
	9.7	*11.3*												
360	9.7													
	10.1													

TABLE S-4 (*Continued*)

ALLOWABLE SHEAR STRESSES (F_v) IN PLATE GIRDERS (KSI)
FOR 36 KSI SPECIFIED YIELD POINT STEEL
(Required Gross Area of Intermediate Stiffeners, as percent of web area, shown in *italics*)

Slenderness ratios h/t: web depth to web thickness	Aspect ratios a/h: stiffener spacing to web depth													
	0.5	0.6	0.7	0.8	0.9	1.0	1.2	1.4	1.6	1.8	2.0	2.5	3.0	over 3
70											14.3	14.0	13.7	13.1
80							14.2	13.5	13.1	12.8	12.6 *0.7*	12.3 *0.3*	12.1 *0.4*	11.5
90					14.4	13.9	12.6	12.3 *0.6*	12.1 *0.9*	11.9 *1.1*	11.7 *1.2*	11.4 *1.3*	11.2 *1.2*	10.2
100				14.0	13.0	12.4 *0.5*	12.0 *1.4*	11.7 *1.8*	11.4 *2.1*	11.2 *2.1*	11.0 *2.2*	10.4 *2.3*	10.1 *2.1*	8.4
110			14.0	12.7	12.3 *1.0*	12.0 *1.8*	11.6 *2.5*	11.1 *3.1*	10.6 *3.5*	10.3 *3.6*	9.9 *3.6*	9.3 *3.4*	8.9 *3.1*	6.9
120		14.4	12.8	12.3 *1.1*	12.0 *2.1*	11.6 *2.9*	10.9 *4.1*	10.4 *4.7*	9.9 *4.9*	9.5 *4.9*	9.1 *4.8*	8.5 *4.3*	8.0 *3.8*	5.8
130		13.3	12.4 *0.9*	12.0 *2.2*	11.6 *3.2*	11.1 *4.3*	10.4 *5.6*	9.8 *5.9*	9.3 *6.0*	8.9 *5.8*	8.5 *5.6*	7.8 *5.0*	7.4 *4.4*	5.0
140	14.3	12.5 *0.3*	12.1 *1.9*	11.7 *3.2*	11.1 *4.8*	10.6 *5.9*	9.9 *6.7*	9.3 *6.9*	8.8 *6.8*	8.4 *6.6*	8.0 *6.3*	7.3 *5.5*	6.8 *4.9*	4.3
150	13.4	12.3 *1.2*	11.9 *2.8*	11.3 *4.7*	10.8 *6.1*	10.3 *7.1*	9.5 *7.6*	8.9 *7.7*	8.4 *7.5*	8.0 *7.2*	7.6 *6.8*	6.9 *6.0*	6.4 *5.2*	3.7
160	12.6 *0.1*	12.1 *2.1*	11.6 *4.1*	11.0 *6.0*	10.4 *7.2*	10.0 *8.0*	9.2 *8.4*	8.6 *8.3*	8.1 *8.1*	7.7 *7.7*	7.3 *7.3*	6.6 *6.3*		
170	12.4 *0.9*	12.0 *2.8*	11.3 *5.3*	10.7 *7.0*	10.2 *8.1*	9.7 *8.7*	9.0 *9.0*	8.3 *8.9*	7.8 *8.5*	7.4 *8.1*	7.0 *7.7*			
180	12.3 *1.6*	11.7 *4.0*	11.0 *6.4*	10.5 *7.9*	10.0 *8.8*	9.5 *9.4*	8.8 *9.6*	8.1 *9.3*	7.6 *8.9*	7.2 *8.5*	6.8 *8.0*			
200	12.0 *2.9*	11.3 *6.0*	10.7 *8.0*	10.1 *9.2*	9.6 *10.0*	9.2 *10.4*	8.4 *10.4*	7.8 *10.0*	7.3 *9.5*					
220	11.6 *4.8*	10.9 *7.5*	10.4 *9.2*	9.8 *10.2*	9.4 *10.8*	8.9 *11.1*	8.2 *11.0*	7.5 *10.6*						
240	11.3 *6.2*	10.7 *8.6*	10.1 *10.1*	9.6 *11.0*	9.2 *11.5*	8.7 *11.7*	8.0 *11.5*							
260	11.1 *7.3*	10.5 *9.5*	10.0 *10.8*	9.5 *11.6*	9.0 *12.0*									
280	10.9 *8.2*	10.3 *10.2*	9.8 *11.4*	9.3 *12.1*	8.9 *12.4*									
300	10.8 *9.0*	10.2 *10.8*	9.7 *11.8*	9.2 *12.4*										
320	10.7 *9.5*	10.1 *11.2*	9.6 *12.2*	9.1 *12.8*										

Girders so proportioned that the computed shear is less than that given in right-hand column do not require intermediate stiffeners.

29. Web Shear between Stiffeners.[5] The largest average web shear f_v in any panel between stiffeners (total shear force divided by web cross-sectional area), in pounds per square inch, computed for any condition of complete or partial loading, shall not exceed the value given by Formula (8) or (9), as applicable.

$$F_v = \frac{F_y}{2.89}\left[C_v + \frac{1 - C_v}{1.15\sqrt{1 + (a/h)^2}}\right] \qquad \text{Formula (8)}$$

[5] See Table S-4 for numerical values of allowable web shear for various grades of steel corresponding to the provisions of this section.

when C_v is less than 1.0;

$$F_v = \frac{F_y}{2.89}(C_v) \qquad \text{Formula (9)}$$

but not more than $0.4F_y$, when C_v is more than 1.0 or when intermediate stiffeners are omitted;
where

a = clear distance between transverse stiffeners, in inches

h = clear distance between flanges, in inches

$$C_v = \frac{45{,}000{,}000k}{F_y(h/t)^2}, \text{ when } C_v \text{ is less than } 0.8$$

$$= \frac{6{,}000}{h/t}\sqrt{\frac{k}{F_y}}, \text{ when } C_v \text{ is more than } 0.8$$

t = thickness of web, in inches

$$k = 4.00 + \frac{5.34}{(a/h)^2}, \text{ when } a/h \text{ is less than } 1.0$$

$$= 5.34 + \frac{4.00}{(a/h)^2}, \text{ when } a/h \text{ is more than } 1.0.$$

When a/h is more than 3 its value shall be taken as infinity. In this case Formula (8) reduces to Formula (9) and $k = 5.34$.

30. Stiffener Spacing. Intermediate stiffeners are not required when the ratio h/t is less than 260 and the maximum web shear stress f_v is less than that permitted by Formula (9).

The spacing of intermediate stiffeners, when stiffeners are required, shall be such that the web shear stress will not exceed the value for F_v given by Formulas (8) or (9), as applicable, and the ratio a/h shall not exceed $\left(\frac{260}{h/t}\right)^2$ nor 3.0.

End Panels. The spacing between stiffeners at end panels and panels containing large holes shall be such that the smaller panel dimension, a or h, shall not exceed

$$11{,}000t/\sqrt{f_v}.$$

31. Area of Stiffeners. The gross area, in square inches, of intermediate stiffeners in pairs of the same material as the web, spaced in accordance with Formula (8) shall be not less than that computed by Formula (10).

$$A_{st} = \frac{1 - C_v}{2}\left[\frac{a}{h} - \frac{(a/h)^2}{\sqrt{1 + (a/h)^2}}\right]ht. \qquad \text{Formula (10)}$$

The *moment of inertia* of a pair of stiffeners, or a single stiffener, with reference to an axis in the plane of the web, shall not be less than $(h/50)^4$.

32. Stiffener Connections. Intermediate stiffeners required by the provisions of Spec. 30 shall be connected for a total shear transfer, in pounds per linear inch of single stiffener or pair of stiffeners, not less than that computed by the formula

$$f_{vs} = h\sqrt{\left(\frac{F_y}{3{,}400}\right)^3},$$

where F_y = yield point of web steel.

Rivets connecting stiffeners to the girder web shall be spaced not more that 12 in. on center. If intermittent fillet welds are used the clear distance between welds shall not be more than 16 times the web thickness nor more than 10 in.

33. Reduction in Flange Stress. When the web depth-to-thickness ratio exceeds $24{,}000/\sqrt{F_b}$, the maximum stress in the compression flange shall not exceed

$$f_b' \leq F_b\left[1.0 - 0.0005\frac{A_w}{A_f}\left(\frac{h}{t} - \frac{24{,}000}{\sqrt{F_b}}\right)\right]. \qquad \text{Formula (11)}$$

34. Beam and Girder Deflections. Beams and girders supporting floors and roofs shall be proportioned with due regard to the deflection produced by the design loads.

Beams and girders supporting plastered ceilings shall be so proportioned that the maximum live load deflection will not exceed 1/360 of the span.

The depth of beams and girders supporting flat roofs shall be not less than $f_b/600{,}000$ times their span length whether designed as simple or continuous spans.

Gross and Net Sections

35. Net Section. In the case of a chain of holes extending across a part in any diagonal or zigzag line, the net width of the part shall be obtained by deducting from the gross width the sum of the diameters of all the holes in the chain, and adding, for each gage space in the chain, the quantity

$$\frac{s^2}{4g}$$

where

s = longitudinal spacing (pitch, in inches) of any two consecutive holes
g = transverse spacing (gage, in inches) of the same two holes

The critical net section of the part is obtained from that chain which gives the least net width; however, the net section taken through a hole shall in no case be considered as more than 85% of the corresponding gross section.

In determining the net section across plug or slot welds, the weld metal shall not be considered as adding to the net area.

36. Angles. For angles, the gross width shall be the sum of the widths of the legs less the thickness. The gage for holes in opposite legs shall be the sum of the gages from back of angles less the thickness.

37. Size of Holes. In computing net area the diameter of a rivet or bolt shall be taken as 1/8 inch greater than the nominal diameter of the rivet or bolt.

38. Pin-Connected Members. The width of the body of the eye bar shall not exceed 8 times its thickness, and the thickness shall not be less than 1/2 in. The net section of the head through the pin hole transverse to the axis of the eyebar, shall not be less than 1.33 nor more than 1.50 times the cross-sectional area of the body of the eye bar. The diameter of the pin shall not be less than 7/8 the width of the body of the eye bar. The diameter of the pin hole shall not be more than 1/32 in. greater than the diameter of the pin.

The minimum net section across the pin hole, transverse to the axis of the member, in pin-connected plates and built-up members shall be determined at the stress allowed for such sections in Spec. 11. The net section beyond the pin hole, parallel to the axis of the member, shall not be less than 2/3 of the net section across the pin hole.

The distance transverse to the axis of a pin-connected plate or any separated element of a built-up member from the edge of the pin hole to the edge of the member or element, shall not exceed 4 times the thickness at the pin hole. The diameter of the pin shall preferably not be less than 5 times the thickness of the member or separated element at the pin hole. If a smaller size is used, the bearing stress shall not exceed that allowed by Spec. 15. The diameter of the pin hole shall not be more than 1/32 in. greater than the diameter of the pin.

39. Effective Areas of Weld Metal. The effective area of butt and fillet welds shall be considered as the effective length of the weld times the effective throat thickness.

The effective shearing area of plug and slot welds shall be considered as the nominal cross-sectional area of the hole or slot, in the plane of the faying surface.

The effective length of a fillet weld shall be the overall length of full-size fillet including returns.

The effective length of a butt weld shall be the width of the part joined.

The effective throat thickness of a fillet weld shall be the shortest distance from the root to the face of the diagrammatic weld.

The effective throat thickness of a complete penetration butt weld shall be the thickness of the thinner part joined.

The effective throat thickness of single-V or single-bevel groove welds having no root opening and having partial penetration into their joints shall be 1/4 in. less than the depth of the V or bevel groove.

Connections

40. Minimum Connections. Connections carrying calculated stresses, except for lacing, sag bars, and girts, shall be designed to support not less than 6,000 lb.

41. Placement of Rivets, Bolts, and Welds. Except as hereinafter provided, the rivets, bolts, or welds at the ends of any member transmitting axial stress into that member shall have their centers of gravity on the gravity axis of the member unless provision is made for the effect of the resulting eccentricity. Except in members subject to repeated variation in stress, as defined in Spec. 22, disposition of fillet welds to balance the forces about the neutral axis or axes for end connections of single angle, double angle, and similar type members is not required. Eccentricity between the gravity axes of such members and the gage lines for their riveted or bolted end connections may be neglected.

42. Unrestrained Members. Except as otherwise indicated by the designer, connections of beams, girders, or trusses shall be designed as flexible, and may ordinarily be proportioned for the reaction shears only.

Flexible beam connections shall permit the ends of the beam to rotate sufficiently to accommodate its deflection by providing for a horizontal displacement e of the top flange determined as follows:

$e = 0.007d$, when the beam is designed for full uniform load and for live load deflection not exceeding 1/360 of the span.

43. Connections of Tension and Compression Members in Trusses. The connections at ends of tension or compression members in trusses shall develop the strength required by the stress, but not less than 50% of the effective strength of the member.

44. Compression Members with Bearing Joints. Where compression members bear on bearing plates, and where tier-building columns are finished to bear, there shall be sufficient rivets, bolts, or welds to hold all parts securely in place.

Where other compression members are finished to bear, the splice material and its riveting, bolting, or welding shall be arranged to hold all parts in line and shall be proportioned for 50% of the computed stress.

All of the foregoing joints shall be proportioned to resist any tension that would be developed by specified lateral forces acting in conjunction with 75% of the calculated dead load stress and no live load.

45. Rivets and Bolts in Combination with Welds. In new work, rivets, *A*307 bolts, or high strength bolts used in bearing-type connections, shall not be considered as sharing the stress in combination with welds. Welds, if used, shall be provided to carry the entire stress in the connection. High strength bolts installed as a friction-type connection prior to welding may be considered as sharing the stress with the welds or with rivets.

Rivets and Bolts

46. Effective Bearing Area. The effective bearing area of rivets and bolts shall be the diameter multiplied by the length in bearing, except that for countersunk rivets and bolts half the depth of the countersink shall be deducted.

47. Long Grips. Rivets and *A*307 bolts which carry calculated stress, and the grip of which exceeds 5 diameters, shall have their number increased 1% for each additional 1/16 in. in the grip.

48. Minimum Pitch. The minimum distance between centers of rivet and bolt holes shall be not less than 2⅔ times the nominal diameter of the rivet or bolt but preferably not less than 3 diameters.

49. Minimum Edge Distance. The minimum distance from the center of a rivet or bolt hole to any edge, used in design or in preparation of shop drawings, shall be that given in Table S-5.

TABLE S-5.

Edge Distances from Holes

Rivet or Bolt Diameter in.	Minimum Edge Distance for Punched, Reamed or Drilled Holes in.	
	At Sheared Edges	At Rolled Edges of Plates, Shapes, or Bars or Gas Cut Edges†
½	⅞	¾
⅝	1⅛	⅞
¾	1¼	1
⅞	1½*	1⅛
1	1¾*	1¼
1⅛	2	1½

* These may be 1¼ in. at the ends of beam connection angles.

† All edge distances in this column may be reduced ⅛ in. when the hole is at a point where stress does not exceed 25 per cent of the maximum allowed stress in the element.

50. Maximum Edge Distance. The maximum distance from the center of any rivet or bolt to the nearest edge of parts in contact with one another shall be 12 times the thickness of the plate, but shall not exceed 6 in.

Welds

51. Weld Materials. *E*60 and *E*70 series electrodes for manual arc welding and Grade *SAW*-1 or Grade *SAW*-2 submerged arc process may be used for welding *A*7, *A*373 and *A*36 steel. Only *E*70 low hydrogen electrodes for manual arc welding or Grade *SAW*-2 for submerged arc welding shall be used with *A*441 or weldable *A*242 steel, except that fillet welds or partial penetration groove welds may be made with *E*60 series low hydrogen electrodes and Grade *SAW*-1 submerged arc process. Welding *A*440 steel is not recommended.

52. Submerged Arc Welding—Properties. The bare electrodes and granular fusible flux used in combinations for submerged arc welding shall be capable of producing weld metal having the tensile properties given in Table S-6 when deposited in a multiple pass weld.

TABLE S-6

WELD METAL PROPERTIES

PROPERTIES	GRADE *SAW*-1	GRADE *SAW*-2
Tensile strength	62,000 to 80,000 psi	70,000 to 90,000 psi
Yield point, min.	45,000 psi	50,000 psi
Elongation in 2 in., min.	25%	22%
Reduction in area, min.	40%	40%

53. Minimum Size of Fillet Welds. In joints connected only by fillet welds, the minimum size of fillet weld to be used shall be as shown in Table S-7. Weld size is determined by the thicker of the two parts joined, except that the weld size need not exceed the thickness of the thinner part joined unless a larger size is required by calculated stress:

TABLE S-7

MINIMUM SIZE OF FILLET WELDS

MATERIAL THICKNESS OF THICKER PART JOINED (IN.)	MINIMUM SIZE OF FILLET WELD (IN.)
To ½ inclusive	3/16
Over ½ to ¾	¼
Over ¾ to 1½	5/16
Over 1½ to 2¼	⅜
Over 2¼ to 6	½

54. Maximum Effective Size of Fillet Welds. The maximum size of fillet weld that may be used along edges of connected parts shall be:

1. Along edges of material less than ¼ in. thick, the maximum size may be equal to the thickness of the material.
2. Along edges of material ¼ in. or more in thickness, the maximum size shall be 1/16 in. less than the thickness of the material, unless the weld is especially designated on the drawings to be built out to obtain full throat thickness.

55. Length of Fillet Welds. The minimum effective length of a strength fillet weld shall be not less than 4 times the nominal size, or else the size of the weld shall be considered not to exceed ¼ of its effective length.

If longitudinal fillet welds are used alone in end connections of flat bar tension members, the length of each fillet weld shall be not less than the perpendicular distance between them.

56. Intermittent Fillet Welds. Intermittent fillet welds may be used to transfer calculated stress across a joint or faying surfaces when the strength required is less than that developed by a continuous fillet weld of the smallest permitted size, and to join components of built-up members. The effective length of any segment of intermittent fillet welding shall be not less than 4 times the weld size with a minimum of 1½ in.

57. Plug and Slot Welds. Plug or slot welds may be used to transmit shear in a lap joint or to prevent buckling of lapped parts and to join component parts of built-up members.

The diameter of the holes for a plug weld shall be not less than the thickness of the part containing it plus 5⁄16 in., rounded to the next greater odd 1⁄16 in., nor greater than 2¼ times the thickness of the weld metal.

The minimum center-to-center spacing of plug welds shall be 4 times the diameter of the hole.

The length of slot for a slot weld shall not exceed 10 times the thickness of the weld. The width of the slot shall be not less than the thickness of the part containing it, plus 5⁄16 in., rounded to the next greater odd 1⁄16 in., nor shall it be greater than 2¼ times the thickness of the weld. The ends of the slot shall be semicircular or shall have the corners rounded to a radius not less than the thickness of the part containing it, except those ends which extend to the edge of the part.

The minimum spacing of lines of slot welds in a direction transverse to their length shall be 4 times the width of the slot. The minimum center-to-center spacing in a longitudinal direction on any line shall be 2 times the length of the slot.

The thickness of plug, or slot welds in material ⅝ in. or less in thickness shall be equal to the thickness of the material. In material over ⅝ in. in thickness, it shall be at least one-half the thickness of the material but not less than ⅝ in.

Built-up Members

58. Compression Members. All parts of built-up compression members and the transverse spacing of their lines of fasteners shall meet the requirements of Specs. 23 and 24.

At the ends of built-up compression members bearing on base plates or milled surfaces, all components in contact with one another shall be connected by rivets or bolts spaced longitudinally not more than 4 diameters apart for a distance equal to 1½ times the maximum width of the member, or by continuous welds having a length not less than the maximum width of the member.

The longitudinal spacing for intermediate rivets, bolts, or intermittent welds in built-up members shall be adequate to provide for the transfer of calculated stress. However, where a component of a built-up compression member consists of an outside plate, the maximum spacing shall not exceed the thickness of the thinner outside plate times $4{,}000/\sqrt{F_y}$ when rivets are provided on all gage lines at each section, or when intermittent welds are provided along the edges of the components, but this spacing shall not exceed 12 in. When rivets or bolts are staggered, the maximum spacing on each gage line shall not exceed the thickness of the thinner outside plate times $6{,}000/\sqrt{F_y}$ nor 18 in. The maximum longitudinal spacing of rivets, bolts, or intermittent welds connecting two rolled shapes in contact with one another shall not exceed 24 in.

59. Tie Plates for Compression Members. Open sides of compression members built up from plates or shapes shall be provided with lacing having tie plates at each end, and at intermediate points if the lacing is interrupted. Tie plates shall be as near the ends as practicable. In main members carrying calculated stress the end tie plates shall have a length of not less than the distance between the lines of rivets, bolts or welds connecting them to the components of the member. Intermediate tie plates shall have a length not less than ½ of this distance. The thickness of tie plates shall be not less than 1/50 of the distance between the lines of rivets, bolts, or welds connecting them to the segments of the members. In riveted and bolted construction the pitch in tie plates shall be not more than 6 diameters and the tie plates shall be connected to each segment by at least 3 fasteners. In welded construction, the welding on each line connecting a tie plate shall aggregate not less than 1/3 the length of the plate.

60. Lacing for Compression Members. Lacing, including flat bars, angles, channels, or other shapes employed as lacing, shall be so spaced that the ratio L/r of the flange included between their connections shall not exceed the governing ratio for the member as a whole. Lacing shall be proportioned to resist a shearing stress normal to the axis of the member equal to 2% of the total compressive stress in the member. The ratio L/r for lacing bars arranged in single systems shall not exceed 140. For double lacing this ratio shall not exceed 200. Double lacing bars shall be joined at their intersections. In determining the required section for lacing bars, Formula (1) or (3) shall be used, L being taken as the unsupported length of the lacing bar between rivets or welds connecting it to the components of the built-up member for single lacing and 70% of that distance for double lacing. The inclination of lacing bars to the axis of the member shall preferably be not less than 60 degrees for single lacing and 45 degrees for double lacing. When the distance between the lines of rivets or welds in the flanges is more than 15 in., the lacing shall preferably be double or be made of angles.

61. Tension Members. The longitudinal spacing of rivets, bolts, and intermittent fillet welds connecting a plate and a rolled shape in a built-up tension member, or two plate components in contact with one another, shall not exceed 24 times the thickness of the plates nor 12 in. The longitudinal spacing of rivets, bolts, and intermittent welds connecting two or more shapes in contact with one another in a tension member shall not exceed 24 in. Tension members composed of two or more shapes or plates separated from one another by intermittent fillers shall be connected to one another at these fillers at intervals such that the slenderness ratio of either component between the fasteners does not exceed 240.

62. Tie Plates for Tension Members. Either perforated cover plates or tie plates without lacing may be used on the open sides of built-up tension members. Tie plates shall have a length not less than 2/3 the distance between the lines of rivets, bolts, or welds connecting them to the components of the member. The thickness of such tie plates shall not be less than 1/50 of the distance between these lines. The longitudinal spacing of rivets, bolts, or intermittent welds at tie plates shall not exceed 6 in. The spacing of tie plates shall be such that the slenderness ratio of any component in the length between tie plates will not exceed 240.

Fabrication—Tolerances

63. Finishing. Column bases shall be finished in accordance with the following requirements:

1. Rolled steel bearing plates, 2 in. or less in thickness, may be used without planing, provided a satisfactory contact bearing is obtained; rolled steel bearing plates over 2 in. but not over 4 in. in thickness may be straightened by pressing; or, if presses are not available, by planing for all bearing surfaces to obtain a satisfactory contact bearing.
2. The bottom surfaces of bearing plates and column bases which are grouted to insure full bearing contact on foundations need not be planed.

64. Riveted and Bolted Construction—Holes. Holes for rivets or bolts shall be 1/16 in. larger than the nominal diameter of the rivet or bolt. If the thickness of the material is not greater than the nominal diameter of the rivet or bolt plus 1/8 in., the holes may be punched. If the thickness of the material is greater than the nominal diameter of the rivet or bolt plus 1/8 in., the holes shall be either drilled from the solid, or sub-punched, and reamed. The die for all sub-punched holes, and the drill for all sub-drilled holes, shall be at least 1/16 in. smaller than the nominal diameter of the rivet or bolt.

Surfaces of high strength bolted parts in contact with the bolt head and nut shall not have a slope of more than 1:20 with respect to a plane normal to the bolt axis. Where the surface of a high strength bolted part has a slope of more than 1:20, a beveled washer shall be used to compensate for the lack of parallelism.

65. Straightness. Compression members shall not deviate from straightness by more than 1/1000 of the axial length between points which are to be laterally supported.

Completed members shall be free from twists, bends, and open joints. Sharp kinks or bends shall be cause for rejection of material.

66. Length. A variation of 1/32 in. is permissible in the overall length of members with both ends finished for contact bearing.

Members without ends finished for contact bearing, which are to be framed to other steel parts of the structure, may have a variation from the detailed length not greater than 1/16 in. for members 30 ft. or less in length, and not greater than 1/8 in. for members over 30 ft. in length.

Rules for Plastic Design

67. Scope of Plastic Design. Subject to the limitations contained herein, simple or continuous beams, one and two-story rigid frames classified as Type 1 construction in Spec. 1, and similar portions of structures rigidly constructed so as to be continuous over at least one interior support, may be proportioned on the basis of plastic design, i.e., of their maximum strength. This strength, as determined by rational analysis, shall not be less than that required to support 1.70 times the given live load and dead load for simple and continuous beams. For continuous frames it shall not be less than 1.85 times the given live load and dead load, nor 1.40 times these loads acting in conjunction with 1.40 times any specified wind or earthquake forces. These are termed *Load Factors.*

Connections joining a portion of a structure designed on the basis of plastic behavior with a portion not so designed need be no more rigid than ordinary seat-and-cap angle or standard web connections.

Where plastic design is used as the basis for proportioning continuous beams and structural frames, the preceeding provisions relating to allowable working stress are waived. Except as modified by these rules, however, all other pertinent provisions of specifications for allowable stress design shall govern.

It is not recommended that crane runways be designed continuous over interior vertical supports on the basis of maximum strength. However, rigid frame bents supporting crane runways may be considered as coming within the scope of the rules

68. Structural Steel. Structural steel for plastic design shall conform to one of the following specifications, latest edition:

*Steel for Bridges and Buildings, ASTM A*7
*Structural Steel for Welding, ASTM A*373
*Structural Steel, ASTM A*36

Note. Abbreviated specifications have been given in §197 for plastic design covering columns, stiffness of beams, connections, bracing and workmanship. For full details see Part 2 of *Specification for the Design, Fabrication and Erection of Structural Steel for Buildings* published by the American Institute of Steel Construction, current edition.

NATIONAL LUMBER MANUFACTURERS ASSOCIATION

309. Abbreviated[6] National Design Specifications for Stress-Grade Lumber.

GENERAL—STRESS-GRADE LUMBER

101. Scope. This specification defines the practice to be followed in design with, and in fabrication and erection of, stress-grade lumber (see Spec. 102), and structural glued laminated lumber and also in design with, and installation of, the fastenings defined herein.

102. Grade Names. Stress-grade lumber consists of lumber classifications known as "Beams and Stringers," "Joists and Planks," and "Posts and Timbers," to each grade of which is assigned proper allowable unit stresses.

103. Beams and Stringers. Lumber of rectangular cross section, 5 in. or more thick and 8 in. or more wide, graded with respect to its strength in bending when loaded on the narrow face.

104. Joists and Planks. Lumber of rectangular cross section, 2 in. to but not including 5 in. thick, and 4 in. or more wide, graded with respect to its strength in bending when loaded either on the narrow face as a joist or on the wide face as a plank.

105. Posts and Timbers. Lumber of square or approximately square cross section 5 by 5 in. and larger, graded primarily for use as posts or columns carrying longitudinal load but adapted for miscellaneous uses in which strength in bending is not especially important.

ALLOWABLE UNIT STRESSES

106. Allowable Unit Stresses for Service Conditions. The allowable unit stresses in Table 9 and adjustments thereof apply to sawn lumber used under conditions continuously dry such as in most covered structures. The allowable unit stresses for glued-laminated timber for this condition of use are given in Table 11.

Tables 9 and 11 are found on pages 280 and 284 of Chapter 11.

107. Saturated Timber. The allowable unit stresses in Table 9 and adjustments thereof apply to lumber used under conditions where the moisture content of the wood is at or above the fiber saturation point, as when continuously submerged, except that under such conditions of use the allowable unit stresses in compression parallel to grain shall be reduced 1/10, in compression perpendicular to the grain shall be reduced 1/3 and the values for modulus of elasticity shall be reduced 1/11. For glued-laminated timber under wet conditions of use the following maximum percentages of the allowable stresses from Table 11 shall be permitted: for f (bending) and t (tension)—80%; for H (shear and E (modulus of elasticity)—90%; for c (compression parallel to the grain)—70%, and for $c\perp$ (compression perpendicular to grain)—67%.

108. Treated Lumber. The allowable unit stresses in Table 9 and adjustments thereof apply to lumber pressure-impregnated by an approved process and preservative.

109. Full Permanent Loading. Where a member is fully stressed to the maximum allowable stress for many years, either continuously or cumulatively under the condition

[6] For complete specifications consult the most recent revision of *National Design Specification for Stress-Grade Lumber and Its Fastenings,* National Lumber Manufacturers Association.

of maximum design load, use working stresses 90% of those in Table 9. This provision applies to mechanical fastenings where the strength of the joint depends upon the strength of the timber.

110. Continuous Spans. Beam grades ordinarily are graded for use on simple spans. When used as a continuous beam, the grading provisions customarily applied to the middle third of the length of simple spans shall be applied to the middle ⅔ of the length of pieces to be used over double spans and to the entire length of pieces to be used over three or more spans.

111. Shear in Joints. Allowable unit stresses for shear in joint details may be 50% greater than the horizontal shear values otherwise permitted.

112. Increased Compression. In joists supported on a ribbon or ledger board and spiked to the studs, the allowable unit stresses for compression perpendicular to grain may be increased by 50%.

113. Modulus of Elasticity. The values for modulus of elasticity in Table 9 assume the lumber will be surface seasoned before it is fully loaded to the maximum allowable load. With sawn members thicker than 4 in., which season slowly, care should be exercised to avoid their being overloaded before an appreciable seasoning of the outer fibers has taken place, otherwise the values for modulus of elasticity in Table 9 should be reduced $1/11$.

114. Uplift of Roofs due to Wind. All roofs, as well as other affected portions of the structure, shall be designed for anchorage to resist uplift from wind. For uplift, the design values for the withdrawal and lateral resistance of metal fastenings in wood and allowable unit stresses for lumber may be increased 33⅓% above those for normal loading.

115. Bearing. For bearings of less than 6 in. in length and not nearer than 3 in. to the end of a member, the maximum allowable load per square inch is obtained by multiplying the allowable unit stresses in compression perpendicular to grain by the following factor: $(L + 3/8)/L$ in which L is the length of bearing in inches measured along the grain of the wood.

116. Lateral Deflection. Beams and Roof Joists. The designer should apply the following approximate rules in providing lateral restraint for rectangular beams and roof joists.

(*a*) If the ratio of depth to breadth is 2 to 1, no lateral support is needed.

(*b*) If the ratio is 3 to 1, the ends shall be held in position.

(*c*) If the ratio is 4 to 1, the piece shall be held in line as in a well-bolted chord member in a truss.

(*d*) If the ratio is 5 to 1, one edge shall be held in line.

(*e*) If the ratio is 6 to 1, bridge at intervals of 8 ft. or 6 h.

(*f*) If the ratio is 7 to 1, both edges shall be held in line.

(*g*) If a beam is subject to both flexure and compression parallel to grain, the ratio may be as much as 5 to 1, if one edge is held firmly in line.

117. L/d Limitations.

(*a*) For simple solid columns, L/d shall not exceed 50.

(*b*) For individual members of a spaced column, L/d shall not exceed 80, nor shall L_2/d exceed 40 where L_2 is between centers of spacer blocks.

AMERICAN ASSOCIATION OF STATE HIGHWAY OFFICIALS

310. Abbreviated[7] *AASHO* Specifications for Highway Bridges.

ALLOWABLE STRESSES FOR STEEL

201. Steel Structures. Unless otherwise specified or noted on the plans, it shall be assumed that the steel is to be Structural Carbon Steel, *ASTM A7*. The modulus of elasticity for all grades of steel shall be assumed at 29,000,000 and the coefficient of expansion .0000065 per degree Fahrenheit.

202. Permissible Unit Stresses *A7* Steel.

Axial tension, structural steel, net section .... 18,000 psi

Tension in extreme fibers of rolled shapes, girders and built sections subject to bending 18,000

Tension in bolts at root of thread 13,500

Compression.

Stiffeners of plate girders 18,000

Concentrically loaded columns having values of L/r not greater than 140:

Riveted ends .... $15{,}000 - \frac{1}{4}\frac{L^2}{r^2}$

Pin ends .... $15{,}000 - \frac{1}{3}\frac{L^2}{r^2}$

L = length of member, in inches

r = least radius of gyration of member, in inches.

Compression in extreme fibers of rolled shapes, girders and built sections, subject to bending, gross section

(*a*) When compression flange is supported laterally for its full length 18,000 psi

(*b*) [8]When compression flange is partially supported or is unsupported .... $18{,}000 - 5\frac{L^2}{b^2}$

b = flange width in inches.

For values of L/b not greater than 30 where L = length, in inches, of unsupported flange between lateral connections, knee braces or other points of support. For continuous beams and girders, L may be taken as the distance from interior support to point of dead load contraflexure if this distance is less than that designated above.

Compression in splice material, gross section .... 18,000 psi

[7] For complete specifications consult the *AASHO Standard Specifications for Highway Bridges*, as revised periodically.

[8] Continuous or cantilever beams or girders may be proportioned for negative moment at interior supports for an allowable unit stress 20% higher than permitted by above formula but in no case exceeding allowable unit stress for compression flange supported for its full length. If cover plates are used, the allowable stress at the point of cut-off shall be as determined by the formula.

Flexure.

Stress in extreme fiber of pins	27,000 psi

Shear.

Shear in girder webs, gross section	11,000
Shear in power-driven rivets and pins	13,500
Shear in turned bolts and ribbed bolts	11,000

Bearing.

Bearing on pins not subject to rotation	24,000
Bearing on power-driven rivets, milled stiffeners, and other steel parts in contact (Rivets driven by pneumatically or electrically operated hammers are considered power driven.)	27,000
Bearing on pins subject to rotation (not due to deflection)	12,000
Bearing on turned bolts and ribbed bolts	20,000

Bearing on expansion rollers and rockers, pounds per linear inch:

Diameters up to 25 in. .... $\frac{p - 13{,}000}{20{,}000} 600d$

Diameters from 25 to 125 in. .... $\frac{p - 13{,}000}{20{,}000} 3{,}000\sqrt{d}$

d = diameter of roller or rocker, in inches

p = yield point in tension of steel in the roller or the base, whichever is the lesser.

Rivets. In proportioning rivets the nominal diameter shall be used.

The effective bearing area of a pin, a bolt, or a rivet shall be its diameter multiplied by the thickness of the metal on which it bears.

In metal less than ⅜ in. thick countersunk rivets shall not be assumed to carry stress. In metal ⅜ in. thick and over, ½ the depth of countersink shall be omitted in calculating bearing area.

High Strength Rivets. High Strength Structural Rivet Steel, *AASHO—M*·98 (*ASTM—A*195).

Shear	20,000 psi
Bearing	40,000

*High Strength Bolts, ASTM—A*325. Joints required to resist shear between their connected parts are *friction type* or *bearing type* connections. Shear connections subject to stress reversal or where slippage would be undesirable shall be friction type. Bolts in bearing-type connections shall have the threads excluded from the shear planes of contact surfaces between the connected parts.

Applied direct tension on nominal area of bolt	36,000 psi
Shear, friction-type connection	13,500
Shear, bearing-type connection	20,000
Bearing	40,000

203. Unit Stresses for Welding. The allowable unit stresses in pounds per square inch of effective area of weld shall be as given in the current specifications of the American Welding Society for Welded Highway and Railway Bridges.

OTHER MATERIALS

204. Bearing on Masonry.

Bearing on granite masonry	800 psi
Bearing on sandstone and limestone masonry	400
Bearing on concrete: Under hinged rockers or bolsters	1,000

205. Concrete, Allowable Stresses.

Flexure.		Values if $f_c' = 3000$ psi
Extreme fiber in compression	$f_c = 0.4 f_c'$	1200
Extreme fiber, in tension plain concrete, primarily in footings	$f_c = .03 f_c'$	90
Extreme fiber in tension, reinforced concrete..	None	
Shear.		
Beams without web reinforcement:		
Longitudinal bars not anchored or plain concrete footings	$.02 f_c'$ (Max. 75)	60
Longitudinal bars anchored	$.03 f_c'$ (Max. 90)	90
Beams with web reinforcement	$.075 f_c' bjd$	225
Horizontal shear in shear-keys between slab and steam of T-beams	$0.15 f_c'$	450

206. Reinforcement, Allowable Stresses.

	STRUCTURAL GRADE	INTERMEDIATE HARD RAIL STEEL
Steel reinforcement.		
Tension in flexural members	18,000	20,000 psi
Tension in web reinforcement	18,000	20,000
Compression..........................	13,200	16,000
Bond, deformed bars.		
Straight or hooked ends, exclusive of top bars:		
(1) In beams, slabs, one-way footings......	$.10 f_c'$ (maximum 350)	$.10 f_c'$ (maximum 350)
(2) In two-way footings	$.08 f_c'$ (maximum 280)	$.08 f_c'$ (maximum 280)
Top bars—Bars near top of beams and girders having more than 12 in. of concrete under the bars	$.06 f_c'$ (maximum 210)	$.06 f_c'$ (maximum 210)

207. Bearing Power of Foundation Soils. When required by the engineer, the bearing power of the soil in excavated foundation pits shall be determined by loading tests. The following tabulations of the bearing power of broad basic groups of materials may be used as an aid to the judgment in the absence of more definite information:

MATERIAL	SAFE BEARING POWER TONS PER SQUARE FOOT Min.	Max.
Alluvial soils	½	1
Clays	1	4
Sand, confined	1	4
Gravel	2	4
Cemented sand and gravel	5	10
Rock	5	..

AMERICAN CONCRETE INSTITUTE

311. Abbreviated[9] *ACI* Building Code Requirements for Reinforced Concrete

GENERAL DETAILS

301. Definitions.

Compressive Strength of Concrete (f_c'). Specified compressive strength of concrete in pounds per square inch (psi). Compressive strength shall be determined by tests of standard 6 × 12-in. cylinders made and tested in accordance with *ASTM* specifications at 28 days or such earlier age as concrete is to receive its full service load or maximum stress. Wherever this quantity appears under a radical sign ($\sqrt{f_c'}$) the root of only the numerical value is intended; all values are in psi.

Deformed Bar. A reinforcing bar conforming to "Specifications for Minimum Requirements for the Deformations of Deformed Steel Bars for Concrete Reinforcement" (*ASTM A*305) or "Specifications for Special Large Size Deformed Billet-Steel Bars for Concrete Reinforcement" (*ASTM A*408). Welded wire fabric with welded intersections not farther apart than 12 in. in the direction of the principal reinforcement and with cross wires not more than 6 gage numbers smaller in size than the principal reinforcement may be considered a deformed bar.

Effective Area of Concrete. The area of a section which lies between the centroid of the tensile reinforcement and the compression face of the flexural member.

Effective Area of Reinforcement. The area obtained by multiplying the right cross-sectional area of the reinforcement by the cosine of the angle between its direction and the direction for which the effectiveness is to be determined.

Prestressed Concrete. Reinforced concrete in which there have been introduced internal stresses of such magnitude and distribution that the stresses resulting from service loads are counteracted to a desired degree.

302. Hooks. The term "standard hook" as used herein shall mean either

(1) A semi-circular turn plus an extension of at least 4 bar diameters but not less than 2½ in. at the free end of the bar, or

[9] For complete specifications consult the most recent revision of the *ACI Building Code Requirements for Reinforced Concrete* (ACI 318–63).

(2) A 90-degree turn plus an extension of at least 12 bar diameters at the free end of the bar, or

(3) For stirrup and tie anchorage only, either a 90-degree or a 135-degree turn plus an extension of at least 6 bar diameters but not less than 2½ in. at the free end of the bar.

303. Spacing of Bars. The clear distance between parallel bars (except in columns and between multiple layers of bars in beams) shall be not less than the nominal diameter of the bars, 1⅓ times the maximum size of the coarse aggregate, nor 1 in.

Where reinforcement in beams or girders is placed in two or more layers, the clear distance between layers shall not be less than 1 in., and the bars in the upper layers shall be placed directly above those in the bottom layer.

In spirally reinforced and in tied columns, the clear distance between longitudinal bars shall be not less than 1½ times the bar diameter, 1½ times the maximum size of the coarse aggregate, nor 1½ in.

304. Lateral Reinforcement. Spiral column reinforcement shall consist of evenly spaced continuous spirals held firmly in place and true to line by vertical spacers, using at least 2 for spirals 20 in. or less in diameter, 3 for spirals 20 to 30 in. in diameter, and 4 for spirals more than 30 in. in diameter or more than 24 in. in diameter if composed of spiral ⅝ in. or larger in size.

The material used in spirals shall have a minimum diameter of ¼ in. The center spacing of the spirals shall not exceed ⅙ of the core diameter. The clear spacing between spirals shall not exceed 3 in. nor be less than 1⅜ in. or 1½ times the maximum size of coarse aggregate used.

All bars for tied columns shall be enclosed by lateral ties at least ¼ in. in diameter spaced apart not over 16 bar diameters, 48 tie diameters, or the least dimension of the column.

Compression reinforcement in beams or girders shall be anchored by ties or stirrups, which shall be not less than ¼ in. in diameter spaced not farther apart than 16 bar diameters, or 48 tie diameters.

305. Shrinkage and Temperature Reinforcement.

Slabs with plain bars (ratio A_s/A_c) 0.0025
Slabs with deformed bars, $f_y < 60{,}000$ psi.......................... 0.0020
Slabs with deformed bars, $f_y = 60{,}000$ psi 0.0018

306. Concrete Protection for Reinforcement. The reinforcement of footings and other principal structural members in which the concrete is deposited against the ground shall have not less than 3 in. of concrete between it and the ground contact.

The concrete protective covering for any reinforcement at surfaces not exposed directly to the ground or weather shall be not less than ¾ in. for slabs and walls, and not less than 1½ in. for beams and girders. In concrete joist floors in which the clear distance between joists is not more than 30 in., the protection of reinforcement shall be at least ¾ in. Column spirals or ties shall be protected everywhere by a covering of concrete cast monolithically with the core, for which the thickness shall be not less than 1½ in. nor less than 1½ times the maximum size of the coarse aggregate.

307. Flange Widths for T-Beams. The effective flange width to be used in the design of symmetrical T-beams shall not exceed ¼ of the span length of the beam, and its overhanging width on either side of the web shall not exceed 8 times the thickness of the slab nor ½ the clear distance to the next beam.

For beams having a flange on one side only, the effective overhanging flange width shall not exceed 1/12 of the span length of the beam, nor 6 times the thickness of the slab, nor ½ the clear distance to the next beam.

308. Minimum Depth of Flexural Members Unless Deflections Are Computed. These values are given in Table S-8 and are the limiting values.

TABLE S-8. Common Minimum Depths of Beams and Slabs

Member	Minimum Thickness or Depth t			
	Simply Supported	One End Continuous	Both Ends Continuous	Cantilever
One-way Slabs	$L/25$	$L/30$	$L/35$	$L/12$
Beams	$L/20$	$L/23$	$L/26$	$L/10$

309. Limiting Dimensions of Columns. Columns constituting the principal supports of a floor or roof shall have a diameter of at least 10 in., or in the case of rectangular columns, a thickness of at least 8 in., and a gross area not less than 96 sq. in. Auxiliary supports placed at intermediate locations and not continuous from story to story may be smaller but not less than 6 in. thick.

310. Limits for Reinforcement of Columns. The vertical reinforcement for columns shall be not less than 0.01 nor more than 0.08 times the gross cross-sectional area. The minimum size of bar shall be No. 5. The minimum number of bars shall be 6 for spiral columns and 4 for tied columns. The ratio of spiral reinforcement, p_s, shall be not less than the value given by

$$p_s = 0.45\ (A_g/A_c - 1)f_c'/f_y,$$

wherein f_y is the yield strength of spiral reinforcement but not more than 60,000 psi.

311. Anchorage Requirements for Main Reinforcement. The calculated tension or compression in any bar at any section must be developed on each side of that section by proper embedment length, end anchorage, or hooks. A tension bar may be anchored by bending it across the web at an angle of not less than 15 degrees with the longitudinal portion of the bar and making it continuous with the reinforcement on the opposite face of the member. Except at supports, every reinforcing bar shall be extended beyond the point at which it is no longer needed to resist flexural stress, for a distance equal to the effective depth of the member, or 12 bar diameters, whichever is greater.

At least ⅓ of the total reinforcement provided for negative moment at the support shall be extended beyond the extreme position of the point of inflection a distance not less than 1/16 of the clear span, or the effective depth of the member, whichever is greater. At least ⅓ the positive moment reinforcement in simple beams and ¼ the positive moment reinforcement in continuous beams shall extend along the same face of the beam into the support at least 6 in.

Plain bars in tension, except bars for shrinkage and temperature reinforcement, shall terminate in standard hooks except that hooks shall not be required on the positive reinforcement at interior supports of continuous members.

Standard hooks (Spec. 302) in tension may be considered as developing 10,000 psi.

312. Anchorage of Web Reinforcement. The ends of bars forming simple U- or multiple U-stirrups shall be anchored by one of the following methods:

(*a*) By a standard hook, considered as developing 50% of the allowable stress in the bar, plus embedment sufficient to develop by bond the remaining stress in the bar. The effective embedment of a stirrup leg shall be taken as the distance between the mid-depth of the member $d/2$ and the center of radius of bend of the hook.

(*b*) Welding to longitudinal reinforcement.

(*c*) Bending tightly around the longitudinal reinforcement through at last 180 degrees.

(*d*) Embedment above or below the mid-depth $d/2$ of the beam on the compression side, a distance sufficient to develop by bond the stress to which the bar will be subjected, but, in any case, a minimum of 24 bar diameters.

313. Torsion. In edge or spandrel beams the stirrups provided shall be closed and at least one longitudinal bar shall be placed in each corner of the beam section, the bar to be at least the diameter of the stirrup or ½ in., whichever is larger.

ALLOWABLE STRESSES—WORKING STRESS DESIGN

314. Allowable Unit Stresses in Reinforcement. Unless otherwise provided in this code, steel for concrete reinforcement shall not be stressed in excess of the following limits:

(*a*) *Tension.*

For billet-steel or axle-steel concrete reinforcing bars of structural grade .... 18,000 psi

For main reinforcement, ⅜ in. or less in diameter, in one-way slabs of not more than 12-ft. span, 50% of the minimum yield strength, but not to exceed .... 30,000 psi

For deformed bars with a yield strength of 60,000 psi or more and in sizes No. 11 and smaller .... 24,000 psi

For all other reinforcement in tension .... 20,000 psi

(*b*) *Compression* (vertical column reinforcement).

Spiral columns, 40% of the minimum yield strength, but not to exceed .... 30,000 psi

Tied columns 85% of value for spiral columns but not to exceed .. 25,500 psi

315. Allowable Unit Stresses in Concrete. These values are given in Table S-9. Note variation of modular ratio with the volumetric weight of the concrete.

316. Wind and Earthquake Forces. Members subject to stresses produced by wind or earthquake forces combined with other loads may be proportioned for stresses 33⅓% greater than those of Spec. 314 and Spec. 315 provided that the section thus required is not less than that required for the combination of dead and live load.

317. Modulus of Elasticity of Concrete. The modulus of elasticity E_c, for concrete, may be taken as $w^{1.5}\,33\sqrt{f_c'}$, in psi, for values of w between 90 and 155 pcf. For normal concrete, w may be taken as 145 pcf.

The modular ratio, $n = E_s/E_c$, may be taken as the nearest whole number (but not less than 6). Except in calculation for deflections, lightweight concrete shall be designed with the same n values as normal weight concrete.

In doubly reinforced beams and slabs, an effective modular ratio of $2n$ shall be used to transform the compression reinforcement and compute its stress, which shall not be taken as greater than the allowable tensile stress.

SHEAR AND BOND RESISTANCE FOR WORKING STRESSES

318. Shear Stress. The nominal shear stress as a measure of diagonal tension in reinforced concrete members shall be computed by:

$$v = V/bd.$$

For design, the maximum shear shall be considered as that at the section a distance d from the face of the support.

319. Web Reinforcement. Wherever the value of the shear stress v, computed from Spec. 318 plus effects of torsion, exceeds the shear stress v_c, permitted for the concrete of an unreinforced web, web reinforcement shall be provided to carry the excess. Such web reinforcement shall also be provided for a distance equal to the depth d of the member beyond the point theoretically required. Web reinforcement between the face of the support and the section at a distance d therefrom shall be the same as required at that section.

TABLE S-9

Allowable Unit Stresses for Reinforced Concrete

Description	Symbols	Allowable Stresses: For Any Strength of Concrete	For Strength of Concrete Shown Below: $f_c' =$ 2500 psi	$f_c' =$ 3000 psi	$f_c' =$ 4000 psi	$f_c' =$ 5000 psi
Modulus of elasticity ratio	n	$\frac{29{,}000{,}000}{w^{1.5}\,33\sqrt{f_c'}}$				
For concrete weighing 145 pcf	n		10	9	8	7
Flexure: f_c						
Extreme fiber stress in compression	f_c	$0.45f_c'$	1125	1350	1800	2250
Extreme fiber stress in tension in plain concrete footings and walls	f_c	$1.6\sqrt{f_c'}$	80	88	102	113
Shear: v (as a measure of diagonal tension at a distance d from the face of the support)						
Beams with no web reinforcement	v_c	$1.1\sqrt{f_c'}$	55	60	70	78
Joists with no web reinforcement	v_c	$1.2\sqrt{f_c'}$	61	66	77	86
Members with vertical or inclined web reinforcement or properly combined bent bars and vertical stirrups	v_c	$5\sqrt{f_c'}$	250	274	316	354
Slabs and footings (peripheral shear)	v_c	$2\sqrt{f_c'}$	100	110	126	141
Bond and anchorage: u						
Deformed tension bar sizes to #11 (*ASTM, A305*)	u					
Top bars	u	$\frac{3.4\sqrt{f_c'}}{D} < 350$ psi	$\frac{170}{D}$	$\frac{186}{D}$	$\frac{214}{D}$	$\frac{240}{D}$
Other bars	u	$\frac{4.8\sqrt{f_c'}}{D} < 500$ psi	$\frac{240}{D}$	$\frac{262}{D}$	$\frac{303}{D}$	$\frac{338}{D}$
Deformed compression bars	u	$6.5\sqrt{f_c'} < 400$ psi				
Plain bars	u	½ of above values < 160 psi				
Bearing: f_c						
On full area	f_c	$0.25f_c'$	625	750	1000	1250
On one-third area or less	f_c	$0.375f_c'$	938	1125	1500	1875

The shear stress v shall not exceed $5\sqrt{f_c'}$ in sections with web reinforcement. Where web reinforcement is required, it shall be so spaced that every 45-degree line, representing a potential diagonal crack and extending from mid-depth, $d/2$, of the member to the longitudinal tension bars, shall be crossed by at least one line of web reinforcement. When the shear stress exceeds $3\sqrt{f_c'}$, every such 45-degree line shall be crossed by at least two lines of web reinforcement.

320. Stirrups. The area of steel required in stirrups placed perpendicular to the longitudinal reinforcement shall be computed by:

$$A_v = V's/f_v d$$

The area of inclined stirrups shall be computed by the equation for bent bars in §321.

321. Bent Bars. Only the center three-fourths of the inclined portion of any longitudinal bar that is bent up for web reinforcement shall be considered effective for that purpose.

(*a*) When the web reinforcement consists of a single bent bar or of a single group of parallel bars all bent up at the same distance from the support, the required area shall be computed by:

$$A_v = \frac{V'}{f_v \sin \alpha}$$

in which V' shall not exceed $1.5bd\sqrt{f_c'}$.

(*b*) Where there is a series of parallel bars or groups of bars bent up at different distances from the support, the required area shall be computed by:

$$A_v = \frac{V's}{f_v d\,(\sin \alpha + \cos \alpha)}$$

322. Shear Stress in Slabs and Footings. The shear capacity of slabs and footings in the vicinity of concentrated loads or concentrated reactions shall be governed by the more severe of two conditions:

1. The slab or footing acting essentially as a wide beam, with a potential diagonal crack extending in a plane across the entire width.
2. Two-way action existing for the slab or footing, with potential diagonal cracking along the surface of a truncated cone or pyramid around the concentrated load or reaction. The critical section for shear to be used as a measure of diagonal tension shall be perpendicular to the plane of the slab and located at a distance $d/2$ out from the periphery of the concentrated load or reaction area. The nominal shear stress shall be computed by:

$$v = V/b_0 d$$

in which V and b_0 are taken at the critical section specified in (2). The shear stress v, so computed, shall not exceed $v_c = 2\sqrt{f_c'}$ without reinforcement.

323. Bond Stress in Flexural Members. In flexural members in which the tension reinforcement is parallel to the compression face, the flexural bond stress at any cross section shall be computed by

$$u = \frac{V}{\Sigma O jd}$$

Bent-up bars that are not more than $d/3$ from the level of the main longitudinal reinforcement may be included. Critical sections occur at the face of the support, at each point where tension bars terminate within a span, and at the point of inflection.

The calculated tension or compression in any bar at any section must be developed on each side of that section by proper embedment length, end anchorage, or, for tension only, hooks. Anchorage or development bond stress u shall be computed as the bar force divided by the product of ΣO times the embedment length.

Columns

324. Spirally Reinforced Columns. The maximum allowable axial load P, on columns with closely spaced spirals enclosing a circular core reinforced with vertical bars, shall be that given by

$$P = A_g (0.25 f_c' + f_s p_g),$$

where f_s = allowable stress in vertical column reinforcement, to be taken at 40% of the minimum specification value of the yield strength, but not to exceed 30,000 psi.

325. Tied Columns. The maximum allowable axial load on columns reinforced with longitudinal bars and separate lateral ties shall be 85% of that for spirally reinforced columns.

326. Composite Columns. The allowable load on a composite column, consisting of a structural steel or cast iron column thoroughly encased in concrete reinforced with both longitudinal and spiral reinforcement, shall not exceed that given by

$$P = 0.225\, A_g f_c' + f_s A_{st} + f_r A_r,$$

where f_r = allowable unit stress in metal core, not to exceed 18,000 psi for steel conforming to *ASTM A*36, 16,000 psi for steel conforming to *ASTM A*7, or 10,000 psi for a cast-iron core.

327. Columns Subjected to Axial Load and Bending. Columns controlled by compression shall be proportioned by the following equation except that the allowable load shall not exceed the load P, permitted when the column supports axial load only.

$$f_a/F_a + f_{bx}/F_b + f_{by}/F_b \text{ not greater than } 1.0$$

where f_{bx} and f_{by} are the bending moment components about the x and y principal axes divided by the section modulus of the respective transformed section, $2n$ being assumed as the modular ratio for all vertical reinforcement, and

$$F_a = 0.34\ (1 + p_g f_y / 0.85 f_c') f_c'$$

Ultimate Strength Design

328. Assumptions. Ultimate strength design of members for bending and axial load shall be based on the assumptions given in this section, and on satisfaction of the applicable conditions of equilibrium and compatibility of strains.

Strain in the concrete shall be assumed directly proportional to the distance from the neutral axis. Except in anchorage regions, strain in reinforcing bars shall be assumed equal to the strain in the concrete at the same position.

The maximum unit strain at the extreme compression fiber at ultimate strength shall be assumed equal to 0.003.

Stress in reinforcing bars below the yield strength f_y for the grade of steel used shall be taken as 29,000,000 psi times the steel strain. For strain greater than that corresponding to the design yield strength f_y the reinforcement stress shall be considered independent of strain and equal to the design strength f_y.

Tensile strength of the concrete shall be neglected in flexural calculations.

At ultimate strength, concrete stress is not proportional to strain. The diagram of compressive concrete stress distribution may be assumed to be a rectangle, trapezoid, parabola, or any other shape which results in predictions of ultimate strength in reasonable agreement with the results of comprehensive tests.

The requirements above may be considered satisfied by the equivalent rectangular concrete stress distribution which is defined as follows: At ultimate strength, a concrete stress intensity of $0.85f_c'$ shall be assumed uniformly distributed over an equivalent compression zone bounded by the edges of the cross-section and a straight line located parallel to the neutral axis at a distance $a = k_1c$ from the fiber of maximum compressive strain. The distance c from the fiber of maximum strain to the neutral axis is measured in a direction perpendicular to that axis. The fraction k_1 shall be taken as 0.85 for strengths f_c' to 4000 psi and shall be reduced continuously at a rate of 0.05 for each 1000 psi of strength in excess of 4000 psi.

329. Safety Provisions. The coefficient ϕ (applied to member resistance) shall be 0.90 for flexure; 0.85 for diagonal tension, bond and anchorage; 0.75 for spirally reinforced compression members with axial load; and 0.70 for tied compression members. The coefficient ϕ provides for such sources of possible undercapacity as workmanship, dimensional and manufacturing tolerances, degree of supervision and control, and strength deficiencies of the material in the structure.

330. Design Strengths for Reinforcement. When reinforcement is used that has a yield strength f_y in excess of 60,000 psi, the yield strength to be used in design shall be reduced to $0.85\,f_y$ or 60,000 psi, whichever is greater, unless it is shown by tension tests that at a proof stress equal to the specified yield strength f_y the unit strain does not exceed 0.003.

Designs shall not be based on a yield strength f_y in excess of 75,000 psi. Design of tension reinforcement shall not be based on a yield strength f_y in excess of 60,000 psi unless tests are made in compliance with §333.

331. Design Loads. The following provide for such sources of possible excess load effects as load assumptions, assumptions in structural analysis, simplifications in calculations, and effects of construction sequence and methods. The design loads shall be computed as follows:

(*a*) For structures in such locations and of such proportions that the effects of wind and earthquake may be neglected the design capacity shall be

$$U = 1.5D + 1.8L.$$

The loads D, L, W, and E are the loads specified in the general code of which these requirements form a part.

(*b*) For structures in the design of which wind loading must be included, the design capacity shall be

$$U = 1.25\,(D + L + W \text{ or } E)$$

or

$$U = 0.9\,D + 1.1W \text{ or } 1.1E,$$

whichever is greater, provided that no member shall have a capacity less than required for dead load and live load.

332. Control of Deflections. The computed deflections of members at the service load level of $DL + LL$ shall conform to the provisions of this code, and the deflections shall always be checked whenever the required net reinforcement ratio for any section of a flexural member exceeds $0.18\,f_c'/f_y$, or whenever the specified yield strength f_y exceeds 40,000 psi.

333. Control of Cracking. Only deformed bars shall be used, except that plain bars may be used as temperature bars and column spirals and No. 2 plain bars may be used as stirrups and column ties. Tension reinforcement shall be well distributed in the zones of maximum concrete tension and in the flanges of T-beams.

The design yield strength f_y for tension reinforcement shall not exceed 60,000 psi unless it is shown by full-scale tests of typical members that the average crack width at service load at the concrete surface of the extreme tension edge does not exceed 0.015 in. for interior members and 0.010 in. for exterior members. These requirements shall not apply to compression reinforcement.

Beam Design for Ultimate Strength

334. Rectangular Beams with Compression Reinforcement. See §277 of text.

335. I and T-sections. See §278 of text.

336. Ultimate Shear Strength. The nominal ultimate shear stress, as a measure of diagonal tension, in reinforced concrete members shall be computed by

$$v_u = V_u/bd.$$

For design, the maximum shear shall be considered at the section a distance d from the face of the support. Wherever applicable, effects of torsion shall be added and effects of inclined flexural compression in variable-depth members shall be included. For beams of I- or T-section, b' shall be substituted for b.

The shear stress v_c carried by an unreinforced web shall not exceed $2\phi\sqrt{f_c'}$ at a distance d from the face of the support unless a more detailed analysis is made in accordance with provisions of this code.

337. Web Reinforcement. Wherever the value of the ultimate shear stress v_u, plus effects of torsion, exceeds the shear stress v_c, permitted for the concrete of an unreinforced web, web reinforcement shall be provided to carry the excess. Such web reinforcement shall also be provided for a distance equal to the depth d of the member beyond the point theoretically required. Web reinforcement between the face of the support and the section at a distance d therefrom shall be the same as required at that section.

338. Stirrups. The area of steel required in stirrups placed perpendicular to the longitudinal reinforcement shall be computed by

$$A_v = V_u's/\phi f_y d.$$

339. Bent Bars. Only the center three fourths of the inclined portion of any longitudinal bar that is bent up for web reinforcement shall be considered effective for that purpose.

When the web reinforcement consists of a single bent bar or a single group of parallel bars all bent up at the same distance from the support, the required area shall be computed by

$$A_v = \frac{V_u'}{\phi f_y \sin\alpha},$$

where V_u' shall not exceed $3\phi bd\sqrt{f_c'}$.

When there is a series of parallel bars or groups of bars bent up at different distances from the support, the required area shall be computed by

$$A_v = \frac{V_u's}{\phi f_y\, d\, (\sin\alpha + \cos\alpha)}.$$

340. Stress Restrictions. The specified yield point for stirrup reinforcement shall not exceed 60,000 psi and f_y shall conform to Spec. 330.

The shear stress v_u shall not exceed $10\phi\sqrt{f_c'}$ at sections with web reinforcement.

341. Web Reinforcement Restrictions. Where web reinforcement is required, it shall be so spaced that every 45-degree line, representing a potential diagonal crack and extending from mid-depth $d/2$ of the member to the longitudinal tension bars, shall be crossed by at least one line of web reinforcement. When the shear stress, v_u, exceeds $6\phi\sqrt{f_c'}$, every such line shall be crossed by at least two lines of web reinforcement.

342. Ultimate Bond Stress. In flexural members in which the tension reinforcement is parallel to the compression face the ultimate flexural bond stress at any cross section shall be computed by

$$u_u = \frac{V_u}{\Sigma O j d}.$$

Bent-up bars that are not more than $d/3$ from the level of the main longitudinal reinforcement may be included. Critical sections occur at the face of the support, at each point where tension bars terminate within a span, and at the point of inflection.

The calculated tension or compression in any bar at any section must be developed on each side of that section by proper embedment length, end anchorage, or, for tension only, hooks. Anchorage or development bond stress u_u shall be computed as the bar forces divided by the product of ΣO times the embedment length, and shall not exceed:

For tension bars conforming to *ASTM A*305:

Top bars $$\frac{6.7\,\phi\sqrt{f_c'}}{D} < 560 \text{ psi.}$$

All other bars $$\frac{9.5\,\phi\sqrt{f_c'}}{D} < 800 \text{ psi.}$$

Top bars in reference to bond are so placed that more than 12 in. of concrete is cast in the members below the bar.

343. Anchorage. Adequate anchorage shall be provided for the tension reinforcement in all flexural members to which the formula for u_u does not apply, such as sloped, stepped or tapered footings, brackets or beams in which the tension reinforcement is not parallel to the compression face.

AMERICAN CONCRETE INSTITUTE

312. Abbreviated[10] *ACI* Building Code Requirements for Prestressed Concrete

DEFINITIONS AND ASSUMPTIONS

401. Definitions. The following terms are defined for use in this chapter.

Anchorage. The means by which the prestress force is permanently delivered to the concrete.

Bonded Tendons. Tendons which are bonded to the concrete either directly or through grouting. Unbonded tendons are free to move relative to the surrounding concrete.

Effective Prestress. The stress remaining in the tendons after all losses have occurred, excluding the effects of dead load and superimposed loads.

Curvature Friction. Friction resulting from bends or curves in the specified cable profile.

Wobble Friction. Friction caused by the unintended deviation of the prestressing steel from its specified profile.

Jacking Force. The temporary force exerted by the device which introduces the tension into the tendons.

402. General Considerations. Stresses and ultimate strength shall be investigated at service conditions and at all load stages that may be critical during the life of the structure from the time prestress is applied. Stress concentrations due to the prestressing or other causes shall be taken into account in the design.

403. Basic Assumptions. The following assumptions shall be made for purposes of design.

1. Strains vary linearly with depth through the entire load range.
2. At cracked sections, the ability of the concrete to resist tension is neglected.
3. In calculations of section properties prior to bonding of tendons, areas of the open ducts shall be deducted. The transformed area of bonded tendons may be included in pretensioned members and in post-tensioned members after grouting.
4. Modulus of elasticity of prestressing steel shall be determined by tests or supplied by the manufacturer.
5. Modulus of elasticity of concrete shall be assumed as prescribed in §317, p. 446.

ALLOWABLE STRESSES WITH PRESTRESS

404. Allowable Stresses in Concrete.

(*a*) Temporary stresses immediately after transfer, before losses due to creep and shrinkage

Compression for initial prestress .... $0.60f_{ci}'$

Tension stresses in members without auxiliary reinforcement (unprestressed or prestressed) in the tension zone .... $3\sqrt{f_{ci}'}$

[10] For complete specifications see Building Code—*ACI* 318–63.

Where the calculated tension stress exceeds this value, reinforcement shall be provided to resist the total tension force in the concrete computed on the assumption of an uncracked section.

(*b*) Stresses at design loads, after allowance for all prestress losses

Compression .... $0.45f_c'$

Tension in the precompressed tension zone with steel reinforcement $6\sqrt{f_c'}$

(*c*) The bearing stress on the concrete created by the anchorage in post-tensioned concrete with adequate reinforcement in the end regions shall not exceed

$$f_c = 0.6f_{ci}'\sqrt[3]{A_b'/A_b} < f_{ci}'$$

405. Allowable Stresses in Steel.

(*a*) Temporary stresses

1. Due to temporary jacking force .... $0.80f_s'$
2. Pretensioning tendons immediately after transfer, or post-tensioning tendons immediately after anchoring .... $0.70f_s'$

(*b*) Effective prestress .... $0.60f_s'$

or if it is smaller use .... $0.80f_{sy}$

406. Loss of Prestress. To determine the effective prestress, allow for the following:

1. Slip at anchorage
2. Elastic shortening of concrete
3. Creep of concrete
4. Shrinkage of concrete
5. Relaxation of steel stress
6. Frictional loss due to intended or unintended curvature in the tendons.

407. Friction Loss. The following equations apply to post-tensioned steel.

$$T_o = T_x\epsilon^{(KL+\mu\alpha)}$$

When $(KL + \mu\alpha)$ is not greater than 0.3, the following may be used:

$$T_o = T_x(1 + KL + \mu\alpha)$$

where α is in radians and L is in feet.

TABLE S-10

TYPICAL VALUES OF K AND μ FOR METAL CONDUITS

TYPE OF STEEL	USUAL RANGE OF OBSERVED VALUES		SUGGESTED DESIGN VALUES	
	K	μ	K	μ
Wire cables	0.0005–0.0030	0.15–0.35	0.0015	0.25
High strength bars	0.0001–0.0005	0.08–0.30	0.0003	0.20
Galvanized strand	0.0005–0.0020	0.15–0.30	0.0015	0.25

408. Ultimate Flexural Strength. The required ultimate load on a member shall not exceed the ultimate flexural strength computed by:

(*a*) Rectangular sections, or flanged sections in which the neutral axis lies within the flange:

$$M_u = \phi[A_s f_{su} d(1 - 0.59q)] = \phi\left[A_s f_{su}\left(d - \frac{a}{2}\right)\right],$$

where $q = pf_{su}/f_c'$ and $a = A_s f_{su}/0.85f_c'$. (See §276 of text.)

(*b*) Flanged sections in which the neutral axis falls outside the flange:

$$M_u = \phi\left[A_{sr} f_{su} d\left(1 - \frac{0.59\, A_{sr} f_{su}}{b' d\, f_c'}\right) + 0.85 f_c'\,(b - b')t\,(d - 0.5t)\right]$$

where

$$A_{sr} = A_s - A_{sf}$$

and

$$A_{sf} = 0.85 f_c'\,(b - b')t/f_{su}.$$

(*c*) Where information for the determination of f_{su} is not available, and provided that f_{se} is not less than $0.5f_s'$, the following approximate values shall be used:

Bonded members

$$f_{su} = f_s'(1 - 0.5pf_s'/f_c').$$

Unbonded members

$$f_{su} = f_{se} + 15{,}000 \text{ psi}.$$

(*d*) Non-prestressed reinforcement (p') in combination with prestressed steel (p) may be considered to contribute to the tension force in a member at ultimate moment an amount equal to its area times its yield point, provided

$$\frac{pf_{su}}{f_c'} + \frac{p'f_y}{f_c'} \text{ does not exceed } 0.30.$$

409. Limitations on Steel Percentage.

(*a*) Except as provided in (*b*), the ratio of prestressing steel used for calculations of M_u shall be such that

$$pf_{su}/f_c' \text{ is not more than } 0.30.$$

For flanged sections, p shall be taken as the steel ratio of only that portion of the total tension steel area which is required to develop the compressive strength of the web alone.

(*b*) When a steel ratio in excess of that specified in (*a*) is used, the ultimate moment shall be taken as not greater than the following:

Rectangular sections, or flanged sections in which the neutral axis lies within the flange

$$M_u = \phi(0.25 f_c' b d^2).$$

Flanged sections in which the neutral axis falls outside the flange

$$M_u = \phi[0.25 f_c' b' d^2 + 0.85 f_c'(b - b')t(d - 0.5t).$$

(*c*) The total amount of prestressed and unprestressed reinforcement shall be adequate to develop an ultimate load in flexure at least 1.2 times the cracking load calculated on the basis of a modulus of rupture of $7.5\sqrt{f_c'}$.

410. Notation Applicable to Ultimate Strength in Shear with Prestress.

f_d stress due to dead load, at the extreme fiber of a section at which tension stresses are caused by applied loads

f_{pc} compressive stress in the concrete, after all prestress losses have occurred, at the centroid of the cross section resisting the applied loads, or at the junction of the web and flange when the centroid lies in the flange

f_{pe} compressive stress in concrete due to prestress only, after all losses, at the extreme fiber of a section at which tension stresses are caused by applied loads

I moment of inertia of section resisting externally applied loads[11]

M/V bending moment divided by shear due to external loads applied for maximum moment at the section

M_{cr} net flexural cracking moment

V_{ci} shear at diagonal cracking due to all dead loads, when such cracking is the result of combined shear and moment

V_{cw} Shear force at diagonal cracking due to all loads, when such cracking is the result of excessive principal tension stresses in the web

V_d shear due to dead load

V_p vertical component of the effective prestress force at the section considered

y distance from the centroidal axis of the section resisting the applied loads to the extreme fiber in tension

411. Shear Resisted by Concrete. The shear V_c at diagonal cracking (for normal weight concrete) shall be taken as the lesser of V_{ci} and V_{cw}, determined as follows:

$$V_{ci} = 0.6\, b'd\sqrt{f_c'} + \frac{M_{cr}}{\dfrac{M}{V} - \dfrac{d}{2}} + Vd \quad \text{(but not less than } 1.7\, b'd\sqrt{f_c'}\text{)}$$

where

$$M_{cr} = \frac{I}{y}\,(6\sqrt{f_c'} + f_{pe} - f_d)$$

$$V_{cw} = b'd\,(3.5\sqrt{f_c'} + 0.3\, f_{pc}) + V_p.$$

412. Shear Reinforcement. Except as provided in §413, the area of shear reinforcement placed perpendicular to the axis of a member shall be not less than

$$A_v = \frac{(V_u - \phi V_c)s}{\phi\, d f_y}$$

nor less than

$$A_v = \frac{A_s f_s'}{80} \frac{s}{f_y} \frac{s}{d} \sqrt{\frac{d}{b'}}.$$

The effective depth d at any section is such that $d/h = d_m/h_m$ at the section of maximum moment.

413. Requirements for Web Reinforcement. Web reinforcement between the face of the support and the section at a distance $d/2$ therefrom shall be the same as that required at that section.

Shear reinforcement shall be provided for a distance equal to the effective depth d of the member beyond the point theoretically required.

Web reinforcement shall be anchored at both ends in accordance with usual practice for reinforced concrete beams.

[11] The term "externally applied loads" shall be taken to mean the external ultimate loads acting on the member, excepting those applied to the member by the prestressing tendons.

Shear reinforcement not less than determined from §412 shall be provided at all sections where any reinforcement is needed, and shall be spaced not farther apart than ¾ the depth of the member, nor 24 in., whichever is the smaller.

A yield strength in excess of 60,000 psi shall not be considered for shear reinforcement.

414. Bond. Three or seven wire pretensioning strands shall be bonded to the concrete from the cross section under consideration for a distance in inches of not less than

$$(f_{su} - \tfrac{2}{3}f_{se})D,$$

where D, the nominal strand diameter, is in inches and f_{su} and f_{se} are expressed in kips per square inch.

Investigation may be restricted to those cross-sections nearest each end of the member that are required to develop their ultimate strength under the specified ultimate load.

415. Placement of Prestressing Steel.

(*a*) All pretensioning steel and ducts for post-tensioning shall be accurately placed and adequately secured in position.

(*b*) The minimum clear spacing between pretensioning steel at each end of the member shall be 4 times the diameter of individual wires or 3 times the diameter of strands, but at least 1⅓ times the maximum size of aggregate.

(*c*) Prestressing steel or ducts may be bundled together in the middle portion of the span, provided the requirements of (*b*) are satisfied.

(*d*) Ducts may be arranged closely together vertically when provision is made to prevent the steel, when tensioned, from breaking through the duct. Horizontal disposition of ducts shall allow proper placement of concrete.

(*e*) Where concentration of steel or ducts tends to create a weakened plane in the concrete cover, reinforcement shall be provided to control cracking.

(*f*) The inside diameter of ducts shall be at least ¼ in. larger than the diameter of the post-tensioning bar or large enough to produce an internal area at least twice the gross area of wires, strands, or cables.

Concrete Cover. The following minimum thicknesses of concrete cover shall be provided for prestressing steel, ducts and nonprestressed steel.

Concrete surfaces in contact with ground	2 in.
Beams and girders	
Prestressing steel and main reinforcing bars	1½
Stirrups and ties	1
Slabs and joists exposed to weather	1
Slabs and joists not exposed to weather	¾

416. Scope. All provisions of §311, p. 443, on reinforced concrete not specifically excluded and not in conflict with the provisions of this chapter are to be considered applicable to prestressed concrete.

INDEX

A

B

C

D

E

S